Seed, Soil and Science

Eugene D. Funk

Seed, Soil and Science

THE STORY OF EUGENE D. FUNK

By Helen M. Cavanagh

The Lakeside Press

R. R. Donnelley & Sons Company

Chicago

TO MY FATHER
ALSO ONE OF THE
ADMIRABLE GENERATION
BORN IN 1867

Foreword

FAMILIES WHOSE INTERESTS are chiefly agricultural seldom receive attention from historians commensurate with their significant contributions to American life and institutions. Here is the story of a family through four generations whose basic interest is the Betterment of Agriculture. Through the years their counsel has often been sought in agricultural and civic affairs. By their recognition of responsibilities and a sensitive appreciation of able and scientifically trained minds their commercial organization has attained recognized leadership.

The center of activity is the rich black lands of Mid-America where the elongated outline of the Central Corn Belt is located in the United States. Bloomington, in McLean County, Illinois is situated deep in the heartland of the Mississippi Valley on the Illinois prairie. Funk's Grove can be seen wrapped in a blue haze some twelve miles south of this city. Agricultural leadership of unusual calibre developed for more than a century near this Grove where families have made contributions quietly. One family among others put deep in the soil an unrecorded but significant story of achievement. Descendants of Isaac Funk, who named the Grove in 1824, have not sought recognition. Far-flung acres of improved crops throughout the world are among the testimonials to their foresight and courage.

Isaac Funk acquired more than 25,000 acres in McLean county during the years 1824–65. He and his descendants retained the land and in return it bound them close to the soil. The faith of the early settlers was justified by the efforts of succeeding generations to preserve the fertility of these acres. Children of Isaac, including eight sons and one daughter, cooperatively decided upon an acceptable division of his estate at the time of his death in 1865. Their strength through unity became apparent. The brothers followed in their father's footsteps assuming responsibilities in civic and agricultural groups. Their children realized about the turn of the twentieth century that they must plan for the future if the land were to withstand the constant drain upon it and meet the competition of newer agricultural communities.

Eugene Duncan Funk, Sr., grandson of Isaac, particularly recognized this responsibility. With the cooperation of his cousins he initiated the organization of Funk Bros. Seed Co. in 1901.

With characteristic determination and tenacity, Eugene Funk, Sr., developed his idea. By hewing to a line of action and thought he lived to see his dream materialize in a Better Agriculture for many people of the nation and the world. With other responsible members of the Funk family he accepted the obligation inherent in the wise use of wealth and power. Elder members of the family often reminded younger generations that they were only tenants on the land.

Upon approaching Funk's Grove by transcontinental highway U.S. 66 the speeding traveler may notice that it is the home of Funk's "G" Hybrids, "Consistently Good Year After Year." Arrows pointing to Research Acres appear at Shirley and Funk's Grove. There is little in written form to tell of the long years of patient effort, expenditures and disappointments before Success and Betterment of Agriculture became realities. Long esteemed for integrity, leadership, and courage, the well-known Funk family is deserving of a chronicled place in the history of Mid-America. Their contributions are recognized in local, state, national and world communities.

This history of interwoven economic and political family associations together with technical scientific information could not have been assembled and written without the advice and aid of Mr. Eugene D. Funk, Jr. His knowledge of family activities and business operations has been an invaluable source of information. He carefully safeguarded a large collection of thousands of items including personal papers, diaries, journals and records. By his recognition of their possible historical value the work of reconstructing almost a century has been greatly facilitated. He also gave generously of his time for critical evaluation and for making available many contacts where additional information could be obtained. Gladys Funk Rehtmeyer contributed effectively by a series entitled *Remembering* (I, II, III). Mrs. Eugene D. Funk, Sr. was especially helpful. Other members of the Eugene D. Funk, Sr. family who contributed information included his three sons, LaFayette, Sr., Paul and Theodore, and his brother, De Loss.

Information was also secured from Mrs Madeline Funk McCullough, Mr. Arthur Funk, Mr. Dana Rollins, Miss Florence Funk, Mrs. Hazel Funk Holmes, Mrs. Florence Funk DeVries, Mr. Benjamin Funk, Jr., Mrs. C. A. Ewing, Mr. Julius Funk, Mr. Donald Funk, Mr. Jacob Funk, Mr. Lawrence Funk, Jr. and Mrs. Frank Funk.

Friends and associates of Eugene D. Funk, Sr. have been equally cooperative including Dr. James R. Holbert, Mr. Campbell Holton, Mr. Dave Thompson, Mr. Frank Fulkerson, Mr. Joseph Fulkerson, Professor W. L. Burlison, Professor P. G. Holden, Mr. Edward J. Dies, Mr. W. A. Wheeler, Professor H. H. Love, Professor C. P. Bull, Mr. Fred McCulloch, Mr. William Heckendorn of the American Seed Trade Association, Mr. A. W. Tibbits of *Seed Trade News,* Mr. Frank Bill of the Bloomington *Pantagraph,* Mr. J. S. McKeighan, Mr. and Mrs. R. B. Best, Mr. Claire V. Golden, Mr. I. C. Bradley, Mr. O. J. Sommer, Mr. J. A. McConnell and Colonel Edward N. Wentworth. Company employees and officials also contributed valuable information as citations to their interviews will show.

Manuscript collections examined include: Records of the Funk Bros. Seed Co.; Papers and Diaries of LaFayette Funk and Eugene D. Funk, Sr.; Papers of Leonidas Kerrick; The Frank Lowden Papers in the University of Chicago Library; the P. G. Holden Papers in the Library of Michigan State University; the J. R. Holbert Papers.

The author worked independently with no restrictions placed by the Funk family upon the use of materials in manuscript collections or in company records. The family of Eugene D. Funk Sr., and the Directors of Funk Bros. Seed Co., were generous in their grants of time and support for the project. Through Research Funds they made possible the publication of the book. They were objective in their judgments and willing to make every effort to produce an authentic record for future generations. This type of co-operation and desire to add to the quantity and quality of business history rendered the monumental task of sifting materials a rewarding research responsibility. The preliminary manuscript was read in entirety by LaFayette Funk and by Eugene D. Funk, Jr.; parts were read by Gladys Funk Rehtmeyer, Paul Funk and Theodore Funk. They made valuable suggestions, helped to correct errors and advised the author on technical information.

The author is indebted to Professors Avery Craven and William T. Hutchinson of the Department of History in the University of Chicago, who gave valuable time to read the manuscript and offer constructive criticism. Professor W. L. Burlison of the Department of Agriculture in the University of Illinois was also consulted. Dr. Earl Sieveking of Funk Bros. read the chapters relating to hybrid corn.

The competent staffs of the following Research Libraries were especially helpful; University of Illinois, Illinois State Historical Society, Chicago Historical Society, John Crerar Library, McLean County

Historical Society, Michigan State University, Agricultural Division United States Archives, Illinois State Normal University, University of Chicago, Manuscript and Newspaper Divisions of the Library of Congress, the Files of the American Seed Trade Association and of the *Seed Trade News* as well as the *Seed World.*

Miss Margaret Schertz, Secretary to Eugene D. Funk, Sr. and Eugene D. Funk, Jr. typed the manuscript.

HELEN M. CAVANAGH

Bloomington, Illinois

Contents

PART ONE

One Family

CHAPTER I

The Heritage · 1865–1890

AN UNUSUAL CHAPTER in the history of the Old Northwest began when Isaac Funk and his brother Absalom settled in the central Illinois prairie world of waving blue stem grass and stately groves. Their family originally migrated from the Germanies in 1733 to Pennsylvania. They moved into Virginia, west to Kentucky where Isaac was born and on to Ohio. From Washington Court House, not far from the Cincinnati sphere of influence, the two Funk brothers found their way in 1823 to land north of Springfield, Illinois. They staked their claims during May 1824 on the central prairies where the wide stretches of level land had long awaited the recognition of men who knew their value. Their log cabin was built on the eastern edge of the Grove that bears their name.

Pioneer life at Funk's Grove was typical of the development of many other settlements in central Illinois. Beginnings were modest but opportunities for leadership and wealth were present if settlers remained and prospered with the new country. Soon after selecting their location, Isaac decided to remain some months near Fort Clark, now Peoria, where he raised a crop of corn on bottom land. There he met and married Cassandra Sharp, whose family also migrated to Illinois from Ohio. They established their home in a log cabin near Funk's Grove. George, the first of ten children, was born in 1827; Adam, Jacob, Duncan, LaFayette, Francis and Benjamin followed in that order by 1836, and a younger group of children—Absalom, Isaac and the only daughter, Sarah—completed the group by 1846. The family circle was broken when Adam died in 1847.

With foresight and courage Funk acquired a concentrated holding of land in Funk's Grove and Mount Hope townships of McLean County, Illinois about twelve miles south of Bloomington. Estimates show a holding of between 6,000 and 6,300 acres by 1840. Between the years 1848–51 about 3,000 to 3,600 acres were added. The largest block was obtained 1851–63 when 12,000 to 13,500 acres were acquired through assignment and purchase from the Illinois Central Railroad. Total land holdings approximated 25,000 acres.

3

Isaac Funk concentrated early on the feeding of livestock for distant eastern markets, for Galena and later for Chicago. He turned some of this land to the cultivation of grain. As a result of these activities he also recognized the need for adequate arteries of transportation, especially railroads, across the level land. He, therefore, gave his support to plans for railroad development and watched with interest the building of two lines near his original holdings.

The completion of the Chicago and Alton railroad traversing the Funk lands and the Illinois Central in the early 1850's with the main line only a few miles distant provided two major lines of communication from the central prairies to the fast-developing lake city of Chicago and the significant river city of St. Louis. With the timber of Funk's Grove and the water of Sugar Creek, the Funk enterprises of cattle raising and crop production expanded appreciably. Often the droves of Funk were the only ones mentioned in the accounts of the growing packing industry in Chicago during the fifties. Funk did not cultivate intensively, thus preserving the fertility of the unusually deep top soil. The land appreciated in value, and since Funk did not speculate in land his holdings provided the basis for one of the large fortunes of the Old Northwest in the pre-Civil War days.[1]

The growth of the cattle industry in the central Illinois prairies during the pre-Civil War decade was accompanied by similar expansion in corn production. The relationship of these increases in certain parts of the state suggested the widespread use of corn in fattening livestock. Illinois became the first state in corn production in 1860 whereas Ohio held the honor in 1850 and Tennessee in 1840. Counties in Illinois raising large quantities of corn in 1860 also provided large numbers of livestock. McLean county including Funk's Grove Township was one of the five counties producing over three million bushels of corn in 1860.

Isaac Funk became a member of the lower house of the Illinois State Legislature in 1840 and a member of the State Senate from 1862 until the time of his death in 1865. He also served as a member of the County Board of Supervisors from 1858 until his death. Leadership was not suddenly thrust upon Isaac Funk. He was well known for fair dealing and prompt payment in purchasing stock from the local farmers. For many years he provided a local market for them. It can be fairly said that although other leaders from Bloomington-Normal rose to recognition in other fields of endeavor Isaac Funk also became an effective spokesman from this significant agricultural area. Few contributed more to both the economic and political development of

George W. Funk   Jacob Funk   Duncan M. Funk

ISAAC AND CASSANDRA FUNK AND FAMILY

LaFayette Funk   Francis M. Funk   Benjamin F. Funk   Absalom Funk

Isaac Funk   Sarah Funk Kerrick

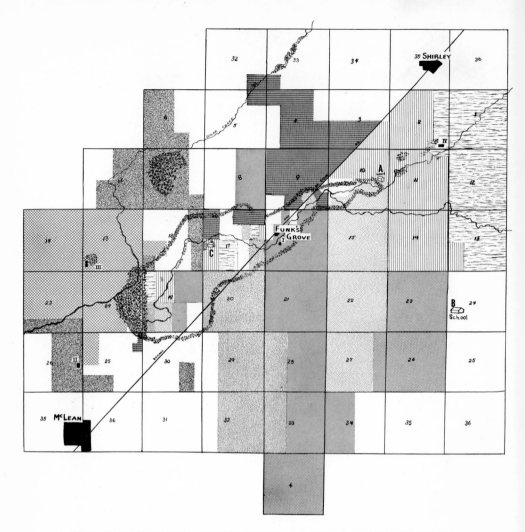

1874 MAP SHOWING DISTRIBUTION OF ISAAC FUNK HOLDINGS
AT TIME OF HIS DEATH

George Funk

Jacob Funk

D. M. Funk

LaFayette Funk

F. M. Funk

Ben Funk

Absalom Funk

Isaac Funk II

Sarah Funk Kerrick

HOMES:

  I Homestead (Isaac Funk)
 II George Funk
III Jacob Funk

IV LaFayette Funk

Outline of Funk's Grove Timber

Creeks

Railroad

A   E. D. Funk, Sr.,
     Country School

B   McIlvain School

C   Church

TOWNS:

Shirley

Funk's Grove

McLean

this prairie world in the pre-Civil War days. He affiliated early with the new Republican Party and was, according to one account, a trusted lieutenant of Jesse Fell and David Davis when Abraham Lincoln, who had often visited in the Funk home, was nominated in 1860 for the Presidency.

Before his sudden death in 1865 Isaac Funk was well known as a state legislator, cattle king and successful farmer. His able speech in the legislature against the Copperheads during the Civil War in 1863 sent his name ringing throughout the nation. As a spokesman for the rich agricultural lands of the central Corn Belt in Illinois he left to his descendants a heritage of responsible citizenship and agricultural leadership as well as wealth.[2]

Isaac and Cassandra Funk died within a few hours on January 29, 1865. No will remained to distribute the estate. Difficulties could easily have developed since the total value was estimated at more than one million dollars, including approximately 25,000 acres of land.[3] Succeeding generations pointed with pride to an amicable agreement by the nine descendants, concluded without benefit of legal aid. Each son and one daughter by mutual agreement received a fair share of the estate. Additional acreage was assigned to George, the eldest son, in recognition of his years of service as manager for his father. One of the great grandsons later recalled that George and Duncan were chiefly responsible for the business decisions necessary for the division. The eight brothers agreed to give to their only sister, the youngest child of Isaac, what they considered to be two choice sections of land.[4]

During the years following the Civil War, the children of Isaac followed chiefly their agricultural interests. Many also became legislators, buinessmen and bankers. They continued without exception to supervise, and in some instances, to live continuously on the land. Some moved to "town" in Bloomington where they established substantial residences. As a result of their inheritances they were individually large land owners. There was little doubt about their collective influence in agricultural affairs. The Funk brothers of the second generation were described as "farmers," in the real sense of the word, by their neighbors and friends because they lived and worked on the land. Their country homes were so located in the original holdings, that Funk's Grove Township became a community inhabited among others by many families of Funks. The central location of Funk's Grove, with its church, school and cemetery, drew the family as a magnet. The Church in the Grove, built in 1864–65, was of mid-

western carpentry construction with classical revival. Decoration
above windows and doors was distinctive. The beauty of the structure
was in the unpretentious simplicity of the straight lines.[5] A calm and
quiet atmosphere pervaded the surrounding countryside. This calm
and peaceful haven exerted deep influence upon those who lived
nearby.

Men of this second generation of Funks answered to the following
names: George was known to his brothers as the "General." He was
the oldest and often strict with his younger brothers. Jacob was called
"Jake" or "Javen"; A. B. was designated as "Abb" or "Stokey"; Duncan,
who had a foot ailment, was dubbed "Grunt" or "Dunc"; Isaac became
"Green" or "Ike"; Ben was called "Trott" and LaFayette answered to
"Att." Francis Marion was always called "Pete." By the turn of the
century there were eight Mrs. Funks, Senior, plus eight or nine Mrs.
Funks, Junior. Family custom employed to this day in order to avoid
confusion was to add the husband's name to that of the wife as "Aunt
Mary Jake"; "Aunt Fannie Ike"; and "Cousin Mamie Gene."[6] Many
others were designated in the same manner.

The country homes of the second generation were spacious and
comfortable. Some of the oldest sons established their residences before the death of their father. There is reason to believe that certain
sections of land were designated before his death and that the division
of the estate was rendered less difficult by this fact. For example, the
family homestead of Isaac and the homes of George in the southwestern corner of the holdings and of LaFayette in the northeastern
corner were all built according to the same basic floor plan. The home
of LaFayette, was the first to be erected according to this plan in
1863.[7] Center halls and straight stairways with music rooms or parlors
on one side, a living room with marble fireplaces, a large dining room
and possibly a study or library were usually included. The kitchens
were large and porches were considered a necessity.[8]

Funk's Grove was the central gathering point through the years for
the entire Funk family during reunions and other happy as well as
sad family occasions. Not far from the homes of LaFayette, F. M. and
Duncan, the non-incorporated village of Shirley was laid out and sur-
veyed by John Foster, September 14, 1866.[9] The Shirley hill on the
old Alton (now the Gulf, Mobile and Ohio railroad) was said to be
the second longest and heaviest grade on the route before the cut in
1912. The small community of Shirley provided a stopping place for
the Funks who lived in the northern part of the township. McLean
served equally well for those of the family who lived farther south.

These small communities, with Funk's Grove Station, were the station stops, in a manner of speaking, for the Funk family. Funk's Grove Township was ideally located to enable its inhabitants to live through every significant change that came to the Middle West in the late nineteenth and early twentieth centuries.

The problems confronting agriculture in the Middle West after the Civil War, became complex and difficult as new wests and competing crops developed. The rising tide of industrialism pressed upon the people in this section of the country. Pulsing lines of transportation passed their very doors. Yet something of the directness, simplicity and individualism characteristic of agrarianism remained with those who lived close to the land. Fundamental courtesies of ruralism as well as the inherent dignity of a gentry close to the soil clung to their everyday lives.

This community of Funk families located near Funk's Grove was so numerous that they were usually occupied in visiting among themselves. As a consequence the family was closely knit. Cousins were to each other almost like brothers and sisters. Joys and sorrows were shared by these families, especially by those of the same age groups. Although there were differences of opinion and possibly unconscious and unimportant rivalries, there was, in the long run, a strong blood bond between these members of the Isaac Funk family. One young woman was heard to remark that she never could understand why a Funk girl had to change her name when she married. This occurred before she herself became interested. The family possessed strong and identifiable characteristics reflected in succeeding generations. Men of the family kept these bonds securely cemented and the women originally named Funk were mindful of the fact.

The eight brothers and one sister composing the second generation of the Isaac Funk family were born on the Illinois prairie in the days when the Old Northwest was fast attaining recognition in the Union. They grew to adulthood in the middle part of the nineteenth century. As the children of an agricultural pioneer who attained economic success before 1865, they also for the most part were successful in their own right. Some received considerable recognition. Their conversations, activities and interests provided rich background for the training of young men destined to meet problems in the twentieth century. There was little in the agricultural world that escaped their attention. In these years they were individually and collectively interested in local, state and national affairs.

The small towns of Shirley and McLean witnessed the comings and goings of those who lived nearby. When the roads were bad or impassable there was only one way out—by the railroad. The way freight or "weigh freight" carried its share of traveling Funks back and forth. Traveling to Bloomington in the morning and back on the evening train was an easy trip.

When the second generation established their homes in Bloomington they lived near each other. George was located on East Washington at the corner of Gridley and about three blocks from the court house square. Jacob first located on the northeast corner of Gridley and Front streets and later remodeled the home of Judge Weldon near this corner. At the southwest corner of Gridley and Grove, A. B. 's residence was number 310 Grove. Almost directly across from George, the Cheney home was located. Descendants of those who named Cheney's Grove in the early years were lifelong friends of the Funk family. Another concentrated group of Funks lived around Franklin Square, only some six or seven blocks north. The homes of Duncan, F. M., Isaac, II, and of Lon and Sarah Kerrick as well as Frank Funk in later years were found near the Fifers, Burrs and Stevensons. Ben was located not far away on North Main Street.

Several of the brothers became bankers. Jacob was president of the State National Bank of Bloomington for thirty-six years. Duncan held the presidency of the First National Bank of Bloomington for thirty-nine years, and was a stockholder in the First National Bank of Shelbyville. These long-term presidencies are probably records with few parallels in Illinois history. F. M. was a stockholder in the First National. LaFayette was a director in the State National and First National Banks of Bloomington. A. B. was also a stockholder and director in the First National Bank. George was interested in banking in Atlanta, Lincoln and Springfield. These affiliations served to consolidate the economic position of the Funk brothers.[10]

Bloomington was the county seat of one of the most productive agricultural counties in the United States. The county court house stood directly in the center of the square. The commercial area surrounded the square on all sides. Among the familiar structures was a two story wooden building known as Adam's Ark run by Adam Guthrie who also came to the community as an early settler in 1826. This store was the gathering place for the Funk brothers, George Stubblefield, Ike Lasch, Adlai Stevenson, Sr., Jim Ewing, Jake Lindley, Jim Neville, Joe Fifer, John Dawson, Guy Carlton, Sr., and many others. The stories repeated around the circle often grew in the telling; the "deep snows" somehow became deeper each year.

The Funks usually appeared in cowhide boots, broad brimmed black hat and long frock coat. Sometimes Duncan and A. B. and Ben would come in from the farms. These men discussed any major issue in current politics. Civic responsibility was as much a part of their lives as raising livestock and crops. If the conversation was punctuated with a little profanity, the exchange of ideas was nevertheless genial and amiable. The Funk brothers were held in high regard. Often they asked Adam Guthrie for his opinions. Adam's Ark was in reality the public forum of the day.

These men were the immediate descendants of the pioneer age. If their manner was a little rough, their integrity was unquestioned and their words were as good as their bonds. They talked of cattle, crops, weather and of the Good Old Times. Better than anything they loved a good joke on each other. They were men of rugged individuality, of spiritual unity, of loyalty to their immediate area, their state and nation. The brothers considered themselves to be an integral part of the community. They welcomed newcomers and in these discussions they did not "put on the dog" in the vernacular of the times.[11] The successor to Adam's Ark was Cash Harlan's Cigar Store located south of the site of the present McLean County Bank. George Funk for many years occupied "his chair" here. He took delight in putting young upstarts in their place when with a twinkle in his eye he set the record straight.[12]

LaFayette was one son of Isaac who lived consistently on the land, never establishing a residence in nearby Bloomington. He built his home from lumber felled in the Grove. Three years were spent in the process of building. Everything was done by hand. He promised his father that he would not marry until he reached the age of thirty, but an attractive young woman, Elizabeth Paullin, changed this program slightly. When they were married in Columbus, Ohio January 12, 1864 he lacked eight days of reaching the required date. Mrs. LaFayette Funk was born on a farm near Charleston, Ohio. The couple proceeded to Illinois where an "in fair" was held at the home of Isaac to welcome them. The members of the large family and their guests sat in a circle. Two chairs were placed in the center for the couple who were the center of attention. With a remarkable show of independence this young couple refused to take the designated chairs.

Many times Mrs. LaFayette Funk saw dozens of prairie chickens on the lands surrounding her new home. Sometimes a continuous line would perch on the fence around the house. She traveled back and forth on horseback in the early days to take corn for meal to Moore's

Mill west of McLean, riding side saddle with the bag of corn behind her. She recalled that the entire estate of Isaac was surrounded by a boundary fence, but with no line fences. Inside of the boundary hundreds of cattle grazed.[13] She was the first to introduce angel food cake to her new neighborhood. Grandsons fondly recalled Grandma's well-filled cookie jar.

The interior of the home of LaFayette has been so well preserved that descriptions applicable to the late nineteenth century seem to fit in with the comfortable rooms as they appear in 1958. Many of the valuable early pieces of furniture have been wisely retained in their original places. The central entrance was seldom used by the La-Fayette family because the double doors were constantly locked. Gypsies might wander that way. Peddlers were seldom welcomed. As a consequence, from the iron fence and hitching post visitors followed a limestone walk to the porch where another doorway brought them into the living room. On cool days a fire burned in the marble fireplace. The library was back of the living room. One of the most interesting pieces of furniture was an eight by ten foot desk, reaching to the ceiling. The parlor in the front part of the house demanded proper behavior especially from the children. The grand piano was not to be played for amusement, and children must look carefully at the glassed-in cases of coral and other rare stones and prized pieces. Gold cornices adorned the long windows. A large mirror built on marble footing reached to the ceiling. The dining room table could seat sixteen and the sideboard with its marble top matched the desk in height. These large pieces of furniture were ordered in Philadelphia by Mrs. LaFayette Funk. A ten-foot orange tree stood in the big bay window of the dining room.[14]

The barn stood a distance of more than a city block away from the house. A long brick building near the walk leading to the garden and grape arbor included the ice house, smoke house and tool room. When hogs were butchered, the smell of hickory smoke foretold burlap-sacked hams and bacon hanging from the rafters.[15]

A typical winter spent in the country on his farm ten miles south of Bloomington was described vividly in the partial *Diary* kept by LaFayette Funk during the early part of the year 1867. New Year's Day was not one of rest. The stock was fed and a new gate was hung. Daily activities in January included a trip to the timber, gathering corn, salting the cattle or possibly walking about a mile to Shirley. Business problems often necessitated conferences with the brothers. On his way to Jake's to visit George, LaFayette met him instead at the Old Homestead. Often George spent the night with LaFayette. There were always necessary trips to Shirley or McLean to pick up the mail or to the timber for a load of wood. Hogs were butchered for meat, and lard was rendered on the farm. Storms were frequent and often severe, as on January 25, 1867, when more snow fell than for many past years. A trip to Bloomington by sleigh while the sleet clung to the trees was always a beautiful sight.[16]

The creeks were high in February. Again it was impossible to make a contemplated journey to see brother Jake. Again LaFayette stopped off at the Old Homestead. When the roads to Bloomington were impassable in February, LaFayette walked the ten miles. As a constant and accurate observer, LaFayette rarely failed to describe the weather conditions in his *Diaries,* usually arising at five a. m. to make his first observation. Trips to Bloomington were not uncommon every few weeks. Once in a while the "hired girl" made the trip with Mr. and Mrs. LaFayette. Business in Bloomington was never very brisk when the roads were poor. Often roads were a foot deep in mud and at times frozen into hard, bumpy ruts.[17]

There were community responsibilities such as improvement of roads and new school districts. LaFayette, during the absence of his wife "Lib" who was visiting in Ohio, was busy hauling loads of posts, planting early potatoes and working in the garden.[18] The year of 1867 was a memorable one because the oldest son of LaFayette arrived in the early fall.

Eugene Duncan Funk was born September 2, 1867, near Shirley, in Funks Grove Township near the city of Bloomington, McLean County, Illinois. A second son born in 1871, Edgar Paullin, died in 1873. A third son, DeLoss, arrived in 1882. The Funk family of Funk's Grove was already widely recognized in the state, region and nation at the time of Eugene's birth. During his childhood his parents, uncles, aunts and cousins exerted influence upon his thinking and his actions. His rise to agricultural leadership during about four score years included more than the story of one locality.

As a child, Eugene heard many stories of his grandfather, for his father and uncles never tired of retelling them. His father's hearty laugh emphasized their importance. One remained in his thinking over the years. Isaac rode a dun pony on his many trips to Chicago before the days of train transportation. Once he was offered in exchange for his horse, the land where the Palmer House now stands at State and Monroe streets. The exchange was refused, enabling Isaac's descendants thus to account for their continued attachment to the countryside. They often humorously thank the dun pony and Isaac's good judgment for delivering them from life in the big city. Another story repeated at many Funk gatherings emphasized the traditional honesty of grandfather Isaac. When he owed a sum of money at a Springfield bank he sent two of his sons posthaste from Chicago with gold to cover the amount. The two sons divided the distance with the second reaching the bank before it was opened on the appointed day. When the banker arrived to open the bank he remarked to Funk, "What are you doing here?" His reply, "I came to pay my father's note, due today," The banker said, "It wasn't necessary to be so prompt." Funk replied, "You don't know my father." Love of country life, attention to integrity and honesty became part of the heritage of young Eugene.

According to one account, Isaac Funk was at the Battle of Kellogg's Grove June 25, 1832 during the Black Hawk uprising. He had made a trip to Galena and was returning to his home in McLean County when he came upon the fresh trail of Indians and informed Major John Dement. Funk is said to have stopped at Kellogg's Tavern for the night. Some accounts referred to Isaac Funk as "Captain" and declared that he volunteered and rode to Dixon's Ferry for help. The act was considered a very brave one in face of grave danger.[19]

The boy, Eugene, attended the one room country school across the road and down the creek from his home. Often he was the only pupil in attendance. About 1878 he was described as playing with his big Newfoundland dog, a pet deer or an antelope or riding his pony after his father's herd of buffalo. Both play and work were part of his boyhood schedule. Early in the 1870's he tried to help his father plant the Osage Orange hedge that borders Research Acres made famous by Eugene Funk in later years.[20] One of his first literary efforts, "The Walnut Tree," was written in 1879.

The horse and buggy age developed and prospered; a pleasant age despite limitations, because horses watched the road for the driver. Probably those who lived through it never grasped in entirety "that this level land with every acre in intensive production was one of the wonders of the world." More often those near Funk's Grove were concerned with looking for timber mushrooms or admiring a solitary white heron watching for fish along the edge of the small lake in the grove.[21] This was the Bloomington, Shirley, Funk's Grove, McLean scene during the early years of the life of Eugene Duncan Funk, Sr. He learned to love the level lands, for here were family and home. Funk's Grove, famous Illinois landmark, always reminded him of the pioneer's faith in the soil of the central prairies.

CHAPTER II

Cattle, Crops and Land · 1865–1890

A PERIOD OF RAPID GROWTH in the western range cattle industry occurred following the Civil War. For some years in the far west cattle had prospered on the trails followed by both the southern and northern herds. A widening network of railroads beyond the Mississippi insured supplies of red meat for America and Europe. This expansion presented a challenge to the descendants of the beef kings on the Illinois prairies. The Funk brothers, sons of Isaac, inheriting their father's reputation as one of the leading cattle men of the pre Civil War days, also acquired experience during their early years as his assistants. The expansion of the range cattle business into the far west presented alternatives to men in Illinois. They could continue, as their father before them, to obtain cattle from the west and bring them to the grass and corn of central Illinois. They could secure their own western ranches in order to produce their supplies of cattle and thus avoid the high prices charged by dealers in Nebraska, Wyoming and in Montana. The activities of the Funk brothers 1865–90 indicate that they were well aware of the problems inherent in both their business activities and in their location. As suppliers of livestock their location near the expanding meat packing industry of Chicago proved to be advantageous.[1] They were alert to all important changes affecting the livestock industry.

During twenty-three years, 1867–1890 when Eugene was growing up on his father's farm, he learned how to raise and finish fine cattle. His father, LaFayette, with his uncles participated in the new organizations, bought cattle in the west and fattened them on the Illinois prairies. Eugene often traveled with his father. He also learned how the farms in Funk's Grove Township were managed. Land values and proportion of acreages in corn and pasture as related to breeding and feeding of livestock became part of his everyday knowledge.

One of the earliest group meetings in the area occurred when stock dealers of McLean County in August 1868 met in Bloomington, with John Nicholas as chairman and B. F. Funk as secretary. They took decisive action in regard to Texas cattle. William Thomas, J. K.

13

Orendorff and L. F. Funk reported resolutions expressing the sense of the meeting and a plan of action to prevent the spread of Texas fever prevalent in the eastern part of the county. These resolutions requested and required that citizens of Bloomington and vicinity who had such cattle should not remove them from present herding grounds until the disease disappeared. A committee of three was appointed to visit herds in the eastern portion of the county and to notify herdsmen, "that the community will not tolerate their removal." Railroads were requested to cease unloading Texas, Cherokee or diseased cattle within the limits of the county. The committee of three included B. F. Funk, J. K. Orendorff and James Rayburn. A kind of local vigilante arrangement thus developed for checking the dreaded Texas fever.[2]

The first oral report indicated that the Texas cattle were healthy but communicated disease to the native cattle. Of one herd of 125 native cattle, 14 died in one day. The loss in the county was estimated at over $25,000. A committee of ten including B. F. Funk and D. Funk was appointed to visit those owning Texas cattle. The last three named, on motion of B. F., were to start legal proceedings against any person who owned or had Texas cattle in their possession. The Association undertook permanent organization with President William Nicholas, Secretary B. F. Diggs and Treasurer Duncan Funk.[3] The Association also undertook to prevent transportation of hides from dead cattle to Bloomington for sale or shipment.[4]

The directors of the recently formed Union Stockyards in Chicago reported in 1869 that despite the declining numbers of Texas cattle during the summer because of disease and the restrictions in Illinois that the business was growing. With the extension of the railroads through Kansas and into Texas the Chicago market was bound to expand. For seven months during the year herds could be brought through the state without harm to native herds.[5]

According to the *Pantagraph* in 1874, "McLean County has become the most important in the State in the fine Stock business and it was proper that she should lead off in this enterprise" by organizing a Stock Breeders' Association. The Committee appointed to prepare a constitution and a plan of organization included LaFayette Funk.[6] A Blooded Stock Sales Association was also reported. Among those interested were LaFayette and F. M. Funk.[7]

The Funks purchased cattle during the seventies in Kansas and Colorado and Kentucky.[8] During 1877 there were 46,136 head in McLean county; of this total there were 21,266 in the western part of the county.[9] Funk's Grove Township took the lead over other townships in McLean County with 3,315 head of cattle. There were fed on the Funk Farms in 1880 some two thousand head of cattle and about the same number of hogs. In addition about 1,200 yearlings were wintered through for next winter's feeding.

The Funks aimed to feed cattle that would eventually weigh from 1500 pounds upward so that they would be heavy enough for foreign shipment. They depended on selection of good cattle because they knew that their excellent blue grass pastures, shade and running water would contribute the necessary aids. The Funks mowed about two thousand acres and fed up all their hay. They purchased upward of sixty thousand bushels of corn and raised some two hundred and fifty thousand bushels, growing in corn and oats over six thousand acres.[10]

An account of the acquisition of land by Isaac Funk, 1824-65 including estimates of the initial cost of the land has already been given.[11] The average value of the land in McLean County, according to the census of 1880 fifteen years after the death of Isaac, was $30.00 per acre.[12] A few tracts sold as high as $35.00 per acre. Many acres were disposed of at $25.00 each. There were instances where the best prairie land within ten miles of Bloomington, the county seat, was disposed of at $20.00 per acre. These tracts by 1890 were worth $75.00 per acre. Sales were made throughout the county at $60.00 and the general average was not less than $50.00 per acre. This situation probably accounts for the interest of the Funks during the decade of the eighties in western lands.

The western range cattle industry was naturally of interest to the Funks who were among the first producers and feeders on Illinois prairie land. Mr. A. B. Funk returned in 1881 from a brief tour in Nebraska, where he looked over ground with the possible thought of establishing a "mammoth cattle ranch in conjunction with his brothers Isaac, Duncan and Jacob." Northwestern Nebraska appeared to be the best possible place. Their idea was to stock the ranch with 1,200 to 1,500 cows as the beginning of a vast herd. They had a cousin in the state who could manage the estate if it should be established. According to one account, the activity of the Funks was centered in the Loup River country where the Loup Cattle Company was formed in the 1890's.

Trips to the far west were not unusual. As early as 1874 several members of the George, Duncan, Jacob and LaFayette Funk families made the journey to Yosemite in California.[13]

A record of a western trip in 1883 to New Mexico included LaFayette, B. F. and young Gene. A committee was sent to New Mexico by the J. D. Gillette Cattle Company for the purpose of locating a ranch. Members of this committee were Captain Isaac Keayes of Springfield, Isaac Van Ordstrand of Heyworth, Andrew Turner of Atlanta, B. F. Funk of Bloomington, LaFayette and son, Gene, of Shirley, Illinois.

LaFayette described the route and territory. The group traveled via the Chicago, Alton and St. Louis to Kansas City, thence by the Atcheson, Topeka and Santa Fe to Socorro, New Mexico. They continued their trip some 128 miles westward proceeding by train and wagon. LaFayette commented that the territory was not so well adapted as he expected for grazing and rearing livestock. They climbed for 100 miles to a summit of 8,000 feet above sea level where the divide sloped to the Pacific.[14] He observed that the formation was mostly plains and low hills with mountain ranges on either side of the road. As a veteran cattle feeder he was constantly aware that the grazing was not what an Illinoisian would call very good. He noted that grass of different varieties of gramma was thin on the ground unlike the blue grass, timothy or white clover farms he was accustomed to see in the states. LaFayette estimated that half a ton could be cut to the acre although the natives claimed that two and a half tons would be a possible total. Scarcity of water was the greatest objection he could find in this territory. The trip included visits to Snake Ranch owned by a Mexican and stocked with about 700 cattle, located fifteen miles from Socorro; then to Pueblo Springs, fifteen miles from Snake Ranch where there was a good but limited supply of grass; and finally to Datal Springs some fifty miles from Pueblo. "This ranch has the surroundings" was the only comment made in the *Diary*. [15]

Eugene, at the age of seventeen, also kept an account of the trip to Socorro, particularly as it pertained to his own experiences. Although he may not have recognized the potential advantages or disadvantages of the land, he could scarcely avoid learning in the company of these experienced cattle men. While his father wrote of the grazing areas, young Gene concentrated on hunting. One hundred and twenty miles from Socorro he was expected to remain behind because there was no horse for him to ride when the other members of the party left on a hunting expedition. When his father and the guide returned they reported seven deer feeding. Young Gene recorded: "I was not long in strapping on my cartridge belt and hunt-

ing knife and filling my Winchester magazine full of fresh cartridges."
Seated behind his father, they departed on a wild Mexican pony that
did not particularly enjoy carrying the weight of two men. When
Gene saw his first doe he was so excited that he neglected to tell
his father. In his haste he landed flat on the ground, scrambled to
his feet, fired and missed the shot. At the second shot the deer
scampered. Distrusting the horse, the young hunter walked the remainder of the distance. Soon he saw five deer, some still feeding and others lying down. A bullet fired at the buck struck the
ground beyond its mark. The other deer took to their heels. Realizing that his record as a young hunter was lost at this point, Gene
determined not to return to camp without something to show for
his efforts.

After three hours he turned back to camp. As he blazed away at a
cottontail he suddenly and unexpectedly caught sight of four deer.
He first shot the one that was lying down so it would not frighten
the others. This shot hit the mark. He shot the second. Success again!
The third animal, a young buck, was not over forty yards away. He
hit the target. Only fifty yards distant the fourth animal was
wounded. Time consumed in killing these four deer did not exceed
ten minutes. The young marksman was a mile from camp. Upon his
return the older men insisted that he must have bought the deer
from some old hunters. They later discovered that the bullets went
through the hearts of three animals—but it took five bullets to kill
the fourth one. The hides were salted and dried on top of the covered
wagon. As a result of this experience the trip was delayed for two
days, but young Gene no longer worried about his reputation as a
hunter.[16]

During the year 1885 A. B. Funk and Isaac II obtained sheep in
Montana. Interests developed near Miles City. "Uncle" John Lisk's
grandchildren were in charge there.[17] Centers in Cheyenne, Wyoming and Miles City, Montana also developed. The western range
cattle business reached its highest point in the eighties.[18] A year after
his trip to Socorro young Gene and his Uncle Jacob departed July
1885, from Shirley via the Chicago and Alton Railroad to Chicago,
thence by the Northwestern Railroad to St. Paul with their destination Miles City, Montana. A day by day record of this trip again
revealed the attention given to close observation by this eighteen
year old. He noted that barns were often larger than houses and
that the fields across the prairies showed few fences. Wheat fields
near Fargo, North Dakota, good grass, absence of timber, and

small railroad stations located every twenty-five or thirty miles caught his attention. Miles City, Montana:

> ... like all other Western towns is situated in a small valley between two small mountains or two chains of "Bad Lands" as the Montana folks call them. The Yellowstone River runs close by with its rushing and surging torrent.[19]

Miles City claimed 2,000 inhabitants living for the most part in frame houses. Some brick stores, according to Gene's account, were located in the business district. The ranch where "Uncle" John Lisk was working for the Funks was located seventy-five miles from the city. Following a route across the Yellowstone River north of Miles City, they found buffalo bones and heads of animals killed three or four years previously. During the afternoon they came upon the Bad Lands:

> A description of which it is almost impossible for me to give to any who has never seen anything of the kind. Geysers that have once been on fire and burnt & cooled off are the only thing I can think of to describe them with. They consist of a chain of butes or hills several miles long and of different widths. They look as though they had at some time been just one mass of melted rock and fire and some act of Providence has put the fire out before it had all been burned out.[20]

A small dugout once used by buffalo hunters provided shelter for the first night out of Miles City. The next morning they passed "Crow Rock" where Eugene wrote: "The Crow and Sue [sic] Indians a few years ago, had a big fight." He carved his name there along with the other "hunters." The ranch, sighted about four o'clock in the afternoon, consisted of one main house with a fifteen by twenty-five foot room. Beds stood in two corners of the room, one above the other, each wide enough for two cowboys. A cooking stove and a table supported on four stakes driven into the ground were located in the same room. Chairs and stools were made from logs sawed in two, with three legs driven into them. Two storehouses and a stable for ten head were half dugouts with dirt roofs. The most disturbing factors were the strong alkali taste of the water and the departure of the cook in the morning, without notice. The visitors slept in a tent on the nearby hill, rising to prepare their own breakfast of coffee, cold biscuit, bacon, rice and canned corn. Their first activity was to obtain more hay for softer beds.[21]

One purpose of the expedition was to sight some game if possible. Young Eugene did not hesitate to catch "Old Blue" for a ten mile solitary and unsuccessful ride in search of antelope. Upon his return to camp ten cowboys arrived with over 600 head of cattle later separated for their various owners. The cowboys "cut" the cattle by grouping them in small numbers. This process intrigued the young man from the Illinois prairies, who wrote as follows:

With all the cowboys around holding them up together then two or three of the men on very quick and active ponies go in among the cattle and drive or "cut" out the separate brands of cattle into different bunches. Some of the cattle are very wild and mean about driving & the horses had a great deal of running and quick turning to do. Then when the cattle were all cut we took the calves that belong to this ranch over to the corral and brand them with the ⱬ brand on both sides.[22]

Eugene was also impressed by the effort of eight cowboys, including himself, to bring about 200 head of cattle into a pen covering less than an acre. They "bunched" the "cattle" a few rods from the yard and then from a circle drove them into the pen. The cowboys broke into song, possibly to let the cattle know they were surrounded. Eugene had never heard anything like the resulting noise, "Not even when I hear my Father loading cattle at Shirley." The cow punchers did not choose to sleep indoors after an afternoon temperature of 114°. They threw their blankets down on the ground.[23] They saddled the ponies on the next afternoon to hunt for antelope and to count the 743 head of cattle.[24] When Uncle Jake's horse was bitten by a snake, the remedy was "to put onion on it."

A thirty mile ride took them to the top of Three Top Mountain, where it was almost possible to see the Missouri River about 40 miles away. Frank Lisk and Gene traveled to Buffalo Gap to look for antelope. The following day they departed for Red Water Camp. Uncle Jake and Gene searched for water and a possible location for a shack next winter. They saw bear tracks,[25] scared up a large black tail buck and succeeded in killing a sage hen for supper.[26] The next day found them at the top of Little Sheep Mountain spending the hours hunting with no results.[27] They slept on the ground "with bumps and stones as large as my fist punching me right in the ribs all night." The morning's hunt produced only six young grouse. By this time they were more than ready to return to Red Water Camp. On August 7 they left for the home ranch on Timber Creek. Frank Lisk and Gene took the route by Dry Creek about twenty-five miles, saw twenty antelope but failed to get one.[28]

On August 10 the day before departure for Miles City, Gene determined to try his luck once more. Before noon he had succeeded in killing two antelope about ten miles from camp. His arrival at camp with the game surprised the older men. They departed the next day from the ranch to the heart of Timber Creek, thence to "Crow Rock" and Coal Bank Springs to Owen's Ranch and finally to Miles City. There they visited the city and Fort Keitch, where Gene purchased Indian moccasins and buckskin for whip crackers. Gene, Sr. in his later years retold with enthusiasm the events of this trip to his four young sons.[29] After three western trips Eugene realized that the far west was no imaginary place. At the age of eighteen he saw the wide expansion of the frontier west and realized that the agricultural areas of Illinois must compete effectively. Efficient farm operations could be the difference between profit and loss on the Illinois prairies.

Land management by the Funks in Illinois followed a recognizable pattern. LaFayette leased some of his 2,000 acres of land, or about half of it, for grain rent, receiving two-fifths from the tenant. He farmed some land but left considerable acreage in meadow and pasture. He cut his own meadow and put up large quantities of hay for the winter. He had in June 1888, from 300 to 400 head of cattle on hand. Each season 75 to 100 Christmas beeves weighing about 1800 pounds were sent to Chicago. From 40 to 50 horses, mostly Percherons, with a few road horses known as roadsters were also profitable. F. M., located one mile south of Shirley, with approximately 2,000 acres, also kept part of his land in pasture and meadow. He also put up his own hay and let tillable land for two-fifth grain rent. F. M., in 1888, was a member of the firm of Funk and Johnson, stockmen, who bought and shipped on the market. Although at one time he was of the firm of Funk and Lachey, druggists, his principal business was cattle raising with 300 on hand. By 1888 he had from 80 to 100 good grade colts for sale including mares, work horses and good road horses. He raised up to 20 Percheron colts for sale each year.

L. H. Kerrick, husband of Isaac's daughter, Sarah, followed the same procedure regarding hay and grain rent, and kept 60 to 80 Percherons and 200 to 300 head of cattle. B. F. also operated on the same basis. He, in common with his brothers, bought all of the grain raised by tenants, if they wished to sell. Tenants, however, were at liberty to sell to whom they pleased. He kept a number of hired hands to feed and care for the cattle and to cut and make the hay. Isaac II followed the same method and fed about the same number of cattle. He owned 30 to 40 head of grade Percherons and three imported horses, one a trotting horse and the other two Percherons. A. B. managed his farm near Shirley with 300 to 400 head of cattle and the same two-fifths arrangement for grain. He maintained 40 to 50

Stone Marking Site of
First Log Cabin

Last Home of Isaac Funk
. . . Homestead

George W. Funk Home

Jacob Funk Home

LaFayette Funk Home

Eugene D. Funk Farm

Eugene D. Funk Home

Deane Funk Home

Percherons. Duncan employed the same program, owned 50 head of horses, mostly Percherons. These horses he raised himself, usually keeping them until they were about three years old. Then he shipped them east, where they sold in numbers from three to twelve. These animals were widely known in eastern markets as "Funk Colts."

Jacob, located two and one-half miles north of McLean with 2,500 acres kept 600 head of cattle, 60 to 80 horses, mostly Percherons, with some roadsters. He also owned at this time 15 to 20 pure blood Angus cattle. He also rented land for two-fifths grain raised. Charles, eldest son of Jacob and one of the firm of Funk and Carr, importers of Percherons, held 600 acres of land near McLean. He devoted his entire attention to horses. In 1886, Funk and Carr imported seven horses from Perce, France. Two years later Frank Carr, along with George Stubblefield of Bloomington and J. N. Franklin of Lexington, journeyed to France to make another importation.

George, the eldest of the Funk brothers, held 3,500 acres of land, largely located in the vicinity of McLean, Old Town and Heyworth. He kept, in 1888, about 700 to 800 head of cattle but only enough horses for his necessary work. He was not interested in raising horses. He also operated his farms for two-fifths grain rent.[30]

The Funk estate shipped in 1888 more than 3,000 head of fat cattle, and more than 1,000 head of fat hogs, besides some horses and sheep. The principal activity of raising cattle allowed most of the land to remain as pasture. Isaac Funk II, in addition to his cattle business, owned over 100 head of finely bred horses and about 300 sheep. Jacob Funk was also interested in horses.[31]

The LaFayette Funk farm was provided with numerous barns, sheds, granaries, all models in their way, kept up to a high degree of usefulness. Stalls for horses and cattle as well as the ground around the barn were paved with brick. Near the house there was a beautiful deer park. The fish ponds were stocked with bass, cat and pike.[32] LaFayette at one time maintained a herd of buffalo.

LaFayette Funk devoted much of his time to the raising of cattle. Shorthorns were his specialty. His seventy Shorthorns were among the best in Illinois. Approximately 800 head of cattle and 150 hogs were sold each year.

Feeding occurred generally through the summer and fall because of the trend away from feeding cattle through the winter. Extra fat cattle ready for shipment would weigh from 1,600 to 2,000 pounds each. They consumed about one-half bushel of corn per day, gaining two or three pounds per day. LaFayette Funk proceeded on the theory that feeding old corn was a better idea. His pastures were never overcrowded with stock. The entire farm was divided into fields of about 160 acres each. Different kinds of cattle were kept apart. Calves were allotted to one field; yearling steers to another. Cattle of different ages were also separated by fields. Calves were fed oats the first winter and kept on pasture. Little corn was fed except to the fattening stock.

More than sixteen miles of tile with outlets to a branch of Sugar Creek were located on the LaFayette Funk farm. Bored wells and one flowing well afforded an ample supply of water for the cattle. Salt, protected by a self feeding device introduced by Eugene Funk, Sr., was constantly before all of the cattle.

Approximately 1,300 acres on this farm remained in native grass, thought to be sweeter and better than the cultivated grasses. LaFayette Funk stated emphatically that his pastures would not be plowed up during his lifetime. About one-half of the remaining land was given over to the cultivation of corn and oats, with the rest in meadow and timber. All of the grain was raised by the tenants who gave two-fifths of the oats and two-fifths of the corn in the crib or in the shock, as Mr. Funk directed. There were only two tenant houses in 1881 on this extensive farm and only two hired hands were employed. Mr. Funk remarked, "I do lots of work myself." About as much grain was raised as was fed, with Mr. Funk purchasing the greater portion of the tenants' shares. Only enough horses were kept to do the work of the farm.[33]

Rotation of crops was practiced, with corn planted where oats had grown. Every few years some of the land was put down to clover. Roads in and around the farmstead were gradually being gravelled with material from the place. LaFayette Funk was enthusiastic about good cattle and good farming, taking great pride in the best methods for obtaining these results. The *Pantagraph* wisely stated, "He is an independent farmer of whom there are scores in this vicinity. But few of them are as well fixed financially as is Mr. Funk, but it shows what well-directed energy and careful management can accomplish within one generation here in central Illinois." [34]

Under dateline from Kansas City, an article entitled "Cattle Kings in Convention" reported the election of Senator LaFayette Funk of Illinois as permanent chairman of the National Association in November 1887. Mr. Funk announced that the most important work to come before the convention was the pleuro-pneumonia question considered of vital importance to all stock men. He also observed that there was a universal complaint by stock men all over the country regarding the depression of the market. He saw no immediate prospect for better prices. He also thought that Kansas City was destined to become a great cattle market. During the morning sessions of the Consolidated Cattle Growers Association, a report from the legislative committee was read and referred to the committee on resolutions. The report reviewed the work accomplished in efforts to procure congressional assistance in destroying contagious diseases. There was included a denunciation of the chairman of the House Committee on Agriculture to whose influence the committee attributed the defeat of the Miller-Campbell bill. Several papers were read including one by Dr. Campbell entitled "The Lesson of the Chicago Outbreak of Pleuro-Pneumonia." Among the large numbers of resolutions was one denouncing the oleomargarine tax.[35]

Well directed energies enabled LaFayette Funk to do more than supervise his agricultural holdings. He noted as usual in his *Diary* the condition of the weather when he proceeded to the meeting of the State Board of Agriculture at Springfield, January 1, 1889. It was clear and pleasant. Two days later he observed that there was no snow or rain at any point in the United States "a phenomena that has never occurred since the Signal Service has been in operation." [36] He conferred in Chicago with a committee regarding the New Horse Show.[37] His family attended the inauguration in Springfield of Governor Joseph Fifer, also from Bloomington, and a close friend of the family.

Frequent trips to Bloomington, shipping cattle to Chicago, attending farmers' institutes, trips to Chicago with the cattle and hogs kept LaFayette almost constantly on the road.[38] A trip to St. Louis to attend the Convention of States on "the proposed cattle combine of Chicago and Kansas City" occurred in February 1889.

When at home he busied himself with selecting trees to be cut from the timber, measuring the inside content space of corn cribs, receiving cattle shipments from Chicago, planting potatoes, sending money to young Gene at school, attending township elections or looking after sick animals. His work with the State Fair at Peoria, directors' meetings of two banks in Bloomington, with many other responsibilities kept LaFayette thoroughly occupied.[39]

There were days when he would work around the farm in the morning and be off to Springfield in the afternoon or to Chicago to attend a Shorthorn sale. On Sundays, when visiting among relatives for dinner and the afternoon was usually the order of the day, he was almost always at home. A drive to Jake's, to Kerricks', Ike's or Dunc's, or perhaps dinner in town at one of the brothers' homes was possible.[40] Their hospitality was soon returned.

Interest in the stock growing activities of his neighbors and brothers took him on Sunday visits to Tom Rusk's, to Lon Kerrick's or to George Funk's place, to look over their cattle.[41] On occasions, the preacher and his wife took Sunday dinner with the family. A cattle sale at Stephens' and Ewings' or a horse sale by Dillon also attracted attention but not always purchases.[42]

A local newspaper mentioned the fact that friends of the Hon. LaFayette Funk would recommend him for the position of Commissioner of Agriculture in President Harrison's cabinet. A dispatch from Washington appearing in the *Chicago Herald* declared that Senators Cullom and Farwell were supporting him. They also supported a candidate for Commissioner of Internal Revenue. It was thought that two appointments from Illinois would not be received. LaFayette Funk does not mention the possibility in his *Diary* 1889,[43] nor was he selected.

When the stock show of 1889 opened in Chicago, Mr. and Mrs. LaFayette and DeLoss, age 7, attended. Weighing the show cattle often kept LaFayette at the job until 10 o'clock at night. Sometimes there was dissatisfaction on the part of spectators with the decisions of the judging committee and decisions regarding awards would have to be made.[44]

Corn, other field crops and livestock were the chief products of the Funk Farms. Gene realized that the wide range of information acquired by his father and his uncles through travel, observation and active participation enabled them to compete successfully. He recognized early in his life the necessity for a combination of scientific and practical knowledge with civic leadership in order to secure programs beneficial to agricultural interests.

CHAPTER III

Civic Responsibility · 1865–1890

IMPORTANT ISSUES with effective spokesmen developed after the Civil War in the agricultural community surrounding Bloomington, Illinois in McLean County. When railroad and warehouse rates became burdensome to agricultural interests the Funks clearly stated their positions. Young Eugene soon realized that his well-known grandfather, Isaac, had been one of the leaders of the new Republican Party in the formative years along with his contemporaries Abraham Lincoln, Jesse Fell, David Davis, Leonard Swett and many other friends from the region.[1] He heard of the consistent support given by his father and uncles to that party. He also learned that a Funk was expected to participate, to speak up and to assume responsibilities of leadership. He became aware that such responsibilities required a well-seasoned knowledge of men and events.

While Eugene remained at home during his first seventeen years, 1867–1884, major problems of state and national government were often under discussion. Three significant changes were gradually and steadily taking place on the national scene including (1) the economic, social and political changes in the South; (2) the rise of the industrial Northeast; (3) the widespread and intensive agricultural revolution in the West. Illinois was affected by all these changes as were her sister states, Indiana, Ohio, Michigan, and Wisconsin in the Old Northwest. The effects of these changes were not immediately discernible. Legislative answers to the problems they created were not quickly forthcoming. Illinois was primarily an agricultural state up to 1870, with the major part of the population following agricultural pursuits. Manufacturing, trade and transportation were dependent upon the basic activity.[2]

On the regional scene, spokesmen for the Old Northwest had emphasized many of its problems and crystallized its economic needs in the rise of the new Republican Party of 1854–60. With continuing ascendancy during and after the Civil War this political party was believed by spokesmen to be the party of "victory, salvation and progress." The Old Northwest produced impressive leadership. The

President of the United States elected in 1868 was the western war hero, Ulysses S. Grant from Galena, Illinois; the Vice President was Schuyler Colfax of South Bend, Indiana.

The position taken by the elder Funks during these years had considerable influence upon their descendants. Their loyalty to the Republican Party, however, did not blind them to the fact that a "good" Democrat was often preferable to an incompetent Republican. They seldom hesitated to speak up for what they thought to be right. Their civic activities in the years 1865–90 were chiefly in local and state positions.

The important central Illinois agricultural area including McLean County produced effective leadership during the sixties and seventies. Certain phases of the story such as the Lexington case are well known to constitutional historians and to lawyers. This area was a focal point, and the Funks as one of the largest landholding families in the immediate vicinity were among those who recognized the problems. Their viewpoints and activities are of interest.

As early as April 1868 a convention was called to meet in Bloomington known as the Farmers, Mechanics and Laboring Men's Convention of the Republican Party of McLean County, Illinois. The object of the meeting was to further an "organization among the farmers, mechanics and laboring men of this country to secure a recognition of their rights as the majority of the population." D. M., F. M., Ben and George participated during April.[3]

With the nomination of Ulysses S. Grant for the Presidency on the Republican ticket, Farmers' Clubs supporting him appeared. L. H. Kerrick spoke in Chenoa and in Bloomington to these groups.[4] Ben Funk, along with Jacob Bohrer, was a member of the committee on arrangements for a Republican rally.[5] The election in November 1868 resulted in majorities for Ulysses S. Grant for President and John Palmer for Governor, both in Funk's Grove Township and in McLean County.[6]

The second generation of Funks accepted its responsibility by participating in local government. F. M. and George became members of the Board of Supervisors.[7] The new state constitution of Illinois in 1870 included recognition of these economic problems confronting the farmers. George Funk, eldest son of Isaac, was one of four elected from McLean County as members of the lower house when this new constitution was put into effect. He supported his colleague from McLean County, William Smith, who was elected to the Speakership, thus giving the county recognition and power.[8] Funk held three important appointments as a member of Committees on Railroads, Banks and Banking, as well as Agriculture.[9] George Funk took his responsibilities seriously, as records of attendance and voting indicate. He supported the bill providing for regulation of railroad rates when it reached the House. A bill important to farmers was enacted, providing for the creation of a State Department of Agriculture.[10] Funk supported John Logan for the Senatorship. A "Farmers' Ring" was organized during this session of the legislature, antedating some of the Granger efforts a few years later.[11] Although there is no available evidence that George Funk was a member of the Ring, which was probably a Democratic group, he voted in favor of legislation regulating railroads and warehouse rates.

A test case arose involving the constitutionality of the law signed in 1871 regulating railroad rates. The suit was brought in McLean County by the Railroad and Warehouse Commissioners in the name of the people of the State of Illinois against the Chicago and Alton Railroad. The railroad was accused of charging $5.65 per thousand on lumber from Chicago to Lexington, a distance of 110 miles, while the rate on 125 miles to Bloomington was only $5 per thousand. The defendant admitted the facts and that its action was not in accordance with the law of 1871, claiming that the Bloomington rate was too low because of the competition with the Illinois Central; that only the company was injured and that it was not illegal because the act of 1871 was illegal.[12] The people's case was presented by Attorneys Rowell and Reuben Benjamin.

John Tipton, then presiding over the McLean County Circuit Court, heard the case in November 1872 and decided against the company. He based his decision upon the ideas that the state in giving citizens equal protection of the law must insure them against discrimination; anything in the railroad charter construed differently must be void. The railroad companies could not have rights contrary to the welfare of the people. This was indeed far-sighted and prophetic reasoning as presented by counsel from this area and upheld by a judge from this county.[13]

The *Pantagraph* stated editorially, "The real question is whether the state has the right to interfere to protect its citizens who are practically helpless against the exactions of immense corporations whose wealth makes them stronger than any power short of the State. The people who live along the line of a railroad have practically no choice where they will do their business; they must ship by the railroad and must travel on it when they travel at all." [14]

Upon appeal to the State Supreme Court the decision was reversed in 1873 on the basis that the law of 1871, although a law to prevent unjust discrimination, included *all* discrimination and therefore was contrary to the constitution. The disappointment of the farmers was great.[15] No additional law was passed until 1873.

In the meantime farmers' organizations began to grow. The Chicago Grange was the first to be organized in Illinois in the office of the *Prairie Farmer* during the last of April in 1868.[16] The State Grange was not organized until March 5, 1872.[17] Farmers continued to face the problems of increasing crops, high railway and grain elevator rates and grain as fuel.[18] The decision of the Supreme Court in 1873 had not increased their support of existing party leadership.

The State Grange had been organized only a few months before the State Farmers' Association. The Secretary of the State Farmers' Association, S. M. Smith, called attention to the jealousy existing between the two groups.[19] He pointed out that the Grange had been well treated by the Associations and that Grangers participated in the Associations.[20] Although the Grange later took the lead, it is apparent that when the law of 1871 was passed there was extensive farm organization in effect.[21]

Leonidas Kerrick, brother-in law of the Funks, was elected to the legislature for the second session in 1871. He and George Funk completed the term.[22]

When the campaign of 1872 brought forth the Liberal Republican movement, it was supported by a number of staunch Republicans from Illinois. Again the McLean County area contributed leadership for this movement through David Davis from Bloomington. Other leading Liberal Republicans who had supported Abraham Lincoln included Jesse Fell from Normal, and Asahel Gridley and Leonard Swett from Bloomington. Others from Illinois were Gustavus Koerner, Jesse K. Du Bois and Lyman Trumbull. Davis [23] and Trumbull were contenders for the Liberal Republican nomination, eventually obtained by Horace Greeley of New York. John Wentworth from Chicago addressed the McLean men at the Cincinnati convention of this party.[24] A Greeley ratification meeting was held locally May 17, 1872.[25] The Funks, however, maintained their place in the regular Republican organizational activities. Funk's Grove produced a majority of 50 for the party and McLean County returned majorities for Ulysses S. Grant for President, McNulta for Congress and Oglesby for Governor in 1872.[26]

By January 1873 there was a meeting of citizens of Mount Hope and Funk's Grove Townships in caucus at McLean to appoint delegates to attend the Farmers' Convention at Bloomington on the 15th and 16th. William Darnell was appointed chairman. Jacob Funk was one of five delegates chosen from Mount Hope Township, and L. F. Funk was one of three delegates from Funk's Grove Township.[27] There were no members of the Funk family mentioned in the delegate groups to the McLean County Farmers' Convention held in February.[28] The Board of Supervisors, however, requested the State to conduct railroad suits testing the constitutionality of railroad law and relief for individuals. F. M. Funk, who was then a member of the Board, supported this idea.[29] The *Weekly Pantagraph* of March 28th recorded that the McLean County Supervisors took action. The newspaper also called attention to the fact that two other resolutions were offered but were not published. One of these was presented by F. M. Funk, providing that the Legislature of Illinois be instructed to make necessary appropriations out of the State Treasury to enable the State Board of Railway Commissioners to prosecute the railroad companies for any and all violations of the law in reference to passenger and freight traffic.[30]

A local meeting was held after the decision by the Illinois Supreme Court of 1873 in the railroad case for the purpose of counteracting and neutralizing "the enormous abuses being perpetrated upon the people by all kinds of monopolies." The meeting was well attended. James F. Boulware presided, urging the necessity of a Farmers' Club. The election resulted in the choice of F. M. Funk as president.[31] Mr. Funk, upon taking the chair, spoke for twenty minutes and was "lustily cheered by the audience." George Funk in June of 1873 was quoted as saying that while farmers were a unit in the contest for their rights he saw no necessity for going into a new party to obtain them. He thought such a move would receive no support in the vicinity except from Democrats.[32]

Popular Reuben M. Benjamin was nominated by both parties and elected as county judge again. Funk's Grove, however, returned a 14 majority vote for the Anti-Monopolists. McLean County returned a Republican majority, whittled down from 2,500 in 1872 to 200 in 1873.[33]

The famous case of Munn vs. Illinois, well known in United States history, instituted in 1871, was decided by the State Supreme Court in October of 1873. Again the Bloomington area was represented when R. M. Benjamin was associated with the People's Attorney General for the State.[34] The arguments closed with repeated emphasis upon the police powers of the State. McLean County again was a vital center for the crystallization of ideas and for courageous leadership.

Local public meetings, such as the celebration of the Fourth of July in 1875, found members of the family seated on the platform, including Isaac Funk, II as chairman. Republicans in the immediate Congressional District lost the Congressional election in 1874 to Adlai E. Stevenson, Sr. They were hopeful of returning one of their own again in 1876. Some favored the candidacy of ex-president of Illinois State Normal University, Richard Edwards. Among these were Lon Kerrick, Duncan Funk and LaFayette Funk. The latter wrote to the *Pantagraph:*

I have not spent much time thinking of Congressional matters but I can say this: I am for the man who will stand up to those rebels in Congress and hurl back in their teeth any and all of their threats or intimations of disunion principles that still lurk within them. And then again we want a man who will go to Congress content with the salary the law allows him, and not be guilty of concocting any scheme to swindle the government or any of its employees out of anything that may be due them. What I have heard of Mr. Edwards leads me to believe he is the man. It is a fact that some of our leading men in office are becoming very corrupt, and we want to weed them all out as fast as they may be found guilty, and then be cautious whom we fill their places with. No doubt the principles of our party are the best any Government ever had if we can only find men who will carry out the principles correctly. To be successful in this campaign, we must put forward our very best men.

> *Your obedient servant*
> LaFayette Funk.[35]

B. F. Funk was urged again to run for the mayorship of Bloomington but decided to decline after five years in the office. The *Pantagraph* was complimentary in its remarks. With the exception of 1875, B. F. had never had an opponent in the field, and since 1871 the Democratic Party had not offered a candidate. No other occupant up to that time had ever held the office so long as B. F. Funk. The newspaper pointed to his prudent management, to the transformation of the fire department from a volunteer organization to a paid one, to the increase and reorganization of the police force, and to the installation of a complete system of waterworks located in northwestern Bloomington at a cost of $80,000.[36]

During this important period LaFayette Funk became a member of the House of Representatives (1883) in the Thirty-third Assembly of Illinois.[37] During the Thirty-fourth (1885) and Thirty-fifth (1887) sessions he became a member of the Senate of Illinois.[38] From 1882 to 1894 and after he was a member of the State Agricultural Board.[39]

The Funks remained within the Republican Party during the post-war years. They did not hesitate to speak out for the farmer and his interests within this party throughout these years. Some leaders from the county sought legal and judicial expression while others participated politically. The rank and file possibly admired the positions taken by Judge Benjamin and by the Funks who remained as spokesmen for the farmer within the Republican Party. These efforts enabled people to believe that remedies could be found within the regular organization. The position of the Funks was a strong one by 1876. With the leadership of such men remaining within the party and the Liberal Republican movement omitting strong agricultural planks [40] and passing over two Illinois candidates, David Davis and Lyman Trumbull in 1872, future protest movements were destined to seek expression and recognition in the newer wests beyond the Mississippi. The Funks apparently judged the political situation with considerable accuracy during the post-Civil War years.

Consistent support of the Republican Party became an inherited pattern in the Funk family. Through the years they continued to seek remedies for agricultural problems within their chosen party. Often their ideas and statements marked them as progressive and independent in their judgments.

PART TWO

Wider Horizons

CHAPTER IV

Leadership in State and Nation
1890–1893

LaFayette Funk continued to accept his civic responsibilities, building a foundation of experience and acquaintanceship that proved invaluable to his descendants. Reflections of the type of leadership that he and his brothers displayed can be observed in the present generations.

The early 1890's were perilous. Agricultural protest movements were rising in the South and West. The Populist Party gained twenty-two electoral votes in 1892 for its Presidential candidate, James B. Weaver. Demands for "free silver" or more money in circulation were heard on all sides. President Benjamin Harrison's administration was ushered out March 4, 1893 under a cloud of impending panic which culminated during the second administration of Grover Cleveland, 1893–97. The legacy of the high McKinley Tariff, the Sherman Silver Purchase law and the Sherman Anti-Trust act, all passed in 1890, increased problems for future legislators. Unifying events such as the World's Columbian Exposition of 1893 focused international attention on Chicago, key city of the Midwest.

LaFayette was among those known not only for his skill and leadership in producing fine stock but also for good judgment in agricultural problems. Unlike some of his brothers he contributed time and energy to activities that carried him throughout his native state of Illinois and gave him opportunity to participate in events of national significance. His brother, Benjamin F. Funk, who was elected to the United States House of Representatives in 1892, also was concerned with national problems.

Busy days were ahead for LaFayette in 1891. As a member of the State Board of Agriculture and the committee for the World's Fair to be held in Chicago, his time was well-occupied. As early as January of 1891 he consulted with architects in Jackson Park, Chicago regarding a site for the Illinois State Building.[1] Between frequent trips to Chicago in connection with the Fair, he was expected to attend the usual number of weddings and funerals and to arrange for livestock shipments at Shirley.[2] Other interests also demanded his attention.[3] He attended a Congressional district meeting, judicial trials of local interest, Farmers' Institutes and meetings of the State committee [4] regarding appropriations for the Fair. He also met with the trustees of the University of Illinois hearing statements from students and faculty about the differences then existing between them.[5] On April 10th he made a quick trip from Chicago to meet the trustees in a tied vote failing to select a regent.[6] In June he attended a meeting of the directors of the Agricultural Experiment Station.[7] At the meeting of the trustees in June they again failed to choose a regent.[8]

Interest in legislative action relating to the Fair continued into June when the State House of Representatives, by a vote of 76 to 73, appropriated $50,000 and advanced the bill to the third reading.[9] The bill passed the House on the 12th, much to LaFayette's satisfaction.

He also participated in a meeting of the committee on the Fat Stock Show to be held in Chicago. The World's Fair Commission was completely organized by July 1, 1891, with all members spending the entire next week in meetings.[10]

Mrs. LaFayette Funk, Gene, De Loss and Miss Alice Harpole departed for Oregon [11] early in June 1891. LaFayette accompanied his family to Chicago where they spent the evening and he remained for a meeting of the State Board of Agriculture.[12] This western trip proved to be a memorable one in the life of Eugene, for he met an attractive young lady, Mary Anderson, who later became his wife. LaFayette, meanwhile, attended the meetings of the World's Fair Commission. A few days at home, one in Champaign, shipping two loads of cattle, and then to the Chicago Stock Yards the following day kept LaFayette occupied.[13] His days were crowded with activity. Arrangements were made in Peoria for the State Fair. From there another trip to Chicago, returning two days later to attend the fair in Bloomington and to spend Sunday afternoon with brother Jake.[14] Between September 1 and 22 he attended the Old Settlers meeting at Farmer City Fair, where he was president of the day,[15] the Atlanta Fair, the Springfield Board meetings, the reunion at Funk's Grove, the Springfield Fair, Saybrook Fair and made another trip to Champaign to meet a committee of the trustees of the University regarding the location of the new building.[16] On the 25th of September he departed to spend the week at the State Fair then held at Peoria. Finally he arrived at Shirley, "tired but pretty well satisfied with the result of the fair." [17] After spending part of the following Sunday at Jake's, he was off again for Chicago and Jackson Park and the problems of the World's Fair.[18]

A trip east to South Charleston, Ohio during October took Mr. and Mrs. LaFayette to Ohio with "Pancake's" folks,[19] cousins of Mrs. La-Fayette. They started home again on November 3rd with a stop-off in Springfield.[20] A few days later LaFayette was in attendance at the Fat Stock Show in Chicago, home on a Sunday, back again for the killing of the premium cattle and the opening of the bids for the building at the World's Fair. The following week end he repeated the same schedule and attended a meeting of the University trustees.[21] The following Sunday brought another trip to Chicago and Commission meetings. Finally the Commission adjourned until January 7th,[22] but meetings on exhibits continued through December.

Gene and Mrs. LaFayette journeyed to South Charleston, Ohio in December, at the time of the death of George Shinn, but LaFayette was again caught in a round of meetings including Chicago and Springfield. The Stock Yards subscription for the Stock Show took him away on December 30th.[23] With all of this responsibility and activity he noted in his *Diary* that the year was successful, with bountiful crops and satisfactory prices.[24]

The same general pattern of almost continuous trips followed in 1892. The same responsibilities as a member of the State Board of Agriculture, of the World's Fair Commission for Illinois in charge of Illinois activities, the Peoria Fair, the Fat Stock Show, as well as state and county Republican conventions, and continued meetings with the trustees of the University of Illinois found LaFayette traveling a good portion of the time. Yet with all of these outside activities he found time to plant some corn and attend church occasionally at Shirley with his family. In addition there were shipments of cattle to be made to Chicago.[25]

Mrs. LaFayette Funk, not to be entirely overlooked, visited Hot Springs in April 1892. She later attended the dedication of some of the State Buildings on the Midway in October of 1892. In general, 1892 was a busy one for this family.

The opening of the World's Fair on May 1, 1893 was a high point for all of those who had worked so faithfully toward that end. The fair continued until the 20th of October. One author has said "The World's Columbian Exposition of 1893 marked an era in the general development of the United States. Especially strong of course was its influence on the state of Illinois and on the city of Chicago." [26]

LaFayette was appointed to the National Commission for the duration of the Fair requiring frequent attendance during the summer months. He refused to accept an appointment as chairman of the Committee on Live Stock of the National Commission.[27]

Two central figures at the opening of the World's Fair were the President of the United States, Grover Cleveland, and a descendant of Columbus, the Duke of Veragua. Members of the Cabinet, Congress and other high officials attended the celebration. The young ladies of Vice President Adlai Stevenson's party were accompanied by the son of the Vice President. As the *Chicago Tribune* recorded: "Those who dreamed of the Exposition were sharers in the triumph of their city and of the Mississippi Valley, whose pulse throbs with it." [28]

The agencies through which the Government worked to produce the Fair included the National Commission consisting of 108 men and their alternates, headed by Thomas M. Palmer of Michigan, and a corporation of the State of Illinois known as the World's Columbian Exposition composed of forty five directors and presided over by H. N. Higinbotham of Chicago, together with a Board of Lady Managers of 115 members led by Mrs. Potter Palmer.[29] The formal opening of the Illinois Building occurred May 18th. The General Assembly of the State passed a resolution providing for adjournment in order that members might attend the opening of the building.

The Illinois Building occupied a conspicious position in the north part of the park. A large relief map of Illinois was compiled by the Board from a survey of the state made under their direction for this purpose in 1892 at a cost of $15,000. A picture on the wall was made entirely of grains and grasses, representing a typical Illinois farm.[30]

LaFayette Funk, president of the Board of Agriculture for the State of Illinois, officiated at the dedication ceremonies. The front of the Illinois Building was draped with two large American flags. Seats were arranged on the plaza in front of the building and in the grand entrance. Camp chairs and standing room were at a premium before eleven o'clock. Members of the legislature were grouped as a body, and members of the National Commission as well as the Japanese, German and Austrian Commissioners, Governor Altgeld and Mayor Harrison of Chicago were present. Others who attended included ex-Governor Oglesby, Congressman Joseph Cannon, ex-Senator Charles B. Farwell and Mrs. Farwell, Marshall Field, Congressman B. F. Funk of Bloomington, and James S. Ewing of Bloomington.

After the singing of "America," President Funk raised his hand and opened the ceremonies by referring to the generous appropriation from the legislature, to the effective work of the Board of Illinois Women and to the State Board of Agriculture in preparing the general exhibit. He explained the purpose of representing diversified industries and the moral and intellectual development of the people of Illinois. He called attention to the fact that Illinois held a high place in the sisterhood of the states as third in population with the richest and broadest agricultural expanse dominated by any government. The Illinois Commission had labored with this thought:

That this exhibition would be the greatest the world has ever seen, and even to have already justified that belief. This marvelous white city by the lake aggregates and epitomizes the industrial progress of the world, and we of Illinois hope that in the laudable competition of which this is now for some months to be the scene of our Illinois, though only founded but in the yesterday of history, will not be found last in true development and progress.[31]

President Funk presented the building to Governor Altgeld, who also spoke. After the close of this speech a question arose as to whether the Fair should remain open on Sundays. Mayor Harrison of Chicago interpreted the vote on the question as favorable.[32] It appeared that the authority of the Board of Commissioners regarding this matter had been overlooked. President Funk, with considerable presence of mind, called on the next speaker to continue [33] thus avoiding dissension.

Dedication of the Illinois State Building was of particular interest to LaFayette, who noted in his *Diary* that "a good day with grand success" was experienced.[34] The "illumination of the grounds" on June 1st was "very handsome." [35] When this was over he declared: "I will go home tonight to plow corn for two days." On the following day he wrote:

At home in the corn field plowing—
Corn small but growing. Pretty tired when night came—but done pretty well for a fellow nearly 60 years old.[36]

After the Fair closed October 30th meetings continued into November in order to dispose of some of the property, to hear grievances of the exhibitors, to sell some of the furniture from the Illinois Building. Attendance at the Stock Yards also took some time.[37] All in all the expenditure of time and energy was well worth the effort.

Responsibilities, however, did not cease with the ending of the Fair. The choice of a permanent site for the location of the Illinois

State Fair now devolved on the State Board of Agriculture. Open bids were disposed of on January 3rd. Four cities—Bloomington, Peoria, Decatur and Springfield—were interested in securing the site. Springfield was selected on the 11th.[38] Inspection of fair grounds in Indianapolis, Indiana and in Columbus, Ohio with a committee of the Board enabled LaFayette to stop off at South Charleston, Ohio.[39] Meetings of the committee in Springfield regarding matters of construction necessitated frequent trips. On April 5th he wrote, "The full Board saw fit to undo everything the committee had done," so that improvement was exactly where it had begun the previous January.[40] Bids were opened by April 24th for erecting the new Exposition Building and on May 3rd it was laid out.[41] Meanwhile the usual marketing of cattle, hogs and sheep demanded occasional trips to Chicago. The disposal of the Illinois Building of the 1893 Fair occurred January 18th.[42]

LaFayette was not the only member of the Funk family who attained national recognition. Ben Funk, also represented the central Illinois agricultural area on the national scene as a member of the United States House of Representatives.[43] He was elected a member of the Illinois delegation in November 1892. Joseph Cannon from Danville was among his colleagues elected from Illinois. This election returned to the Presidential office the Democratic candidate, Grover Cleveland for his second term. The Vice President as noted was Adlai Stevenson Sr., from Bloomington, Illinois.[44] Other colleagues in the House of Representatives with Ben Funk included "Silver Dick" Bland of Missouri, W. J. Bryan from Lincoln, Nebraska, Nelson Dingley from Maine and "Sockless Jerry" Simpson from Medicine Lodge, Kansas. The Republicans were the minority party. Funk attended the opening session. He became a member of the standing committee on agriculture.[45]

President Harrison's concept of a billion dollar country was about to backfire in 1892 when the gold reserve became alarmingly low. Signs of economic difficulty were becoming increasingly visible. Unsettled conditions among western and southern agricultural groups strengthened protest movements culminating in the formation of the Populist party.

By the time this Fifty-third Congress met in 1893, the panic of that year had broken. Among the problems recommended by the President for immediate action was the repeal of the Sherman Silver Purchase act. Although Funk spoke on other important matters, he did not express views on this subject. He presented a petition, however, from businessmen and bankers of Clinton, Illinois requesting the repeal of the enacting clause of the bill.[46]

Although a new member of the House does not often speak, Ben Funk appeared to be the exception. This may have been due to the fact that the Republicans were in need of spokesmen from strong agricultural areas during this particular session. Funk spoke upon the reformation of the law dealing with selling by short weights and measures in the District of Columbia. He was interested in the fees paid to the examiners, which he considered too high.[47] He presented petitions on the various subjects.[48]

When an effort was made to secure the admission of Arizona, B. F. Funk spoke in behalf of an amendment to allow officers determining the price of lands to sell them at less than $5 an acre if they judged the value to be less. He supported the same idea when the question of New Mexico was discussed.[49] The question of pensions aroused heated discussion especially when the identity of the individual was disputed. Several of these cases were located in Illinois.[50] Funk believed that any known irregularities should be reported.

Many people blamed the high McKinley tariff of 1890 for the economic difficulties in 1893. This was particularly true of Democrats and Populists. With Democrats in power this issue quickly came under discussion. "Sockless Jerry" Simpson and W. J. Bryan, also members of this Congress, carried the brunt of the argument. B. F. Funk did not hesitate to join in the discussion. Simpson emphasized the hardships of farmers under high protective tariffs. In his explanation of wheat prices he referred to the "Republican" State Board of Agriculture in Illinois, and its statistical report. This reference to the political coloring of the Board elicited a denial from Mr. Henderson of Illinois. Ben Funk rose to inquire by what authority he referred to the Board as appointed by a Republican administration and declared that the body was not a political group. Mr. Fithian pointed out that the Board was not appointed by the administration but that it was by majority, Republican. Ben Funk observed that the Board was about equally divided between the two parties.

Mr. Simpson then said that he was informed that the gentleman from Illinois, Mr. Funk, had a brother who was on this Board and, he presumed him to be a Republican. All of this discussion was apparently carried in good humor because Simpson obviously wished to use certain portions of the report for his own purposes in discussing the prices of wheat. Ben Funk asked Simpson why he did not read the entire report. Simpson replied, "Because I had only five minutes."

The remarks of B. F. Funk on the tariff gave considerable insight into the reasons why the farmers of agricultural sections, particularly in the Old Northwest, in traditionally Republican sections since 1856, could continue to support high tariffs:

As my distinguished friend from Kansas (Mr. Simpson) would have you believe that the farmers of Illinois are just on the ragged edge of starvation, I want to say that I represent one of the best agricultural districts in this country, in the central part of Illinois; and that to-day in McLean and adjoining counties lands are selling from $75 to $100 per acre (applause on Republican side). Mr. Chairman, what has caused this? A protective tariff system, inaugurated and sustained by the Republican party.

He continued with the thought that with ten-cent corn in 1850–60 and a wagon priced at $130, the farmer was compelled to haul to market 1300 bushels of corn. In 1894 the wagon could be purchased for $50, because laws enacted by the Republican Party had cheapened commodities for the working classes. For a hundred bushels of corn the farmer could buy the same or a better wagon. Farm labor in the earlier period had received $8 per month and in 1894 was commanding $20 to $25 per month. Those better wages were also attributed to the protective system by Representative Funk. "It gave them a better market for their produce at good prices," he said. "Let me give you an illustration of how this works." Here B. F. told of his father, Isaac Funk, who raised the wages of a farm hand in 1850. He added, "It was talked about through the community that Old Ike Funk was ruining the country by raising the wages from $10 to $13." [51]

As a member of the Committee on Agriculture, Benjamin Funk was interested in the remarks of William Jennings Bryan when he referred to the price of nails. Funk asked the price of nails in "the good old days of Democracy" as contrasted to the price under protective tariffs. Bryan then offered the opinion that the price of wheat had dropped under tariffs to that of the good old days. This silver-tongued orator then said that he realized that tariff had not necessarily brought the price of wheat down, but he continued to object to Funk's argument that protection should take the credit for every reduction in the price of manufactured products. After this interlude Bryan returned to the discussion with the gentleman from Maine.

The debate continued. Ben Funk rose again to declare that he would be "recreant in my duty" if he did not voice the sentiment of the farmers in his district against the Wilson-Gorman tariff. He added, "Many Democrats have written to me asking me to use my best efforts to defeat the adoption of the Wilson bill." [52] Funk believed that to enact the lower tariffs of the Wilson bill would prevent prosperity from returning. He must have been aware that lower tariffs had not been passed since 1872. The Wilson-Gorman tariff was so emasculated in the Senate that President Cleveland refused to sign it and allowed it to become a law without his signature.

During the month of December 1894, Mr. B. F. Funk received an indefinite leave of absence because of sickness in his family.[53] He advocated safety in the construction of the Federal Building in Chicago by allowing a period of three years for its completion rather than eighteen months.[54]

Two members of the second generation, LaFayette and Benjamin, participated in events of state and national significance. They secured these positions through the choice and support of their neighbors and friends. The name of Isaac Funk from Funk's Grove had reached the halls of the national Congress. His sons also prepared another generation to carry on the responsibilities of agricultural and civic leadership so clearly outlined by the activities of this early pioneer. Young Eugene and his cousins were aware of these responsibilities. Eugene, son of LaFayette, and Frank, son of Benjamin, also attained national recognition in the twentieth century.

CHAPTER V

Town and Country · 1894–1901

LaFAYETTE FUNK with his brothers and their brother-in-law, Leonidas Kerrick, were recognized agricultural leaders in Illinois during the 1890's. As a member of the State Board of Agriculture, LaFayette for some twenty-two years knew the problems and the spokesmen. One of the brothers, Duncan Funk, was in the State Legislature during the same decade as a member of the Fortieth, Forty-first and Forty-second assemblies.

LaFayette and other members of the Board of Agriculture witnessed the laying of the cornerstone of the Exposition Building in Springfield on July 4, 1894. By the seventh of July only the mail trains were running because as LaFayette recorded "the strike continues." He referred to the effects of the Pullman Strike of 1894.[1] There were many moments of worry regarding the State Fair, for as late as September 7th LaFayette wrote, "[I am] in Springfield and view the work with a good deal of hesitancy as to being near ready for the fair."[2] Exhibits were arriving by the 20th, and on the 23rd he noted "Everything is in a state of commotion."[3] Attendance was satisfactory, in fact, very good. The day after arrangements were made on October first to take care of the Board's property at the Illinois fair grounds, LaFayette was off to attend the St. Louis Fair, arriving home on October third. Undaunted by this schedule, he spent the remainder of the week in Chicago attending meetings of the State Board of Agriculture. On Sundays he was at home, but two weeks later he was in Chicago again in connection with the Fat Stock Show. This project consumed considerable time during the remainder of the year.[4]

When in Chicago with cattle LaFayette often took dinner with a cousin on his wife's side of the family, Bill Harpole, who was a commission merchant in Chicago.[5] They discussed the cattle market. On a Sunday afternoon they strolled through Jackson Park, remarking in 1896 that "a great change has been made here since the World's Fair."[6]

LaFayette was an eminently successful man, a large land owner and a recognized banker, as well as state agricultural leader. His interests widened steadily. In November 1896 he departed for Indianapolis to attend sessions of the Farmers' Congress.[7] He noted in his *Diary* that there was not much of an attendance at the forenoon meeting on the 10th, but that considerable business was dispatched at the afternoon session.[8] This was one of many sessions of the Farmers' Congress attended by LaFayette in succeeding years.[9]

Bills referring to construction at the fair grounds, such as for the Poultry Building, interested LaFayette [10] as a member of the Illinois Board of Agriculture. He followed his usual activities during 1897–98.[11] The recurring pattern was interrupted by the declaration of war with Spain in April 1898. A telegram advised LaFayette to proceed to Springfield to attend to the problems in connection with the mobilization of troops on the State fair grounds. The following morning he found things "pretty lively" there.[12] Eight thousand men were expected by the evening of the 27th of April. By May 3rd the troops were in camp receiving "pretty good military discipline." [13] The fair grounds looked the worse for wear after two regiments departed for the front on May 15th. A few days before, he had been in Chicago with cattle on a "hard market" demoralized by a big run of western cattle. Feeders were selling too high, so he returned home.[14]

During the late spring of 1898 LaFayette met with the county board of supervisors. Trips to Springfield were also necessary to determine damage by troops to the fair grounds and to attend the Republican convention held in the Exposition Building.[15] A trip to Omaha occurred in June, when Mr. and Mrs. LaFayette departed with DeLoss. A stopover in Chicago enabled LaFayette to attend to cattle and sheep at the stockyards. At Omaha there was a good attendance at the dedication ceremonies of the Illinois Building at the Exposition Grounds.[16]

Local agricultural fairs also were attended in the fall. Supervisors' meetings and preparation for the State Fair consumed time in late September. His friend, Joe Fulkerson, became a candidate for the presidency of the State Board of Agriculture.[17] He was also busy with registering the town voters, and helping John Foster, a neighbor, with his father's papers. Another trip to Omaha, in November 1898 to take care of the sale of furniture in the Illinois State Building, kept him occupied.[18]

Always keenly interested in historical information, LaFayette cooperated with Messrs. Prince and Burnham of the McLean County Historical Society in the preparation of a paper.[19] By December 1, 1898 he was hard at work on a memorial address in honor of Senator

McLean.[20] On the day that the address was delivered, LaFayette started for Fort Worth, Texas to attend another session of the Farmers' Congress.[21] He visited Houston, Galveston, San Antonio and Waco.[22] By December 18th he had returned. Plans were laid for Christmas, when Gene's folks came for the day. The Christmas tree was Mrs. LaFayette's orange tree, which produced forty-three ripe oranges for the occasion.[23] The usual winter grippe epidemic occurred. The year 1898 went out "clear and cold with fairly good wheeling." [24]

On LaFayette's birthday, January 19, 1899, a picture was taken of Mrs. LaFayette and her orange tree with forty-five oranges among palms and ferns.[25] Gene presented three dozen oranges to the *Pantagraph*. The orange tree had been brought by Mrs. LaFayette from California in 1873. After the florist from the Old Phoenix Nursery, one of the famous Bloomington-Normal nurseries, grafted a shoot from California, the tree bore fruit. It was often used for a Christmas tree with candles. Mrs. LaFayette also brought back in 1874, a century plant and part of the original root from a Christmas cactus taken by her aunt from Zanesville, Ohio to Oregon in the 1850's.[26]

As the turn of the century drew near, LaFayette was occupied with the affairs of the State Board of Agriculture, copying Grandpa Foster's will for him, attending meetings of bank directors as well as the Supervisors' county and town meetings.[27] He and his wife attended the high school commencement at the State Normal University with DeLoss.[28]

Continuing interest in the McLean County Historical Society took LaFayette to a meeting held at Funk's Grove, September 20, 1899. The day commemorated the 75th year of the pioneer settlement, and as LaFayette wrote, "A very good turn out of the representatives of the first families from different parts of the country" made the meeting a success. Papers relating to the settlement of Funk's Grove were read.[29]

Other activities took this agricultural leader to the laying of the cornerstone of the new Federal Building in Chicago [30] and to meetings of the State Board of Charities.[31]

LaFayette Funk noted in his *Diary* on March 7, 1900, "Great complaint of good seed corn through this section of the country." Gene wrote on May 11th that there was much seed that would not grow. Problems relating to corn, livestock and labor were continuing ones but the Funks turned their minds to solutions and bent their energies and their fortunes in the same directions. Everyday life continued.[32]

LaFayette continued to meet with the boards of directors for two Bloomington banks and with the State Board of Charities.[33] Membership on the State Board necessitated his travel in Illinois in search of proper building sites and to inspect institutions.[34] He was also a member of the Board of Supervisors in McLean County.

Local incidents also received attention.[35] Mr. and Mrs. LaFayette attended the 100 year birthday of William Anthony's father on May 9, 1900. The following day the fifty year incorporation of the city of Bloomington was observed. LaFayette recalled that forty years earlier he had broken the prairies on his own farm with four yoke of oxen and a big 22-inch plow held by tracks and a lever.[36] The forty-fourth anniversary of the founding of the Illinois Republican Party in Bloomington occurred May 29th. The attendance was small "but a few of the survivors were present: General Palmer and others." [37]

LaFayette with Colonel Judy visited Rensselaer and Fowler, Indiana attending cattle sales and looking over Hereford cattle.[38] A Funk-Stubblefield reunion held in June brought only a few from afar, but a good attendance of those nearby.[39] LaFayette attended the 75th anniversary of the settlement of Cheney's Grove, where he heard "some good papers." [40]

Bloomington experienced a disastrous fire on June 19, 1900.[41] LaFayette wrote: "Four solid blocks of the best business houses all gone, the Court House and part of another old block east of the Court House block . . ." [42] Interest in the construction of the new building took LaFayette on trips to South Bend [43] and Fort Wayne to examine possible kinds of construction.[44]

Members of the Funk family continued to enjoy their community settlement in Funk's Grove Township. The close friendships and relationships between the several families kept them busy with each other's pleasures and problems. The "in-laws" and their families also visited back and forth, increasing the number to be found at any family gathering. Mrs LaFayette Funk was frequently visited by her sister, Till Florence, and her daughter, Bessie. Bessie later became Mrs I. G. Funk. This double relationship within the families of George and LaFayette drew the younger members of the families together.

L. H. Kerrick, of the same generation as the Funk brothers, highly respected as a lawyer and beloved by the Funks as the husband of Sarah, spoke the sentiments of many who watched the movement from the farms to the growing urban communities. He delivered an address entitled "The Farm and the Town" before the Sixth Annual

Literary Congress in Bloomington, Illinois, January 13, 1897, representing the College Alumni Club. He believed it unnatural that men
and women should prefer the life of the city to the life of the country.
He pointed to the fact that the census of 1790 showed 3 percent of
the people in cities and towns, whereas that of 1890 showed 30 percent, not reckoning towns of 8,000 inhabitants. He thought that educational advantages drew people to the urban centers. For him
schooling and work together provided proper training. In fact, he
said, "We are going to 'town.' " He then asked, "How is this movement
affecting that great first interest of the world, Agriculture?" and answered, "Most unfavorably." Other ideas included these: (1) Excessive population in cities brought unremunerative prices for farm
products and consequent agricultural depression; (2) Supply and
demand did not, under all conditions, regulate the prices of food
products; (3) The ability of the consumer to pay often regulated the
prices. Kerrick thought that the world's consumers were poor because
two had gone to town where one was enough to do the work there.
He disposed of the argument that farm machinery enabling the
farmer to produce a surplus created lower prices. He recalled that
low prices had existed for only eight years, whereas the improved
machinery had been in existence thirty-five to forty-five years.[45] Kerrick believed that:

> The two-row corn planter—the greatest single improvement in agricul-
> tural machinery ever invented—thirty-six years ago. One man and a team
> and plow could stir three acres of fallow ground sixty years ago as well as
> now. One man could husk sixty or seventy bushels of corn sixty years ago
> as well as now. It may be we have some bigger corn husking liars now than
> formerly.

Kerrick deplored the transfer of controlling political power to the
city. On the matter of surpluses he declared the chief purpose of the
farmer should be to produce necessities, conveniences and luxuries
of life. A large surplus should not be the objective.[46] The overgrowth
of cities destroyed this purpose and forced the farmer to produce surplus to pay his heavy taxes. He believed that when the farm population lessened, civilization and national strength decreased and de-
cayed. He thought that men who stayed with land had the blessings
of earth.[47]

Mr. Kerrick exhibited in 1897 sixteen high grade Angus steers, sold
December 15th at the stockyards by Robinson Company to Armour
at $8.25. These were the highest priced cattle sold in Chicago for
sixteen years.[48] These steers were raised in about the same way that

Mr. Kerrick had been raising steers for a good many years. He advocated the best sires and insisted that attention be given to the cows before the birth of the calves. Gentle handling of the young animals made them more manageable.[49] The *Breeders' Gazette* in November 1897 noted that Aberdeen Angus cattle bred and exhibited by L. H. Kerrick were winners of Clay Robinson's special prize of $300. Judging was by a committee of stockyard buyers. The average age of bullocks was thirty-one months and their average weight was 1660 pounds.[50]

The western range cattle industry in Wyoming reached its zenith in the year 1886, according to the *Chicago Daily Drovers Journal.* From this time until 1898, numbers fell off rapidly. There was a slight increase in 1899.[51] As a consequence L. H. Kerrick advocated the production of "baby beef" in the central corn country. At last the central Corn Belt had found an answer.

Stock growers in the Middle West were particularly interested in the status of the western production of cattle. This was the period when cattle men from the Illinois prairies who were accustomed to fattening their cattle for the Chicago market on corn and grass spoke with some emphasis. Among those from McLean County were Frank Funk who told the McLean County Farmers' Institute, January 17, 1900, that annually half a million dollars or more for cattle left McLean County. A *Pantagraph* reporter inquired about this cattle situation from L. H. Kerrick. Experienced cattle men according to Kerrick could buy fairly well in western markets. Inexperienced farmers were not close enough judges either of cattle or markets to be successful.

Kerrick believed that there should be a difference of $1.00 to $1.25 between the buying and selling prices to assure a feeder of making money on his cattle. At the selling price of fat cattle there would be risk in paying more than $4.00 to $4.25 for feeders. When hog prices increased, chances for profit on cattle were improved. Prices of feeders quoted in western markets and in Chicago suggested caution. The cattle feeding problem on high priced lands indicated that "they should breed and raise their own cattle, because the taking of half a million dollars out of the county annually is bad financial policy and must work injury to many interests here." Kerrick did not know whether large buyers in the West would ever change their policy, but he suggested it would be a wise and safe thing for every small farmer to begin raising a few cattle. Kerrick thought this program could be advantageous to an owner or to a renter. He stressed the necessity for building up the fertility of the soil. With improved western cattle the western man knew that the purchaser from Illinois would pay the western price for feeders or return home without the cattle. The buyer could refuse to buy until prices came down.[52]

Kerrick was in a position to speak. He received the highest price paid for cattle on the Chicago market in over fifteen years. These cattle were highly bred and scientifically fed. Of his $8.25 "doddies" he said, "They were raised in the same manner we have been raising steers for a good many years."

John G. Imboden of Macon County also stressed before the McLean County Farmers' Institute the importance of "finishing" cattle.[53] Later in the same year Eugene D. Funk expressed ideas similar to those of Mr. Kerrick. Referring to conditions in 1900, E. D. Funk declared that there was no adequate profit in feeding high priced western cattle. He also advised small farmers, whether land owners or tenants, to raise a few head of high grade cattle.[54]

The *Chicago Daily Drovers Journal,* March 20, 1900, stated that the most prosperous farmers raised crops of grain and fed them to well-bred cattle and hogs. Highest priced grain and improved fertility of the land were obtained by this method. Prosperous parts of the nation were found where farming and first-class stockgrowing were combined. Mindful of historically successful feeders in Illinois this publication added:

> The most successful cattle feeders, the Funks, Gillettes and Alexanders of the early fifties and many others well known since, down to the market toppers of the present season, have invariably experienced the greatest care in the selection of the animals to be put in their feed lots.[55]

Everyday activities continued for the Funk family along with their proper concern over the prices and supply of stock. LaFayette Funk added some land from the estate of F. M. Funk.[56]

LaFayette departed in Mr. Leonard's special car for Fort Worth, Texas during 1900 with a party of eighteen to visit the stockyards. Funk, with C. W. Baker and L. W. Kerrick, also visited Alvarado, Texas to see the Swenson brothers. From there he departed for Dallas and returned home for the Kansas City Cattle Show with General Manager Leonard and General Agent Skinner of the Union Stock Yards. He visited Waco and San Antonio with a group from the Chicago stockyards in March 1901.[57]

During November and December 1900, the stock market, the coming Fat Stock Show, the relationship of corn to stock raising and to the fertility of the land continued to arouse comment. Gene attended the Illinois Livestock Breeders' Association in Springfield, November 15, 1900.[58] Lon Kerrick addressed the Woodford County Farmers at Metamora Institute October 19th on the subject of Beef Cattle. He re-emphasized his earlier statements, declaring in brief that the prosperity of the Corn Belt depended on the fertility of the soil; that they were just entering a period of the restoration of beef production; that knowledge had disappeared when farmers ceased breeding and raising cattle a few years ago; they would never get the right results unless fertility of the soil was returned. Therefore Kerrick advised raising only the best beef on the high priced lands of Illinois. This advice could be practiced better by the average farmer on the farm of medium size and by farmers of medium capital who stayed on their farms than by farmers of large capital who must hire labor. Kerrick reportedly said that the farmers of Illinois were discovering they must have better cattle than they could buy. Kerrick's first step was to breed his own cattle. He advised the same careful selection in the purchase of bulls for producing high grade beef as for obtaining a pure bred herd. Kerrick produced by these methods the best calves ever to appear on his farm. He discovered that cattle were ready for market at twenty-eight to thirty months of age. They possessed all of the characteristics of good beef weighing about 1400 to 1500 pounds at the top price. Kerrick believed that the old fashioned method of allowing a steer to roam about three or four years before fattening him would never again be profitable on high priced lands. The western cattle business proved that this method consumed too much time and resulted in inferior products. He believed that better breeds with more beef to the acre would reach the market in less time. After explaining methods of feeding, he concluded that beef fed on 40 cent corn must be good enough to bring six cents in Chicago for reasonable profit.[59]

An important event in the livestock world occurred at 4 o'clock in the afternoon of September 21, 1899 in Chicago, where fire destroyed the old livestock pavilion. Plans for a new exposition could be traced to a meeting in 1899 of the National Association of Exhibitors of Livestock held in Springfield during the Illinois State Fair. With the promise of support from leading exhibitors of livestock, the Union Stock Yards became the sponsor.[60] Early in the following year livestock interests in the United States actively promoted this project. This proposed event scheduled December 1–8, 1900 was anticipated as the "grandest" event in the entire history of the business. The exposition, it was hoped, would become a kind of an educational center for the livestock industry the world over, greater in scope than that held at Smithfield, England. Agricultural colleges in the United States were to be in charge of feeding demonstrations. Registered breeding associations would be responsible for displays of cattle. The exposition was organized and directed by the pure breeding associations and representative stockmen in the United States. It was organized purely for exhibition purposes without capital stock and without any view to profit with no gate receipts.[61] The exposition was intended to be as complete in agricultural displays as the World's Fair had been in the representation of the general commercial interests of the country.

The livestock interests of the United States and allied industries, with strong commercial interests in Chicago, stated their purpose in organizing "The International Livestock Exposition" to be the holding of annual exhibitions of pure bred cattle of the fat stock show and of the range cattle exhibit, of mutton sheep and draft horses. Exhibitions of feeding methods, transportation appliances, public inspection of animals, meats, refrigeration and packing house processes were to be included. A display of dressed meats and meat products of all kinds and manufactured packing house by-products would show the complete utilization of all parts of slaughtered animals.[62] A board of directors consisted of officers, executive committee and presidents of all recognized breeding associations in the United States and Canada.

LaFayette Funk became one of the directors of the Union Stock Yards and was deeply interested in the proposed "big show," the First International. He described the "reorganization." The new directors included Nathanial Thayer of Boston, Massachusetts; K. Valentine, Chicago; L. B. Doud, Chicago; Fred L. Winston, Chicago; and LaFayette Funk, Shirley, Illinois. Funk was one of two selected outside of Chicago. He commented in his *Diary,* "I was selected as one of its members and as representing the livestock interests of the country." [63] This honor was deserved recognition of LaFayette's knowledge and ability as one of the well known agricultural leaders in the Middle West. He was one of the foremost Shorthorn breeders in the United States.

Preliminary plans were completed by November 17th. The arrival of approximately 3,500 prize cattle and 10,000 head of fat cattle was expected. Premiums amounted to $75,000, and 800 yards of ribbon were calculated for use. It was said that the organization was undertaken more than a year before at the initiation of the Toronto breeders. Kansas City stock interests were also hopeful of obtaining the show, but at the time the indisputable supremacy of Chicago prevailed.[64]

Dexter Park on the south side of Chicago was the revolving point for the livestock world on December third. The *Chicago Drovers Journal* described the event where 15,000 people were turned away as a memorable epoch was begun in the agricultural industry of the United States, symbolizing the founding of a great national institution with ambassadors, governors and national leaders present.[65]

Funk and Kerrick cattle were shown at this time. The Fat Stock Show was described by LaFayette as a "very large exhibit—possibly the largest aggregation of fat stock ever come together at one time." People came by the thousands on December 6th when prize fat cattle were sold at auction at "fabulous prices." Kerrick's carload finally sold at 15½ cents per pound. Gene, Sr. also shipped a carload of Christmas cattle to Chicago. He entered in the show but did not expect a premium. However, he sold his cattle at auction at $6.45, topping the second premium of $6.25, and the third premium of $6.15, that had defeated him in the show ring.[66] L. H. Kerrick easily captured first place in the two-year-old class with his "doddies" over Tom Ponting of Moweaqua, Illinois and James Looman of Hudson, Kansas, both of whom had remarkably fine cattle. In the Grand Champion class for twos, Kerrick's Angus cattle swept the field. The price of $15.50 was described as the highest ever paid for a carload lot.[67] The *Prairie Farmer* noted that "this load of Aberdeen Angus, as compared with Mr. Kerrick's load of Christmas cattle of a year ago, which topped the market at $8.25, were more uniform in height, had a little larger spring of rib and were a little shorter in the leg, while in some shades of appearance to a practiced eye they did not come up to the former load." [68]

Professor C. F. Curtiss of the Iowa Experiment Station commented that no regular quotations for baby beef were possible because it was not a distinct product on the market. The term applied only to cattle finished for the block at an early age without specific limitations. Requirements for weight varied considerably at different times and from year to year. Prices for fat yearling steers were quoted weekly in *The Breeders' Gazette*. The term "doddie" originated in the early Scotch history of Angus cattle to distinguish them from another polled breed known locally as "Sunlies"; baby beef, according to Curtiss, was not calf beef but beef made from cattle that had been pushed by good treatment and liberal feeding to early maturity or finished for market at an early age.[69]

Renewed interest in feeding cattle and intensified experimental work with corn on the Illinois Prairies occurred about the turn of the century. This interest was indicated by increasing numbers of agricultural organizations. The Funks, who were interested in both corn and cattle, participated in new organizations.

The Funks continued to be spokesmen in state affairs. Duncan M. Funk was a member of the lower house of the State Legislature (1896) and LaFayette continued as a member of the State Board of Agriculture.

When "Dunc's" wife became seriously ill in 1896 and died early in January of the next year at the age of 61 years, the occasion took young Eugene and his good friend Dale Evans to remain overnight in "a very sad household." [70] Duncan turned his attention to his responsibilities in the Illinois House of Representatives, where he was a member of the committee to arrange the inaugural ceremonies. He held membership on important committees including Appropriations, Banks and Banking, Claims, Public Charities, Soldiers' Home and Soldiers' Orphans Home, State and Municipal Indebtedness and Committee to Visit Charitable Institutions. [71]

Duncan Funk was the legislative spokesman for the family during 1897–1903. As a member of the Illinois House of Representatives, he held membership on many committees: chairman of Committee on Contingent Expense, member of committees on Retrenchment, Appropriations, Banks and Banking, Building Loan and Homestead Associations, Farm Drainage, Horticulture, Roads and Bridges. [72]

At the end of the century LaFayette wrote:

This day not only closed the year—but also closes the 19th century. What wonderful changes have been wrought in almost everything since 100 years ago. [73]

Little could he anticipate the changes that were to come in the following fifty years.

CHAPTER VI

Education for the Future
Third Generation

GRANDCHILDREN of the pioneer Isaac Funk grew to maturity during the decade 1880–1890. Their parents provided educational opportunity and travel abroad for those who were interested. Horizons widened and ideas crystallized.

Eugene, eldest son of LaFayette, was the first of the older group of grandchildren to begin preparatory education away from home.[1] He departed at the age of seventeen in 1884 to Wyman Institute located in Alton, Illinois. He returned for week ends and holidays to Shirley. Before departing on January 1, 1884, Eugene wrote of a snowy and blustery day when difficulty was encountered in driving buffalo across the creek into the east pasture. The following day the thermometer reached 30 degrees below zero on the east porch. He set forth for the Institute with the thermometer hovering around 24 below zero.

Education received at the Institute was typical of that offered in private schools in the Midwest at the time. Gene's comments and descriptions at the age of seventeen were indicative of his developing thought and character. The boys quickly removed the snow from the school pond to insure better skating.[2] Forgetfulness seemed to accompany interest in outdoor sports, with a result of two checks against Gene's name for leaving his music behind. Mr. Wyman excused him and the young man noted, "I suppose it was on account of me always trying to be a good boy before yesterday." [3]

During January, interest in skating and the weather seemed to overshadow other topics. Chess absorbed attention some of the afternoons. Gene was a good player and often won. Interest in Bloomington prompted a subscription to the *Daily Leader* rather than the weekly edition.[4] Letters from home, from cousins Linc and Deane were welcome. Gymnasium work on the parallel bars was interesting, if tiring.

Trips to Shurtleff College to hear lectures on physics were part of the program at the Institute. Eugene was pleased with one lecturer who came from Bloomington. Studying was not always easy at Wyman, particularly when the gas failed and only coal oil lamps remained. Philosophy lessons often suffered.[5] He also read during the winter. Typical of his choice was the *Sportsman's Club*.

A week end at home required departure from Alton by train at nine o'clock to reach Shirley about two in the afternoon.[6] Always a keen observer of the weather, Eugene made many entries about the approaching spring. Ducks flew north as early as February 25, 1884.[7] The monotony of school life was varied by an occasional trip to St. Louis.[8] Perhaps the appearance of the carriage from Monticello might bring forth a reasonable observation on the appearance of some good looking girls.[9] When baseball became possible after the first of April, the *Diary* for 1884 stopped abruptly. Apparently he could only find time to record the insignificant days of the winter months when it was difficult to enjoy sports or outdoor activities. With spring the out-of-doors offered every possible opportunity to keep the hours well filled.

Young Eugene entered Andover Academy, near Boston, Massachusetts during the following year of 1885. Three years later he entered Yale University where he remained for two years. He chose a European tour in place of graduation. These steps in his education influenced profoundly his later activities.

Twenty miles from Boston on the Boston and Main Railroad, Andover Academy, the oldest classical academy in America, was located in the historic city of Andover. When Eugene D. Funk, Sr. attended the Academy there were two departments—Classical and English.

The faculty, according to reports, endeavored to instill in their students studious habits with a healthy enjoyment of athletic activities when recitations were over. Occasionally the boys attended the theatre in Boston on Saturdays with a dinner at the Parker House, Boston headquarters of Professor Phillips. Attendance was required at chapel on Sundays. Long walks in the pleasant streets, rendezvous at Indian Ridge and the Shawsheen River, or a ramble to the surrounding hills made school life a happy one. The boys became a part of the community, often answering the fire alarms to assist with the old-fashioned hand engine. Students were not all required to live in the institution. Many were housed among the residents of the town. There were also English and Latin Commons belonging to the Academy. Graduates usually attended Yale, Harvard, and Dartmouth.

Eugene D. Funk lived during his first year 1885, at Sanborns. He was enrolled in the English Department. Interest in athletics became predominant during his years at Andover. At one time he was President of the Athletic Association. During the year 1887–88 he lived at Mr. Blunt's house with eleven other young men.[10] Funk joined a local Greek letter organization II A. E.[11]

Some of the other younger Funks attended eastern colleges. The choice of Yale was not unusual for young men whose families were large landowners although Dana Rollins, grandson of Duncan, attended Amherst. State Universities were in the process of developing and land grant colleges could not offer facilities for agricultural education equal to the best equipped farms in the country. Both Deane, son of Jacob, and Frank, son of Benjamin, attended eastern preparatory schools. Deane graduated from the Sheffield School at Yale in 1888. Eugene and Frank were of the class of 1891. The Sheffield School grew because of the continuing interest in the importance of natural and physical sciences during the last half of the nineteenth century.

There were numerous illustrations of the acceleration of interest in scientific subjects.[12] The names of Benjamin Silliman and Denison Olmstead were well known at Yale. As early as 1847–48 a School of Applied Chemistry was included in the Department of Philosophy and Arts.[13] The Yale Scientific School opened as early as 1854.[14] Darwin's *The Origin of Species* appeared in 1859. During the same year Mr. Joseph E. Sheffield donated a sum of $10,000 to aid the growth and purchased Sheffield Hall thereby assuring the home of the Scientific School. It became the Connecticut College of Agriculture and Mechanical Arts.[15] A well-defined course in agriculture was announced in 1865. By 1886 the school numbered 100 in the freshman class. During 1892–93 the freshman class was increased to 207. Of 528 students only 201 were from Connecticut. The Storrs Agricultural College, however, became the Land Grant College of Connecticut in 1893,[16] and thus absorbed some of the attention given to scientific training.

Notification of his acceptance as a freshman at Yale reached Eugene September 20, 1888. He chose enrollment in Sheffield Scientific School with conditions in solid and spherical geometry, Caesar, Latin grammar and exercises. His studies at Andover had not included any preparation in these subjects. Again his deep interest in athletics became apparent during his first year at Yale when he was chosen captain of the freshman football team. Among the items in his carefully kept scrapbook appears a telegram in 1888 from Walter Camp. The telegram to Captain Funk said: "Choose the wind and get lead early. Telegraph me result." [17] Captain Funk played one of the rushing positions at right tackle. Yale lost the Harvard freshman game by the score of 36–4. The *Boston Sunday Globe*, December 2, 1888, in commenting upon the play, called attention to Funk's playing as follows: "He was downed in great style by Funk," and "Yale's ball and play was begun by Funk making a desperate rush." [18]

Social events occupied some of the time including an invitation to attend the Philalethean Society's activities at Wellesley College. Equally enjoyable were the summers between school years on the farm at Shirley and in the city of Bloomington, Illinois. Opportunities to entertain were not lost by four young men of the various Funk families, Charles A., Deane N., both sons of Jacob, Eugene D., and Frank H. Funk. An evening event of August 30, 1889 was described by the local paper in the extravagant language typical of the 1890's as a "revelry of the elite." The young men were said to have provided one of the most delightful gatherings in the annals of Bloomington.[19]

The young men of the third generation were destined to carry the interests and activities of the family outward toward wider horizons. Information regarding their education, activities and travel reveals their comprehensive purposes and wide acquaintanceships in later years. Their fathers built wisely for their sons and they in turn also left a widened circle of interests and activities to their descendants. The third generation might easily have followed that old adage "From shirt sleeves to shirt sleeves in three generations." These sons of the second generation, grandsons of Isaac, in almost every instance returned to the land of their fathers to participate in agricultural groups and in civic responsibility.

This ten-year period often described as the Gay Nineties also saw the culmination of the Agricultural Protest movements in 1892; the heyday and decline of the far western range industry; the depression of 1893; the beginnings of the deeper struggle between capital and labor as well as the increasing demands for social justice. Expanded markets and territorial interests after the Spanish-American War gave rise to wider knowledge of world problems. Within the national and international framework the second generation of Funks consolidated their position in the Old Northwest. The third generation also prepared for the responsibilities of the future.

Gene chose the opportunity of a tour in Europe to observe agricultural developments in place of graduation from Yale. As a result,

Eugene D. and Linc with a cousin from Ohio, Howard Bateman, sailed from New York in July 1890. The trip, including many observations recorded in the *Diary* of Gene Funk, is reported here in some detail because of its deep influence upon his later life. He was particularly aware of the contrasts in agricultural methods then operative in the Old and New Worlds. The long attachment of European families to the land and their inherited responsibilities reflected through generation after generation, later influenced his thinking in a profound and recognizable manner. Arthur Funk, son of Isaac II, also traveled in Europe during the 1890's and studied violin in Germany.

Eugene and I. Linc Funk, son of Duncan, left Bloomington July 16th via the Chicago and Alton for Chicago, and departed for New York at 5:30 the same day on the Lake Shore and Michigan Southern Railroad. On the crowded train Gene read *Nelly Bly and Her Travels.* Upon arriving in New York they stopped at the Gilsey House where their passports were waiting.[20] Howard Bateman of South Charleston, Ohio accompanied them on the remainder of the trip.

The Atlantic crossing was made on the *Etruria,* boarded at Pier No. 40 in New York. Gene recorded that there were no friends there to wave them farewell at the wharf and "that big lump comes up in our throat just the same as it did when we left B." [21] As he observed the tugs turning the big ship around, his description reads:

One each on opposite corners of the ship bunts its nose up against the huge vessel and grunts and groans like a little pig two or three days old trying to persuade its mother to roll over and give it room to lie down.

The first day out on the ocean was calm, but a slight attack of seasickness marred the second day of the voyage. Staying on deck in the air was as good as any other remedy. About ten o'clock they sighted a large school of porpoises. Rough weather continued,[22] but the trip was uneventful.

When the Captain signalled the lighthouse with sky-rockets off the coast of Ireland, excitement like that of the Fourth of July prevailed. This was done so that telegraphic word could be sent sixty miles to Queenstown. A tug met the boat and took the passengers to shore.

Upon leaving the *Etruria,* Gene was impressed by its size in comparison to the small tugs. After a night's rest and breakfast the boys decided to take a walk. They encountered an old Irish beggar woman at least eighty years old who insisted on their having some of her "Irish Shamrock" for a bouquet and good luck. During their walk they saw St. Paul's and were impressed by the many old and wrinkled peddlers with their small two-wheeled carts and small mules. They set out by train for Cork, where they took a drive in a "jaunting car." This conveyance was a two-wheeled vehicle with one horse and three seats, one for the driver in front. The two additional seats accommodated four persons who sat with their backs to each other, allowing their feet to hang down, resting on an outside step. A six-mile trip to Blarney enabled them to see linen factories, the Blarney Castle and the Blarney Stone. They inspected the castle and kissed the stone. Later, after dinner, they heard the Shannon Bells.[23]

The beauty and grandeur of the scenery impressed the young travelers who concluded that in some respects Ireland surpassed their homeland. They departed to the Black Water River, or the "Irish Rhine," and were interested in seeing the residence of Sir Walter Raleigh and the hill behind it where he planted and thus introduced "Irish" potatoes brought from America.[24] The scenery along the river caused Eugene to reflect that it was a great pity there should be such poverty.[25] A tour of Ireland followed to Banty and Glengarreff. Here the country appeared to defy description:

> We have seen more lovely country today. I cannot describe it. To ask one to imagine he saw a large crazy quilt enlarged and everything colored with green—the seams to be stone fences. Allow the quilt to be lower in the center—that would represent a valley—then one might have some vague idea of these valleys and hills. Little groves and forests—every tree in green from root to tip of limb, being covered with Irish ivy—so is every old castle or ruin and every stone. The ground in the woods is covered with the greenest of moss and ferns. It is a scene that I have wished many times already that *all* my folks at home could be with me to enjoy.[26]

A distance of forty-two miles to Killarney was covered in the rain with beggars following their cart to ask for pennies. Some had flowers to sell, and others were accompanied by musicians.[27] The next day brought a journey to the Gap of Donloe. Rain interfered with the view but the boys covered four miles on foot down to the river and back to their starting point.[28]

Crowds on their way to the "Steeplechase" race were encountered when the young men set out for Dublin. They decided it was a good opportunity to see Irish people and to study their habits. After watching them for some time Eugene recorded, "My opinion of poor starving Ireland has gone through a remarkable change since we landed in this country." [29] They visited the central part of Dublin, Guinesses, then the largest Brewery, and the Old Irish House of Parliament. They crossed the Irish Sea to Holyhead on the English shore.[30]

As a final thought on Ireland, Funk noted that he was doubtful if all the dollars collected in the United States for the poor Irish ever reached that country. He also noted that many of the absentee landlords who lived in England were Irish. Funk was astonished to find that tenants who had lived on the land for years and improved it in many ways were turned out when higher rents were required by the landlords.[31]

The passage across the Irish Sea was unexpectedly calm. A glance around the town of Liverpool revealed six miles of docks along the water's edge. Funk noted Birkenhead where American cattle were received and slaughtered. When the boys arrived they were warmly received. They returned to Liverpool by the way of the tunnel under the bay.

Ayr, Scotland was the next stop. The home of Robert Burns' monument and "Tam O'Shanter's Bridge" attracted their attention. Glasgow appeared to be the famous salt market where many riots previously occurred. Five thousand men worked at the shipyards. Here the young travelers received their first word from home in twenty days—two welcome newspapers. They continued to Ballock with a ride on Loch Lomond and to Inversnaid for the night. The cave of Rob Roy was a mile and one-half distant.[32] At the head of Loch Katrina, they boarded a steamer. Flock after flock of grouse were visible. Funk was impressed by the fact that each landowner possessed his own hunting grounds where he often invited friends to bring their dogs and spend several weeks.

Upon leaving the boat, the young men enjoyed a drive through the Trossacks or "bristling country" of Scotland. A walk through the private grounds of one estate revealed about one hundred acres laid out in magnificent drives, walks and by-ways winding among shrubs, rocks and flower beds. A trout stream ran through the grounds. The stone mansion was surrounded by a lawn of velvet green grass. The journey took them on the Sterling where they saw the famous Sterling Castle, Holyrood Palace, the home of John Knox, the old Scottish Parliament building, Edinburgh Castle and Greyfriars Church.[33]

A chance acquaintance arranged a visit to one of the best Scotch farms. Funk summarized his impressions. The men they saw were all land renters for a number of years at a time, some ten, some forty. Some families had lived on the estate for many years, paying a cash rent, so much per acre. A farm of 290 acres had sold the previous winter for 160 pounds or $800. Wheat production averaged fifty bushels per acre; oats, 77 cents a bushel; potatoes brought $90 per acre.[34]

The itinerary included Melrose Abbey,[35] old Roman walls, York Cathedral and Birmingham. The large pen works and the Humber bicycle factory held their interest. Kenilworth, Warwick and finally Stratford, where they saw the Shakespeare museum, the church of his burial. The inscription here impressed Funk.[36]

The boys returned by way of Warwick where they were impressed by the grounds surrounding the castle covering a stretch of land ten miles long and five miles wide. Originals by Rubens and Van Dyck were noticed favorably. At Oxford, Funk recalled "Tom Brown" and the crew.

Concern regarding finances and expense of living in hotels influenced the travelers to seek less expensive accommodations while in London for they wisely concluded they were at home only in the evenings and certainly were not expecting many callers. First to be visited in London was the National Gallery at Trafalgar Square, where there were more fine pictures than they could possibly remember. They moved on to the British Museum to look at books, manuscripts and mummies. The original of the Magna Charta, some proof sheets of Scott's novels, letters by Bacon, Washington and Napoleon attracted their attention.[37]

They made their way to the Tower of London, noted the historical associations and gave some time to examining the crown jewels.[38] St. Paul's and Westminster Abbey impressed them profoundly. Often they attended the theatre in the evenings,[39] but sightseeing followed the next day. They encountered some difficulty in observing Parliament in session because Minister Robert Todd Lincoln, son of Abraham, was out of the city.[40] A pleasant drive took them through Hyde Park, St. James and Green Parks; they passed Rotten Row, a monument to Albert and Buckingham Palace. Another trip took them to Hampton Court.[41] In London rain made the city dark like night.

An effort was made to locate the office of the editor of *Farmer and Stock-Breeder* who was out of town until the following Thursday.[42] They went out to Windsor Castle because the Queen was reported to be entertaining the German Emperor on the Isle of Wight, but they found they were not allowed to go through the castle on Wednesdays. A search for Dickens' Old Curiosity Shop was successful.

Living was reported to be cheaper on the Continent. Expenses in Ireland, Soctland and England while traveling had averaged about $10.00 a day, while in London they cut them down to about $4.00 per day.

The first installment of Eugene Funk's European *Diary* ends at this point. He forwarded the entries to his parents. The record was apparently kept to aid in informing them of the details of his trip. Before departing for Holland, the young men spent a Sunday at Brighton. They left in London a newly purchased trunk and their silk plug hats "which we were obliged to buy when we arrived in the city in order to be 'English, you know' and to keep the little boys from crying out as we passed 'there goes a Yankee.'" Howard proceeded to Berlin while Linc and Eugene sailed from Harwich to Rotterdam. The decision to travel with second class tickets was sufficient to convince them of its inadvisability. The crossing was rough. The distance of 101 miles across the North Sea brought them to a good view of Holland's dikes and breakwaters.

A trip to Amsterdam was reported as follows:

Our train carried us through a low flat, but beautiful country. Mostly grazing land for stock—and well stocked it is too with the black and Holstein cattle. The land is very rich and as near as I could tell there were from two to three head of cattle for every acre of ground. It is all very flat and low land, there is not a hill to be seen. There are also *no* fences, but like Ireland it is cut up into little patches of from one to ten acres—surrounding each of these is a deep ditch or canal, which answers all the purpose of a fence. These ditches are several feet deep—dug with steep banks and once an animal gets into one—it cannot get out without help. Little bridges are built across wherever needed and used by the cattle and horses. What seemed odd to us was the mammoth and old fashioned wind mills and so many of them—stood around everywhere—used by the peasant for grinding his corn and pumping the water off his land into large canals which run out to sea.

The city of Amsterdam was described as an odd, neat and clean city built almost entirely on piling, with a canal fifty miles long. The broad streets and thoroughfares were on either side of the canal where most of the heavy freight was carried on boats from one part of the city to another section. These boats were propelled by two men with long pike poles. The boys returned by train to Rotterdam,[43] and then proceeded to Brussels where they encountered some language difficulty. The cathedral defied Gene's description. A lace factory employing three to four thousand people attracted attention. A journey to the famous Waterloo battlefield drew forth, "I would not have missed this trip this afternoon and what I saw for all the cathedrals and old ruins of castles in the Kingdom." [44] Yet Funk recognized the immense amount of labor, time and money that had been spent on the cathedrals and he expressed wonderment at the glory of the stained glass windows depicting so many different Biblical events.

At Cologne the boys tried a bottle of Rhine Wine but decided that it had a queer taste. The Cathedral at Cologne impressed the visitors because of the fine stained glass, pulpits, altars and chapels. Later they crossed the Rhine on a pontoon bridge of boats. And at this point Eugene, Sr. expressed a wish that they might be able to drop in on the folks at home. They hoped for letters at Frankfort.[45]

Ten hours were consumed in the trip from Cologne to Bingen where the train took them to Frankfort on the Main. Several Americans were on board the boat. One gentleman and family were from Chicago, and two young gentlemen who were from Jersey City and Concord, presently studying at Vienna, knew some Andover classmates. No letters from home awaited them at Frankfort.

The cleanliness of the city impressed the travelers. They visited the home of Goethe and the place where kings and emperors had been chosen. They moved along to Giessen where they visited Herr Bar for whom Mr. Livingston of Bloomington had given them a letter of introduction.[46]

Comments on German farms included:

And the farmers, will they ever invent, manufacture or import into this country implements with which they can in one-sixteenth part of the time and labor—cultivate their land and gather their crops. Here is this country—thousands of years older than ours—the country from which our ancestors originally came, yet to this day we see the men, women, boys and girls—sometimes a dozen on an acre of ground—all mowing with an old straight handled scythe, the blade of which is four or five inches broad and almost straight about two and one-half feet long.

What would our people at home think if they had to put up hay in this way and handle it about ten times in all before it is put into the barn. Then we saw them using the old flail—to thresh their wheat—never heard of a threshing machine, reaper or mower. The plows, the funny things, I cannot describe them. There is a sort of cart runs along in front—pulled by horses or cows—on wheels—and behind this is a beam, sort of this fashion!

The funniest looking plow, I ever saw—worse than the forked stick we saw in New Mexico.[47]

A 500-foot climb enabled them to look over the city of Heidelberg where they also visited the University and an old castle. They discovered a Turkish bath house at Baden-Baden.[48] At Strasburg the clock that tells everything astounded them.[49] Mail from friends caught up with them at Lucerne [50] where they enjoyed the lake and saw lions carved out of solid stone by Thorwaldsen. They took the boat to the head of the lake.[51]

Narrow streets in Berne with houses built out over the street and a sort of arcade or tunnel left open where the walk would ordinarily be, caught their attention. This space was often filled with market goods so one was obliged to walk in the street. A fine view of the city was obtained from a high hill. They saw another old clock with a small rooster perched on the side. He flopped his wings and cried as the clock struck one.

Upon reaching Geneva [52] they visited their bankers, took a ride on the lake and looked at Mont Blanc twenty-five miles distant.[53] They recalled the name of Calvin here. Along the way to Chamonix they noticed:

Little farms scattered all along wherever a patch of ground the size of a good sitting-room or parlor could be found that could be cultivated. The scenery was very fine and Old Mont Blanc could be seen far above any of the other peaks. As in Germany the women seem to work in the fields just as hard or more than the men. Everybody seemed to be making hay today. Some mowing, others raking and stirring the short grass and still others loading small carts with the precious cow feed and storing it in stone barns.[54]

The temptation to climb Mont Blanc was too great. The boys purchased Alpine sticks and heavy woolen socks which they placed over their shoes. After seven long hours with no guide they were thankful to get back to the hotel.[55]

Along the drive up the valley of the Arve and over the boundary into Switzerland children offered plums, grapes and peaches in exchange for pennies.[56] The route continued through the country to Milan [57] where the cathedral was the finest of all they had seen.[58]

The train took them to Verona where fortifications and water systems were of interest. Venice was the city of true enchantment as they stepped into a gondola "and slid silently to our hotel in this queer and wonderful city Venice through the narrow and dark canals." [59] Netting was needed to protect them from mosquitoes at night. Funk noted that if Boston was laid out on cowpaths, the men who built Venice must have followed the fish.[60] The boys were impressed by Venetian glass, by the beautiful mosaics, the Palace of the Doges, the

Bridge of Sighs, the Grand Canal, St. Marks Cathedral, a lace factory and a gondola ride at night.[61]

The treasures of art at the Uffizi Gallery in Florence brought forth the following remark: "And a true lover of art I dare say would want to spend days and weeks going around and among them. But we boys, I am sorry to say, are none of us artists—so we hurriedly pass through these places—taking in as we think the whole beauty of a picture or a piece of statuary at one glance." He spent two or three hours in the Uffizi [62] and then visited another art collection in the Pitti Palace.

A trip around the city of Florence brought them to the Medici Chapel where the masterpieces by Michaelangelo, Day and Night, Twilight and Dawn impressed them.[63] Eugene remained alone at Florence while the others went to Rome. When he met them at Rome they visited the Cathedral of St. Peter, Bridge of Saint Angelo, Castle St. Angelo built by Hadrian, St. Pauls [64] and the Sistine Chapel at the Vatican. The paintings of Raphael and Michaelangelo interested them greatly.[65]

The usual tourist trip to Vesuvius provided them with some excitement when they actually climbed to the top to look into the crater. Naples proved to be both dirty and picturesque. The Bay of Naples by moonlight was truly a sight to remark on.[66] They were interested in the ruins of Pompeii where they spent some time. After returning to Naples the other boys decided to proceed to Paris and London— they were tired of Italy, and as Funk noted:

> Neither of them cares much for art, history and antiquity—none of us know much about these life long studies.

Furthermore they were probably anxious to be on their way "home." [67]

After Linc and Howard proceeded to London, Gene wrote of his plans from Rome, September 29, 1890. He declared his intention to go out "into the country in France to see the big horse raising country and also to see some herds of cattle in England" before returning home. He thought it unwise to hurry away until he had "seen what he could if it takes until the time we originally thought of, about Christmas." [68]

He visited Pisa, Genoa, Monte Carlo, Nice and Marseilles, arriving in Paris October 5th.[69] From October 11th to October 15th there remains a partial record of Gene's activities in Paris. Many years later Gene told of his visit to the Vilmorin estates at Verriers near Paris. He was profoundly impressed by the activities of this family and their contributions to scientific improvement in agriculture.

The European tour left a lasting imprint on the life of Eugene D. Funk. He continued to refer often to ancient history, works of art and the places he visited. He welcomed the opportunity to observe agricultural practices and cultural heritages in the various countries. The visit to the Vilmorin estate proved to be a high point in the entire European tour. The future plans of the young traveler regarding the contributions of his agricultural family in the United States were influenced by the example of the Vilmorins.

CHAPTER VII

Country Life on the Illinois Prairies 1894–1901

GRANDSONS OF ISAAC, members of the third generation were returning after travel and education to establish their own homes and families. The number of Mr. and Mrs. Funks was steadily increasing. Gene, Sr., Deane N., I. G., Frank and Linc were married within the year 1894–95 during this decade.[1] Contemporary accounts by LaFayette and Eugene D. in their diaries record the constant interest of the members of this one family in all other members. It is seldom possible to see the events of the passing years through the eyes of two different generations in the same family. These diaries and other records reveal the agricultural life of the times with remarkable clarity.

Members of this third generation, secure in the dignified atmosphere of their father's town houses and country homes, nevertheless were increasingly aware that effective leadership always begins in a small way among local friends and contemporaries. This idea was accepted by the younger married men of the Funk family. Their names appeared early in many new agricultural organizations sponsored by some far-seeing professors at the University of Illinois. Membership was drawn from the established agricultural families of the state. By the turn of the century agricultural problems were more sharply defined. It became clear to many people that leadership in the central corn belt should quickly be asserted.

Eugene Funk recognized the need for experimentation to attain better varieties of corn when he produced Funk's Ninety-Day in 1892. This was his first contribution during a lifetime devoted to the improvement of field crops, especially corn.

Ex-Governor Oglesby emphasized "The Royal Corn" when he spoke at the Fellowship Club in Chicago during 1894 on the occasion of the Harvest Home Festival. His impressive tribute to corn in 1894 indicates the importance of the plant in the decade of the 1890's. He opened his remarks "The Corn, The Corn, The Corn . . . Look on

68

its ripening, waving field: See how it wears a crown, prouder than monarch ever wore . . . Aye, The Corn, The Royal Corn." Two men, Eugene Funk and ex-Governor Oglesby, certainly understood the problems of the central Corn Belt.

During the decade of the 1890's Eugene D. Funk established his own home, assumed responsibilities for his father's farms and thought seriously about the agricultural problems of the central Illinois Prairies. Among many family weddings of the third generation his occurred miles from Funk's Grove on the Pacific coast in Oregon. Eugene, Sr. brought to central Illinois a bride whose grandfather and grandmother, Charles and Mary Bryant, had made the long trip across the western prairies before the Civil War from New York in 1853.[2] His marriage to Miss Mary V. Anderson, was an especially fortunate one.

Gene departed from Bloomington for Oregon on June 16th, 1894.[3] On an earlier trip as noted, he had met Mary Anderson when he and his family stopped over at Yaquino Bay in Oregon. She was visiting a friend who knew Gene. For a week or so the friendship flourished. Correspondence followed his return to Illinois and a second visit ended in an engagement.[4]

Their marriage occurred July 19, 1894 at Portland in the home of Grandmother Anderson. Dr. Thomas McClelland, president of Pacific University, officiated. Although the president was a little disturbed by the interruption of her studies at the end of the third year in college, he commented when asked to perform the ceremony, "Now I can see why you don't want to graduate." The ceremony was held in the middle of the afternoon. Mrs. Bell, a sister of Miss Julia Hodge, was located in Seattle. The couple stopped there and then proceeded to Minneapolis, Minnesota where they visited Mr. Northrup of Northrup-King Seed Company for two days. Upon arrival in Chicago they proceeded to Funk's Grove where they made their home with Mr. and Mrs. LaFayette for three months until they could locate a house. The first home of Eugene, Sr. in Bloomington was established at 507 East Grove Street. Gene traveled back and forth to the farm almost every day usually driving in good weather. A house built on East Grove by a Mr. Hutchinson became their home the next spring. It was located next door to the Reverend Gilliland, who was pastor of the First Christian Church. The two oldest children of Eugene, Gladys and LaFayette, were born in Bloomington.[5]

Gene spent his days at the farm but returned home evenings and week ends. Little Gladys' health was a matter of record in his diary, and his deep concern over his own difficulties with his left eye early in 1896 necessitated travel to Chicago. Treatments by a specialist and two weeks in Passavant Hospital resulted. The difficulty was diagnosed as hemorrhage of the eye. When in Chicago, the Chicago Beach Hotel on the South Side was often a center of activity. Charles Funk, Belle and Herb Rollins, and F. H. Funk with his wife were welcome callers. Nor was Gene unaware during his illness that his two loads of fat cattle brought $4.10 on the market. He wrote in his diary, "The same as I paid for them last August 7th, outlook discouraging . . . at present there is nothing in this business." [6]

The household of young Gene in Bloomington progressed. When he was on the west coast he was fortunate in securing Fugihara, a Japanese servant. "Fugi" decided to leave for Chicago in search of better wages but in three days returned, henceforth content with the good living in central Illinois. Living in town presented difficulties as well as pleasures. Often when driving back and forth to the farms, storms overtook the families. Time was wasted despite the easy access to the railroad. Often Gene's family stayed overnight with LaFayette. Social responsibilities in town as well as participation in activities in the country provided double sets of activities. Mamie's mother, Mrs. Anderson, was a guest during the summer of 1896.

The market continued "hard" in Chicago with an oversupply of cattle. Gene did not intend to pay 3¾ for cattle and 2¾ for sheep when fattened cattle brought only 4 cents. Later Paul Shinn sent him two loads of cattle on July 30th for 3½. These two loads consisted of eleven yearlings at 750 pounds and thirty-nine head with an average weight 972 pounds. [7] Cattle previously purchased were put on feed January 20th. By October 6th thirty-six of his top cattle sold at 5.15, average weight 1,602. They paid him 22 cents per bushel for 80 bushels of corn, $1.25 per month for grass and made $6. per head in addition. Gene said, "This was the first time we came out ahead in a long time." [8]

Gene was convinced that in the near future he would move to the country. One day he and Mamie drove out south "looking at location for our new house. I do wish I knew just what to do about it and what sort of a house I ought to build."

Gene meantime realizing that effective leadership began at home was beginning to participate in local agricultural activities. Early in January 1898 he attended the Farmers' Institute; he became a member of the nominating committee and was made a delegate to the State Convention. Some of his evenings at home were spent at the club or with Mamie to hear a public lecturer such as one on the Arctic. Often after a hard day's work he was too tired to attend entertainments such as the minstrels in the club rooms. Mamie joined the Second Presbyterian Church by letter January 9, 1898.

Significant ideas crystallized as responsibility for a growing family brought decisions. The following indicates the serious comment expressed by Gene, Sr.:

> May today—sometimes in the future be a historical one to me and to my *family*, especially. May my dear little girl and boy who are now in their babyhood realize some day that we are now planning for their welfare and comfort in future time. May they both live and appreciate what is being done for them. May they in times of despair, misfortune and temptation—read & think of the history of their Great Grandfather, Grandfather & Father's endeavors to beautify, enrich and preserve one of the garden spots of this world. May they be ever inclined to continue [sic] to its preservation & improvement and to hand down to those future generations such ambitions that will forever be an honor to the name by which they are known.[9]

LaFayette on this same day in the morning worked with his son, Eugene, helping him to lay out a piece of ground 200 feet north and south between two rows of hard maple trees and 450 feet east and west. This tract was situated in Section 13 of Funk's Grove Township "on one of the most sightly and loveliest places in existence for a country home in Illinois." [10] Gene was busy setting out plum and pear trees on April 1st. This was the site of his new home constructed later in 1906 and finished in 1907. Planting of trees in sequence around the border was continued by Gene near the chosen site. He included Hard Maple, White Pine, Red Bud, Arbor Rose, Thornless Honey Locust, Hackberry, Sour Cherry, Box Elder, Ash, White Birch, Walnut, Elm, Wild Cherry, Buckeye, White Oak, Tulip, Peach, Crab Apple, Wild Crab Apple, Osage Orange. There were also a Plum Thicket, Shrubbery, and later a Grape Arbor.[11]

Gene and Mamie moved to the country during the middle of April 1898 when they sent two loads of household goods to the farm on the South Place. They definitely "pulled up stakes" in the city on May 2nd, apparently without much regret:

> How beautiful is nature if we can only collect his thought and ideas long enough to see. How sweet and beautiful in the country. How deceitful is the city in its very self. Hot & dusty, bad water, worse milk, continued gossip about someone else. The same old parties and an enormous expense.[12]

Fugihara at first was not so intrigued by the wonders of the countryside. He was sent to LaFayette's for a few days but decided to return to Mamie and Gene.[13] All was not pleasure, for cholera struck the sows and pigs and farming seemed to be "an uphill business" at this point.[14]

Early in the fall the cattle got into the corn and Gene observed: "Another day to almost make one feel discouraged. This life is, of course, a continuous strife of ups and downs. But let us continue to keep up spirits and look for brighter lights behind dark clouds." [15] Gladys had undergone a bad cut on her face and nose just before her third birthday.[16] Tonsilitis set in a few days later and the grippe became a real threat, yet Gene could write on December 31st that the year ended with good prospects for the future.

As the last year of the nineteenth century began January 1899 he added in his *Diary:*

> Let us do what is right. Be honest in our dealings and surely we shall reap a successful reward.[17]

The executive committee of the local Farmers' Institute convened with little evident enthusiasm early in January. Interest, however, increased later in the spring [18] and during the remainder of the year. The McLean County Farmers' Institute was organized on November 23, 1895 with Deane Funk as president, S. N. King of Normal as vice president, and E. O. Mitchell of Danvers as secretary. At the first meeting the opening address was given by Professor Davenport of the University of Illinois with discussion led by Edward Ryburn and LaFayette Funk. On the next day, discussion of a paper on farm fences was led by Noah Franklin and LaFayette Funk. Officers of the Institute during 1899 included President Noah Franklin, and Vice President Eugene Funk.[19]

E. D. observed when yearlings were put on 60 acres of jerked corn January 27, 1899 for about an hour and a half that:

> It is really a shame what little interest a man can take in gathering his own corn. There are bushels & bushels left on the grounds. This corn was averaged by rows through field—and those rows were very scrupulously cleared of their ears. I am glad I am going to make a change. I trust we can have the place put and run in a better condition and with some satisfaction.

An improvement in communications came with the cutting and placing of telephone poles. Distribution and installation of the instruments followed. One of the earliest rural telephone companies was organized by Eugene D., who was one of the directors.[20]

Uncertainties of the market provided eternal problems for farmers. Lambs sold in February 1899 for only as much as they would have brought the preceding fall.[21] Hard luck on the cattle market in March with thirty seven Missouri cattle, one steer crippled, had brought less than Gene had hoped. Later in the summer, however, he met a good market although he anticipated a higher one. If he had fed the cattle until November they would have brought better than 7 cents.[22]

Improvements on the farm included new hog houses described as great successes.[23] Gene also purchased poles to build a new cattle barn. By this time he had determined his general payment plan for single men working for him at $21 per month. If everything proved satisfactory during the corn-husking season he would pay $10 more. He did this for single men as an inducement for them to behave themselves and to hold them during the summer after he had kept them through the almost idle months of the winter.[24] Gene, Sr. always referred to his workmen as "his boys." On June 3rd they finished painting the new sheep barn. During the year a windmill tower sixty feet high had been raised at the South Place.[25]

Trips to town were often overnight events,[26] with the possibility of visiting in the homes of uncles and cousins[27] and then possibly returning home by way of Miller Park to hear a band concert.[28]

An addition to Gene's family arrived July 6, 1899. He wrote:

Again we are blessed with health & Happiness and the addition of a very dear little girl to our house. Let us welcome her and love her as we do her older sister & brother. May she grow up to be a true and noble woman, a pride to her family & nation.[29]

During the fall months of 1899 Gene, on his thirty second birthday wrote that he was in good health with a fine family. He was pleased with his decision to run the entire farm himself. Although he was not yet out of debt he believed that there was every prospect "to be on easy street some day." [30]

With better prices on the cattle market in September for three loads of cattle, Gene estimated that the profit returned was almost 50 cents for corn since last January. At Auxvasse, Missouri, he obtained 144 head of cattle at $3.85 to $4.55 with the greater number between $4.25 and $4.40. The total cost was $6,681.89 plus expenses of $1,375. He owed his father, LaFayette, $1,656.53 on these cattle for money borrowed and taken in draft from Chicago. An oversight in payment of $722.89 at Fulton, Missouri to Mr. W. M. Patterson took him posthaste to Bloomington to send a draft for this amount. His concern was related in his *Diary* when he said that this kind of business might lead strangers to misinterpret his purposes in territory where he was unknown: "Surely it has taught me a lesson to be more careful." [31] A later trip to Auxvasse in November 1899 taught Gene, Sr. additional lessons, such as procuring a written contract and actually seeing his cattle weighed.[32]

Gene was fond of his mother-in-law, Mrs. A. B. Anderson, who left in October after another visit to Shirley with her daughter, Mamie.[33] Other events interesting to the family included the wedding of Miss Grace Cheney, whose family was descended from the pioneer settlers of Cheney's Grove. As a friend of the Funk family for many, many years, her marriage to Attorney John F. Wight brought Mamie and Gene in to Bloomington to stay at Uncle Abb's for the event.[34]

The December 24th entry by Gene, Sr. gives an idea of Christmas in the country: [35]

Christmas comes but once a year and so to-day we arranged our Christmas for the children. Mr. Necessary's little folks were invited for dinner—also Father, Mother & De Loss, Mrs. Turner, Doc & Pearl came after dinner. We had a big turkey gotten up by our ever faithful Japanese boy, Fugihara. I gave two of my men—most faithful to me during the year—each $20.00 in gold for their interest in their work and to show them I value and appreciate their good work.[36]

Eugene attended local and state meetings of the Farmers Institute during February 1900.[37] He was especially proud of his new cattle barn during a severe storm in February.[38] Farmers in the Corn Belt showed increased interest in the improvement of seed corn. At the meeting of the Illinois Corn Growers held in March 1900, corn experts attended including James Riley, Professor Forbes and E. S. Fursman, who was President of the Illinois Association. Professor A. D. Shamel of the University of Illinois was a strong advocate of the score card in judging corn. Fursman advocated closer attention to sowing and caring for seed corn.[39] The Indiana Corn Growers perfected an organization, January 7, 1900, and invited Fursman to address them.[40] Fursman was described as "undoubtedly the most enthusiastic corn-grower in the United States." He was well-known for his work in corn carnivals and for his advocacy of mixing seed at planting time or of "planting every sixth row of some later variety than the main crop, so that the period of pollination may be prolonged." He said a mixed corn always produced more than a single variety.[41] According to Fursman the average yield in Illinois of corn had been increased from 32 to 38 bushels per acre through the efforts of the Illinois Corn Growers Association.[42]

Interest in plant breeding attained added significance. A writer for *The Breeders Gazette* called attention to the long activity of the Vilmorin family near Verriers in France.[43] E. D. recalled the impressions from his European trip of 1890. W. M. Hays and his work with wheat indicated the progress made in the United States. Increased knowledge regarding the sugar beet and the work of Luther Burbank as well as other information regarding the Mendelian theory hastened activity.

The Illinois Seed Corn Breeders organization met in Springfield, Illinois June 1900 with J. H. Coolidge of Galesburg as President and F. A. Warner of Sibley as Secretary. Membership was limited to persons engaged in growing pure-bred corn on land worked by themselves. The members should not sell corn except in the ear unless otherwise ordered by the purchaser. No member was allowed to sell seed corn except that grown by himself. Type, variety, quality must be reported to the secretary by the second Wednesday of December. Seed corn for sale by members must be tested for vitality and show a germinating power of at least 90 percent.[44] At the meeting held in Springfield in October 3, 1901, J. D. Funk and L. H. Kerrick became members.[45]

Interest and necessity during 1900 increased concern over the corn crop. The connection between raising cattle and corn on these rich Illinois lands, with their increased valuation, became obvious to the thinking farmer as he considered his relationship to the problems of expanding production, the price level and to domestic and foreign markets. This was not the day of radio and television as mediums of information. The speaker, the newspaper, the periodical, the institute, the carnival, the fair or the University short course were the only means of communicating the slowly increasing fund of scientific information. Compared to the 1950's the methods seem antiquated. Compared to the 1880's the thinking and the activities were advanced. It is difficult to measure their contribution in the light of the times in which they were made. Sufficient emphasis has not been given to the endeavors of the so-called "Corn crank" or to the "Corn evangelist." E. S. Fursman was one of the first and Professor P. G. Holden one of the latter while E. D. Funk was able to combine the scientific and commercial knowledge through his ability to lead men of all groups.

Annual corn expositions occurred at Mitchell, Davison County, in South Dakota for three years according to an article in the *Orange Judd Farmer*, in October 1900 which printed a picture of the 1900

Corn Palace erected there.[46] Peoria, Illinois held its second successful corn show under the auspices of the Illinois Corn Growers Association and of the businessmen of Peoria under the leadership of E. S. Furs-man early in October 1900. According to the same publication, "It was so successful that it will probably become a permanent institution." It is unique in that no other corn show located in the Corn Belt had been attempted on so large a scale and was a success both financially and in the way of exhibits. Perfect weather had much to do with the outcome of the show, and the farmers of the central west seemed to appreciate the efforts of the managers to present the good points of King Corn. They came from all over the Corn Belt to the third exposition held during 1901 in Peoria.[47]

Early in May as usual Gene took his family to the Grove to pick wildflowers.[48] Mrs. Bryant, grandmother of Mrs. Eugene, arrived from Oregon June 14th. Her uncles, Mr. A. A. Fay of Stanley, Kansas and Mr. Charles Fay of Manhattan, Kansas, arrived for a visit in July.[49] The children were sick during the year. LaFayette, Jr. required a nurse's care in January and Alta Elizabeth was ill in April. Gene, Sr. worried about his wife, Mamie. On January 14th he wrote "Dear little wife, she has her hands full, taking care of our family of little ones. I can see it wearing on her and I worried for fear it may cause her ill health in future years." Alta Elizabeth was not well again in May and in June.[50] A second boy arrived August 25th amid rain, wind and hail storms. Gene, Sr. wrote of his namesake:

God has once more blessed our happy home with another son born this morning 3 o'clock. Another grave and responsible burden added to his mother & father's shoulders which will be lightly and happily borne if he will but turn out to be in every respect an honest and industrious man who in the years that are to come can take up and carry through successfully those ideas and plans so well thought out & prepared by his ancestors.[51]

During the summer Gene drove his father, LaFayette, over the Franklin farm near Lexington where they called on Mr. Spoor, then 99 years old. LaFayette recalled stopping over night here when driving cattle to Chicago, before the railroads were built.[52] Interest in the past became a tradition in the Funk family, chiefly because of the close association of the family with these events and also because of a recognition that out of these everyday activities the history of a region was in the making.

Isolated events indicated other interests and activities of these families during the summer of 1900. Pawnee Bill's Wild West Show was an important attraction because he came from Bloomington, although the street parade was nothing of importance.[53] The fairs at Clinton, LeRoy, Champaign and Springfield drew attendance from LaFayette, Sr.[54] Mrs. LaFayette departed for Ohio to attend Jesse Shinn's wedding.[55] Gene managed to sell cattle at $5.80 (weight 1,482) and bought cattle weighing 1,015 at $4.80.[56] In September he departed for Kansas to purchase four loads of cattle.[57]

A Republican rally, held at Funk's Grove October 10, 1900, was described as follows:

Almost an ideal day. The great barbecue has been held and has gone down in history as one of the greatest political events of this section of the country. People were here from all directions and distances. Providence smiled on the four townships that originated the scene.

According to Eugene's *Diary* an estimated 10,000 people attended the rally. He recorded that seven beef were killed and washed by steam. The menu also included Irish and sweet potatoes, buns, cheese, pickles and cookies. It looked as if the country would support William McKinley for President.[58]

Gene gave the first speech of his life at the Piatt County Farmers Institute on the subject, "How I Handle My Sheep." Several men congratulated him but he was of the opinion that he did not care to make a business of delivering addresses.[59] Before this his ideas on cattle feeding had found their way into the columns of the *Prairie Farmer*. He also thought there was no profit in feeding cattle when western feeders were as high as during the past year of 1900. He and many other McLean County men were refusing to buy unless the price went down. He also advocated that corn farmers raise a few high-grade head, whether landlord or tenant. His blue grass 180-acre pasture furnished feed for cattle all winter except during snow when they were in the barn. He kept 1,400 sheep but 900 would be sold before May 1st. Fifty acres of land made him three crops-oats, clover and rape; rape being practically an extra crop. He grew and fed it successfully last year and this year. Corn was planted after rape.[60]

Efforts to obtain cooperation in the McLean County Farmers' Institute produced results. The closing days of the meetings held in January 1901 brought 1,000 people in attendance. Gene, Sr. hoped that meetings in years to come would be as successful, harmonious and pleasant in committee work as the last two years.[61] He also attended the State meeting of the Farmers' Institute the 21st of February at Jacksonville.[62]

The shipping of stock in February brought 401 sheep and 20 cattle to the Chicago market. A fine price was obtained for the cattle but they made no money since they had been fed for a year and lost weight because of hunters.[63] As a consequence of this situation, Gene, Sr. became interested in proposing a law against shooting on the public highway. Nineteen of the directors of the State Farmers' Institute were in session during a trip he made to Springfield. All signed the petition and helped to carry the measure to the legislature.[64] With LaFayette and Captain S. N. King, Gene called on George Stubblefield to look over the bill. He promised to get someone to introduce it.

LaFayette appeared in April before the Judiciary Committee of the Senate in favor of the bill. LaFayette presided over a meeting of the stockholders of the Union Stock Yards when the former directors were re-elected. On January 20th he celebrated his sixty-seventh birthday and spent some time pointing out dividing lines between his property and those of others in the Grove, finally locating a government post.[65] Continuing interest in historical activities brought LaFayette to the State Historical Society meeting in Springfield January 29–31 where he heard some good papers.[66] Spring came early. By the 17th of March the birds were singing and the prairie chickens could be seen in the pasture. With these signs of spring the mud was knee deep.[67]

When Mrs. LaFayette and DeLoss departed on a trip for Hot Springs, Arkansas, Gene's family moved to the LaFayette home to keep house for Grandfather. A little reminiscing was reflected in Gene's *Diary* for May 15th when he noted:

77 years ago today Grandfather Isaac Funk settled in what is now Funk's Grove.

41 years ago today Father LaFayette Funk began to break prairie sod for himself about ½ mile north and ¼ mile east of his present residence.

38 years ago today Father and Mother began keeping house in this present residence.

Three significant events occurred during the spring of 1901. The first of these was the creation of a route for a new rural mail delivery starting at Shirley. Gene participated in the appointment of a Democrat. He later wrote, "Would rather have a good Democrat than a poor Republican every time." [68] The dedication of the new Agricultural Building at the University of Illinois was the second event. The building was described as the largest and finest of its kind in the world. Of this occasion, Gene wrote:

I predict that not even those who are most enthusiastic in the matter can scarcely realize the outcome and benefit to agriculture that this department in the University of Illinois will be in the next few years to come, not only the state of Illinois but the whole world.[69]

L. H. Kerrick, president of the Illinois Cattle Feeders' Association, was among those who spoke at the dedication of this new building. S. Noble King of Bloomington, chairman of the Legislative Committee of the Illinois Farmers' Institute, 1899, officially represented the farmers of the State. Dean Davenport gave an address and Congressman Joe Cannon also was present.[70] The third event in this series of especial interest to LaFayette was the laying of the cornerstone for the new Bloomington Court House.[71]

Labor problems on the farms, with help coming in from Kentucky, led Gene, Sr. to write at length of the fact that Will Necessary could accomplish as much as two other men. He entered into no groups or quarrels with anyone, always working for the interest of his employer. William Necessary was the recipient of a $2.00 bonus at the end of the week in addition to his employer's verbal statement that if they both lived that was not all he would do for him.[72]

Gene departed on a cattle-purchasing trip to Kansas in late July. He spent some time with Mr. Charles Fay near Manhattan where he found cattle but owners were unwilling to sell. Finally near Lincoln he obtained 100 head at 4 cents to be driven three miles without shrinkage of 3 percent. On August 4th the cattle were loaded.[73] Gene and Deane also undertook to import Shropshire sheep from two leading English breeders.[74]

The last months of the year 1901 were notable for three more important events. E. D. and LaFayette traveled to Pittsburgh with a load of cattle for the Fat Stock Show there. L. H. Kerrick, Uncle Jake and Deane also shipped a load apiece. LaFayette and Gene sold their cattle at $8.00. Kerrick also sent cattle to Chicago November 30th.[75]

Gene's family, including a nurse, set out December 10 at 9 a. m. for Mamie's former home in Oregon.[76] The children were baptized into the Presbyterian Church at LaFayette's home before departing.[77] Grandma Bryant traveled as far as Chicago and then left for Shepherd, Michigan, where some of the Bryants were living. Mamie and Gene arrived in Oregon December 29th, going by train to Oswego and then walking three and one-half miles.[78] On the following day they drove six or seven miles to Grandpa Bryant's farm through what was once the dense forests of Oregon.[79]

A third event of considerable significance in the Funk family history occurred before the departure for Oregon. Funk Bros. Seed Co. was organized in November 1901.[80] After years of experimentation and experience, Eugene Funk and his cousins with the advice and consent of the older members of the Funk family embarked on a new industrial enterprise. The organization of this unusual company occurred at the beginning of the twentieth century.

PART THREE

A Guardian of the Heritage

CHAPTER VIII

The Seed Company
Early Work with Corn · 1901–1903

EUGENE D. FUNK, SR., experimented with corn as early as 1892. During this decade of the nineties he thought seriously of some method whereby the Funk farms, the agricultural colleges and experiment stations, together with the United States Department of Agriculture could find common ground. His trip to Europe during 1890 inspired him to undertake this program. Emphasis upon the study of genetics about this time gave impetus to his crystallizing ideas during the succeeding years. He knew of the work of those who had contributed to the better selection and improvement of crops.

During the last decade of the nineteenth century significant events were occurring at the Agricultural Experiment Station located at Svalof, Sweden, where Dr. Nilsson was placed in charge in 1890.[1] He first tried the German method of "slow amelioration" which was the principle chosen by Charles Darwin in his work, but Nilsson found that it was not applicable to all the needs of the agriculturists (1885–91). He then decided to sow kernels of numerous selected ears separately and in small groups (1891–92). In this way he found that only those kernels derived from one single ear gave "pure and uniform cultures" [2] and the strains were almost always pure and constant. Nilsson's principle was to derive his strains from single mother plants to obtain pure breeds. Also from a selected plant a pure and constant race could be obtained by isolating and multiplying the progeny.[3]

It should also be noted that the company that was organized for the production and improvement of seed-grains for the southern part of Sweden was established as early as 1886 by private agriculturists with their work based on the scientific method. Botanical studies were to contribute to agricultural experiment stations in Europe and America.[4] A company for central Sweden was combined with the first group. In 1891 the General Seed-Grain Trading Company was set up in Svalof to undertake the commercial side of the activity. The

Vilmorins, already referred to as the well known French agricultural family near Paris knew of the Svalof Station inasmuch as they tested their new variety of oats (ligowo) at this station.[5] Problems in Europe were more definitely related to smaller cereals as the prevailing crops.

In the United States, meanwhile, Willet M. Hays conducted independent researches with important results in wheat. He found that in each thousand plants there were a few "phenomenal yielders." Single seed plantings, as he said, made it "practicable to secure these exceptional plants, and from these new varieties can be made." [6] The related strains were found constant and pure and needed only to be multiplied "to give a new race." [7] Problems related to the improvement of corn, however, were somewhat different.

When Eugene D. Funk and his cousins decided to enter into the commercial improvement of corn they knew that they must draw upon the experience of many who had preceded them. Such men as J. L. Reid and J. S. Leaming in the United States had applied the idea of selection. Some scientific activity had been undertaken by W. J. Beal at Michigan Agricultural College, P. G. Holden, C. G. Hopkins and A. D. Shamel at the University of Illinois.

Robert Reid moved from southern Ohio to central Illinois in 1846 bringing with him a semi-gourd seed variety known as Gordon Hopkins Corn. A poor stand was secured in the spring of 1847. The missing hills were replanted with a small local variety called Little Yellow Corn, probably a flinty type. From the resulting crop, the variety Reid's Yellow Dent was developed after many years of selection by Robert's son, James L. Reid. A report appeared in *American Agriculture* by H. S. Bidwell, December 1867, concerning a Tennessee farmer who also experimented with the source of pollen. A. E. Blount from the same state began controlled pollination in a variety of white corn. The resulting variety and accounts regarding it appeared in succeeding years after publication in 1879.[8]

J. S. Leaming, living near Wilmington, Ohio in 1826, originated the oldest known variety of corn. He began selecting seed from the ordinary yellow corn on the Little Miami Bottoms of Hamilton county. For 56 years he selected a slightly tapering ear well filled at butt and tip with straight rows ripening in from 90 to 199 days. E. E. Chester of Champaign, Illinois secured seed from J. S. Leaming in 1885. He selected ears that ripened in 100 to 120 days. J. H. Coolidge of Galesburg secured seed from E. E. Chester and developed a deeper kernel. According to one source, Leigh F. Maxey of Curran, Illinois said that he purchased his first bushel of Leaming seed on March 10, 1897 from Mr. E. E. Chester in Champaign, Illinois. It is probable that strains of Leaming came into Illinois from these sources.[9] Funk's Yellow Dent was developed from Reid's Yellow Dent,[10] and Leaming secured from Chester and Coolidge figures extensively in the early corn experiments of the new Funk Company.

Another early experiment was performed about 1870 by Professor W. J. Beal of the Michigan Agricultural College. He repeated the Bidwell emphasis in 1876 upon the importance of pollen selection He crossed two varieties by detasselling one in 1881 in what was probably the first detasselled growing plot.[11] There followed Kansas experiments by Kellerman and Swingle. Experiments at the Illinois Experimental Station by G. W. McCluer, F. D. Gardner and G. E. Morrow were published 1892–1895.[12] It is possible and probable that Eugene Funk knew of this work when he developed Funk's Ninety Day in 1892.

The ear to row method was emphasized by C. G. Hopkins in 1897 at Illinois to determine protein and fat content of the corn kernel. Eugene Funk was among the first to turn this knowledge to practical commercial use.

During the decade 1890–1900 Gene Funk was on the alert for information concerning Pedigreed corn, as it was then called. Among his papers there is a small pamphlet published in 1894 by Parlin and Orendorff Company of Canton, Illinois. This pamphlet described how to bring the quality of corn above the known standard.[13] Gene Funk also demonstrated in 1892 his interest and knowledge by producing Funk's Ninety Day. This corn originated in the following manner. Gene Funk secured through the University of Illinois in 1892 a half bushel of little Early Murdock Corn. He paid $2.00 for this half bushel of shelled corn. Funk's Ninety Day was a cross between Early Murdock and Minnesota Pride of the North, perfected by C. P. Bull and W. M. Hays. From this variety Funk collected in each succeeding year the early ears. In 1914 he wrote:

> In 1901 I started a breeding block using the ear to row method, such as is generally used now by corn breeders throughout the country. My recollection is that when I started with this work, I had twenty-two different types of corn selected from this early variety of yellow corn.[14]

According to Perry G. Holden, who came as a Professor from Michigan Agricultural College where he was a colleague of W. J. Beal to the Agricultural College at Urbana in 1895, Gene Funk was well informed about the experimental work carried on at the University's Experiment Station in Illinois.[15] Gene's father, LaFayette, as a member of the State Board of Agriculture also knew of the work at the University. Holden's review of early corn breeding work at the University gives an insight into the type of early experiment carried on at the Illinois Experiment Station. Although his story was written some fifty years after the events "almost entirely from memory," this information is important to the Funk story because in 1902 P. G. Holden became the first general manager of the Funk Bros. Seed Co.[16]

Although it is difficult to determine the importance of this early experimental work at the University of Illinois there is little doubt that it was among the early steps in the improvement of corn. Contemporary records of this work are difficult to obtain. Nevertheless the following statement appearing in *The Breeders Gazette* November 14, 1900 gives support to Holden's account that the experiments he described so many years later actually took place:

> At the University of Illinois an experiment in closely inbreeding corn was tried with the result that in four seasons the crops completely "ran out." The silks were covered with paper sacks and in due time fertilized with the pollen from the stalks on which they grew. Then the silks were covered up again until all the pollen had fallen.[17]

The results of the Holden experiments showed that the crosses differed widely in yielding ability and that some produced more than the original seed. Inbreeding experiments reduced the size of the stalk and ears until these characters were nearly constant. Holden observed that an occasional plant in the selfed material looked normal. He thought this result occurred because of accidental crossing. He checked this by making crosses between inbreds and stated, "The results confirmed this explanation; the plants were in great contrast in size and vigor to those from the selfed seed." The main purpose of this experimentation, according to Holden, was to determine "how to use controlled crossing easily and effectively as Beal's work seemed to indicate that crossing was what gave the results we were after. My inbreeding experiment was incidental to find out more about how pollination behaved and the effect of inbreeding on yield."[18]

When "P. G." decided to leave the University of Illinois in 1900 to manage a sugar beet factory at Pekin, Illinois, he established sixteen different centers of beet raising. Gene Funk was among those who grew beets producing 29 tons to the acre at $4.50 per ton. Twenty tons were considered a fairly big yield per acre. One day after breakfast, ostensibly to look over the beets, Holden and Gene Funk visited the Funk Farms. This trip, as Professor Holden recalled years later, was "a history making trip."[19] Gene Funk recorded in his *Diary* in July 23, 1901 that he enjoyed the visit very much. Gene wrote of Holden, "He gave us much valuable information on different subjects and he expressed himself as having had a most delightful time. We drove over the farm and then down through the woods taking dinner at Deane Funk's." [20]

Gene Funk expressed the following general opinion when they discussed at this time the possibility of improving the efficiency of the Funk farms: "We didn't earn these farms, we fell heir to them—if we have them, they ought to do something for the rest of the world." P. G. Holden offered the opinion that before the rest of the world were saved it might be possible to bring more efficiency to the administration of the Funk Farms. The two men discussed the centralization of purchasing power in order to save time and effort. Gene commented: "You've set me to thinking—there's going to be something doing." [21] This conversation was probably the vital spark to the implementation of his developing plans.

The trouble with some of the Funk boys, according to Holden's observations, was their love for extended vacations. Gene, Ben, Duncan and Deane were less inclined to go so often and remain away so long. The early months devoted to the organization of a new company provided opportunity for all to learn about the enterprise. With divided responsibilities and unity of purpose Gene hoped that the third generation would also contribute something of value to the development of agriculture.

After discussion with Gene's father, cousins, uncles and friends, plans for the organization were completed. Funk Bros. Seed Co. was incorporated in November 1901. The first headquarters were located in a room on the third floor of the National Bank Building in Bloomington. Offices were moved during the succeeding year into a store and warehouse building on North East Street in the block where the Post Office building now stands. The seed business was transacted from this point in connection with a large elevator and warehouse built at Funk's Grove during the same year. A few years later in 1907 a half interest was purchased in the property now owned at 1300 West Washington Street. Two years later all of the buildings and grounds at this address were acquired. A house was converted to an office and was occupied until 1938 when a new office building was constructed. These changes were brought about largely because of the abiding faith and courage of Eugene D. Funk, Sr. who launched a business enterprise based upon his ideas first put into operation in 1892.

The commercial development of improved corn and other crops

is a long and complicated story. Eugene Funk, Sr., toward the close of his eventful and interesting life, wrote his old friend and first manager, P. G. Holden:

Hybrid Corn is a long story commencing back as far as 1904. These are only a beginning of a lifetime of experiences . . . but the water has gone over the dam and perhaps it is best that the unruly waters should be allowed to settle into a mirror lake of sunshine and shadow.[22]

This "mirror lake of sunshine and shadow" could reflect years of persistent effort and intermittent discouragement as well as success. Out of these trials, tribulations and determination came a better agricultural life to many American farmers. Gene Funk, Sr. played a leading part in this unfolding drama of the Royal Corn and other crops.

The organization of this new seed company marked a significant event in the annals of the Funk family. A stockholders' meeting was held in November 1901.[23] Thirteen members of the third generation, ranging in ages from 26 to 35 years, undertook as their objective the improvement of grains produced on their farms. Larger yields and better quality became their chief objectives.[24] Thus the dream of E. D. Funk for his family became a reality. He saw in his family's extensive land holdings and in the potential abilities of the third generation an opportunity to convert their heritages into a source of common good. He sought to follow the example of the Vilmorin family of France. His visit to Verriers during his European tour deeply influenced his thinking.

Eugene D. Funk was chosen president of the company, with L. H. Kerrick as vice president, J. Dwight Funk as secretary and Frank H. Funk as treasurer. J. Dwight Funk and L. H. Kerrick became directors for one year; E. D. and Deane were selected for two years and Frank H. Funk for three years. The company was capitalized at $25,000.[25] Five dollars on each share of stock was to be subscribed on or before November 15, 1901. Directors E. D. and J. Dwight were instructed to purchase on behalf of the company seed corn to provide amounts to the several stockholders who intended to raise corn for sale to the company. The stockholders were to repay the company the cost of all corn used by them.

P. G., as Holden was known to his friends, did not decide to join the commercial organization of Funk Brothers immediately. During October 1901 Eugene was somewhat discouraged by preliminary refusals from both Professors A. D. Shamel and P. G. Holden to join immediately in the contemplated project. Gene recognized that the

Funks needed men associated with them who could go before the people, attend institutes and organize groups for the better study of corn and seeds. This same line of thought was emphasized as he told his friend Holden that raising the corn was not enough. The public must learn the facts. Other branches of the contemplated business—"smaller seeds, garden seeds—wheat—potatoes—corn—peas—soya beans would become a dead letter if the Funk family tackled the undertaking alone." Ever mindful that he would not urge a man to leave academic life unless he wished, Gene added that he had written Shamel to that effect, "nor did we wish the impression to get out that we had asked him to leave the University work and go into some commercial business." Observing that since Holden was not connected with the University plans might develop better with Shamel remaining there, Gene said: "In fact, I can see where we can go even further and get better and greater results from our experiments than the University could think of doing—all of which the University would be at perfect liberty to use. For doing the greatest good to the farmers I don't see why this proposal and business properly carried on could be excelled in anything projected at the University." Other ideas occurred to him but this line appeared to be the central theme of his original thinking about the organization of the company.[26]

A fundamental philosophy and a basic understanding of human nature were also expressed in a letter to A. D. Shamel:

> And now, old man, you are having your ups and downs, you are always going to have them. We all of us have them—no matter what business or profession. We may foresee there will inevitably always be present more or less smut in our oats, insects in our orchards, droughts in our corn fields and whirlwinds in our air castles. But do not become discouraged. We must not allow what seems to be a molehill to others to become mountains to us. The public as a rule are our best friends but they are the hardest to reach and often the easiest to lose.[27]

Perry G. Holden became the first general manager of the Funk Bros. Seed Co. Professor Shamel remained at the University for a few years and then joined the United States Department of Agriculture.

Reporters came almost immediately from their individual publications to observe the work on the Funk farms. *The Farmers Voice and National Rural* presented a summary of the activity on the Funk farms in an article datelined Bloomington, Illinois, January 18, 1902. The article began: "Bloomington is the metropolis of one of the greatest agricultural sections of this country." The reporter with J.

Dwight Funk and Professor Holden left Bloomington for Shirley, arriving at the farms of J. Dwight Funk and LaFayette. The home of LaFayette was described as "a mansion in proportions, occupies a handsome site from which is an unsurpassed view of the high rolling lands which give to this part of the great 'prairie' state a beauty at once unusual and charming." [28]

Seed for the corn to be used in the first year's breeding was stored in the barns of J. Dwight Funk, "and thither we went to see the beginnings of the huge enterprise." The gathered seed represented months of correspondence and weeks of travel on the part of the company's secretary, J. Dwight Funk, who was described as "an enthusiastic grower of corn himself and well qualified to pass upon the merits of specimens submitted." [29]

An original account found in the Funk Papers described the methods. After securing the names of all the leading corn growers in the Corn Belt, the list was reduced by correspondence and by examining samples, to about twenty-five men who were visited personally on their own farms. Their corn was inspected as it came from the fields and if it was good or better seed than that of the Funks it was purchased. Some 2,500 bushels of the best seed corn in the world was secured in this manner. From this amount about 3,000 of the finest ears were selected for breeding.

Each ear was given a number in a pedigree book with the following items tabulated: length, circumference, weight, number of rows, number of kernels to the row, space between rows, character of tip, of butt, length of kernel, shape of kernel, shape of ear, shade of kernel, breadth of kernel, shade of cob, percent of oil, percent of protein. These points were employed in determining (1) the amount of grain to each cob, (2) purity, (3) proportion of length to circumference. At this time the ideal ear was thought to be cylindrical and the proportion of length to circumference to be 10 to 7. It was thought that there should be no lost space between rows. The tip and butt should be well filled, the kernel rough, wedge shaped, long, thick grain with sound medium cob and shank.

Isolated plots of ground for breeding blocks were selected on the Funk farms. Each breeding block was situated so that there would be less danger of pollen blowing over on it from other corn. A breeding block contained five acres and from 80 to 100 rows of corn. A single ear was planted in each row and every row was numbered. This number was recorded with the information pertaining to this ear. An expert took notes on its growth and maturity for later use.[30]

During the last part of July and the first of August the pollen flies from the tassel. Stalks were examined before the period of pollenization. If they were barren or inferior in any way they were detassled so that every kernel raised in a breeding block had fruitful parents.

This early work revealed that ordinary corn had low prepotency, namely lack of power to reproduce desirable characteristics. According to this early account, "a fine large ear selected from corn of no breeding when planted will produce 10 to 12 percent barren stalks, 30 to 40 percent nubbins, 40 to 45 percent medium sized ears and only 5 to 6 percent of ears resembling a parent ear." It was believed that by detasseling the weak and barren stalks the strength of the corn in the breeding blocks was increased.

During the harvest each row was gathered separately as the product of a single ear. The entire yield of each row was weighed and the number of ears counted. The average weight of the ears was thus computed. The total weight and the number of hills determined the rate of yield per acre. Then the ten rows giving the largest yield per acre along with the greatest average weight of ears were selected as the "champion rows." Only the best ears from these champion rows were selected from this same breeding block the next year. The account continued, "The rest of the good ears from these champion rows with the best ears from the next highest yielding rows were used for the general field seed." [31]

Detasseling took place on the Funk Farms from the very first year of the company's production as stated in an article appearing in the *Orange Judd Farmer,* November 1902, "Just before the tassels appear the inferior row is detasseled in order to prevent the ears on the vigorous healthy row being pollenized from the poor row."

A large area was devoted to the growing of quality seed corn in addition to the breeding plots where the highest grade of corn was produced. All but a few of the very best ears from the breeding plots were planted in the general fields. When the corn was dry enough to husk it was stored in different seed houses on the various Funk Farms. Small and inferior ears were removed at unloading time. Others were placed on drying racks. [32]

The corn remained in the drying room until all of the surplus moisture disappeared. If the crop matured late, artificial heat was used. After the corn was well matured it was removed to the warehouse at Funk's Grove where it was again sorted and put up in long narrow crates which held the ears of corn for shipment. [33]

Over a dozen varieties of high bred seed corn were produced. In addition Funk Bros. Seed Co. grew and handled large quantities of high grade oats, clover, rape, timothy, soybeans, sorghum and other leading farm seeds.[34]

The third step in the early procedure during 1902 was the chemical breeding of corn. If an ear first proved to be a "champion yielder," its product would go to the laboratory to be analyzed for high oil and high protein. If the ear tested high in either content it was planted in a single row in a chemical block. The selection from these blocks was the same as that described above with the added calculation of high protein and oil. Oil was considered valuable for fattening and finishing livestock. Protein was necessary to develop tissue and bone in growing animals.[35]

As early as May of 1902 C. G. Hopkins, head of the Department of Agronomy at the University of Illinois, wrote to Funk that he had received his letter describing the vast amount of work undertaken to improve corn. He added that he forwarded to Professor Holden results of chemical selection upon "The two varieties to be used in our cooperative work in corn breeding plots in which we used the system which we have followed from the last five to six years." [36]

Dr. R. O. Graham of the Illinois Wesleyan College, who took his first degree at Amherst and his Ph.D. degree under Professor Remstadt at Johns Hopkins, became chemist for Funk Bros. Professor Graham reported the method followed in the laboratories financed by the Funks at Wesleyan. The company desired to increase the protein and oil values in corn. It was thought that each acre might increase by one half the value of its production without unusual drain upon the soil.[37] A young scientist, H. H. Love, was employed to assist Graham.

The methods employed in the chemical analysis required the selection of a large amount of each variety physically of the highest grade. From one variety 205 ears were selected; from each of these ears two grains at a place were taken out. These grains were then placed in an envelope labelled with variety and number and sent to the laboratory to be tested for protein and fat, and the best were selected for planting. The seed corn thus represented ears both physically and chemically of the highest grade.[38] Ears corresponding to the highest marked numbers were planted in rows by themselves in each lot. The ten-acre lots were placed approximately one half mile apart. From year to year this process was repeated.[39]

Scientific analysis was possible because Funk Brothers were willing to equip a laboratory without regard for the expense involved to carry forward this work. The amount of protein was determined by the Kjeldealh process, in which ground meal was boiled up with concentrated sulphuric acid for several hours. The nitrogen of the corn was thus changed to ammonium sulphate, the ammonia was freed and the amount of nitrogen was tested. Ten analyses for protein were carried on at the time. The other process was used to extract the fat. An electric bath was provided for this purpose to heat the ether. Twenty of these analyses could be performed at the same time. The ether process offered advantage because it could be continued during the night without fear of fire.[40]

During the year 1902 the Funks bred corn with high oil and high protein for general feeding; corn with high oil and low protein for glucose factories; corn with high protein without changing the normal amount of oil to be used as a balanced ration for fancy beeves and bacon hogs; corn with high protein and low oil for growing cattle and young hogs.[41] According to the observer from the *Country Gentleman,* ordinary corn contained 10 percent protein increased in Funk Bros. pedigree corn to 12.80 percent. Ordinary corn contained 4.25 percent oil, increased in Funk Bros. pedigree corn to 5.60 percent. The yield of ordinary corn was 50 to 60 bushels per acre where that of Funk Bros. was 80 to 90 bushels per acre.[42] It is significant that this information was published in agricultural papers outside of Illinois.

Eugene D. Funk was given the credit for originating the idea of a company with such purposes. For many years, according to the reporter from *Farmers Voice and National Rural,* he cultivated corn on the lines laid down by Professors Holden and Hopkins, and the results justified the faith he manifested in the new movement. Indeed, the Funk Farms were the scene of many interesting experiments conducted under the auspices of the Agricultural College, and the practical results appealed strongly to President Funk.[43] Funk stated that they proposed to make commercial use of the lessons taught by the experiments at the Agricultural College of the University of Illinois. He noted that they had worked for years with the college, saying, "I have carried forward some interesting and I think valuable experiments during the past eight years."

Among the first speeches delivered by the president of the new company was one given before a group of landowners, tenants and overseers on the Funk Farms delivered at Dwight Funk's Seed House, April 25, 1902:

I feel that not one of us can fully appreciate or realize that the true meaning of this first meeting, coming together as it were, of the owners and tenants and overseers of this body of land, situated as it is, in the center of the corn belt of the United States, the fertility that it possesses, the resources that lie hidden, almost within our eyesight and if properly managed within our pockets. I say I do not believe that any of us are capable today of duly realizing the situation of what we can do, if we will, in the next twenty-five years. No other combination, taking everything into consideration, exists today. The old maxim "United We Stand, Divided We Fall" presents in its true sense, to this gathering of men and this company, that from the first to the last, we must be united and it was with this thought in view that we had asked you all to meet here at this time.

The new president spoke also to those who might wonder what the chief purpose of the organization of the seed company was:

We have launched our boat and the general public is watching and expecting much of us. Let us prove to them that we are equal to this worthy undertaking. Not a dollar has been spent up to the present for advertising, but inquiries are coming to the office already from all quarters, from Michigan to Texas, asking for seed corn. The people have heard of us already and we must bestir ourselves to be ready for them. This summer we shall have many visitors. Let us be in shape to entertain them. Let us take great pride, not only on our crops, but in our fence corners and gates and places where the eyes are sure to wander.

Mindful of tenants in the audience, Gene Funk anticipated for them higher wages because of higher prices for corn. He predicted the construction of the grain elevator at Funk's Grove. Moreover, he advanced the idea of purchasing supplies in wholesale lots whereby the tenants also could benefit. He predicted that in a few years there would be valuable results for future generations in the management of the land.[44]

Gene was busy during the early months of 1902 working with a committee in Springfield to bring the State Breeders Association to Bloomington for the November meeting.[45] Word arrived from Oregon that the two oldest children were ill with scarlet fever.[46] The family did not return to Illinois until May 1902.[47]

During the absence of Mrs. Eugene Funk and the children in Oregon, P. G. and Gene spent the evenings discussing problems related to the improvement of corn.[48] Out of these discussions came many ideas. Once a fire almost destroyed some of the Ninety-Day ears so carefully preserved by Gene. Water was poured on them and the corn froze. Holden remembered testing for germination this Ninety-Day corn taking six kernels from each frozen ear. Joe Henderson who worked on the farm vividly recalled this incident.[49]

The *Orange Judd Farmer*, November 15, 1902, printed an extensive article under the title "Where Pedigreed Seeds Are Grown" with a description of the land acquisitions of Isaac Funk, Sr. It included the activities of the second generation of the Funk family who were designated primarily as farmers, although they had extended their father's operations from cattle raising to become successful bankers, merchants and political leaders. The equipment for scientific breeding of grain now undertaken by the third generation was said to be unequalled. According to this article, "The Funk name is a synonym for business ability, aggressiveness, honesty and integrity. All the Funks have had practical experience in the management of farms and ranches." [50]

Progress was apparent with the construction of the new warehouse and elevator at Funk's Grove, "It is a modern elevator with every convenience and an abundance of light." Seed houses were built on all the main farms where grain was placed and dried directly after it was taken from the field. From the seed house, grain was taken to the warehouse and prepared for shipment to customers.

The operation of this entire program interested the Illinois Stock Breeders who met in Bloomington, Illinois on November 18, 1902. This group was composed of Horse, Cattle, Swine and Sheep Breeders together with Cattle Feeders Associations. [51] Those who visited the Funk Farms were offered a seventeen mile trip where these interesting ideas and experiments were explained. One row of Boone County White Corn showed a yield of 132 bushels to the acre. Nearby a row of the same corn yielded only 47 bushels. [52] A field of 100 acres planted in Reid's Yellow Dent the previous spring was virgin prairie never before plowed. This field yielded at the rate of 101-103 bushels to the acre for the entire field. [53]

The agronomist for Funk Bros. Seed Co., Dwight Funk, explained to the visitors that the family was induced to undertake these experiments on a large scale when they discovered that their land was not paying as it should considering its value. They looked for a method to increase their crops. This meant the production of more corn to the acre. After securing the best seed corn in the country the seed beds were made with the utmost care. Three kernels were planted to the hill. [54]

Professor W. A. Henry, dean of the Wisconsin College of Agriculture, delivered a speech when the visitors reached the elevator located at Funk's Grove. He described the meeting as historically significant. [55]

It is as it were the first crystallization of an effort which has been in progress for some little time. I have a parallel in my mind. It was my pleasure two years ago this past summer to visit the greatest seed farm on earth, historically I refer to the Vilmorin seed farm, Paris. That farm has been under the present management for some 200 years. The name Vilmorin is known all over the world. It had a significance like pure gold; it is untarnished. The head of the family had passed away not many years before I was there. The sons were carrying on the business. . . . The sugar beet industry of the world owes its production largely to the Vilmorin family . . . . After I had visited another, the great Dupres farms, run by another illustrious family, and the children were carrying the work inaugurated many years before by the parent. This has been my third visit to a great seed growing establishment.

Professor Henry recognized the profound beginning made by the Funk Brothers and complimented them for going to the corn itself to learn their lessons. He called attention to the intellectual burden that had fallen to the members of the Funk family who were willing to solve problems rather than merely collect rentals. These men, who acquired a heritage in the reputation handed down to them by those preceding them, were described as follows: "They are studying, thinking I suspect, as they never did before, and in this intellectual work they are getting the best out of life. Without it we are mere animals; with it we are as the Gods." Credit was also directed to the pioneers at the agricultural colleges who undertook, often against opposition, to encourage experimentation.

The director of the Iowa Agricultural Experiment Station, Professor C. F. Curtiss, who was also dean of the Iowa College of Agriculture, called the occasion memorable. He declared: "We are making history here which will be recorded in the annals of American Agriculture, and no one can estimate the influence of such a day as this. . . . It is an occasion so fruitful in its lessons for the betterment of Agriculture that we cannot estimate its influence." He expressed the wish that ten thousand farmers from the Mississippi Valley could have attended this significant meeting. LaFayette Funk wrote in his *Diary:* "Today was the great demonstration of the Live Stock Breeders' Association visiting the Funk Farms. Some very able speeches were made at the warehouse in the Grove." [56]

Professor Holden wrote Gene Funk that Professor Curtiss had a splendid time and that he would not have missed it for anything. He knew about the work but it exceeded anything that he had anticipated.[57] Holden also said he appreciated the difficulty in securing corn free from moisture which he described as "your most serious obstacle, but if there were no great obstacle there would be no excuse for Funk Bros. Seed Co." [58] Later in the same year Holden told

Eugene that he was on the right track and he must keep up the highest possible standards.[59]

Reports of this meeting were published throughout the country. W. B. Lloyd of the *Country Gentleman* wrote that what was seen at the Funk Farms was not for the "gentleman" farmer, but for practical men in moderate circumstances. These were the men the Funks were trying to reach.[60]

The resignation of P. G. Holden as general manager became effective as of September 1, 1902 because of his decision to return to academic life at the University of Iowa.[61] Frank H. Funk became general manager, a post which he retained until 1905.

Lyle Johnstone, who attended the University of Illinois in the fall of 1902 and graduated with a master's thesis on "Seed Corn" in 1905, recalled working for the Funks during the early years of their corn breeding activities. He stated that Lyle Funk used inbreds for crosses. These were line bred of the same families. He had pictures of Lyle making these crosses. Two pictures were included in the Funk Bros. Seed Co. catalogue printed 1903 and 1905. He also made a statement to this effect during the lifetime of Eugene Funk, Sr.[62] He recalled helping with the seed corn breeding plots during the summers of 1903 and 1904 when he took the train from Bloomington to Funk's Grove station each morning, leaving his riding horse at the station. Sometimes he stayed with "Big Jim" Moberly, whom he enjoyed immensely. Invitations to the home of Dwight, Lawrence and Gene Funk were welcome after wandering around the corn plots all day. Johnstone's chief responsibility was to inspect the different plots and from time to time to make notes of unusual changes.[63]

Lyle Johnstone also recalled the process employed on the farms during the summers 1903 and 1904. The breeding blocks consisted of about 100 rows "each planted from a single ear having desirable characteristics to yield well, to stand up, to resist disease and be vigorous and rapid growing." At the end of each row white stakes bore the number of the ear planted. The parentage of the ear could be easily traced. Improved strains of the different varieties were thus discovered. This method was known as that of corn breeding by selection. He continued:

When outstanding characteristics were produced in ears from certain rows and the ancestors of the ears which produced those rows had also been desirable, the next year one or two or both practices were followed. Sometimes what was called a multiplying block was planted to produce commercial seed from that particular ear or two of those outstanding ears were crossed in different combinations to try and produce ears with the outstanding characteristics of both.

Stalks bearing no shoots, or undesirable for other reasons, were detasseled. When the crosses were made sacks were placed upon the tassels and upon the rows "and when the pollen was ready to fall the sacks were removed and pollenization was done by hand, and more than one application was made sometimes." [64] The statements of Mr. Johnstone are especially valuable because he was responsible for keeping the records pertaining to the ancestry of each ear planted in the breeding blocks. Parts of each ear were retained for future use in a long tin container which bore the ear registry number. This was the method of selection and crossing employed as standard practice to improve field corn for many years.

The Agronomy Report made by J. Dwight Funk, April 4, 1903 reveals that the Funks had scattered their thirty breeding blocks during 1902 over all of their farms. Results were described as valuable and encouraging. They showed trueness to type in some rows and lack of it in others. From each block the rows highest in yield (other conditions being equal) were selected for champion rows. Ears of the right types were selected for breeding ears for the next season. Of the 121 champion rows, 28 yielded at the rate of 100 bushels per acre. Of these 28 one was from Leaming, 14 from His Excellency and 13 from Boone County Special. Of 2,100 ears raised in breeding blocks in 1902, only these 121 proved worthy of propogation. The following numbers of ears were selected for chemical analysis:

> *Leaming,* for Protein 290
> for Oil 310
> for high combination 240
>
> *His Excellency,* for Protein 422
> for Oil 372
>
> *Boone County Special,* for Protein..........123
> for Oil 148

At this time 682 tests were made for oil and 835 tests for protein at Illinois Wesleyan; 148 tests for oil and 240 tests for combination were made at the University of Illinois.

The breeding blocks were reduced in number to thirteen. The total number of ears required in these blocks was 582 as against 2,100 of the previous year. Seed patches of ten or twenty acres were established on each farm to take the place of this reduction. These seed patches were planted from the first corn produced by the Funks.[65]

Recognition of the significance of selection was well stated in the report of 1903:

Results depend more upon the selection and grouping of individual ears than upon anything else. Our greatest efforts must be put upon the breeding of valuable and uniform types of the several varieties of corn under improvement. For every separate type of corn that goes into Breeding Block, there will be a specimen saved for reference. All ears will be labelled as to type. In this way better than any other, we will be able to distinguish ears of high prepotency. It is an established fact that there are certain laws of nature governing the propagation of characteristics in plants. Certain individuals reproduce certain characteristics throughout their line of descent, while others yield in their descendent to the influence of the fertilizing plant and result in innumerable different types. In the selection of the so-called dominant types. In the selection of the so-called dominant types lies great development of the different varieties of corn.

New plans were suggested for 1903 such as the breeding of fodder for protein and the crossing of Leaming and His Excellency.[66]

A report dated June 6, 1903 referred to the completion of records and added, "Since the 19th of May we have put in four other plots. Three hybridizing plots and another experiment plot. The hybridizing plots were Leaming on His Excellency and Boone County Special on Leaming." [67] Work progressed. In some of the chemical blocks, ears were covered for pollinating by hand. Three to five of the highest in content for which they were bred were selected. The ears and tassels on these rows were covered. The purpose was to give crosses between parents of the very highest chemical contents.[68]

The end of the second year for Funk Bros. in 1903 indicated progress. A successful catalogue had been issued and plans to improve continued:

The work of carrying on the breeding of corn to a successful result is being worked out in all the little details. The plan is to make such selection that the strains of the different varieties that give the greatest yield will finally be planted on our entire acreage, keeping the blood lines pure and thus establishing the only lines of pedigree corn for sale in the world.[69]

Up to this time three lines of corn proved themselves to possess such prepotency of pollen in the characteristics of yield that all corn from these lines was high in yield. One line planted in different bodies of land gave an average rate of yield per acre 132 bushels.[70] It was also realized that extreme caution must be employed in the regulation of heat when drying corn.[71]

From the breeding blocks of 1903, champion mother ears were selected which had yielded over 100 bushels. Funks Yellow Dent,

Leaming and Boone County Special qualified. These mother ears represented different strains. Results showed remarkable evidences of heredity in corn as to the chemical content. These strains were described as not only uniformly high chemically but also uniformly high in productiveness. By hand fertilization the increase in chemical content was accelerated.

Reference was made in June 1904 to the University of Illinois where an experiment was conducted with detasseled seed then in the third generation. The first generation equalled one and one half bushel increase over tasseled corn; second generation equalled six bushel average increase over tasseled seed. According to Dwight Funk, "This experiment is not directed against inbreeding but against direct self-fertilization of which there is more or less danger as the experiment has so far shown." He added that the Funks had worked out a more elaborate plan than that conducted at the University of Illinois.

The program mentioned provided that in one block of each variety, half of every row in the second division or the last forty rows would be detasseled. All of the even rows were detasseled at one end and all the odd rows at the other end. All rows were on an equal basis for production tests with forty competitive tests of detasseling versus tasseling in each block. The agronomist believed that it was not the operation of detasseling that improved the production but the fact that seeds grown on detasseled stalks were certain to be other than self fertilized. The elimination of this feature produced superior seed.[72]

Improvement of seed for general planting in 1904 was predicted both in vitality and in physical appearance. Endorsements of methods and results in corn improvement were received from Dr. H. J. Webber in Washington, D. C. and from Professor Hays of Minnesota as well as from Professor Henry of Wisconsin.[73]

The Orange Judd Company published in 1903 *The Book of Corn* with Chapter Four entitled "The Breeding and Selection of Corn" written by A. D. Shamel who had been a co-worker at the Illinois Agricultural Station with Holden. He was convinced that corn breeding had by this time become a specialized industry, and that the ordinary or general farmer would never breed corn. Funk Bros. Seed Co. was one of the most extensive producers of seed corn at this time.[74]

A new enterprise was launched with its founders and their contemporaries aware that they were institutionalizing an unusual plan. They knew of no other comparable company in the United States organized on the same principles. The ideas of Eugene D. Funk, his cousins and associates proved strangely prophetic.

CHAPTER IX

Methods and Problems, Corn 1903–1912

THE FUNKS of the third generation did not experiment in a small way. They were acquainted with the leading scientists and agriculturists of the day. They also participated in new agricultural organizations where their views were willingly expressed. Their spokesmen appeared in 1903–07 on programs of the American Seed Trade Association and the American Breeders Association. Eugene, Frank and J. Dwight were the chief spokesmen for the new seed company.

Considerable interest in the problems of plant and animal breeding was exhibited in the meeting held under the auspices of the Association of American Agricultural Colleges and Experiment Stations at St. Louis, Missouri, December 29 and 30, 1903.[1]

Eugene Funk knew Dr. Webber, physiologist in charge of the Plant Breeding Laboratory of the United States Department of Agriculture, personally. "Archie" Shamel, who had moved to the Department of Agriculture in Washington, wrote to Fred Rankin at Urbana to urge Funk to help entertain Dr. Webber when he came to Illinois.[2] Funk observed a few days before this January 16, 1904 that "Webber and Hays are two men it does a fellow a whole lot of good to rub up against."[3] Shamel was rooming at Dr. Webber's home so he was particularly anxious that "the Funk boys show Webber a good time." Rankin also urged Funk to remain as president of the Illinois Farmers Club because all of the boys wished him to continue and "it is no flattery to say that your clear, level-headed judgment is just what is needed. It is not always the loquacious fellow who is the most useful man."[4]

The activities of the American Association of Breeders in St. Louis so stimulated Gene Funk's thinking that he wrote a personal letter to Dr. H. J. Webber. Funk was concerned because Professor Lyon of Nebraska and a man from Southern Illinois had agreed that taking corn from rich fields of Illinois to plant upon their soil would produce

101

poor results. Funk had not sufficient data to enter the discussion but he was interested enough to do some thinking. He expressed the following ideas to Dr. Webber:

> . . . this thought has struck me. For instance the live stock Breeder takes his pure bred bulls and crosses them on his grade cows and the result is often a much better animal than either of their original. Corn is cross fertilized by nature—would it not be feasible to use the argument that to take some of our pure bred corn and mix it in the planter with some of their native corn and thus obtain a better variety for the first two years than to have planted either separately. And I believe by the introduction of a small amount of new seed every year to their fields of native corn, that they could better their hybrids very much.

This was advanced thinking for the year 1904.

He added that demand for Funk corn on land similar to their own was such that they could not at present undertake other demands. But he was interested scientifically in Webber's opinion.[5] Webber answered that they had discussed the problem thoroughly in their laboratories but had been unable to agree upon an opinion. This was Mr. Hartley's reason for raising the question at St. Louis. Dr. Webber pointed to the differences between the nursery and field methods, saying that he preferred the latter but did not have sufficient evidence to draw sound conclusions. He observed that plant breeders could not proceed in the same way as animal breeders who gave more attention to the male, whereas in plants, selection was largely limited to the female "as in this way we are able to handle large numbers." Webber agreed with Funk's idea of mixing pure bred corn with field corn.[6]

The *Corn Register* in the Funk Bros. files for the years 1902–05 refers to hand pollination in 1903; to the record of the sire 1904; to "hybridizing block" in 1904; to Leaming combination crosses to be made in 1905 "and reverse"; to oil "hybridizing plots"; to detasseling. There is reference to the use of same sire four times in crosses in 1905. In one instance "418" was referred to as both sire and dam.[7] These records substantiate statements made in the early catalogue of the company regarding methods followed in the early years and corroborate published statements by reporters.

From various accounts of the work done by the Funks in the early years it is apparent that they thought that:

1. The first and greatest consideration was yield per acre.
2. Inbreeding was injurious on a large scale but did some experimental work.

3. Crossing of strains of high yielding varieties within "families" increased yields.
4. Chemical analysis of corn was the method to obtain better corn for commercial purposes.
5. Detasseling of barren and weak plants improved the quality of seed corn.
6. Higher yields within varieties (corn families) could be secured by selection.
7. They could control the sire as well as the dam by taking stock seed from detasseled rows to insure that pollen came from adjacent rows.

Fortunately for the record, speeches made by Frank Funk in 1904 and by Eugene D. Funk in the same year, as well as two reported accounts of explanations by the agronomist, J. Dwight Funk, are available. Early methods can now be described.

Funk Bros. Seed Co. joined the American Seed Trade Association in 1902. Frank Funk was assistant secretary of the organization in 1904. The annual meeting was held in St. Louis, June 21, 22, 23, 1904, where Frank Funk presented a paper entitled "Breeding of Seed Corn for Increase in Yield." He referred to Indian corn as the greatest staple raised in America and as its most distinctive crop. This crop was grown in every state in the Union on three million out of five million farms according to the preceding census. He pointed out that in 1903 in the United States 88,000,000 acres produced 2,244,000,000 bushels with a value of $750,000,000 as compared with value of all other cereals including wheat of only $585,000,000. Demand in corn was overtaking supply because 108 commercial products also produced from corn were on the market. Since 1896 exports of corn had increased from 4 to 10 percent of the crop. It was estimated that only 25 percent of the crop was moved beyond counties where it was produced, the balance was fed to meat producing animals. Increase in yield was, therefore, important. Seed selection was one method employed to secure this result.

He said that Illinois could feel a sense of pride in the work of the College of Agriculture and in the efforts of the Illinois Seed Corn Breeders Association to bring about a renaissance in corn. Corn breeding at this time meant, according to Frank Funk, "the application of the same laws of heredity to corn that have been in universal use among livestock breeders for many years." This was accomplished by seed selection to increase certain desirable qualities because each succeeding generation showed a tendency to become more fixed in its certainty to reproduce these qualities. Until recently the only effort was to test one variety with another "but since the idea of comparing the yield obtained from one individual mother seed ear has been brought forth", the rate of yield should be greatly increased. He added that it was possible to select families, or blood lines, or strains of corn showing tendencies toward large yield, early maturity, uniform type of ear or increased chemical content.

In a breeding block of one hundred ears planted in single rows, ten could show unusually high yield. From these ten rows would be selected ten of the most perfect ears. These one hundred ears would then be planted in a breeding block the following year. He asserted that repeated experiments through a series of years demonstrated that yield could be materially increased.

He also told members of the A. S. T. A. that "the one factor that should determine the selection of the seed is the statistical record of the ancestors of any family or strain of corn." In other words its "Pedigree." He also referred to the success of W. M. Hays with wheat production in Minnesota. Other factors than these mentioned could be controlled in corn demonstrated at the Illinois Experiment Station. These included the height of ears, width of leaves, and chemical composition.

Upon completing the paper Mr. Funk answered questions. One gentleman inquired about the danger of inbreeding. Frank Funk replied:

The danger of inbreeding is overcome by detasseling the stalks which give no appearance of production of ears. Every other row is detasseled and the stock seed is taken from rows which are detasseled, thus insuring that pollen shall come to the adjacent row.[8]

An account of this early work also appeared in the *Catalogue* of Funk Bros. Seed Co. for 1903:

1. From 20 to 30 of the best corn raisers in the United States we secured 200 bushels of corn. From this collection 3,000 of the best ears were selected. Records were kept of the length, circumference at butt and tip, weight of ear, of cob; percent of protein, of oil and starch. Each of these was planted in a single row of a certain breeding block. Breeding blocks were small plots from 5 to 10 acres placed where they were most isolated— some in the heart of the timber along its edge or in the center of the great pasture lands—to keep pollen from blowing over and mixing with this specially bred corn. There were 30 breeding blocks in 1903, averaging 100 rows, 50 rods long. Three kernels were planted to a hill. When the corn was 10 inches high each hill was thinned to two stalks. Before the period of fertilization barren and inferior stalks in the breeding blocks were removed or detasseled insuring that every kernel in the breeding block was pollinated by a fruitful and vigorous stock.

2. Each row was harvested by itself with the entire yield taken in

pounds. Ears were counted and separated into good, medium and poor yield per acre, with average size of ears forming the basis for selection. The ears for the same breeding block for the next year were selected from the ten champion rows.

3. Seed for the general fields was selected only from rows giving the highest yield per acre "and then it is only the cream of the general fields selected for seed corn to go to the market." Annually the Funks planted about 8,000 acres in corn; 210 acres in breeding blocks. Therefore, every acre was expected to supply enough corn for about 40 acres of general fields. From the general fields about 5 percent was selected for high bred seed corn shipped by ear in bushel crates.[9]

Later in the same year Eugene D. Funk spoke on "Commercial Corn Breeding" before the Congress of Experiment Stations in St. Louis, October 8, 1904. The address was illustrated with stereoptican views. Some introductory remarks were omitted in the printed pamphlet containing this speech. The original copy, however, contained references to the purposes of the Funks in founding Funk Bros. Seed Co. Eugene spoke of his family and of the company:

We are composed of a large family, not all brothers, but descendants of the second and third generation from one Isaac Funk, who settled in Illinois in 1824 on and near the body of land which we are now operating, some 25,000 acres. There are today, twelve young and active members of this company and eight older heads to whom we go for advice and counsel.

He referred to his own idea of promoting the organization of such a company to consolidate a family which had always worked together in harmony. With rapid increases in numbers there would be a tendency to drift apart.[10] Three years were employed to perfect his idea, and at last, he said, "The thought came while attending a meeting of the Illinois Seed Corn Breeders Association in Champaign where discussion centered around keeping the members together and to improve corn." These purposes were the key to the Funk situation, "owning a large body of land, handled under a common system, regulated by an incorporated company, each holding as many shares as proportionate to his acres of land." The original idea embodied the following purposes:

The Funk Bros. are not only developing seed corn and seed oats business but also Pure Bred Stock as well. We have what might be called a department store in an agricultural line; a system whereby at least two members are considered at the head of each department, that is they have in charge, all the detail work of one special line. . . . We have our own business manager. . . . We have an advertising department.

Meetings were held once a month. He who produced the most

gained the most. The company would aid the individual to sell goods at an advantage and could help him to buy at small margins above cost. In the event of the death of any member leaving young children unable to carry responsibility, his estate would be carried along by the company. This introduction was concluded with emphasis upon the fact that all members of the company contributed to the activity in commercial corn breeding.[11]

Eugene Funk mentioned the obvious advantages gained from interest in increased yields of corn. During the past ten years yields had averaged only 28-29 bushels per acre. He also reminded his listeners that corn could be grown to a greater or lesser extent in every state in the Union, with the Corn Belt producing about 80 percent of the world's supply. Demand was increasing because 100 articles of commerce were manufactured from the corn and its plant. A summary of his address included the following points:

1. Within varieties there existed certain strains or families. Inherent qualities produced other ears with characteristics of the mother ear.

2. Breeding of corn was relatively simple, involving Nature's method plus keeping a record. By selection it was possible to increase certain desirable qualities through reproduction in succeeding generations by employing the Ear to Row method.

3. Previous to pollenization, tassels of weak and barren stalks were removed. All ears and rows bore individual numbers and were so recorded. Each row was husked separately and the corn was weighed. From the best rows the mother ears were saved for the next year's breeding plot. Seed was also saved for larger fields from 5 to 10 acres, called multiplying plots.

Funk stated:

The yields of the mother plants, followed by the multiplying plot and then larger fields, become the performance record of the strains of corn the same as the individual track record of his progeny becomes the record of the trotting horse.

4. One to five acre fields where the intensive work and the single row system were carried on, were called breeding blocks. Kernels from a single ear were planted here. For an ear to qualify it was subjected to physical and chemical examination. It must always be equivalent or better than the previous generation.

He added:

The result for the first few generations, while we may have large yield composed of all sorts and sizes of ears—hybrids from many hundreds of other plants—we may find comparatively few ears equalling or excelling the mother ear.

After the type was once fixed, reasonable uniformity was expected.[12]

From the crop of 1904, being harvested at the time of this St. Louis meeting, part of the record of the progeny of No. 120 was available.[13]

Eugene Funk referred to parallels in animal breeding, citing the Duke of Airdrie of Shorthorn fame; the Grove Third of Hereford breed; Chief Tecumseh of Poland China fame. Hambletonian, of American race horse pedigree, was supposed to have been an ordinary looking animal. Then Funk made a significant statement for the year 1904:

> For all fine looking high scoring corn is not from high yielding producers. Corn breeding is not to get more type beauty of ear or maybe a few big ears and the rest nubbins, but it is to produce corn that will increase the average acreage yield per acre of this country from 28-29 bushels to an amount that will justify the labor and expense of raising an acre of corn and that farmers have a right to hope for.[14]

He continued to say in this St. Louis speech that yield per acre was the essential point of interest for most farmers and the corn breeding should be judged not by idealism but by facts. Gene Funk quoted from Dr. Webber of the U. S. D. A. to the same effect and then declared that for himself as a commercial plant breeder:

> Personal experience has proven to us the above facts for *some of our largest yielding* strains of corn to-day are anything but ideal ears from the standpoint of the score card.[15]

Three years were required according to Funks before the commercial corn breeder could furnish pedigreed seed corn from his commercial field to the market.

The First Year—a breeding plot planted with carefully Selected seed—ear to row.

The Second Year—a breeding plot *and* a multiplying plot both planted with registered pedigreed seed from best yielding rows of first year's breeding plot.

The Third Year—a breeding plot *and* a multiplying plot *and* a commercial field—all planted with pedigreed seed. The seed for the breeding plot and for the multiplying block being from the second year's breeding plot and the seed for the commercial field being from the previous year's multiplying block.[16]

Eugene Funk also referred in St. Louis to the application of the experimental ideas of C. G. Hopkins with regard to the increase of oil and protein. He declared that the experiment was adopted as a commercial proposition with other varieties of corn. During the past year Funks placed on the market for seed purposes, corn containing an average of 5.68 percent in oil and 11.94 percent in protein. This corn also came from the breeding blocks containing the highest yielding strains; at the time of the speech they possessed an ear planted with a composition as high as 17.40 percent in protein and 7.70 percent oil.

This important explanation concluded by mentioning again the work of Professor W. M. Hays at Minnesota with his 18 percent increase in the yield of spring wheat; to the increase of sugar in the sugar beet; to the work of Dr. Webber in cotton and to that of A. D. Shamel who began with corn and turned to tobacco in Connecticut. These activities, said the speaker, showed that the Funks were not alone in this type of work.[17]

The chemical analysis of corn undertaken by the Funks at Wesleyan University in Bloomington, Illinois under Dr. Graham's supervision was sharply curtailed about 1905. The Funks concluded that: "The gains added materially to the value of a strain of corn but that the buying public did not recognize the added commercial value."

The cousins decided that expenditures such as they were then making were not warranted, especially since the University of Illinois was desirous of making these tests free. Therefore, the expenditures at Wesleyan were to be curtailed to about $2,000 annually.[18] Dr. Graham and Eugene Funk were instrumental in aiding H. H. Love, Graham's assistant, to secure a position at the University of Illinois. Love worked with C. G. Hopkins and Edward M. East.[19]

A speech given before the American Breeders Association by J. Dwight Funk was reported in the *Prairie Farmer*, May 10, 1906. The following summary of this speech includes procedures followed by Funks:

1. Selection of fertile, well cultivated breeding plots or blocks.
2. Selection of variety or varieties of already proven merit.
3. Within the variety chose 80 ears for breeding purposes.
4. Each ear should be given a number, entered into a record book and with other data describing characters of breeding ear. These breeding ears are called mother ears.
5. Plant each mother ear in a single row in breeding block.
6. To prevent self-fertilization one half of each row should be detasseled and the breeding ears for the next year selected from the detasseled stalks, "In detasseling, alternate the ends of the rows upon which this is performed. For instance detassel the north end or half of all the odd numbered rows and the south half of all the even numbered rows. In this way you are using each breeding block era (sic) as both sire and dam in your breeding block."
7. In harvesting make 4 divisions of the progeny.
    a. ears gathered from the standing stalks of the tasseled end

A GRAPHIC DESCRIPTION OF OUR METHODS

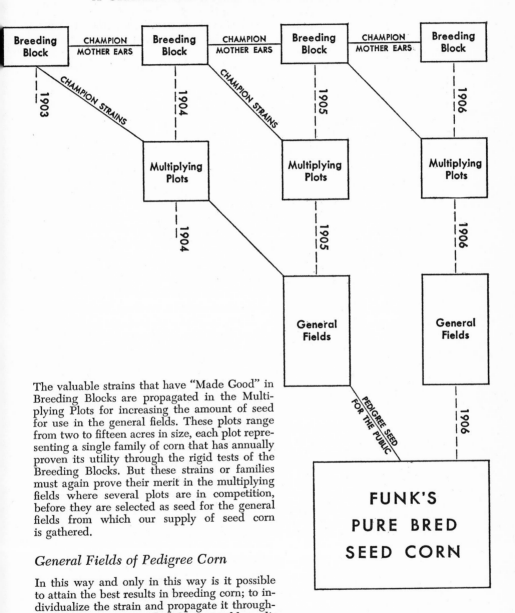

The valuable strains that have "Made Good" in Breeding Blocks are propagated in the Multiplying Plots for increasing the amount of seed for use in the general fields. These plots range from two to fifteen acres in size, each plot representing a single family of corn that has annually proven its utility through the rigid tests of the Breeding Blocks. But these strains or families must again prove their merit in the multiplying fields where several plots are in competition, before they are selected as seed for the general fields from which our supply of seed corn is gathered.

General Fields of Pedigree Corn

In this way and only in this way is it possible to attain the best results in breeding corn; to individualize the strain and propagate it throughout its existence as seed with a traceable pedigree without mixture after their qualities are proven in the Breeding Block.

    b. the ears from the fallen stalks of the tasseled end

    c. the ears from the standing stalks of the detasseled end

    d. the ears from the fallen ears of the detasseled end.

Each of these divisions should be weighed separately and the number of ears in each counted. The sum of the four weights will give the corn production of the mother ear.

    8. All of these rows should have been equal in length and the same number of kernels planted by hand in each hill. At time of maturity inspection of the exact number of stalks and hills in the row should be taken. If the hills are planted 3½ feet each way there will be 35,556 hills in an acre. Having the corn production per hill, the rate yield per acre can be easily obtained.

    9. "The breeding corn should be saved only from the division I previously mentioned, namely from the standing detasseled rows. In your selection of what may be called champion rows, you first eliminate these rows that have failed to meet the requirements in growth."

    10. "The breeding ears for next year's block have been selected from 8 to 10 rows producing greatest amount of Corn per acre and per stalk. They are from standing detasseled plants which did not suck or show a tendency for any undesirable characteristics. In short the dams of these ears have made an excellent record and these characters should appear to some extent in the progeny. But we know only the performance record of one of the parents. To facilitate the development, the influences of the sire must be controlled." [20]

    11. "We have for planting this year four rows of corn retained on the cob of the original breeding ears. Select eight or ten that gave you the best results in the breeding block. Mate these ears in pairs on small isolated plots; plant some five rows from one of the ears and six rows from the others, alternating the rows and detassel the rows and detassel all plants in the even rows."

    12. "One of these ears is being used entirely as the sire. It produces all the pollen used in this miniature block. The other is used only as a dam and from its rows are selected the breeding ears. The kernels of these we know have been fertilized by a sire which the year before proved itself to be a champion."

The best of the ears described above were then planted together in a multiplying plot from three to five acres in extent and one third or one half of the rows were detasseled. From these plots enough seed was procured to plant a large field. Dwight Funk continued:

This corn now has a traceable pedigree on both sides. Its parents have annually been subjected to a rigid test as to yielding power and other good characteristics. And annually the self-fertilization has been eliminated.

There should be four or five of these multiplying plots, according to Dwight Funk, in the same field. The amount of ground in each plot should be gathered by itself, making a division of the tasseled and detasseled corn. The product of each plot should be weighed and the rate of yield per acre computed. Here again was a competitive test. Seed for the general fields should be selected first from the plot giving the greatest yield per acre and then from the next and so on.

13. Another more technical step remained. In the second year, or mating block, some individual plants would be undesirable as sires which could not be identified until too late to prevent pollinating some of the dam rows, "To be able to accurately identify parents of an ear the individual plants should be mated and the pollination of the ear performed by hand from a single apparently desirable sire.

14. Pollination should be carried on between mated individuals as extensively as possible and a correct record kept of such crossing. Plants used as male as well as those used as female should be numbered and tagged in order that the performances of each sire could be identified. A good many crossings would be required to produce one good big ear pollinated entirely from a plant producing a good heavy ear of similar type.

In summary J. Dwight Funk stated that on "our farms" they conducted 15 of the large 80 row breeding blocks, some 50 of the small mating blocks, and "last year we made 600 individual crosses. We have identified at least 12 strains out of an aggregate of over 8,000 in four different varieties that annually head the list as to yield in their variety. Each year of course decreases the number of strains left in the race and increases the amount of seed produced by the remaining strains." [21]

An important event occurred when Dr. Hugo De Vries, the famous botanist from Holland visited the Funk Farms in July, 1906.[22] He formerly lectured at the University of California in 1904 and returned to the United States in 1906. He also lectured at the University of Chicago in December 1906.[23] During 1907 De Vries published his important book on *Plant Breeding* where he showed how the Nilsson principles were applied and also devoted an entire chapter to the discussion of the improvement of corn. Unfortunately the conversations between the Funks and Dr. De Vries were not recorded, but pictures of their observations on the Farms remain. It would seem reasonable that the ideas of Dr. De Vries in regard to the possibilities of adapting the methods of Nilsson and Hays to corn improvement could have been under discussion. The Dutch scientist was apparently impressed by the extensive experimental commercial work carried on by the Funks. He included pictures of the work in his book.[24]

The years 1904–1908 were significant in the development of experiments regarding the improvement of corn. G. H. Shull formulated his ideas about the selfing of pure lines, speaking on the subject in 1908 before the American Breeders Association. Edward M. East was also working independently after he moved from his previous assignment at the University of Illinois to the Connecticut Experiment Station in 1905. H. H. Love, formerly assistant to Graham for Funks in Bloomington, had recognized with East the importance of continuing experiments with selfed lines at the University of Illinois. When East departed he recalled their work and wrote to Love for samples. According to Love's statement he sent to East bulked seed from their early experiments. East continued his work at Connecticut producing results equal in importance to those of Shull. However, he stressed the importance of selfing varieties of corn. Important as the work of these men was they were not able to translate their findings to solutions for improving commercial corn.[25] It was to be a long process. But the years 1908–14 may well be called the formative years when men like Eugene D. Funk held tenaciously to the belief that it was possible to improve commercial corn.

Eugene D. Funk continued to be alert to all possible information that would enable him to improve his product. Despite financial difficulties by 1908 and the realization that there must be other causes for the poor corn that often resulted he held to his original ideas. His activity in promoting the National Corn Association from 1906 to 1914 enabled him to bring many ideas to the public. He also knew the leading scientists and heard them speak. The Geneticists did not find the secret of adapting their ideas to large scale commercial improvement. The Shull ideas were applied in Nebraska but by 1914 Shull himself believed that his ideas were largely theoretical instead of practical. The East inbreds were not adaptable to the middle west.[26] There remained much to be done.

Over a year after the publication of the above article at the first National Corn Exposition held in Chicago October 1907, J. Dwight Funk again spoke on the subject of "Successful Corn Breeding." His opening paragraph was reported as follows:

Originally our system of breeding was simply the selection from comparative yield tests of the most productive. As our knowledge of the work grew we introduced additional methods such as crossing the progeny of proved high yielders and the individual mating of plants.

He described the same methods as related above with this addition: Regarding the mating of individual plants of these proven high yielders, selecting the dam from one champion and the sire from another as follows:

The tassel of a large vigorous plant to be used as a sire is covered before it ripens with an impenetrable bag. This is to prevent foreign pollen from adhering to this tassel, also to preserve all the pollen produced thereon. The young ear of the fine plant used as a dam is covered in the same way before any silk appears.

They believed that they could keep absolute records of sires and dams. Twenty strains gave high performance, "Many crossings between these strains of individual plants have given even better results." [27]

A summary of prevailing methods practiced by Funk Bros. was also offered to the public in 1907, pointing out that the breeding blocks were located "so as to prevent the pollen of other corn mixing with these ears." Records were kept of the performance of each mother ear. Only one side of the pedigree was thus obtained. This description in the catalogue emphasized the fact that they could discover mother ears producing magnificent yields, "but to insure success" this characteristic of yield "must be fixed to transmit it to succeeding generations." The article continued, "Then we can expect with some certainty that ears produced by these champion yielders will in turn give large yields." [28]

Robert Griffin, who came to Funk's Grove Township in 1906, recalled the early breeding blocks. One was located west of the old Jim Moberly home east of the Alton Railroad tracks and east of the road to Funk's Grove Station. Another block was located beyond Funk's Grove railroad station on the road leading to the church near the Dingett place and an apple orchard. Two others were on Dwight's and LaFayette's farms. Griffin also remembered detasseling the corn of these breeding blocks. [29]

The answer in the catalogue was the same as previously pointed out by J. Dwight Funk in his speech:

> To do this it is necessary to control the influence of both parents. That is, the mother ear must be a champion and the pollen which fertilizes her product must be from Champion Rows. In planting the blocks described above of 80 to 100 rows only one-half of the seed is used, the remaining one-half is left on the cob. Now of these 80 to 100 rows, only ten of the largest yielders were selected as Champions. By our records we can, of course, identify the ears from which these champion rows are planted. Taking the remaining one-half of these champion ears we again plant them in single rows in what we call Champion Blocks. In these blocks all of the even rows are *Completely Detasseled*, so as to receive pollen only from the Odd Rows. The detasseling is performed to prevent self fertilization or fertilization from related plants. [30]

The Funks realized that the sire or fertilizing plant was not completely controlled, adding: "This is successfully done only by hand pollination. The young shoots of the detasseled plants are covered with bags before any silks appear and the tassels of the tasselled rows are likewise covered before any pollen is ripe. Then the pollen from fine individual sire plants is used to fertilize ears of the detasseled plants and a record is kept of all these individual 'matings.' Only one sire is used on each ear. Finally the large ears that have been fertilized from good sires (a plant producing a fine large ear) are planted in the breeding blocks the next year." This completed "the Good Pedigree on Both Sides." The seed for the multiplying or increase plots is selected from the detasseled champion rows of these breeding blocks. Breeding ears were selected only from stalks standing at harvest time. The percentage of standing corn of the entire row was recorded. If this percentage was low the entire row was rejected. The same procedure was followed for ears too high or too low on the stalk. Notes were also taken through the growing season on vigor with which corn started and grew, on the amount of quality of foliage and on the construction of the stalk. The following statement appeared:

For proof we refer you to our records on file at the University of Illinois showing the performance of registered ears in the breeding blocks for the past four years.[31]

The breeding methods were summarized in 1908 as follows:

1. Selections of single ears giving high yield.
2. Proving that these ears transmit the quality to their progeny.
3. Mating the ears that give best results in the above test.
4. Mating the individual plants that have the same or differing strong characters.
5. Selecting from these matings, progeny that proves true in remaining all strong characters.[32]

Funk Bros. Seed Co. announced under the heading of "Breeding vs. Selection" in a 1909 advertisement that "We are 'the largest seed corn breeders in the world' and we might well add and with every regard for the truth 'the *only* commercial seed corn breeders in the world.' For when we use the words 'seed corn breeders' we use it in the broadest sense, meaning: Those who work for practical results through scientific methods." In another sentence "We claim to be 'the only commercial seed corn breeders in the world' because no other seed house can show absolute and accurate data in connection with any breeding work done under their own direction nor by their own employees." [33]

Advertising methods employed by the Funks during the early years were directed by Lyle Funk. The chief media for advertising were the

SUMMARY

1. Selection of types.

2. Test ears for yield per acre. The vital point in corn breeding.

3. ½ each ear planted in a row to itself.

4. A check row is planted in *Breeding Blocks* every 5th row in order to observe variation in soil.

5. Once the breeding block has been harvested and the results carefully recorded, the next step is the selection of champions. In breeding for yield per acre, there must necessarily be the highest yielding rows.

6. The next year having preserved the half of the Mother ears giving highest yields per acre, plant these Mother ears all in the same isolated breeding block. In this breeding block the undesirable strains have been eliminated so that they may cross freely. This, of course, does not mean that the strains are all pure, but they are much purer than anything in the test breeding block and thousands of times purer than anything grown in a general field from straight selected seed.

7. Selection of champions from Breeding Blocks. Hand pollinating of mated stalks.

8. Selection of three stalk hills—an ear to be planted in the General Field must first be found in a hill containing three or more stalks— must show by size, weight and vigor that it is stronger than the other two ears in the hill.

9. Now we have seed for General Field which is planted much the same as all corn fields are planted. When General Fields show first sign of ripening—start picking seed corn to sell. Only largest, heaviest ears selected for this purpose. The best 3% are packed in boxes and are shipped in the ear. The second 10% to 15% are shelled and shipped in bags.

agricultural publications and the catalogue. The amount expended in 20 agricultural papers in 1904 was $648.01. The average cost per inquiry for this type of advertising was estimated to be 16⅔ cents. Orders immediately traced to the advertisements amounted to $3,836.78. On this basis Lyle W. Funk recommended the expenditure of $2,500 in those publications producing these results. An exhibit at the Illinois State Fair was also a profitable undertaking with cash prizes received against expenses of $127.02. Part of this exhibit was a cabin completely covered on the outside with yellow corn, with a roof of red corn and a chimney of white corn. At the St. Louis Fair in 1904, 25,000 souvenirs in the shape of an ear of corn were distributed. There were 38,026 names on the mailing list in 1904, with 20,259 in Illinois, 9,438 in Iowa; 2,770 in Indiana; Kansas 789; Missouri 1,710; Nebraska 528; Minnesota and Mississippi Northwest 75; Misc. States 1,457.[34]

Thirty-three papers were selected for advertising in 1905. Ads were included in "Hospodar," a Bohemian paper in Omaha, Nebraska; in a German publication, "Deutsch American Farmer" and in "Skandinavian," a Swedish paper. Fifty thousand catalogues were ordered for 1905. The State Fair premiums in that year were $365.[35]

General business affairs brought about many problems through the experimental years 1901–1908. W. K. Bracken, who married Grace Funk, daughter of F. M. Funk, acted as attorney for the company.[36] The indebtedness of the company investment July 12, 1902 was $27,698. An assessment of 20 percent on all capital stock was voted August 1902.[37] As has been stated, Frank H. Funk became general manager in 1903.[38] The number of directors was increased from five to seven, November 14, 1903. E. D. Funk continued as president, L. H. Kerrick as vice president, D. N. Funk as secretary and F. H. Funk as treasurer [39] and general manager.

The board of directors authorized the borrowing of $10,000 December 13, 1903,[40] and an additional $5,000 July 9, 1904.[41] Thirteen thousand was authorized to be borowed October 1, 1904. Julius Funk [42] was employed by the general manager in 1905.[43] At the stockholders meeting held July 15, 1905, a committee composed of D. N. Funk, A. B. Funk, I. G. Funk, with E. D. Funk ex officio member, was selected to investigate the financial condition of the company and report to the stockholders meeting August 5, 1905. A report was made September 2, 1905. This report showed $18,750 paid in; net assets, $10,605.64; a net loss of $8,144.36. There was a profit of $990.34 in 1904–05 (to July 1st) on a business amounting to $119,933.32.[44]

At the directors meeting of November 1, 1905, F. H. Funk and D. N. Funk resigned. L. P. and L. W. Funk were elected directors. E. D. Funk was reelected. He also continued as president of the company; L. H. Kerrick as vice president; J. D. Funk continued as agronomist and J. L. Funk as assistant agronomist.

Changes occurred in the directing personnel during 1906. Frank Funk resigned as general manager and treasurer effective June 30, 1906. E. D. Funk gave up the presidency and his directorship as of the end of the fiscal year.[45] D. N. Funk was elected director in his place and became president of the company September 1, 1906.[46] L. P. Funk became vice president and L. W. Funk was secretary; J. L. Funk became manager and treasurer; J. Dwight Funk agronomist. An assessment of capital stock was made payable by September 15, 1907. There was some consideration of a possible amalgamation with Garton Bros. of Warrington, England [see chapter Field Seeds]. J. L. Funk and W. K. Bracken were appointed to make a visit to England to investigate, and returned with a report which was placed on file August 23, 1907.[47] The idea was abandoned.

Records of meetings are not extensive for the year 1908. However, Eugene D. Funk kept a fairly good account in his *Diary* which helps to fill in the story. Although some disappointments crept into his notations, he kept the analysis remarkably clear. He was aware that some of the members of his numerous family including himself had spent the best part of the past seven years in building up the company. On the other hand he realized that some of the officers needed to go through a course of experience and training "that means years yet before we can get settled down to facts and figures." [48]

To complicate matters the seed gathered from the special patch in October 1908 was "mighty poor stuff." [49] A finance committee was to go over the books and make a monthly report in September.[50] E. D. attended an advisory board meeting in November. He had also been present the previous June by request at a directors' Meeting. The company became interested in offering $6,000 for one-half interest in the Bloomington Pickle Factory.[51] Later in the month authorization to pay $7,500 for one-half interest was given by the board.

At the annual meeting November 1908, J. D. and E. D. were elected as directors for three years.[52] It was recognized in the spring of 1909 that the report of the past year's busines was not very flattering. The demand for seed corn was not up to that of the previous year. During the summer there had been some complaints.[53] E. D. met with Deane and Lawrence and decided upon instructions to curtail all possible expenses. E. D. recorded that he preferred not to take any decided position on matters until he had familiarized himself with the office and business details again.[54]

LaFayette attended the seed company meetings in 1910. Often no quorum was present.[55] Early in this year E. D. reviewed the financial condition of the company.[56] The amount borrowed from two Bloomington banks, from banks in Springfield, McLean and Heyworth as well as the Portable Elevator Company amounted to $45,500.[57] Gene was constantly paying interest and renewing notes.

TOTAL DOLLAR VOLUME OF
BUSINESS
FUNK BROS. SEED CO.

1904–05	$119,933.22
1905–06	100,619.13
1906–07	115,662.09
1907–08	174,407.26
1908–09	112,687.75
1909–10	92,346.81
1910–11	89,999.59
1911–12	98,385.95
1912–13	120,445.15

When E. D. was elected Director for three years in 1908, D. N. continued as president.[58] The capital stock was increased from $25,000 to $50,000 November 1908.[59] In 1909 D. N. continued as president with E. D. elected as general manager. An informal meeting was held April 2, 1910 and a stockholders meeting occurred July 9, 1910. These were the only recorded meetings from November 6, 1909 to May 5, 1911.[60]

The crop of 1911 was described as producing more rotten corn than usual. Indebtedness for the company by this time included $43,500 borrowed from the two Bloomington banks and one in Springfield. In addition $20,000 was owed to the banks.[61] The years 1909–12 were difficult ones for the company.

By May of 1912 conditions changed. Orders were coming in for corn by long distance, by telegraph and through the mail. At a called meeting of stockholders of the seed company it was decided to pay them in full for all seed corn and other farm seeds amounting to a little over $9,000. At this time liabilities included $39,000.67 to the banks and $16,000.02 to the Funks, a total of $55,002.69. Assets totaled Cash, $11,000; grounds and building, $25,000; stock, $5,000; Bills, $5,000; total $46,000.[62] Although indebtedness was apparent, a loss of $10,000 for a new enterprise was not extraordinary.

During the middle of the summer at a meeting of the company a committee was appointed to draw up a proposition to the stockholders to sign including a deficit amounting to $36.00 per share. For those who wished to remain in the company there would be an additional $40.00 per share assessed.[63]

In September of 1912 Gene recorded that he visited the Ninety Day breeding plot with Dwight and Northcott and found "some extremely interesting characteristics brought forward." [64]

Interesting visitors came to the farms in 1912 from foreign countries, including James Sandiago Campion of "La Nora" Diareaux, F. C. S. Argentina, who came through the introduction of Mr. Hartley of the U. S. D. A.[65] Mr. Campion was a large land owner living 250 miles from Buenos Aires on 10,000 acres and renting 15,000 additional acres. He raised 3,300 acres of corn and 8,000 head of hogs. For his own benefit and as an agent of the Argentine government he was touring Europe and the United States to examine practical farming.[66]

Four visitors arrived from Uruguay, including Hugora, Surraco Cantera and Nipilite Gallinal, from Montevideo.[67] An old friend of Frank and Eugene at Yale, Issa Tammura of Tokyo, Japan arrived in September 1912.[68] He represented Japan as Commissioner of Live Stock. Mr. Hopkins of the University of Illinois and Dr. Russell of the Department of Agriculture in England arrived July 30th.[69] Dr. Edward John Russell was director of the famous Rothamsted Soil Experiment field, the oldest in the world at Harpenden, England. He visited the S. Noble King farm near Bloomington as well as the Funk Farms. It was at Rothamsted that Lawes and Gilbert worked together for half a century. The use of phosphorous there confirmed the results of the Illinois soil investigations. The result of the use of phosphates on five corn plots of the King Farms near Bloomington-Normal Illinois, resulted in corn two feet taller than other plots.[70]

Professor Wianko with eighteen students from Purdue University looked over the corn breeding grounds. They were escorted over the farms in five automobiles under the direction of Deane, Arthur, Lyle, Charlie and Uncle Jake with Gene.[71]

The dream of Eugene Funk, Sr. to unite the members of the third generation in a business enterprise crystallized during the first decade of the twentieth century. He turned directly to the corn plant to learn its secrets. Despite financial losses there were many positive gains during these years. Members of the various Funk families experienced a common center for their activities while the Funk product was carried to many agricultural areas in the world.

Gene Funk realized that a successful seed company must include many field crops. He benefited throughout his lifetime by the lessons he learned in these early years. Many of his original ideas regarding the organization of the company prevailed and determined the course of development in succeeding years.

CHAPTER X

Alfalfa, Silage and Organizations 1901–1903

WHILE COUSINS of the third generation were carrying forward their new enterprise the brothers of the second generation continued to follow their usual lines of activity. They looked with encouragement and some indulgence upon the new ideas of their sons and heirs. Fortunately there was sufficient financial security to permit experimentation for the future. The Funk family contributed effectively to what may be described as a progressive period in commercial seed research. This interest and activity in agriculture paralleled a general progressive period in United States History 1900–17. Automobiles and new types of farm machinery revolutionized the industrial world. The farm was no longer isolated. As the years slipped by, older settlers slowly passed from the scene. New leadership, new organizations, agricultural interests, problems and responsibilities appeared.

Although the third generation joined forces to organize Funk Bros. Seed Co. in order to produce more and better corn, they also favored experiments with other crops. These experiments included alfalfa, silage and clover before 1903. An experiment with alfalfa occurred in 1901. In connection with the University of Illinois, Eugene Funk carried on one of the first silage Experiments with Professor Mumford. Charles Brand of the United States Department of Agriculture conducted an experiment with red clover.

Gene Funk reported a trip to Minneapolis and Madison in 1902 where he visited the agricultural stations of the State Universities in Minnesota and Wisconsin. The greater part of a week was spent with Professors W. M. Hays and C. P. Bull in Minneapolis—St. Paul, where breeding plots of wheat, barley, hemp, oats, corn, alfalfa, clover, timothy, Canada field peas, broom grass and sugar beets presented a large field for study and information. The methods of plant breeding were reported by Gene to his company to be the same in each case with maize, grains and grasses. He noted that their corn work was just beginning with Minnesota 13 ahead of others. They were con-

ducting the same experiment with red clover that the Funks undertook on their farm with Mr. Brand from the U. S. D. A.[1] Gene also
reported that Professor Moore of Madison had covered the tables in
his classroom with "our Leaming corn" sent to him the previous year.
He reported that the Funks were well-known in this area and that he
was often asked, "Are you the man who lives on that large farm in
Illinois and raises seed corn?" [2] Professor Moore promised to send a
variety of Soybeans as a sample to the Funks in 1902.

Co-operative programs were undertaken with the United States
Department of Agriculture as early as 1902. At this time A. D. Shamel
who left the University was located with the Department in Washington. A plan for cooperative experiments together with the different
methods of sorting seed corn was forwarded to Funk October 20,
1902. Shamel wrote, "Following this plan, will be sent to you an outline for a report of your test of vitality. With this matter we will send
you envelopes and vials for the samples which we desire to test in the
Seed Laboratory of the Department of Agriculture." [3] A report indicated great variation in results of germination and moisture tests of
samples which were secured during 1903.[4] The Department was,
however, desirous of securing additional varieties for further tests.
Samples of Funks Ninety Day and Leaming High Oil from the crib,
and Boone County White, Reids Yellow Dent, Leaming and High
Protein both from the crib and from the field were requested. Arrangements were made to cooperate in making tests to determine:

1. Relative vitality of different varieties.
2. Effect of early, medium and late picking on vitality.
3. Relative advantages of different storehouses.[5]

The heavy freeze of November 1903 brought a request for varieties
still in the field so that valuable information as to the effect of freezing on vitality might be determined.[6]

Gene wrote to Professor Hopkins of the University of Illinois June
4, 1901, expressing his interest in the cooperative ideas for the expansion of agricultural knowledge throughout the state. He was particularly concerned about alfalfa and commented to Hopkins as
follows:

Referring to my alfalfa field and the information you so kindly gave me
regarding the bacteria or parasites on the roots, I have been unable to
discover any at all. The clover roots in the same field are full of them.
Now I have a cousin in Nebraska who raises many hundreds of acres of
alfalfa and have sent for three sacks of infected dirt. I expect to cut the
alfalfa in about ten days. Now how large a space and how would you

suggest that I proceed to put this imported dirt on the field or part of it so as to get a piece of ground started with the innoculated roots.[7]

The cooperation between the Funks and the Department of Agriculture in the University of Illinois is shown by a statement from C. G. Hopkins who expressed pleasure in the interest of Eugene Funk who offered to cooperate whenever possible.[8]

Hopkins commented in this same communication upon the problems with alfalfa, telling Funk that the trouble with his alfalfa was the same that Hopkins had encountered in all others that he had examined in Illinois, i. e. without tubercles. Hopkins believed the plants needed nitrogen, and added, "Next week we expect to apply to a portion of this field some old alfalfa soil which we have had shipped to us from Kansas." He then described two methods of applying this soil and advised Funk to remove the first crop soon, "then sow soil which you are obtaining from Nebraska at the rate of about 1,000 pounds per acre."

Funk noted on the back of this letter that he did not know whether there was anything in this "importing tubercle business" or not, but he was willing to try almost anything to get a stand of alfalfa. He was well acquainted with these people and they had helped him in several other matters all right. He and Herb decided to go by their instructions until they proved they were on the wrong track.[9] On July 26, 1901 Funk noted in his *Diary:* "Alfalfa Experiment—Nebraska Dirt." [10]

In a communication to the *Breeders Gazette* December 31, 1902, C. G. Hopkins wrote that Eugene Funk "partly to please me and partly to make an honest trial of a scientific theory" scattered a few hundred pounds of soil infected with alfalfa bacteria over part of a newly seeded field. At the Illinois Live Stock Breeders meeting when they observed the experimentation with corn in 1902, Mr. Funk stood on that alfalfa field surrounded by nearly two hundred members and pointed out the distinct line between the strong and vigorous alfalfa plants on the inoculated soil and the weak and sickly looking plants on uninoculated soil. Inoculated soil, according to Funk, produced fully twice as much alfalfa hay. Inoculation, he believed, was essential to growing alfalfa on his soil.[11]

Gene Funk often told the story of his importation of "foreign" soil to put on good Illinois land. His help on the farm laughed so heartily when they heard of the two sacks of imported dirt that Funk left them in the barn. One day he gave all hands a holiday to attend the circus. During their absence Gene Funk hitched two mules to an old wagon filled with dirt and sowed it on his alfalfa field, in two different strips about 30 feet wide and 150 feet long, leaving an open space between. He disked the first strip, not the second.

On Sundays he often drove Mrs. Funk around the farm. He visited the alfalfa field so often that she finally asked "why." He declined to answer. There was no encouraging result that fall. But the next spring with the frost out of the ground there was one green strip. Mrs. Funk always insisted that she knew all along what he had been doing.[12]

Soon the supply of *Bulletin* 76 on "Alfalfa on Illinois Soil" was exhausted. In the second edition Hopkins wished to insert statements from two or three men including Gene Funk.[13] An account of this alfalfa experiment was written on the back of an old envelope by Eugene Funk when he returned from his alfalfa field. It was later found in his files for 1903. He wrote C. G. Hopkins that he was more convinced than ever about alfalfa inoculation. Hopkins had advised him three years before to try introduction of bacteria by placing infected dirt from a strong, vigorous alfalfa field over his own alfalfa field. Funk continued:

I sent to Nebraska and obtained three common grain sacks of dirt from an old alfalfa field. I received many a laugh from my neighbors. The stuff came and lay in the barn several weeks before I could make up my mind to take the time to scatter it. I finally mustered up the courage and sowed two strips about 30 by 300 feet, almost in the center of the field. That summer and fall I saw no apparent results, but the next spring and summer following we could readily see that something was causing the alfalfa plants to become much darker shade of green and they looked more vigorous.

Last year being very wet all but about four acres of my 22 acre field was covered with water at times for a few hours for several inches and I attribute it to over flowing water carrying the bacteria practically all over the field but the four acres which is higher ground did not overflow. Today the alfalfa is three times thicker and twice as large on our infected ground. . . . I think without doubt the introducing of a small quantity of infected soil upon a young alfalfa field will solve the question of growing alfalfa on Illinois soil where red clover and corn will grow.[14]

As the third generation continued to experiment for the future, the second generation gradually growing older continued in the settled patterns of their established way of life. LaFayette Sr. was well aware that the old settlers were slowly passing from the scene. When George Stubblefield died January 10, 1902, he noted in his *Diary* that only one more of the first settlers, John Stubblefield, then eighty-two years of age, remained. In addition to his usual activities as director for the two Bloomington banks and for the Union Stock Yards, LaFayette was also a member of the Court House Committee in Bloomington.[15] He also became a director of the National Live Stock Bank in Chicago. A new interest developed near Chanute, Kansas when Deane and LaFayette set out to see oil and gas wells in that vicinity.[16] About a month later the Kansas and Texas Tank Line was organized in Atlanta, Illinois with seven Directors. These meetings continued through the next few years.

Local politics continued to interest LaFayette. The spring Republican primaries revealed scratching of ballots. A lively Republican convention in McLean County as well as township business relating to the new Township Highway Commission held his attention.[17] LaFayette departed to Chanute, Kansas to inspect the gas fields,[18] and looked up some lots in Kansas City which he concluded were a poor investment.

LaFayette was elected chairman of the Board of Supervisors in April for the year.[19] During this year a bond issue for the new Court House was authorized.[20] Neuralgia of the face and neck troubled him. He concluded by May 12 that his trouble was erysipelas.[21] The usual dividend declared by the Stock Yards was 4½ percent with 2 percent on the 14th of June and 2½ percent on the 20th of June, all in New York. Another dividend was declared September 6 of 2 percent to be paid September 20th.[22] This pattern was repeated throughout the following years.

Gene and DeLoss visited Colonel W. H. Fulkerson near Jerseyville, June 7, 1902 to attend the Illinois Farmers Club. Gene became the president of this new and important organization.[23] An executive committee included the officers and F. H. Rankin, C. A. Shamel and A. D. Shamel.[24] In Illinois this group was supposed to meet four times a year at the homes of the various members. The subject for discussion at this first meeting was "Farm Accounts." The Fulkerson, or Hazeldell Stock Farm, included 1500 acres of land. W. H. Fulkerson and Sons controlled 635 acres. The home was described as a splendid brick building. From the tower a view of the surrounding land could be obtained. An upright clock from colonial times stood in the hall. One of the saddle horses was a descendant in five generations in the Fulkerson family directly from a Revolutionary war horse! [25]

As president of the club Gene Funk was called upon to say a few words. He referred to the fact that within two weeks he had attended two original meetings for organizations interested in agriculture. While meditating on something to say he recalled that a few days before this meeting:

My attention was suddenly called to a small object. A mere caterpillar struggling for its life and endeavoring to cross a small pool of water by crawling upon a blade of grass until its weight would bend the grass over onto another. Down that blade it would go and up another, finally reaching the other side of the water without even getting its feet wet.

He was of the opinion that the twenty-six able bodied charter members of this new organization were also "endeavoring to cross and gain with safety, the other side of a wide pond of agricultural knowledge. Tell me how many of us do you think have the natural born instinct and ability to cross this pool without getting our feet wet?"

Fifty years ago, Gene said, there was no real need for an Illinois Farmers Club. The grandfathers of these young men all knew each other. Mr. Piatt of Piatt County would visit in McLean county to buy mules. Mr. Harris of Champaign, Mr. Gillette of Logan and the Brown brothers of Sangamon were all close neighbors in those days. Gene asked, "Can it be that railroads and modern methods have caused us to be strangers?" He added that regardless of politics a man could prove himself worthy and by unanimous approval be considered a member, "If we can by meeting together in this way, carry home to others, a few ideas of our experience and observation all the more glory and honor to the Illinois Farmers Club." [26]

Other organizations flourished as communication became easier. The seventh annual convention of the Illinois Live Stock Breeders Association was held at Urbana, November 22, 1901. L. H. Kerrick was president of the Cattle Feeders Association. He presided at one of the morning sessions and spoke on the subject of exhausted land.[27] Again Kerrick emphasized the importance of sustaining the fertility of land in Illinois by raising corn and feeding cattle. He believed that people came to the corn belt for good beef but he recognized the problem of raising the highest priced beef on the highest priced land.

The Breeders Association elected as president, A. P. Grout; first vice president, John Kincaid, and second president, L. H. Kerrick. The executive committee included Eugene D. Funk who was also secretary of the Illinois Sheep Breeders' Association.[28]

The Illinois Seed Corn Breeders, organized in 1900, met in Champaign February 15, 1903 and returned the same officers. President, J. H. Coolidge; vice president, E. E. Chester; Treasurer, F. A. Warner. The board of directors included Coolidge, Warner, E. Davenport, J. V. Toland, J. L. Reid and J. Dwight Funk. A. Shamel was named official inspector. The Illinois Corn Growers Association met at the College of Agriculture with E. E. Chester reelected as president.[29]

The *Breeders Gazette* noticed that LaFayette Funk was returned to the Board of Agriculture at the State Fair where the "Golden Jubilee" was held. The article said, "Stockmen will be especially pleased to see that Mr. LaFayette Funk returns to activity of the board after some years of rest." [30] He continued as a member of the board of directors of the Union Stock Yards.[31] LaFayette also continued as a member of the Board of Review regarding township assessments and as a member of the special county Court House committee.[32]

During the fall of 1902 Gene worked along on the silo business. Mr. Sam Fry of the commission firm of the U. S. Yards, Harpole, Shinn and Fry, visited the farms.[33]

LaFayette applied the old Dutch adage regarding the weather. As it was on December 1st, so would it be during the month of December. If weather on the second of December controlled the month of January he predicted a bad month, if the third of December foretold weather for February it would be a little better.[34] As Christmas, 1902 drew near, a custom long established was continued when a Christmas roast and steaks arrived from Louis Pfaelzer.[35] Dinner for both Christmas and New Year's were held at LaFayette's home.

Lon H. Kerrick continued his views on the American farmer before the Ohio State Board of Agriculture. Although he believed the American farmer to be a great Institution he was equally as certain that the farmer was too concerned with what he was, and not enough concerned about what he had done with the great wealth left to him; "the truth is we have not been doing much but use it up." He advocated the raising of livestock in order to maintain the fertility of the soil. He added that he now saw the Ohio farmer fleeing from livestock and livestock from the Ohio farmer. He stated that there was no good agriculture that was disassociated with the raising and feeding of livestock. Grain farming was but half farming according to his ideas. He added, "I have pleaded with our people, the people of Illinois on that rich soil, where it is even more difficult to exhaust than here, to come back to their safe and sane methods and combine livestock breeding with farming." He believed that if he robbed the land, he robbed the children. Kerrick turned to his favorite subject, the raising of beef. He told of the plight of McLean County in regard to western cattle.

At the preceding International he lost the highest ribbon because the judge thought that his cattle were too fat. Kerrick said that nine out of ten people thought that these cattle were "overdone" but after they were slaughtered before competent judges he could say:

Now let me tell you something which will be easy for you to remember; the average percent of fat of the 32 two-year-old steers slaughtered and judged on the block was 8.83. The steer to which they gave the first prize on the block was 8.77 percent fat. Finally by the judgment of these men the best beef on the block had 8.77 percent fat. My cattle showed (which were too fat you understand, and which looked too fat and which I wanted to look too fat) 4.14 percent fat, less than one-half the average of the whole lot, half the percent of the first prize steer on the block. These are the official figures and you can find them. I did not make them.

He then said, "We do not know how to tell from the outside what is inside unless we put it there." [36]

About the same time that Lon Kerrick was pleading for the return to raising of cattle on the Illinois prairies, E. D. Funk allowed Professor Mumford of the Agricultural Department of the University of Illinois to bring students to his farm to judge his Shropshire flock and to visit the Kerrick farm the same day.[37] Late in the year 1901 a steer feeding experiment was under discussion with a young man from the University placed on the Gene Funk farm.[38] While Gene was in Oregon with his family in the late months of 1901 he received a communication from Professor Mumford who thought it a little late to begin that year.

The experiment was carried out, however, and the results were published in *Bulletin* 73 showing the comparison of silage and shock corn for wintering calves intended for beef production. This experiment was undertaken with the cooperation of Gene Funk on his farm. Fifty head of eight-month-old grade Herefords and grade Shorthorns were fed eighty-eight days. Equal areas of the same kind of corn were harvested as silage and shock corn. The calves were purchased in Kansas during a few weeks before the experiment began. They received shock corn and mixed hay. The experiment began February 5, 1902, when the calves were divided into two lots, twenty-five each.[39] The experiment also included measurement of the advantages of having hogs follow cattle with reference to corn and silage.[40]

A silo was constructed on the Gene Funk farm with the bill paid by the University. Mr. Dorsey was the young man who kept the records. According to the *Drovers Journal* the experimental cattle sold well and attracted considerable attention. Professor Mumford requested suggestions from E. D. Funk in a letter written July 17, 1902.[41] Arrangements for the continuation of the experiment during the next year were soon made.[42] Professor Mumford stated that he liked the suggestions of Gene Funk and added his appreciation for Gene Funk's interest and help for the future. He offered cooperation from the Experiment Station in any practicable way.[43] Funk had commented that Professor Shamel had some very valuable ideas to be ferretted out of the silo in connection with his corn work, and suggested that all work together.

The experiment in feeding of steers on the E. D. Funk farm was conducted early in 1902. The University was to pay a young man to help by the month and Funk was to provide him with board. *Bulletin* 73 contained Professor Herbert W. Mumford's conclusions with respect to this experiment. The calves on the Funk Farms were fed liberally through the winter months without attempting to fatten them or to secure great gains. The experiment was to determine whether silage or shock corn produced the best cattle. Fifty head of eight-month-old grade Herefords and grade Shorthorns were fed eighty days. Equal areas of the same kind of corn were harvested as silage and shock corn. Early in the fall of 1901 the calves were purchased in Kansas. They received shock corn and mixed hay. The experiment began February 5, 1902 when two lots of twenty-five calves were selected, equal in age, thrift and quality.[44]

Funk informed Professor Mumford that he was of the opinion some valuable information could be obtained if data were collected in a systematic way about the various methods of feeding cattle on the Funk Farms, although he had no desire to tie the Farms to the University nor the University to the Farms, he was willing to contribute his share to valuable information.[45]

The experimental cattle sold well and attracted attention. The experiment was continued in the fall of 1902.[46] Funk wrote:

If there is really any thing in the silo for the farmer I believe it is the corn growers whom we should interest fully as much if not more than the corn feeders and the farmer is constantly robbing his soil while the latter is retaining his fertility, but marketing his crop as a rule on very small margins. Where you people of the University are going to do the most good is by combining your (? free) bulletins and showing that these experiments work out not only for the benefit of one but for all.[47]

Funk explained in detail how to proceed with feeding for the fall of 1902.[48] He also referred to different methods on the different Funk Farms and thought that a comparative study might be valuable. An ensilage cutter was to be obtained by the Animal Husbandry Department for use in the experiment. C. P. Bull also aided in the construction of the silo, building a good proportion of it.[49]

The discussion of the best way to feed and finish cattle for the market continued. The block test was the subject of action by the executive committee of the International Life Stock Exposition. The *Breeders Gazette* commended this action. Previous to the discussion by the committee the *Gazette* made a vigorous plea to do away with the test by saying:

> The winners on foot cannot be expected to kill out a carcass that will win in an edible meat contest. It is purely folly to test that proposition further. It is settled for all time. They cannot win on the block if fat enough to win on the foot. No student of the fat stock show dare risk his reputation on a denial of this proposition.

The *Prairie Farmer,* however, observed that it was folly for an ordinary layman or general newspaper to quarrel with so great an authority as the *Breeders Gazette* but L. H. Kerrick "whose practical success in producing beef and showing cattle cannot be questioned" has been "repeatedly quoted in the *Pantagraph* in opposition to the above idea." Mr. Kerrick believed that the block test should be retained. He demonstrated not only with one but with carloads of steers that beeves can be brought to the highest show form by correct feeding. These cattle when judged on foot will show no excess fat on the block. He believed that it was far easier to finish a steer to pass only the live test.[50]

On the other hand, A. B. Funk stated that he had nothing new to offer in cattle feeding. He recently sold steers at $8.25 in Chicago which were fed after the old style, on blue grass pasture giving them all the ear corn they could eat. He added, "I do not claim that this is the best way to feed, in fact, I am satisfied that it is not."[51]

The year 1903 brought few changes for LaFayette who continued as director for two local banks and for the Stock Yards, his membership on the State Board of Agriculture then seeking funds for new fair buildings. He was also interested as a member of the special committee in the progress made in constructing the new court house in Bloomington. He noted on January 1st that he had been working with seed corn affairs, "It is work beyond any question."[52]

The growing family of Gene Funk welcomed another boy, Paul, February 8, 1903.[53] Gladys, LaFayette, Jr., Elizabeth, Eugene, Jr., and Paul now kept both households busy with their chatter and play.

Experimentation with cattle continued on Gene's farm into 1903. Lee Sutton took Dorsey's place with $30 per month paid by the University's Experiment Station and $10 paid by Funk.[54] Professor Mumford said that he would pay for the board of the cattle this year. William Necessary stopped working February 9, 1903. Joe Henderson returned February 17, at $22 per month. E. D. wrote, "Joe has stood by me in times past and I want in some way to show him I appreciate that way of doing." [55] Mumford advised certain rations for the cattle fed on silage and shock corn.[56]

On May 8, 1903 Gene wrote: "A day that shall be long remembered. The noted cereal and grass breeder, Professor W. M. Hays of Minnesota, visited our farm today. Frank, Dwight and I accompanied him over the place and he really seemed to enjoy it. We gathered much valuable information from him." [57]

At a meeting of the board of directors for Funk Bros. Seed Co. held in June, Gene said: "One of the most interesting (to me) meetings held yet. The subject of livestock was more or less talked of and I think the time is about ripe when this branch of the company can be added." [58] The foundation for the seed house on LaFayette's farm was begun. Work was completed September 25th.[59]

Life was not all cattle and crops and trips. Mr. and Mrs. LaFayette, DeLoss and Mr. and Mrs. Eugene Funk entertained about two hundred people at LaFayette's home, bringing them down from Bloomington to Shirley on a special train at a cost of $40. Some came in picnic hacks and in carriages as well as in hay racks from Shirley to the house. The day was perfect and all declared they had the "best time of their life." [60]

During the last of July and the first of August, 1903, LaFayette was busy with the work of the Board of Review and of the Special Court House Committee of Bloomington. Mr. G. R. Lawson of Utica, Missouri and Mr. E. L. Halsell of Nara Visa (?) New Mexico visited the farms. They looked over seed corn and wished to sell some X. I. T. calves for feeding.[61]

The neighborhood of Shirley was deeply moved by the passing of Mr. Anthony who had reached his 103rd birthday last May 9th. A large attendance was reported at the funeral in the Grove cemetery September 1, 1903.[62]

Gene was on the Chicago market with hogs and cattle September 9th. Fifty cattle were among those fed during the last year as "experiment cattle" in connection with Professor Mumford's ideas.

50 cattle av. wt.	24 silage ....@	$5.70
	1 silage 1420	5.25
	24 Shock Corn ....@	5.70
	1 Shock Corn	5.25

When LaFayette needed to attend the directors meeting of the

Union Stock Yards he asked George Funk who was also a member of the Supervisors Court to call the meeting to order and to preside in his absence.[63] The dedication of the new County Court House in Bloomington occurred September 24, 1903. Mr. and Mrs. LaFayette attended and were pleased with the ceremonies.[64] Immediately LaFayette set out for Springfield where he found work lagging on the buildings for the State Fair.[65]

These were the days of the country club activities. Mrs. LaFayette and Mrs. Eugene attended a reception given at the club October 16, 1903.[66] Visitors came often to see the farms. Frank Funk, Frank Aldrich with a third person described by LaFayette "as some German Count" were looking over the barns October 29th.[67] Clay & Robinson from Chicago also looked over the farms.[68]

Interest in rapid transportation between communities aroused some conversation with those who talked of interurban lines in McLean County.[69] The business affairs of the K. & T. P. L. & O. Company were, according to LaFayette, not in a very healthy state.[70] Eight well-defined small pox cases in the county caused apprehension.[71]

The International Live Stock Show was attended by Mr. and Mrs. LaFayette and Mr. and Mrs. Eugene D. They saw their good friends, Colonel and Mrs. Judy, there Dec. 1–3, 1903. Mr. Kerrick's Grade Aberdeen Bullocks were Champion 2 year olds and winner of Simon O'Donnell's cup for the Best Load of Angus Steers at the International.[72] A writer for the *Breeders Gazette* while admitting that Baby Beef was the coming thing argued:

It is indeed true that Mr. Kerrick's calves are ruined at an early stage by feed, that his calves are too soon yearlings, his yearlings are too soon two's; thus the calf lives but part of his allotted days, though they may be happy ones.[73]

The Funks of the third generation were aware that the maintenance of soil fertility in the central Corn Belt was the essential responsibility. They considered cattle raising and fattening to be an important industry for this purpose. They became active during these early years in new organizations to aid the farmers. They sought high yields in grains and grasses in order to increase productivity of their lands, thus meeting the demands of higher valuation and taxation. Knowledge of the farmers' problems and needs became their business. The resulting confidence that was built up over the years was endangered only because their willingness to experiment did not produce immediate desired results. Of greater significance was the fact that their experimentations eventually paid the farmer increased dividends.

CHAPTER XI

Oats, Soil and Cattle · 1903–1907

THE THIRD GENERATION of Funks put into practice the accepted philosophy of many leaders in the family. An article in the Sunday edition of *The Inter-Ocean* of Chicago in 1904 emphasized this philosophy as "Wealth is power, but use it wisely, enjoy life—and work." The article, entitled "Funk Family's Unique Place in Central Illinois History," described the part the family played in Illinois farm life and politics.[1] Their concern for the preservation of the rich Illinois soil and their willingness to cooperate with all who were experimenting in many fields was apparent in the years 1903–07.

Funk believed that preservation of the fertility of the rich soil in the Corn Belt required experimentation and soil surveys to inform the individual farmer of his responsibility in this program. Phosphates were thought to be essential. Their deposit and exploitation were unfortunately possibilities for speculation and high prices. E. D. Funk inquired of Robin Jones, Nashville, Tennessee regarding prices. Jones replied March 12, 1903 that the price to dealers was $4.00 per ton f.o.b. mines, in sacks.[2] Farmers in Illinois were alerted to the situation largely through the efforts of Professor C. G. Hopkins, head of the Department of Agriculture at the University of Illinois, who was also concerned about phosphates at this time. He replied to a question from E. D. Funk, saying that $4.00 per ton in bulk or $4.40 per ton in bags f.o.b. cars Nashville was the regular quotation he had also received from Jones. The freight from Nashville to Chicago was $3.22 per ton of 2,000 pounds.[3]

Hopkins believed that there were four materials necessary not only in maintaining but in markedly increasing productive capacity of the land: (1) farm yard manure, (2) nitrogen direct from the atmosphere, (3) general limestone and (4) ground rock phosphate. For root crops, possibly potassium should be listed. He then changed the subject in his letter to Gene, Sr., declaring that if he were to come to a board meeting of the seed company he would prefer to come on a Saturday. He asked that Deane Funk be informed that "Mr. A. A. Hinkley, Du Bois, Illinois has been growing soy beans for several

132

years and he now has land which is becoming fairly well infected." [4]

Eugene D. Funk was interested in the choice of some other person as President of the Illinois Farmers' Club,[5] because his time was taken in organizing the new seed company. He also believed in passing the presidency around to others.[6] Fred Rankin replied that there was no need for a change and that "the boys" all felt the same way about the subject.[7] Fred Rankin was deeply interested in Masonry and urged E. D. to take the Consistory Degree on April 19th, 20th, and 21st. Frank and Newt Harris were expected to join. Funk decided to accept.[8]

Early work in the breeding of oats was undertaken on the Funk Farms during the summer of 1904. Little attention had been paid to this promising field of crop improvement. Twenty-one varieties were tested on half plots during the third year of the work. A number of these under different names proved to be of the same variety. It cost $9.00 to select seed for a half acre of land. Breeding was undertaken on the E. D. Funk farms to improve yield, weight, resistance to lodging and for uniformity. According to the *Pantagraph* this activity proceeded on the same principle as corn breeding.

Mr. Funk explained that in a short distance north of his home there were twenty-one varieties of oats grown side by side on half acre plots in the form of narrow stripes about two rods wide and extending from one end of the field to the other. Funk identified the twenty-one varieties. He observed that about 99 percent of the oats of the country were a conglomeration of everything in the oats line. Experiment stations had undertaken some breeding of small grain. Something of this kind had also been done in England, France and Germany, "but to bring it on the farm in a large and practical way in this country, the Funks are the pioneers, so far as the *Pantagraph* has been able to learn." [9]

The Funks were undertaking this program in order to (1) increase the yields per acre, (2) increase the proportion of twin oats and (3) decrease the awns on the oats. The article noted that it should not be understood that some varieties of oats are all twin oats and other varieties are all double oats. Both kinds were in all varieties with a difference in the proportion.[10] The proportion in any variety could be increased by breeding. The threat of smut was almost removed by treating before planting. Mr. Jesse D. Norton of the United States Department of Agriculture, was conducting a long list of experiments for the Department.

Probably the most interesting part of the experiment was the true breeding of oats by selection and separate planting of single heads.

A narrow strip of land was divided into a string of plots about the size of onion beds where the crop from ten heads each of nineteen varieties were planted, producing about 18,000 plants in all. To obtain the seed the very best individual heads were chosen from half acre plots and general fields, and these heads were gone over again and the best taken from each variety. The description continued:

Data is recorded. Our breeding plot contained the planting from ten heads of one variety. Each head was planted separately making 3 to 7 rows across the plot. The head from which the berries are taken was saved and made a part of the record. From now on the whole parent plant will be saved.

Two small machines were bought to plant a single berry. They did not work well, so the Funks invented a better planter. Prepotency became the invisible factor to be judged only by its results, its record or pedigree. In all of this work Mr. Funk was "not inclined to make any strong claims on theory or probability, but to proceed for several years according to well proven principles and see what his results figure out." [11]

J. B. Norton conducted the experiment for two years. He began his work with the United States Department of Agriculture on oats in 1902. He was connected with the plant breeding laboratory of the Bureau of Plant Industry. In 1903 he had some oats grown on the Funk Farms "and since the beginning of 1904 he has transferred his whole work here". The principle breeding plots were located on the Julius Funk farm, where he stayed but he was also conducting work elsewhere on the Funk Farms. The object at first was to find out what could be done to improve the conditions of oats in the United States. It was found that nothing could be done with the existing varieties except to establish them as pure. Two lines of work resulted: (1) to establish the pure strains and (2) to test other varieties and find out which were identical and what the relation between the different varieties actually were.[12]

Great interest was shown in the soil survey undertaken by Professor C. G. Hopkins of the University of Illinois. It included chemical analysis. A. J. Bill of the *Pantagraph* said: "He has applied fertilizer tests for three years to the principal type of McLean county soil (Marshall Silt Loam) on the farm of S. Noble King east of Normal, Illinois, and demonstrated the marked benefit of using phosphorous in addition to the usual clover or manure treatment in growing corn and oats." [13] The greatest value of the survey was its presentation of a means for identifying the type of soil on every farm in the country. Its real use had only begun.

L. H. Kerrick continued to prepare cattle for the International. A visit to his farm in July, 1904 brought forth this comment:

These are not common cattle and a common fellow can't say much about them. They are not 'dumb, driven cattle': they own the place, receive homage from every visitor and converse freely with the keepers. . . . Somebody has called 'em Angus; This word comes from the adjective 'august' and they look it; their bearing is dignified mildly contemplative, aristocratic and altogether self-satisfied. To be truthful about these black pets one must say they look rather lazy and glutenous and very much at ease.

There were thirty-six two-year olds. A carload was to be sent to St. Louis in the fat cattle competition at the World's Fair and fifteen to the International at Chicago. There were also nineteen yearlings; fifteen of these were also to go to Chicago. Uniformity was stressed as a great point in building up this herd. There was a very large proportion of the real Angus type. There were 135 purebred cows of breeding age and 275 purebreds in all. There were 583 black cattle in July and there were 610 a few weeks before, the largest number ever on the Kerrick place up to this time. Edwin J. Oelze was the herdsman and Mr. William Butler was the feeder. The feed of the thirty-six two-year old steers was as follows: Six bushel of chopped ear corn (measured by the scoop, three scoops to the bushel), four bushel of ground corn, about two bushel of oats, about 50 pounds of wheat bran. This is for the morning meal at 6 a. m. At 4:30 they received the same less the bran plus 100 pounds of oil meal. This has been their feed for six weeks. Previous to that they ate soaked shelled corn. They were encouraged to eat all that they would clean up well. For roughage they ate clover, hay, corn fodder and the finest blue grass. They had the run of the pasture. There were no fancy features or conditions that many breeders gave to a few head of cattle.[14]

Lon Kerrick won at the International, $700 in cash premiums with his three carloads of Angus steers. All of his forty-five cattle won high place. Kerrick counted this a far greater thing than taking ribbons with a single animal or two. According to the *Pantagraph*, Mr. Kerrick "calls the exhibiting of single animals sport, while competing with carloads represents practical farm production and is directly related to the real business at the stock yards and packing plants." He prepared six loads of show and Christmas cattle; three won at the International, three awaited the Christmas market.[15] There was no Second Championship award but Kerrick's load of two-year olds stood next to Krambeck's Grand Champions. Wellington Leavitt, chief buyer for Swift's, judged the loads. He was quoted in the *Breeders' Gazette* as saying:

I did not give the Grand Championship to a yearling load simply because there were three loads of 2-year olds of decidedly superior finish to any yearlings on exhibit. If Krambeck's load had not been an aspirant, Kerricks cattle would have taken the Grand Championship against any yearling lot on the Ground and eliminating both the Krambeck and Kerrick loads, I would have given the coveted prize to D. W. Black's cattle.

Kerrick received in the Southwestern district second best load of two-year olds. First on two-year old Angus and First on Angus; in the Eastern district, Second best load of two-year olds. Second on Angus and Third on Angus yearlings; also Third Angus special on two-year olds, and first K. I. T. special; the total equalled eight premiums. In his load of two-year olds, one weighed a ton although he was not then weighed separately. The symmetry of the animal was described as almost faultless. John Roos, the English judge, and Professor Curtiss, the eminent stockman of Iowa, found the animal without being told of him. At a dinner in the Saddle and Sirloin Club they pronounced the animal "the best steer in the show". The steer did not compete separately. He was shown as one of fifteen in a carload lot. Kerrick was reported as satisfied with the judging.[16]

Funk Bros. Seed Co. took the following prizes at this International in 1904 with three carloads: In the North central district three-year olds, first and second, Second Grand Champion, three-year olds in the Show; Eastern district, two-year olds, Second; Angus Special, two-year olds, Fourth. In the single Steer class an animal known as "Curly" won four prizes in the dressed cattle contest. First in two-year old carcasses, Grand Champion of all ages. A fine steer "Jerry" fed by Deane N. Funk did not win a premium but brought next price to the Grand Champion Steer in the sale of single steers.[17]

The first prize two-year old and champion carcass was a grade Aberdeen Angus, named Funk's Choice. He dressed 66.7 and showed "a beautiful smooth side, with light tallow inside, a medium quality of outside fat of beautiful color and grade, fine and it was marked about right. The lean was carried thickly down the rib in rare fashion". Live weight, 1,235; Dressed, 824; Percent beef, 66.7; Weight fat pounds, 105; Price 15¢. The success of the Funk Bros. confirmed the ideas of Professors Mumford and Henry in the use of silage for beefmaking.[18]

Mr. and Mrs. LaFayette planned a trip to California in February of

1905. An attack of "la grippe" had so exhausted Mrs. LaFayette that after leaving home she was forced to remain for a few days at her niece's home, Mrs. Humphrey of Bloomington. Mrs. Humphrey was about to depart for Florida. Finally both families left the city February 26th and 27th. Before departing, LaFayette had attended to a $450 subscription to the Interurban through Frank Aldrich and attended the State Board of Agriculture in Springfield; the meeting of the stockholders of the Union Stockyards; the Livestock Breeders' meeting in Champaign; the directors' meeting of the K & T O & P Company and the bank directors' meetings in Bloomington.[19] Their western trip took them via Chanute, Kansas City, El Paso and thence to Pasadena, California. Upon arriving seven hours late in Los Angeles, LaFayette wrote that the country they traversed that day had been worse than worthless.[20] He was impressed later with the orange groves and the electric cars running to Long Beach, a distance of twenty-one miles in 45 minutes.[21] He returned to Bloomington March 9th in time to attend a meeting of the Board of Supervisors where he thought the tax situation was a muddle.[22] He attended the funeral of Mr. Adam Brokaw and noted that the body of Judge Weldon arrived from Washington April 13, 1902.[23] LaFayette left for Kansas the last of April, and Gene and Mamie attended a cattle convention at Amarillo, Texas for about a week.[24] Uncle Bill Harpole, the well known commission man since 1873, died May 17th in Chicago. The funeral brought Aunt Till Pancake and Norma Harpole to visit Mrs. LaFayette.[25]

Travel by automobile was less infrequent. DeLoss started with two other boys on a trip to Princeton, Illinois. He, his mother and his father drove to Jake's for Sunday dinner in 49 minutes and home from Charlie Funk's in 32 minutes.[26] A new automobile recently purchased by DeLoss enabled him to turn over his old machine to Eugene who encountered some difficulty when he replenished the oil supply. The motor would not operate. Gene and DeLoss took the machine apart only to discover that Gene had been sold kerosene in place of gasoline.[27]

Messrs. Eugene, Lyle, I. G. and Lawrence Funk returned early in September 1905 from the Swenson ranches in Texas where they visited and contracted for 500 feeding cattle to be shipped to them in November. The Swensons owned four ranches forty to sixty miles apart with more than 50,000 acres in each. The Funks were pleased with the plan for breeding cattle on these ranches and gratified to find that the corn grown on the ranches was from their own seed company and yielded about double that of the native corn.[28] Six hundred and seventy-seven cattle were divided as follows: I. G., 110; Lawrence, 110; Lyle, 55; Dwight, 55; and Gene, 297.[29] Cattle were marked on the ears.[30]

At the International in 1905 in the carload lots, Funk Bros. yearlings were first; in the South central District, carload of grain fed three-year olds Funk Bros.[31] Shorthorns also took first prize. The net return on the carload of show cattle was $1,680.67.[32]

The problem of adaptation of seeds and plants to certain soils, generally referred to as acclimation, continued to worry E. D. He wrote his friend, C. G. Hopkins, about the problem:

> For instance we are told by some people that corn shipped more than fifty miles from home will not do well, yet we are discovering by actual experience among our customers that corn from the same seed sent to Oklahoma and to Canada and some of the same kind sent the year previous to Oregon . . . in each case the soil was similar to our black Illinois soil.

Heretofore they reasoned that in their own state, poor yields meant poor farmers. If Funk's corn does not do well in Iowa, Gene thought it might be because of loose, sandy soil with more moisture. He asked:

> In connection with your soil survey of the State would it be possible to run some experiments along the line above indicated and eventually when a customer writes for corn or other seeds—by a glance at the soil survey, map, salesmen . . . can readily tell whether black prairie land grows corn.[33]

Along this line the *Farmers' Voice and Rural Outlook* carried an interesting article two years after Funk's first inquiry entitled "A Romance in Phosphate". The author traced the warnings of Professor Hopkins regarding the loss of phosphates in the soil. He believed rock phosphate, used together with legumes and farm manure was the most economical method of supplying phosphorus to the land. About twelve years ago an explorer had found what he thought was coal in the forest lands of Tennessee. He learned from a chemist that it was rock phosphate worth more than coal if found in quantities. The land was located in Hickman County about forty miles southwest of Nashville. Investigation suggested an extensive deposit. Companies were formed and enthusiasm was high. This was the year of the Panic of 1893. The product was on the market at too low a figure in order to divert trade from South Carolina interests which then held a practical monopoly on the trade. Shrewd capitalists bought up nearly all of the lands. The original discoverer, a lumberman, held the 10,000 acres on which the discovery had been made at a price which the combine would not pay.

This tract had not been developed. Charles Willard Hayes, in charge of geology for the United States Geological Survey in Vol. 2 of the Seventeenth Annual Report of the United States Geological Survey, reported the high grade phosphate rock in quantity on this land. Finally the option on this land was secured by a Nelville B. Coburn of St. Louis. He worked for years to obtain financial backing to develop the land. The trust waited patiently for him to sell out to them. Despairing of help he accidentally came upon a bulletin written by Professor Hopkins and contacted him. Hopkins visited the tract. After tireless examination of deeds and the tract itself, Hopkins contracted such representative men in Illinois as A. P. Grout of Winchester; L. H. Kerrick of Bloomington; G. W. Gale of Galesburg; E. E. Chester of Champaign; N. B. Morrison of Odin and others. It was agreed that if sufficient interests were shown that Illinois farmers would take over the company known as the New York and St. Louis Mining and Manufacturing Company. Illinois men became officers and a majority of the stock was placed in escrow in the hands of a board of trustees consisting of S. Noble King of Bloomington; C. G. Hopkins of Urbana; Judge Edward Kirby of Jacksonville; Col. George D. Reynolds of St. Louis; and M. B. Coburn. Stockholders included Dr. Frank H. Hall, Aurora; Frank Funk, Bloomington; H. D. Hughes, Antioch; A. A. Hinckley, Du Bois; J. H. Kincaid, Athens; Julius Strawn, Jacksonville and many others.[34]

This phosphorus was obtainable at $8.00 per ton, depending on the section of Illinois. According to the article, this plain non-acidulated rock phosphate cannot be bought from the fertilizer trust, for the trust prefers to make up its rock phosphate into what it is pleased to call "complete fertilizers". The article concluded with the thought that the acid phosphate selling at $30 per ton would contain little more than one ton of rock phosphate, costing four times more than the Illinois men would sell for. One ton of rock phosphate contained as much phosphorus as four tons of "complete" commercial fertilizer. Furthermore this company proposed to keep its phosphate for domestic use. Of the one and one-half million tons of rock phosphate mined annually, one million tons or 66 2/3 percent was shipped abroad. This was described as an effort on the part of the Illinois men to secure a "Square Deal."[35]

A meeting of the Illinois Farmers' Club was held at the Beardsley Hotel, Champaign, Illinois on May 31, 1905. It was called to order by

President Joseph R. Fulkerson.[36] The subject for general discussion was farm accounts. The system applied by E. D. Funk was described in some detail. Funk said that he thought out a plan last year (1904) that pleased him so much that he put it into practical application. He described the system as follows:

He has numbered all his fields and provided the foreman with a printed form on which is to be entered each night what each man has done that day, the number of the field he has worked on. The left hand side is for forenoon; the right hand side for afternoon, the foreman's entry is simply dittoed, but if the team or field is different in the afternoon the entry must show it. The entry will show for instance that on the forenoon of April 7, John Jones plowed corn with four horses in field No. 60. Another entry may show that this man fixed fence between 69 and 70. This form is made out every night and handed to Mr. Funk Saturday night. At the bottom is a blank for remarks for noting unusual happenings as the foaling of a mare.

Mr. Funk then went through the daily reports and made up a record of the various kinds of accounts that he wished to keep. He could determine work done in every separate field and find the cost of production in that field. He said that the system was simple and would tell what it cost to produce corn. Professor Mumford had men who kept this record. He also numbered his horses so that hired men should designate the teams used.

Deane Funk believed that the most difficult problem to determine was the winter feeding of cattle. To obtain the average amount of grain that a steer ate then to tell the proportion of that grain that goes to the hog following the steer presented a real problem. B. F. Funk called attention to the fact that crop yields for different years may vary. It would not be the same for any two years. It was answered that the average cost over a period of five years would be something of a standard. One person said he would need to know the answer because he could not tell whether it was too little to allow a tenant 8 cents for producing a bushel of corn or 14 cents as too much.

Deane Funk figured carefully that it cost $3.25 to break and work an acre of ground until harvest time. President Fulkerson observed that the farmer could not get at the cost of production in such an exact way as the manufacturer. Deane Funk had determined that with corn at 30-40 cents per bushel plus the feeding of oats and hay that the cost of feeding a horse for one day was about 20 cents. He himself fed his horses about fifteen pounds of hay a day. He believed the average farm horse was fed too much.

Lyle Funk was called upon to speak of his European trip. He gave an interesting description of the famous Vilmorin farm ten miles from Paris. He met Philip Vilmorin, grandson of the man who organized their outstanding experimental farm in 1815. There were only 145 acres in the place and it was detached in tracts of ten to forty acres. People from anywhere sent seeds there for testing. Two hundred varieties of wheat and 800 varieties of potatoes were grown there. They also had laboratories and a chemist. He also spoke of his observations in Holland.

The older members of the Funk family, B. F. and LaFayette, expressed interest in the meetings wishing that it had been possible for them in earlier days to have attended such gatherings of farmers. E. E. Chester also congratulated the young men. Joe Fulkerson, E. D. Funk and Mr. Harris were voted as a Committee on Cost of Production Statistics.[37]

Governor Deneen appointed LaFayette to the Illinois Road Commission. He confided to his Diary that "I am not very favorably inclined toward the proposition." [38] On March 7th he met with the commission. His old friends, James and Joe Fulkerson, were present. Work on experimental hard roads continued through the year. McLean was especially interested in the project. Dedication of the road was September 26, 1906.

LaFayette, whose disapproval of automobiles was not always carefully concealed, was "kidnapped" as he described it but in the hands of friends on July 22, 1906. The night before his good friend, Col. Judy, came home from the State Fair and State Convention meetings in Springfield. Mr. and Mrs. Joe Fulkerson were already there. The automobile trip took the "captive" first to Dwight, then to Kankakee over night. The next day found the party in South Bend, stopping at the Oliver Hotel. LaFayette recorded: "The day has been rather against the kidnapers, they having bursted two automobile tires. The roads have been pretty rough in places." The Oliver factory was inspected before their departure to LaFayette, Indiana where they visited Purdue University. Their route took them through Crawfordsville and Danville to Champaign, where they found it "good wheeling to within 10 miles" of that place. After that "we had it good and muddy." After breakfast they visited Professor Hopkins, seeing most of the breeding plots of grains and grasses on the south farms. The distance traveled was about 550 miles. This was quite a trip for the early days of automobile travel. From this point forward LaFayette rode "*on* the automobile" more often.[39]

The fall of 1906 produced "a great deal of rotten corn." As LaFayette described it, "Five bushels to the hundred of worthless, damaged and rotten corn would not be too high an estimate." [40] LaFayette attended the seed company meetings during 1906.

Gene did not keep his Diary during 1906 until September 17th when he recorded that he "commenced unloading car load brick for new house." A month later carpenters were at work.[41]

On December 7th Gene attended the Farm Institute at Lincoln, Illinois where he talked on "Alfalfa". He recorded that he "got along fine" and received many compliments. "Good audience and splendid meeting." [42]

The Funks were strong supporters of President Theodore Roosevelt in the years after McKinley's death. L. H. Kerrick speaking at the First Baptist Church in Bloomington in October 1904 stressed his belief in the "efficiency of fair, temperate, candid discussion" in order to gain common ground. Differences of opinion, he said, were bound to produce patriotic divergencies. Taking note of the 1904 Presidential campaign he mentioned the questions of Philippine policy, the race question at home, the Tariff laws, the Trusts, the money question. He then said:

I have been over the ground carefully, and I shall vote the Republican ticket and counsel my fellow citizens to do the same; and all with good conscience, without which, I could not.

No one shall have the right to call me an unthinking unreasoning partisan.

I shall at all times scrutinize and question the policies of my party closely.

As I see it, I thereby prove my loyalty to my party. By such a course I prove that I am a better citizen and a better Republican than any who without thought and blindly, toss the cap in the air and yell their approval of everything and anything the party stands for.[43]

Kerrick's individuality in politics was emphasized by the position he took regarding the question of commercial reciprocity as an important issue on 1908–09 during the Presidency of William Howard Taft. Kerrick said, in a speech before the Farmers' Institute:

Reciprocity presupposes the existence of protective Tariffs. It has been called the hand-maiden of protection. If there were no protective Tariffs in the world, we would have free trade, all over, leaving no demand for reciprocity. But the American example and practice have proved exceedingly contagious. Almost every country has, or is building strong protective Tariff fences. Our hope of holding our good foreign customers and securing others lies now in the possibility of negotiating Reciprocity Treaties or conventions which may accomplish the end.

Kerrick declared he was a protectionist as were Hamilton, Clay and Blaine and McKinley except that he could never be one who favored "prohibitory or exclusive Tariffs". Then he added, "But McKinley lived to say, referring to our system, 'the period of exclusiveness is past'". Blaine became an apostle of reciprocity. Mr. Kerrick pointed to the fact that the Dingley Tariff had prevailed eight and one-half years with over 700 articles scheduled with duties ranging from 45 to 100 percent. He believed that such protection was formerly advisable. But at the present time he believed the Dingley law to be a monstrosity. Kerrick's analysis of the law and his reference to the reciprocity section of the bill indicated an independent interpretation of these problems. Senator Cullom of Illinois, chairman of the Foreign Relations Committee, said the ratification would result in gains to trade.

Kerrick pointed to the fact that not one in a thousand people had ever read the Dingley law. He had never seen it himself in a newspaper or in campaign literature. Campaign speakers did not refer to it. He declared that the American public had nothing to do with the procedure. Only representatives of manufacturing industries were heard. Kerrick declared the method of tariff-making was vicious. He referred to labor cost differences in Europe as one-half of those in the United States. If the difference was 10 or 12-1/2 percent or possibly 25 percent it scarcely seemed necessary for the same manufacturers to enjoy protection of 45 to 100 percent. This he called "Graft".

He also had the courage to point out that anyone who opposed the Dingley Tariff or who talked of revision was called a "free trader" or described as disloyal to the party. Then he added:

I think that keeps many from speaking their minds. It does not bother me. I believe in parties. The country is better off for having them. A man should belong to a party and be loyal to it. I do not leave my party nor permit anybody to thrust me out because I believe and say the Dingley law should be revised promptly and radically.

He then said an honest but ignorant person might attribute prosperity to the Dingley Tariff but an intelligent person would attribute it to the fact that "We have had that all but incalculable amount of surplus farm products to sell the rest of the world." The Dingley law, he said, was not made to benefit farmers.

Here was a clear voice from central Illinois speaking with courage and insight to his farmer friends on one of the major political issues of the day. The tariff was such a troublesome political issue that Theodore Roosevelt saw fit to ignore it during his seven years in the Presidency. President Taft had the courage to bring it up but with other divisive problems in the Administration his party split on the issue. Mr. Kerrick closed his remarks with a reminder that the markets of Europe were being closed against the farmers' surplus and that exhorbitant protection of American manufacturers was the cause.[44]

During the early years of the twentieth century, while the seed company developed as a family enterprise, experiments on the farms were not confined to corn. Other field crops, soil improvement and methods of feeding livestock received attention. The interdependence of these activities contributed to the efficiency of the farms.

CHAPTER XII

The Old Order Changes · 1907–1912

THE FIRST DECADE of the twentieth century brought forth renewed emphasis on progressive ideas in the history of the United States. Increasing international prestige, ideas of social justice including regulation of trusts, programs for conservation, new methods of transportation, and new ideas in education required noticeable adjustments. Rural life underwent considerable change. Population movements to urban areas increased. Immigration reached a high point. Those who lived in the agricultural center of the elongated Corn Belt felt the impact of these changes. The Funks retained their land and continued to work and speak for the betterment of agriculture. A succession of deaths among the second generation during the first two decades of the new century placed more and more responsibility upon the third generation as new problems and new opportunities appeared.

Lon Kerrick continued to maintain that agriculture was the greatest industry in the United States. He and others of the Funk family regretted the lessened emphasis on stock raising in grain growing areas. In January 1907 he delivered an address before the Indiana Livestock Breeders' Association in Indianapolis.[1] His previous ideas regarding baby beef remained unchanged. He continued to advocate the idea that "the best beef, the cheapest lean meat with the most perfect admixture of fat, will be produced by liberal use of the proper feedstuffs during the period of the most rapid growth of your calf or steer." This practice was best for producing profit on high priced lands. Kerrick personally examined this kind year after year and found no other beef equal to it.[2]

The voice of one of the strongest champions of agriculture was stilled March 13, 1907 with the unexpected death of Leonidas Kerrick. His loss was a great shock to the Funk family who regarded the husband of Sarah Funk as a member of the family. They respected his legal ability and his knowledge of live stock. He was well known throughout the United States and abroad as an authority on highest quality beef and for his prize winning Angus steers

145

at International Livestock Expositions.[3] The local *Pantagraph* said:

> He had the instinct of a farmer and a thorough appreciation of the
> practical problems of the farm as well as confidence in science to solve
> those problems. Then to these qualities were added his remarkable ability
> to sift a subject to the bottom and his always attractive form of state-
> ment with many a frill of fine humor, his addresses took hold of the people
> with peculiar force. He had a fearless purpose to say the right things and
> the high character of the man was always a part of what he said.

During his life Lon Kerrick spoke often and wisely in the state of
Illinois and in the region. He helped to shape definite movements in
agricultural education, especially in Illinois. He was a member and
president of the Board of Trustees for the University of Illinois. Eugene wrote "a heavy and sad blow to all of us and especially Aunt
Sallie who is lying at almost point of death." [4] After a long and linger-
ing illness she followed her husband in death on May 15th.[5] The passing of Sarah marked the second of the children of Isaac to leave the
scene. Others of her generation followed in rapid succession within
the next decade. Benjamin F. Funk died February 16, 1909 after a
long illness caused by stomach trouble. Isaac II was killed a few
months later, May 1, 1910, by a train at Funk's Grove station. These
changes left four of the brothers as advisers for the younger members
of the family.

When George, the oldest son of Isaac, also passed along July 16,
1911 [6] the realization that familiar faces at family gatherings were no
longer present was increasingly impressed upon the family. Duncan,
LaFayette and Jacob of the original eight children of Isaac remained.
Duncan also died in 1911 after a stroke of paralysis. Gene realized the
situation when he wrote:

> One by one our uncles and aunts are leaving us and more and more is
> Life a heavy burden being thrust upon the third generation of Isaac
> Funk's family to uphold the honor and dignity and to maintain and keep
> together a family relation which has no equal anywhere and may I be
> permitted to do my part.

Gene became more aware of these successive losses in the family
when the wife of Jacob, his Aunt Mary, died July 14, 1912. His father
LaFayette suffered a stroke early in January 1911.[7] Only LaFayette
and Jacob remained of the original family of Isaac. They continued
to be active until 1917, when they died within a few hours on the
same day.

The decision to build upon the site selected when Gene and Mamie
Funk moved to the country was carried out in 1907. When the family

moved into the new home the event was indeed a red letter day as the following entry shows:

May we all live to a ripe old age and enjoy the many comforts that we have placed in this new home. To those to whom this house and estate may eventually fall heir—may they appreciate that it was for them as well as for ourselves that we have tried to look into the future—and may their appreciation of our efforts and their honesty and character of themselves be as strongly and enduringly built as is this house. Let them think and act also for not only themselves, but for future generations as well. Thus handing down from generation to generation some of the finest farming land that the sun ever shined upon. Who are the persons by the name of Funk who can say we have kept and preserved our share of this grand estate which was founded by Isaac Funk in 1824 and has been handed down to us.[8]

Two more children were added to the family group when Ruth arrived in August 1907,[9] and Mary was born May 17, 1910 increasing the number of children to eight. Gene commented "a large family for these trying times" and expressed the hope that all of his children would grow up to prove the worthiness of the name Funk.[10] Concrete gate posts were set around the new residence in May 1908. He hoped that his grandchildren would look upon them and learn from their lasting qualities that it pays "to build, to plan to think not only for yourself, but for others who may follow." [11]

While these changes were occurring 1907–12, three generations of Funks were participating in the current activities. LaFayette, always close to Eugene's family, celebrated birthdays and anniversaries with his son's family. He spent considerable time with his three oldest grandchildren. Gladys was a frequent visitor as were LaFayette II and Eugene Jr. The youngsters often remained overnight with their grandparents and their Uncle DeLoss, whose ability with electronics was fast becoming evident. A new sled was brought to Grandfather for inspection and Grandmother's two comforts were carried home with pleasure. When the two boys went fox hunting with their Grandfather the day was indeed important. These were happy and formative years for the fourth generation and Grandfather LaFayette's advice was welcome and long remembered. Both of the boys gained immeasurably from the knowledge of the many activities of LaFayette as they heard him and his brothers talk of their problems.[12]

There were also new interests in the West. After attending a reunion of his class at Delaware, Ohio, and a visit with the Sigma Chi boys, LaFayette left with his brother Jake and their friend, Mr. Hoblit, for Montana. When they arrived at Billings they were met by

Dr. Sudduth of Normal, Illinois, who hired an auto and took them to a field of winter wheat "of what they call dry farming." On the next day they traveled to the Sudduth ranch. On the third day they continued twenty-five miles to a neighboring ranch and then about sixty five miles over territory without roads. During thirteen miles of their trip the visitors saw three herds of sheep, some 8,000 in all. There were also some 500-600 cattle within sight. LaFayette attended a Shorthorn sale held by the assistant secretary of the Shorthorn Breeders Association for people in Ohio and Missouri.[13]

Gene Sr. and his cousin Deane were especially interested in raising fine cattle. Gene also acted as judge in carload lots of feeding cattle at the International. Isaac G., son of George, and Emirl Engerson accompanied him. The responsibility was difficult only in one or two lots when the competition was close. He recorded that he gave the Grand Championship to the yearlings because it was believed that the feeder could realize more out of them than the calves. Deane Funk's car lot received the Grand Sweepstakes,[14] first in class and fourth. Ike received second in Class and first in the district.[15]

Deane won the Grand National in 1908 also as in 1906. The young men recalled when Lon Kerrick won in 1900. The same kinds of grass and the same kind of good corn and climate were cited as reasons for the excellent competition from the Funk Farms. As the *Breeders' Gazette* stated:

The creation of a carload of Grand Champions necessitates as a preliminary, the possession of the necessary raw material. . . . The feeder must have the cattle and unless, taking by the forelock, he has bred them, his search is likely to be unrewarded.

When Deane Funk was requested to give a prescription for success he expressed surprise saying, "Nothing to it but a bunch of good steers and plenty of feed . . . If you haven't got good cattle to start with it would be better not to feed them good corn and if the feed isn't good I wouldn't advise you to waste it on the cattle, no matter what quality they possess."

With the exception of a few, these cattle were bred on the Funk Farms. If they had not been intended for show purposes, they would have been handled in the same manner. If marketed in the usual manner, they would have consumed a little less oil meal and instead of being held on corn ten months, the market would have received them sometime in August. In 1906 a close account was kept with the object of determining the relative cost of finishing native and range bred steers as well as those of various ages. The expense of one pound gain during a long feeding period ranged from 9 to 13 cents. This series of tests, according to the *Breeders Gaeztte,* "convinced the Funks that long feeding is not generally consistent with satisfactory financial results." [16]

Compared with the Kerrick Grand Champions of 1900 the standard in 1908 appeared to be higher with animals smoother and more even in every respect. The Funks were aware that the making of Grand Champions was not necessarily an avenue to wealth. Grand Champions had sold as high as $17.00 per cwt. and as low as $8.35. The price in 1900 was $15.50; in 1906 it was $17.00.[17] After winning the Grand National in 1906 and 1908 there was a decrease in emphasis by the Funk family on the production of champions.

Eugene Sr. took his two boys, LaFayette and Gene Jr., to Crawfordsville, Indiana where they showed sheep and hogs. They took 14 firsts, 6 seconds and 2 thirds with a total of $81.00 to their credit. This exhibit included Chester Whites and Berkshire hogs, shropshire sheep and seed exhibits. Gene Sr. wished to take this exhibit to the Springfield, Illinois Fair under the name of Funk Bros.[18] He was in demand as a speaker. As president of the Illinois Livestock Breeders Association he spoke on "Correlation of Types of Corn Yield" and delivered an address at Madison, Wisconsin on "Some Corn Problems."

Gene, Sr. also became indirectly active in politics during this first decade of the twentieth century. He hoped to secure the placement of representatives who were sympathetic with the needs of agriculture.

According to Wm. T. Hutchinson, few political battles in Illinois have been more complex than the legislative contest for the Senatorship through the first five months of 1909.[19] Early in 1909 some agricultural spokesmen in Illinois were becoming more articulate in their demand for a farmer as United States Senator. A resolution to this effect was adopted by the Livestock Breeders and Corn Growers who disapproved the re-election of Albert J. Hopkins. Resolutions called for the election of an agriculturist as Senator and requested the appointment of A. P. Grout of Winchester as United States Secretary of Agriculture.[20] By February 20th E. D. Funk had informed A. P. Grout that he had sent a letter to all Republican members of both the State Senate and House who classified themselves as "farmers." [21] He informed Governor Deneen of the action, saying that if this movement conflicted in any way with what the Governor had in mind "it gives me pleasure to abide by your request." [22] Funk believed that Mr. Lowden would be a strong candidate after Hopkins showed his strength and that Mr. McKinley would see what he could do. He advised letting them fight it out for a few days before they showed themselves.[23] Between trips to Omaha Gene Funk was thus well occupied. Apparently Grout was to be supported for Senator if the appointment occurred. Grout was informed that resolutions quietly pursued at Springfield were not to be made public until March 4th. Their strategy was to keep Governor Deneen informed on the strength of the vote; if Hopkins could not win on the strength of the Primary Law then Grout was to be the accepted choice.[24] Either Hopkins would be elected or left out of the vote with only about a dozen followers. Then favorite sons and dark horses were expected to appear. This activity would consume a few days. They expected Lowden to be presented both as an agriculturist and as a livestock man. No one knew his strength. McKinley also would come in for a few votes. The committee passed a resolution that Funk appoint two gentlemen besides himself to act as steering and advisory committee with power to act. Funk asked Grout's opinion.[25] Gene realized that "politics are about as uncertain as the weather." [26] By April things seemed to be at a standstill.[27] Lorimer was finally chosen as Senator. These delays and difficulties served to widen divergencies in the Republican Party of Illinois.

Concern was expressed over the reduction of appropriations for livestock investigations and for horticulture at the University of Illinois. Professor Mumford requested Eugene Funk's help when the bill came up for a second reading as the only time it would be amended on the floor of the House.[28] Funk complied with the request. After the 18th Mumford stated:

> I want you to know that I am expressing the unanimous feeling of the Agricultural College and Experiment Station when I say that we all feel greatly indebted to you for your active, efficient and unselfish efforts in behalf of the College and Experiment Station Bill and especially do I feel grateful for your work in connection with restoring Section 2, the part of the bill affecting his stock investigations. From Dean Davenport, Professor Blair and Professor Rankin, I have heard the most complimentory expressions concerning your help.[29]

Funk quickly recognized what he considered to be a mistake on the part of Professor Cyril Hopkins in advocating the elimination of the livestock industry. He believed this would discourage young men from staying on the farm and thus increase tenancy. He feared that any need for an agricultural college would be lessened. He wrote his good friend, Fred Rankin, that he approved Rankin's idea that all associations and agricultural interests should affiliate closely. He said he formerly sponsored this idea in the National Corn Association at Omaha. His hope was to impress people with the idea that agriculture was not a narrow chanel and a monstrous road. He was aware that the livestock interests in Illinois were having their troubles at this time. Funk was not in favor of any precipitous action as suggested by the Stock Yards people until the Investigating Committee on Bovine Tuberculosis had made some move. Knowing the committee was probably unfavorable to a tuberculosis test he counseled delay, adding, "When we are fighting the Indian we must take the Indian's tactics or he will get our scalp." [30]

Dr. Peters of Nebraska was appointed as the head of the Biological Laboratory established near Springfield.[31] Again Funk urged strong reorganization among livestock men in order to obtain support for a man of Dr. Peters' ability.

Activities other than the seed company and the corn associations kept Gene occupied. As president of the Illinois Livestock Breeders' Association in 1909, leadership was necessarily exercised in a different field. There were two other problems of importance, such as the bovine tuberculosis disease and the appropriation for the Agricultural College.

In regard to bovine tuberculosis, the State Board of Livestock Commissioners were also concerned. Phil S. Haner of Taylorville was chairman. A letter from the animal farm department of Swift & Company included a statement giving a summary of slaughtering of cows and heifers for Libby, McNeil & Libby for the first three months of 1909. Since only a portion of cattle infested with tuberculosis were ultimately condemned by United States Government inspectors it appeared fair to estimate the number of condemnations at 50 percent for the number of animals found infected. Officers of the association were particularly interested in legislation to prevent the spread of tuberculosis and were in favor of a bill to manufacture hog cholera serum for free distribution to swine interests. The association emphasized its non-political purposes and stressed its emphasis on the betterment of livestock.[32] Circular letters were mailed from Shirley.[33] Efforts were under way to make the Breeders Association a strong one in all parts of Illinois.[34]

Funk favored a site for the Bovine Laboratory near Springfield, eventually obtained, with easy access to the secretary of the Livestock Commission.[35] His correspondence with Phil A. Haner, secretary, revealed a strong desire to benefit the livestock industry.[36] The bovine tuberculosis legislation and the enforcement of city ordinances with regard to this question required time. P. R. Barnes urged Gene Funk to speak in Chicago during November on the general purposes of the Livestock Breeders in the matter of securing legislation on bovine tuberculosis. Funk was asked to urge cooperation and unity among interested groups.[37] A joint investigating committee met in Chicago. Aware that certain leadership was not in sympathy with clearing up the problem, Funk moved cautiously but effectively.[38]

A new investment activity, the "Golden West," opened up with Curt N. Treat of Chicago. This was a gold property under development. Those investigating were waiting for someone to buy the property.[39] The old stockholders of the Mid-Continent Oil Refining and Manufacturing Company, who were approached, included members of the Funk families.[40]

Another interest claimed the attention of Eugene Sr., when he explored the possibilty of securing stock in *The Farmers Voice* in 1910. Eventually the investment in this agricultural paper cost him $5,000 for 100 shares of stock.[41] A visit to Captain R. M. King's farm included LaFayette, LaFayette, Jr., Gene and Gene, Jr. to inspect experimental wheat plots. The phosphorous application showed up well.[42]

After the so-called paper panic of 1907 there was apprehension regarding financial affairs in the country. The Department of Agriculture at the University of Illinois felt the pinch in reduced budgets. Something of the philosophy of Gene Funk is revealed in 1910 when he tried to analyze the influence of agricultural education at a state university during these years. Although he hoped that something could be done to remedy the crippled condition of the Agricultural College he stated that he never would go back to the legislature at the cost to himself of $7.25 to $10.00 a day to accomplish so little. He questioned whether a boy of sixteen to twenty years of age received the right sort of education when he left home and was thrown into a town with thousands of other boys and girls. He favored teaching the fundamental principles of agriculture, mechanical art, engineering and some chemistry in every county, township high school and consolidated rural school. This would relieve the anxiety of any mother whose boy left home "to get an education" before he knew what he was interested in. These young people often acquire such a "surplus amount of supreme knowledge" from starting so soon in life that they had to wait until becoming forty or forty-five years old to realize that there was a whole lot to learn.[43]

Changes immediately affecting the Middle West in methods of

communication also directly influenced the lives of the Funks. The automobile brought many changes to central Illinois. The Funks were among the early purchasers. When Gene Sr. discovered in 1907 that he could drive from his new home to Bloomington in thirty minutes he exclaimed, "That is going some!"

The construction of a deep waterway from Lockport to Utica provoked some discussions. The Chicago *Examiner* reported Funk's opinion regarding a commission. He advocated a non-partisan group with members passing an examination before being confirmed. Although he had not studied the question except from a distance, he thought the rights of the Sanitary District of Chicago could only be in the flow of water for sanitary purposes, at the same time taking into consideration such increase as the city of Chicago would require in the future He concluded:

I voice the sentiment of 99 percent of the farmers of the State by saying that the agricultural interests of Illinois are always willing to join in a movement that is for the greatest good to the state and to the people. We have voted for our share of the expense of twenty million dollars for deep waterways to the Illinois River and we would ask and expect of those to whom the duty of supervision of construction is given that business methods, wise counsel and honest thoughts be expended.[44]

The day of the interurban as a rapid transit system between communities was thought by some to be one of the wonders of the age. A line between Lincoln and Bloomington seemed possible to the Funks. The Funks corresponded with Mr. H. F. Allan, an Englishman who was interested in investing money in the United States. They helped to pay his expenses to visit the area. There were some ideas of connecting such a line with Chicago. Allan arrived in Bloomington, remaining over night with LaFayette. Funk already held $3,000 worth of bonds and 30 shares of stock in the Springfield and Northeastern Traction Company. A French syndicate also looked into the proposition.[45]

Changes in transportation other than the automobile and the interurban were apparent. An airship made the trip from Chicago to Springfield for the opening of the State Fair. It traveled faster than the special train.[46] LaFayette was also interested in a National Good Roads meeting in Indianapolis in December where he obtained valuable information.[47]

Gene's children were growing up. Elizabeth sang at exercises at McIlvain School during 1911. The boys decorated the automobile with corn, wheat, oats and rye to participate in the Merchants' and

Manufacturers' parade with 48 other cars. The children were dressed up in white suits and dresses. The fourth of July, 1911 was a gala day with 36 people present for fireworks. The families of Jake, Deane, Ike and LaFayette participated. The boys shot off the sky rockets and balloons.[48]

LaFayette continued to receive recognition, and he was appointed by Governor Deneen in 1910 as a delegate to the Conservation Congress held in St. Paul, Minnesota. He heard President Taft deliver an address and when "Teddy" Roosevelt spoke, he filled the auditorium.[49] An able address was also delivered by James J. Hill, according to LaFayette's *Diary*. One deep disappointment, however, came to him in this same year when he was not reappointed after long service to the State Board of Agriculture.[50] After many years he missed the activities and responsibilities.

Some of the Funks became interested in the rich swamp lands of Louisiana. E. D. Funk and Deane Funk decided to visit the area. E. D. became ill but arranged for Julius Funk to take the southern trip.[51] Deane and Julius Funk became interested in forming a local syndicate to develop Louisiana land.[52] E. D. finally made the trip to New Orleans with Deane, Julius, Barnes and Fred Rankin and parties from Wisconsin, Chicago and New York. Julius, however, undertook the venture without the assistance of E. D. and Deane.[53]

E. D. noted again the tightening money markets at the end of the year. He observed that the price of grain dropped off about 30 percent and that the livestock market was doing about the same, yet railroads charged high freight rates. He said he was trying to get out from under before the crash came.[54]

Christmas was spent at Gene's, with Joe Henderson acting as Santa Claus to the great delight of the children.[55] The continuing problem of securing domestic help led Gene to follow a new plan by writing N. Kaumans that he would be glad to secure two German girls to work in his country home.[56] The difficulty in obtaining efficient help was especially acute since Fugihara, the Japanese boy, had returned to his homeland. As a result, the Kessel Family came to live on the E. D. Funk Farm.

Another new departure was emphasized when the Bankers' Association of the State of Illinois, president E. E. Crabtree and vice president B. F. Harris of Champaign, through its secretary R. L. Crampton, wrote Gene Funk that "The Association has never taken so much interest in anything as it has recently in The Betterment of Agriculture—using your expression." The membership of the association needed awakening. Their plan included division of $6,000 in cash prizes in ten counties. E. D. asked Lyle Funk to attend the meeting.[57]

A. P. Grout informed E. D. Funk that the new Illinois Alfalfa Growers' Association was to be organized at Grout's farm near Winchester June 29, 1911. E. D. was elected vice president.[58] Gene later spoke upon the subject, "Some Results from Ten Years' Corn Breeding" at the University of Illinois short course.[59]

Concern over the trend of affairs in Washington prompted Gene, Sr. to speak out against reciprocity July 15, 1911. Writing in *Farm Magazine* he pointed out in an article, "Look Ahead, Farmers", that "certain interests" were doing everything they could to lower farm wages. He stated that peasantry could result under this plan for reciprocity. He expressed surprise that more agricultural papers had not taken the matter seriously. His experience, he said, in the past few years had given him opportunity to note how far some of the "interests" would go to gain their point. Agricultural interests should wake up to the fact that Argentina, South Africa and other countries were taking away the export business. The high price of land was forcing the small producer to sell, thus increasing larger farms. This brought the tenant sytem and the policy of working the land for all possible profit without thought of the future. Then would come peasantry, where the tenant no longer existed. E. D. urged against being carried away with the idea that the American farmer is independent and wealthy. If facts were known, he said, "There is more farm indebtedness than ever before in the history of the country." [60]

Financial worries caused Gene some concern. His personal indebtedness was about $56,484. The debts of the seed company over against assets amounted to about $10,000 and ventures like the National Corn Association and an agricultural publication, *The Farmer's Voice*, were costing plenty of money.[61] Added to this situation cholera continued among his hogs.

Gene gave freely of his time when he was elected as one of eight directors of the Illinois Good Road Improvement Association.[62] A meeting was held in Bloomington November 30th when a party of thirty examined the hard road to Shirley and also near McLean.[63] LaFayette at this time was a member of the State Highway Commission. He was especially interested in these activities.[64] Interest in good roads throughout the state increased. A report from 486 bankers on roads in 430 townships in 98 Illinois counties gave answers to some of the questions. This report merited attention because 65 percent of Illinois bankers were farmers on their own land, and 40 percent of the bankers lived in towns of less than 2,000 people. S. E. Brandt of DeKalb was chairman of the Bankers Committee on Good Roads, Thomas Sudduth of Springfield was secretary.

In the 430 townships there were 26,000 miles of road, 27 percent of the total mileage of the state. With an indication of about 10.3 percent of road mileage improved, Illinois lagged behind Massachusetts with 50 percent; Indiana 38 percent; Ohio 28 percent; Kentucky 20 percent and Wisconsin 18 percent. Stone roads were favored by 127 townships, gravel roads by 95 percent and dragged roads by 124. Where improved roads existed people favored their increase. Over 80 percent of the townships in Illinois raised only $500 to $4,000 for road purposes. Local bankers, merchants and professional men showed little interest in 267 townships, yet they felt that the present system was inefficient. Ninety percent of the bankers advocated revision of the laws. With this nucleus of influence behind them the Commissioners for Good Roads foresaw success.[65]

The year 1912 was an exciting one from the political viewpoint. The split in the Republican Party between President Taft and ex-President T. Roosevelt, together with the nomination of Woodrow Wilson by the Democrats, gave rise to efforts to determine which of the three candidates was the most progressive. If there were any measure of their progressive ideas, William Howard Taft with his control of the party organization and the support of men like Elihu Root was believed by some to be more conservative. He received criticism for his conservation program and the Payne-Aldrich tariff. "Teddy" Roosevelt maintained an enthusiastic following, especially in Illinois. When the Progressive Party was formed, the Funks were torn between admiration for "Teddy" and party loyalty to a midwesterner, President Taft. Gene was in Chicago July 17th when the regular convention was held. He noted in his diary:

In Chicago on morning train. Hang around Republican Headquarters—convention. Much excitement for Roosevelt. Very little enthusiasm for Taft. The People want the former and the interests have control of the latter. Out to Coliseum—can't get in.[66]

Gene spent only a short time in Chicago since he was on his way to Mt. Carroll, where he visited Gladys at Frances Shimer School for girls.

Before the Republican convention in June, Theodore Roosevelt visited Bloomington in the spring on April 7th. Frank and Gene Funk accompanied his train to Springfield. Large crowds met the ex-President in both cities.[67] On the 10th of April, Illinois gave strong majorities for Roosevelt, Deneen for Governor and Frank H. Funk for State Senator.[68]

Later in the year after Theodore Roosevelt became the Presidential candidate for the Progressive Party, his running mate, Governor Johnson of California also visited Bloomington. Gene accompanied his party to Champaign and Decatur. He noted:

People are not going wild over political situation. People are thinking and listening and reading, but the mass of the people are not expressing themselves out in open discussion or demonstration.[69]

The Progressive movement drew little enthusiasm from Republicans of McLean County during February 1912 when Professor Charles C. Merriam of the University of Chicago led a group in Springfield. No delegates were present from Bloomington. The *Pantagraph* described the conference as a farce. Although resolutions endorsed no specific candidate, this Bloomington newspaper said that Robert La Follette of Wisconsin was highly praised and T. Roosevelt and G. Pinchot complimented.[70] Frank Funk favored the direct primary, the income tax and free sugar at a Republican county convention in April.[71] When he joined the new Progressive party in August to address a county convention, his action was interpreted as an admission of candidacy for the Governorship.[72] The first state convention of the new party was held in Chicago on August 4th, where Frank Funk was nominated for Governor. Medill McCormick called the convention to order. In his acceptance speech Funk said:

Most of us, my friends, really understand what this Progressive movement means. Mighty forces are moving humanity the world over. Our enemies are the enemies of attempts the world over to give the 'square deal' to all mankind.

He also said that the state "must be the principal instrument in bringing forward" the mighty movement led by Theodore Roosevelt, "but that does not make it socialistic any more than the state activities for the protection of life vs. health are socialistic or that the postoffice as run by the federal government is socialistic."

Then he added:

How long will it take our reactionary brethren to learn that when we provide legislation by which the states step in and accord to every being better opportunity that we are really making a new individualism rather than socialism?

He believed this was the only true meaning by which prosperity could be attained. He stated that he entered the campaign without obligation or promise.[73]

The *Pantagraph* supported the Republican party and noticed that the *Chicago Tribune,* although posing as the leading Progressive organ, did not support Funk's candidacy. This local Bloomington newspaper expressed the opinion that the purpose of a Progressive state ticket was to obtain the necessary 2 percent of the vote and that "an effort to use the Funk name, the Funk character and the Funk money" was thus made to give the new party legal standing.[74]

The Democrats carried the state in the election. Frank Funk carried 21 counties in comparison to the successful Democrat, E. F. Dunn with 67 and the Republican, C. S. Deneen with 14 to his credit. Funk's vote trailed T. Roosevelt in the state by approximately 83,000 votes. The split in the Republican Party contributed to the success of the Democrats in Illinois.[75] Gene wrote on election day, November 5th, that the Democrats won "hands down." No other comment was needed.[76]

A Good Roads Convention was held in Peoria, Illinois, September 27, 1912, revealing information that Illinois possessed a great network of 95,000 miles of country wagon roads. These were the responsibility of haphazard efforts of 4,800 highway commissioners working independently of each other. They were poorly paid and largely inexperienced. They operated with inadequate funds.

The Illinois Highways Improvement Association argued that improved roads would bring to Illinois

> Better schools and larger attendance
> Better health and quicker medical attention
> Better farms and more cultivated land
> Better crops and cheaper transportation
> Better economic conditions and more producers
> Better social conditions and less isolation
> Better church attendance and better citizens
> Better postal service and closer friends.[77]

Other activities also demanded attention. Meetings of the Mid-Continent Refining Company, chartered in Illinois and capitalized for $53,000, demanded time. A company to establish a plant at East St. Louis was organized in 1913.[78] Some of the Funks participated.

During these years 1907–1912, when members of the third generation continued their experiments in agriculture and their new company, Eugene Sr. also took a leading part in the organization of the National Corn Associations. He accepted in 1907 the presidency of the N. C. A., where his work for the Betterment of Agriculture brought him national recognition and continuing influence.

PART FOUR

The Betterment of Agriculture

CHAPTER XIII

National Corn Association and
Expositions · 1907 · Chicago

THE WORD "Corn" to Americans in 1907 meant Zea Maize or Indian Corn. The broader biblical definition of "Corn," including almost all seeds and plants of the various cultivated crops or domestic grasses as wheat, oats, barley, millets and others exclusive of corn, was not usually applied. However, when the originators of the National Corn Association chose its title they thought in terms of the broader interpretation.[1]

A clear distinction must be drawn between the National Corn Association, made up of a group of men primarily interested in the Betterment of Agriculture, and the National Corn Exposition. The Exposition was always organized in a city chosen as the site in cooperation with a committee of local businessmen. The secretary of the National Corn Association worked closely with this committee. The National Corn Association, during its active years 1907–14 and thereafter, elected only one president, E. D. Funk, with one continuing board of directors.[2]

The Congress of the United States passed the Morrill Act in 1862 providing for the establishment of Colleges of Agriculture. A subsequent act of March 2, 1877 provided for Agricultural Experiment Stations in conjunction with the colleges provided by the Morrill Act. An indirect basis for the expansion of all agricultural work was thus provided. The National Corn Expositions from 1907–14 presented outstanding experiments provided by scientific investigations. These ideas were brought to thousands of people and they in turn disseminated this information to their neighbors. Charts, placards, samples of grains and grasses called attention to the new methods and advancement in agricultural science.[3] This was a time of numerous fairs, group meetings and conventions. The Corn Association filled a need on a national basis by employing this typical method of communication during the first part of the twentieth century.

For several years the idea of a Corn Exposition was in the minds of some leading spokesmen for agricultural interests in Illinois. Their persistence and endurance despite many difficulties culminated in the presentation of six Expositions in seven years. The first of these meetings was held in Chicago (1907), two in Omaha (1908 and 1909), the fourth in Columbus, Ohio (1911), the fifth in the southeast at Columbia, South Carolina (1913) and the last in the southwest at Dallas, Texas (1914). Before the Columbia gathering, E. D. Funk, president of the Corn Association, called attention to the contributions of E. S. Fursman of El Paso, Illinois. Fursman had visited Funk's office and home periodically for years to talk about "a great and glorious" National Corn Association. He visited presidents of railroads, of colleges, and governors of states in behalf of the idea. Corn was E. S. Fursman's hobby. He talked of it constantly whether in a railroad car, hotel or at home. Some called him, "The corn crank of Illinois." Funk recalled that Fursman came to his office one day and insisted upon a National Corn Association with Eugene Funk as president, Professor P. G. Holden as vice president and Fursman as secretary-treasurer and general manager of an association that should eventually cover the entire United States from Maine to California. He urged that literature and letterheads be obtained to interest all friends in a series of National Corn Expositions.[4] This activity occurred in the winter of 1906. For a year the membership consisted of these three men.

Financial interests in Chicago were eventually contacted. A guarantee fund of $40,000 was raised for the First Exposition in October 1907. Mr. Edwin D. Conway, a businessman of Chicago, became president of the Exposition. Fursman spent time in Chicago trying to push the activity along. Some discouragement entered into his enthusiasm because Chicago leaders moved slowly. Articles in Chicago papers mentioned Eugene D. Funk of Funk Bros. Seed Co. as one of the promoters.[5] The *Prairie Farmer* wrote that there was no great Corn Exposition in the United States although the idea was suggested in several cities. Corn was called "King of the Cereals" because it fed more people directly or indirectly than any other cereal. Cities strove to immortalize corn, but only local success was achieved.[6] Recognition by leaders in Chicago of the significance of the movement was a forward step.

Continued delay was apparent in June 1906. Fursman described his business contemporaries in Chicago as "too slow for me . . . they are no further advanced than they were eight weeks ago." [7] It was suggested confidentially to Fursman after the Exhibition was assured that Charles A. Stevens become business manager of the Exhibition to serve with Fursman. Funk and Fursman spent the day in Chicago with Curt Treat. Mr. and Mrs. E. D. Funk, with their two oldest daughters, attended Ringling Brothers Circus and also looked over the Coliseum as a prospective site for the Exposition.

The president of the Chicago Commercial Association sent out to some 200 prominent businessmen a notice for a meeting during January 1907, for the purpose of organizing the International Corn Exposition. Fursman was urged to invite E. D. Funk, Professor Fred Rankin, Professor P. G. Holden and C. A. Shamel to be present.[8]

Later in the spring Fursman remarked, "Funk, the Exposition is going to be the greatest event that ever happened and we will be the proudest men in the world because we have started people to thinking about the 'Betterment of Agriculture.' I never felt so happy in my life." These were among the last words of the man from El Paso who made corn his hobby. He died suddenly April 12, 1907.[9] His death brought a change in officers, but his idea lived on through the leadership of E. D. Funk and others.

C. A. Shamel, associated with the *Prairie Farmer* of Chicago, was appointed in Mr. Fursman's place. Eighteen states sent exhibits to this first exposition. The Illinois Agricultural Experiment Station sent the only Agricultural Educational Exhibit.[10] One of the most interesting attractions was the model of a farm. Daniels' Scenic Studios offered to locate a miniature farm on the floor in the middle of the Coliseum Building. This idea provided a change from a horse and plow piece at an expense of $2,000 to the studio.[11] The model farm was 20 feet square with everything built in proportion including growing corn, buildings, houses, stables, "as realistic as real." Mr. Shamel and Mr. Treat began to say, "Meet me at the Farm." This miniature was called "Funk Farm."[12] E. D. Funk requested a two-foot border of corn around the farm. Curt Treat and C. A. Shamel opposed the idea but were willing to allow a sign to read "Fac-similar of one of the celebrated Funk Brothers Corn Farms, the largest Seed Corn Growers in the World."[13]

C. A. Shamel suggested that the president of the National Corn Association issue a call for a Corn Congress and appoint twenty delegates to attend from each state. At this meeting the Temporary National Corn Growers' Association would become a permanent organization. The National Corn Congress[14] was scheduled under the auspices of the National Corn Growers' Association to meet October 9–11, 1907. The Congress was in charge of Eugene D. Funk of Shirley, Illinois, president of the Corn Growers' Association.[15]

According to C. P. Bull, Crop Improvement Associations such as those in Minnesota and Wisconsin cooperated in making the Chicago Exposition possible.[16] The Chicago meeting was held at the Coliseum October 5–19, 1907. Officers of this first National Corn Exposition were Edwin D. Conway, president; C. A. Shamel and P. G. Holden, vice presidents; Curt M. Treat, secretary; Henry A. Wheeler, treasurer; and C. A. Shamel, general manager.

Twelve states were represented at the first meeting of the Association. Delegates were interested in a permanent organization. An appointed committee reported the following officers: E. D. Funk, president; P. G. Holden, vice president; and J. W. Jones, secretary-treasurer.[17] C. P. Bull, present for this organizational activity, recalled that the original group sat among the girders in the gallery of the Coliseum organizing their Association while the band played below.[18]

President Funk called attention in his address on October 11th to President Theodore Roosevelt's reference to the deep water channel to the Gulf of Mexico. He urged farmers to stay on the land; to learn to grow better crops and to retain the fertility of the soil. Funk stated that the President of the United States was probably not aware that the movement had already begun. Then characteristically, he paid tribute to E. S. Fursman "who to my personal knowledge worked most faithfully for the last ten years to bring about what we are now witnessing—the greatest show of its kind ever produced." He urged farmers to learn how to improve the quality of grain, enlarge quantity and extend markets.[19]

The Exposition opened with a fine display of corn and a chorus in Grecian costume composed of fifty men and women. The twenty foot square model farm in the center of the floor created considerable interest. Harlow Higinbotham declared that Corn had proved its right to be called King; it was worth roughly a billion dollars each year; it was equal in value to two thirds of all U. S. exports; and its value was twice that of the world's yearly output of gold and silver.[20] He also quoted from Governor Oglesby's "Royal Corn." [21] Among other addresses given was one by J. Dwight Funk on "Successful Corn Breeding," referred to in Chapter IX.[22] There was also an exhibit of household articles made from different parts of the corn plant.[23] The Honorable Willet M. Hays, assistant secretary of the United States Department of Agriculture, said such a display in the Coliseum would have been impossible five years ago.[24]

A. D. Shamel represented the United States Department of Agriculture at the Exposition. He called attention to "Corn, King of Kings," in an article written on the eve of the Exposition for the *Chicago Evening American,* and gave a short summary of the scientific raising of corn dating from 1825. He referred to the activity of J. S. Leaming of Wilmington, Brown County, Ohio.[25]

The choice of Eugene D. Funk as president of the Association brought forth favorable comments. He was described as one of the strongest men in the corn business, a supporter of agricultural organizations and an advocate of advanced work in agriculture. His record as a corn breeder proved, according to the *Prairie Farmer,* "that his judgment is sound; his counsel is safe and his energy is well directed. The corn growers, distributors and manufacturers of the many corn products will readily acknowledge his leadership." [26]

Although some thought that farmers did not support the Exposition in great numbers, plans were made to hold another Exposition. Some expressed the opinion that the railroads ought to sign an agreement to pay part of the guarantee fund another time. Mr. Charles A. Stevens became chairman of a committee to implement these plans. Officials of the Chicago Board of Trade indicated their intention to assist, but could not as an organization make an appropriation to a guarantee fund. The first edition of the publication *Corn* was approved.[27] P. G. Holden urged the appointment of J. Wilkes Jones as general manager for the next year.[28]

F. H. Rankin of the University of Illinois observed that the Exposition was a new event. He was of the opinion that the organization should proceed. The importance of incorporation should be urged among corn men. He wrote Funk, "Our farmers as a class are a little conservative and slow to act, but if the business men of Chicago realized how fully and heartily the corn men appreciated their interest and cooperation in financeering [sic] the recent Exposition, they would certainly feel encouraged to continue." Rankin believed that it was the very best advertising they could undertake. The educational value of the exhibits would encourage the University of Illinois College and Experiment Station to support the Exposition.[29]

These were busy days for Eugene Funk. He had expected to see W. M. Hays at the American Breeders meeting at Washington in January 1908. He did not attend when word was received from people in Omaha, Council Bluffs and South Omaha of a proposition to hold the National Corn Association meeting there. Funk hoped that many western states would be interested in displaying smaller grains, grasses and forage crops.[30] Five days later on January 30th, Funk wrote Jones, the general secretary, about the situation in Omaha. He felt that a very dark cloud was hanging over the future of the National Corn Association. He sometimes wondered if they had started at the wrong end of the ladder. Instead of building up to the top they were attempting to build down from the top. He believed that agricultural activities must be handled by agricultural leaders. There was no other way to success. Omaha's interest, he thought, could be handled best by Omaha people.[31]

As plans progressed, Jones suggested that, if possible, President Theodore Roosevelt should be invited to speak, and Secretary of Agriculture James Wilson and Assistant Secretary W. M. Hays, also should be asked to attend. He also suggested a Roosevelt Day with the President, including J. J. Hill of the Great Northern Railroad and others taking some part. A Grain Dealers' Day should attract not less than 100 of the Chicago Board of Trade. Enthusiasm was high in Omaha. Pledges were increasing. One man who pledged $1,000 was never known to subscribe for anything before.[32]

The dates December 3rd to 12th, 1908 were selected for the first Omaha Exposition. Leading agricultural workers in fifteen states had pledged their active support by February, 1908. Jones, as general manager, informed Secretary of Agriculture "Tama Jim" Wilson that he was communicating with the Assistant Secretary of Agriculture, Hays, regarding the conduct of an Agricultural Congress throughout the entire period of the Exposition. Railroads offered substantial aid. They proposed to employ one man whose salary and expenses would be paid, to share cost of posters and other material as well as to feature the Corn Exposition in their newspaper advertising. Jones hoped that a large attendance would result from such cooperation.[33]

Jones explained to Assistant Secretary Hays that a committee of the National Corn Association met after the first Exposition in Chicago and again undertook to put the Exposition on there. Finally they concluded that it would be impossible to meet the demands of the Chicago interests. Jones expressed pleasure with the Omaha arrangements where they obtained a better building for $2,000 rental for two weeks than was available in Chicago where a rental of $10,000 was asked. Jones relayed another suggestion from Davis of the Pioneer Implement Company of Council Bluffs, Iowa, to show a miniature plant converting waste farm products into alcohol.[34] Professor A. D. Shamel of the United States Department of Agriculture at Washington, D. C., was also informed by Jones of the decision to change the location from Chicago to Omaha.[35]

The *Prairie Farmer* recorded that Omaha had been selected as the site of the Second National Corn Exposition, saying it was to be regretted that Chicago had lost the enterprise. The article continued, "But it seems that there has been a growing fear among the interests behind the International Live Stock Exposition that in the event of the Corn Show proving a permanent success the latter would necessarily detract some from the prestige of the farmer." [36]

Omaha subscribed $25,000 for the guarantee fund. Jones hoped that Professor Hays would attend for the entire period, especially since an Educational Congress was to be held, "A sort of cereal school throughout the entire exposition period." Jones urged Shamel to discuss the plans with Secretary Wilson and Assistant Secretary Hays, adding, "It will be necessary for us to make an unusual effort and put the exposition upon a high educational basis, and it must have the support of the workers in agriculture who are recognized as leaders, in order to make it win out." Jones observed that the great trouble with the agricultural shows in the past, particularly corn shows, had been that promoters believed it necessary to allow the show to degenerate into a sort of street fair and attract the rabble in order to make it pay its way. The leaders of the National Corn Association could not afford to allow such a policy to prevail.[37]

The letter heading for the Association in 1908 carried the slogans, "Betterment of Agriculture in Its Broadest Interpretation" and "More Corn, Better Quality, Wider Markets." Officers of the Association during 1908 included president, Eugene D. Funk; vice presidents, P. G. Holden, Ames, Iowa and E. G. Montgomery, Lincoln, Nebraska; and secretary-treasurer, J. Wilkes Jones, Ames, Iowa. The National Corn Exposition officers were: president, G. W. Wattles, Omaha; vice president, H. H. VanBrunt, Council Bluffs; treasurer, C. F. McGrew, Omaha.

Funk encouraged Jones, stating that he also would write Secretaries Wilson and Hays. Funk agreed to the Railroad and Grain Dealers' Days: "I advocated that very thing at Chicago last year but it did not materialize." He doubted that a government exhibit could be displayed without an act of Congress, but believed the idea worthwhile and of great value, "not only as an attraction but in an educational way it would be hard to estimate its value." [38] Regret was expressed by the President that no full time person was available to devote time to the publication *Corn*. Someone should have been present at all state institutes to secure the "rich articles that were given and so few received the benefit." One issue could have been for Iowa, one for Illinois, one for Ohio and so on.[39] Jones was in thorough agree-

ment with Funk's suggestion relative to the issues of *Corn*. He hoped
to obtain some samples and prices of buttons and pins for the organization. Proof for the next issue of *Corn* was to be forwarded for
Funk's approval.

Funk, in a speech delivered before the Commercial Club of Omaha,
March 7, 1908 developed the same theme and summarized his thinking up to this time. "Corn Shows are not 'new fangled' affairs," he
said. The National Corn Exposition, he explained, was the latest
up-to-date method of presenting to the people at large, modern methods of improvement in agriculture. "Corn, leader of all in the Middle
West, should be entitled to the best." With this slogan, Funk turned
to statistical proof of his contention. He stated that over 90 million
acres were planted annually to corn with value twice that of the crop
of cotton and equal in value to wheat, oats, barley, rye and the total
value of stock; horses, mules, milch cows, other cattle, hogs and
sheep. He then asked, "Why should we not bow our heads to this
most wonderful of all grain-producing plants? Yet be it known that
we are only at the beginning—in the primary class, if you please—
studying the elementary principles of grain production." [40]

Here was an opportunity in one of the centers of the growing west
to emphasize significant problems of the Corn Belt farmer. Funk declared that the soil was the farmer's bank account; only a bankrupt
nation could result if the wealth of the land was not retained as it
was removed.[41] He added, "You ask what has this to do with an Exposition?" and then answered, "Everything!" Funk continued with
another question, "Are the most important ideas gained from the lessons dug out of the text books or from experience and actual observation?"

Funk explained that directly or indirectly agriculture was depended upon almost entirely by the merchant, the banker, even the
little store around the corner. The corner grocery became a center for
the exchange of ideas because the man informed of improvements had
money in the bank and could also pay cash for his groceries. A neighbor who had a poor crop asked for credit. Exchange of ideas at the
grocery store often influenced the less successful to try his neighbor's
way. Funk described this exchange as "A small Exposition on the village corner." Persuasively he advocated magnifying this idea in a
place and a city like Omaha where experiences with corn could be
exchanged.[42]

He continued, saying that Illinois, during the last seven years,
had raised the annual yield by five bushels of corn to the acre on

nine million acres. With enthusiasm and conviction he concluded: "Plant breeding, corn breeding is the study of the hour. We must have Expositions where we can bring our samples of produce." [43]

Inquiries regarding the Omaha Exposition began to pour in. Among the questions asked were these: "Can the Exposition be developed in a manner fair to all with chief emphasis on its agricultural aspects?" "Can selfish interests be removed from influencing by their cut and dried plans?" Funk answered that he hoped and expected to make the Exposition as fair as possible with "Let the Best Man Win" as the slogan. He remarked that judges' associations often seemed unfair when to the best of their knowledge they acted as honest men.

Secretary Jones expressed the hope that the Exposition would be an incentive toward the Betterment of Agriculture in its broadest interpretation. Several manufacturing industries were anxious to cooperate because they recognized an opportunity to share in the development of the agricultural west. New interests might act as a spur to prompt grain growers to "look carefully into the future and anticipate some of the problems that have proven so costly to farmers in the other settled states where the fertility of the soil is already a vast and extravagant problem with them." The growing of better crops meant more careful conservation of soil fertility. It also meant better livestock and better farming generally.[44] Railroad officials were also interested in bringing increased freight and passenger traffic.[45]

The purpose of the National Corn Association was to assist the members of the commission in the various states and to keep them in touch with the work being done in other states and to receive suggestions from them for a similar purpose.[46] Eugene Funk constantly stressed cooperation.

Interest in the forthcoming Omaha Exposition increased. Problems relating to the Illinois State Corn Show also caused Funk some concern. He was apprehensive about limiting the exhibits exclusively to Illinois as too narrow and exclusive, "I am looking forward to the future when other states will say to Illinois: 'You barred us, we bar you.'" Funk interpreted this type of limitation as the elimination of the small corn breeder:

I am in favor of local, county, state and National Corn Shows having a class of some kind wherein the other fellow is invited to come and show his corn . . . it is by the possibilities of spreading out *as* it were, from local to county and from county to state fairs, from state to international that has brought out the live stock interests of this country and hundreds and thousands have their hopes built on the future that some day they too may reach the top. Thus we reach the masses.

The words of the Corn Exposition, *Betterment of Agriculture in its Broadest Interpretation,* according to Funk, suggested that they were looking for the most practical way to spread the gospel of corn improvement. He opposed excluding anyone. Limitations would place the president of the National Corn Association in a bad light before fellow corn breeders throughout the states if he advocated anything but at least one open class. After expressing himself he received notice that the executive committee by unanimous vote had decided upon opening the Pure Bred Corn Class to the world. Funk noted, "There must have been someone else stirring up the hornet's nest. However, I am sure this is the right thing to do in justice to everybody." [47]

Courage, determination and purpose enabled these men who formed the National Corn Association to adhere to their original idea. Their decision to change the location from Chicago resulted in the opening of the second and third Expositions in the western city of Omaha, Nebraska.

CHAPTER XIV

Omaha · 1908 and 1909

EUGENE D. FUNK constantly thought in terms of improved corn and greater yield. Corn, he said, was a great prosperity-preserving product. He believed that modern methods of corn breeding and corn culture could bring to every farmer an average increase of from 20 to 50 percent. Hundreds of progressive farmers had found this to be practical experience, not theory. Funk figured that to Illinois alone an increase of ten bushels an acre would mean an annual revenue of $50,000,000. He pointed to the man who did not obtain part of that increase as the one who would not learn at the Illinois Corn Show how to improve the yield of his farm. The National Corn Exposition also could become the medium for learning about modern methods, more careful study of details, corn breeding, cultivation and rotation of crops. New thoughts and modern ideas would go home with the visitor.[1]

A Union Pacific folder, *The Automatic Flagman,* announced the National Corn Exposition would be held in Omaha in 1908. Besides the regular corn exhibits there would also be small grains and grasses. According to this folder the purpose of the management was to provide a clearing place for the progressive ideas of well-directed and intelligent labor with the best products of the season's harvest. There were to be six thousand individual exhibits. A miniature corn palace with a moving picture exhibit in continuous operation could be found at the west end of the large auditorium located in the center of the city between the wholesale and retail establishments. While "Corn is King" at this Exposition, "Alfalfa is undoubtedly Queen of the West" and would also have a palace of her own. Omaha was known as "The Market Town" because almost everything was bought and sold within its limits. During the preceding year, while Omaha sold $88,048,000 worth of merchandise it furnished a market for 1,158,716 head of cattle, 2,253,562 hogs and 2,038,777 head of sheep, besides handling through the elevators and buying on the cash grain market 42,538,800 bushels of grain from western fields.[2]

Funk continued his efforts to bring the central purpose of the Na-

171

tional Corn Association to his friends. He explained to Professor W. H. Olin of Fort Collins, Colorado State College:

You understand the word "Corn" included the English term of all grains and grasses. There is an opening and opportunity for an organization throughout the agricultural world of this country, that if properly and honestly conducted, would in time be the strongest and most uesful to our people of anything yet attempted.

Funk also warned that the same agricultural problems of the East would soon arise in the West unless "we take time by the forelock and begin to systemize in order to retain the good things and yet enjoy the luxuries." [3] The National Corn Association would help to attain this goal.

He wrote to Jones, who had inquired about taking motion pictures on the Funk Farms: "In regard to the moving pictures, think next Tuesday or Wednesday will be all right. You can get at least three if the weather is good: (1) working on the corn (hand pollinization), (2) a steam threshing outfit, (3) a steam hay baling outfit. We can discuss the divisions of the state into zones when you are here . . . you know, the fast trains do not stop at Shirley and we would have to get an auto or carriage at Bloomington." [4]

The Funk exhibit had not been decided upon. Funk himself thought it wise to keep before the public and was willing to use the same Holland windmill that was used at Chicago. However, a majority of the directors of Funk Bros. Seed Co. decided against an exhibit for the Omaha Exposition and opposed entry for any of the premiums as a company. They decided against participation because E. D. Funk was connected with both the Corn Association and the company. There might be comments, "As we have learned the same was done last year, although our experience at the Corn Show cost us $1,300 and neither personally or as a company did we receive 'thank you' from the Chicago end of it." [5]

The directors of the Postum Company of Battle Creek, Michigan among others authorized a display at the Exposition. They requested a space 10 by 20 at the cost of $200 to show "our process indicating the kind of wheat, barley and corn in use in our products and demonstrate our goods." [6]

Modest as usual, Funk thanked Dewitt C. Wing, Associate Editor of the *Breeders' Gazette* for an article on behalf of the National Corn Exposition in that publication: "I have only one comment to make and that is you gave the writer more credit than he deserves. . . . A successful National Corn Exposition is only the beginning from which to select the material to build the future prosperity and education of our coming generations in the agricultural lines." [7]

The Omaha Exposition proved to be a success. Funk presented a bill of $190.65, explaining: "Now that such a thing has happened and as I have gladly given many days and weeks of my time and thought during the last year, to say nothing of the past ten years, I will for the first time present a bill of expense, or rather railroad and hotel expenses." [8]

The National Corn Exposition was described as the first great national agricultural show ever held in a country more dependent on agriculture than on any other industry. Four great movements influenced governors, county and state agricultural societies, railroads and businessmen to participate: (1) The "short courses" of agricultural colleges begun in Wisconsin and Iowa in 1899; (2) local Agricultural Experiment Stations on county poor farms, begun in Iowa in 1903: (3) "Seed Corn Specials," flag-stop educational service started in 1904 by P. G. Holden. During 1904–5–6, these trains traveled 11,000 miles, enabling more than 150,000 people to hear 1,265 lectures at 789 stops; (4) short courses held in towns. [9] Seed trains carrying wheat, oats and other grains were organized in other states. C. P. Bull carried this out in Minnesota about 1904. [10] Competition for international markets and land values increased in the Corn Belt year by year. It was necessary for leadership to become vocal.

Members of President Roosevelt's Commission on Country Life, [11] organized to recommend remedial legislation, also cooperated with the managers of the Exposition in Omaha in 1908 by scheduling a series of conferences in Omaha at this time for the purpose of gathering data and information. A report was to be made to its president. [12] Governor's Day was scheduled for December 9th, and Agricultural College Day on December 11th. W. M. Hays, Assistant Secretary of Agriculture; H. M. Collingwood, Editor of *Rural New Yorker;* W. J. Bryan; E. S. Conway of Chicago; Lic Lwis Gorozpe, Mexico; T. R. Garton, Warrington, England; Samuel H. Smith, Chicago Board of Trade, and various Governors were scheduled to speak. Bands gave concerts. There were women's exhibits, and domestic science departments and model kitchens were included. Foreign countries making exhibits included Mexico, England, Canada, Hawaii and Argentina. Zeferino Dominguez of Mexico arranged the Mexican exhibit. The Mexican Government offered a solid silver trophy costing $1,500. A. D. Shamel of the Bureau of Plant Breeding in the United States Department of Agriculture was in charge of judging. [13] The first Omaha Exposition was successful enough to encourage the promoters to plan for another Exposition in 1909.

The report of the Second Annual Exposition but the first held in Omaha summarized the activity as follows:

Attendance 105,661; grain and grasses exhibits, 7,773; farm implement exhibits, 441; ears of corn sold at auction, 43,000; amount distributed in premiums, $54,000; 14 agricultural colleges represented.

Foreign countries with visiting delegations included Mexico, Canada, Hungary, England, China, Cuba, Philippine Islands, and Germany.[14]

During the first four months of 1909 problems relating to the administration and organization of the second Exposition were discussed in correspondence between Funk with C. C. Rosewater, J. W. Jones, T. F. Sturgess, W. O. Paisley, R. A. Moore and G. I. Christie. Experience gained during the first two Expositions proved to be a wise teacher. The major difficulty was to determine the proper relationship between the civic interests whose financial backing was essential and the agricultural educational interests. These difficulties often found reflection in the efforts of the general manager to direct activities. Consequently questions of policy and those rising from personality were constantly brought to the attention of the president of the National Corn Association, E. D. Funk.

Funk's ideas in January 1909 included special entertainment for the city crowds in the evenings and a well-conducted restaurant. From the agricultural viewpoint he regretted that the corn at the last Exposition was placed up in the gallery. He recommended many changes in enforcement of rules and regulations. He added:

As to the administrative part of the exposition I feel that it would be wise to divide it into two parts: One to be known as the Agricultural interests; and the other the Omaha or Exposition interest. As a matter of fact it is that way now but let it be understood more clearly. One cannot well exist without the support of the other; therefore each should be on equal terms with the other in the general arrangements, but the details should be looked after by separate departments and not allowed to conflict with each other."[15]

J. W. Jones decided to give up his position as general manager to attend to his own interests in Idaho.[16] Differences of opinion arose in connection with the responsibilities of Sturgess. Funk took hold of the situation in February, asking that the Rosewater-Sturgess interests and any others attend a meeting at the Great Northern Hotel in Chicago.[17] A copy of a letter found its way to Funk, asking that copies of all National Corn Exposition correspondence be sent to Sturgess.[18] Office personnel was confused as to the source of direction. Neither Rosewater nor Sturgess attended the meeting, as the result of some misunderstanding. Information, however, was received concerning the proposed raising of $40,000 by Omaha interests as a guarantee fund to bring the 1909 Exposition again to that city.[19]

Messrs. Sturgess, Paisley and George Stevenson outlined the 1909 campaign. Last year's direction centered around Mr. Jones. During 1909, according to Sturgess, "With our present arrangement, in determining our policy and general plan of action from an agricultural standpoint, it will be put up to you for approval." Questions for immediate decision in March included: (1) Amount of money to be used for educational promotional work and its apportionment. Some states spent their apportionment long before the Exposition and then asked for additional money or their exhibit would not be made. It was, therefore, suggested that since their exhibits came from the agricultural colleges and experimental stations they should be prepared ready for shipment and installation by the colleges. The management of the Exposition should only pay for the transportation, installation and care of exhibits; (2) Mr. Stevenson, as assistant secretary of the National Corn Association, should visit each of the state experiment stations, consult with the vice presidents and point out the campaign for each state. Each state should emphasize some special feature of its own work; (3) In going over the junior work, Mr. Hildebrand was to work out the list of premiums for juniors and visit county institutions to work in their interests.[20] Funk approved, in general, the above ideas, but suggested that Stevenson estimate amounts for each state. After talking with them, he also urged that Stevenson search for some plan whereby the National Corn Association could become self-sustaining.[21]

The Nebraska Press Association endorsed the Association and the Exposition. Local editors estimated that if the National Corn Exposition could be the means of raising the average yield of corn per acre by five bushels, twenty million dollars could be added to the wealth of the Nebraska farmer. A resolution of the press association recommended the permanent establishment of a Corn Exposition of a national and educational nature in the West. If neighboring press associations would take a similar attitude, the future of the National Corn Exposition and of increased yields would be assured.[22]

A letter written by Funk to Professor Moore at the University of Wisconsin at Madison carried these same thoughts. No general manager was appointed after Jones' resignation. Funk told Moore that there was at one time an attempt made to crystallize the whole affair under the management of certain interests "which eventually would have been used for political purposes entirely for Omaha." He continued: "I got onto this during a show last fall and foresaw the situation would develop and did develop up to a certain point a few weeks ago." [23] He felt that Jones was an able person but because of some deficiencies in qualities of management he gave his critics their opportunity. Sturgess and Jones could not agree. With Jones' resignation Sturgess might have become manager, but he was unknown in agricultural circles. A new difficulty arose with the scheduling of a State Corn Show in Des Moines, Iowa at the time of the National Exposition. They asked the National Corn Association to change dates. Funk told the Iowa people they were expected to make a showing atOmaha in order to determine which faction in Iowa was cooperating.[24]

Funk's comment to Jones regarding payment for expenses included this statement: "Have not received any payment for my expenses last year. I did not receive one cent for my time at the Chicago Exposition, not even 'thanks' (they did pay my railroad fare to Chicago twice, I think, during the summer). I paid all my expenses to Springfield in the interest of the State Corn Exposition, so up to this time I don't feel under obligations to anyone and I hope to remain free to say as my judgment dictates." [25]

Funk was again concerned about the Illinois Corn Show. He described the show held the previous year at Springfield as the best he had ever attended. It cost the people of Springfield nearly $14,000. It was for the benefit of the farmers, but the farmers did not attend in numbers. He was of the opinion that the people of Springfield would not respond again when the farmers themselves took so little interest.[26]

Inquiries from the New England states, information that Missouri, Oklahoma and Arkansas would be represented, and a letter from Mexico saying that 100 Mexican landowners were planning to attend the next Omaha Exposition were encouraging. The Mexican, Señor Dominguez, was responsible.[27]

As he traveled about the United States, Funk concluded that a movement among the agricultural classes was necessary. He believed the movement was, in a measure, being forced upon farmers "through the strife for higher education and competition, coupled on to the fact that the demand from the farmers' resources are growing greater, greater and greater with a depleting soil." He added:

I care not so much about the Corn Show as an exhibition in itself as I do to use it as a means whereby we can put the greater numbers to thinking, both about themselves and future generations to come.

He continued to emphasize his belief that the nation was at its highest point of prosperity derived mainly from the resources of the soil, "a great National Bank, if you please." With no return at the present rate of drawing on the deposit, he asked, "What will become of the future generations that are to follow?" [28]

Reference was made to an *Omaha Bee* article in the May 11, 1909 edition. This article reportedly referred to an attempt to change the name of the Exposition and stated that the National Corn Association was trying to assume that the Exposition was theirs, and theirs alone. Funk feared the wrong impression despite the fact that those concerned with the problem knew the charge was ridiculous. He thought there had been enough "house top explosions" last year. Neither did he approve of efforts to belittle the importance of the Omaha leadership. He cared little who received the glory and was aware that some sections:

especially the North and West, were anxious that the name be changed, and in order to keep them in line, and not let them think we were throwing cold water in their face, it became necessary to have the words "grains and grasses" . . . I am writing at length because I do not wish to be misunderstood or misrepresented. I have had reasons for thinking that unless we are careful, narrow and perhaps selfish, interests might attempt to drive a wedge between the Omaha and agricultural interests. . . . You may show this letter (confidentially) to Mr. Rosewater. This letter was accompanied by one to Stevenson carrying the general idea that Omaha interests were bound to assume responsibility since they were financing the Exposition. Funk said "Let Omaha call it 'ours'—and let the agricultural interest do likewise." [29]

He drew upon the example of Springfield, Illinois, which failed to bring the agricultural interests into the planning and operation.

Mindful that years bring changes, Funk was of the opinion that eventually Omaha would give up the show:

I speak in this way from experience and I am taking this stand from history of the Old Mechanical Exposition on the Lake Front in Chicago, later on, the Fat Cattle Show, and now the International Life Stock Exposition. All of which my father had had more or less to do from weighmaster to ring-master and from director to president for the last thirty years. Chicago got tired of each one of these during the course of time and it was only the bulldog tenacity of a few live stock men of the country that held the interests together. [30]

Finally after considerable correspondence regarding the Iowa situation, it developed that expenses for the Iowa display at the last Exposition had been shouldered by individual professors. Professor Holden, now in charge of extension work, said that his busy schedule kept him from attending the meetings of the vice presidents of the Corn Association. The *Omaha Bee* in an article June 20, 1909 stated that as a result of a conference between officers of Iowa State College and the executive committee of the National Corn Association. The exhibit at Des Moines was to be brought to the Omaha Show. By June 20, 1909 harmony seemed to have been established.[31] Apparently Funk had scored again in his handling of this matter, sending Stevenson directly to see Professor Curtiss.

By June 25, 1909 Funk recognized that the Corn Association was growing rapidly. At this time he felt that the next vital question was whether to continue the old conservative lines or to allow outside influence to creep in and finally ask for recognition.[32] Favorable reports were coming in. One called attention to the fact that there was less "splurge and splutter" this year. As Funk said, the splurge and splutter had little importance in final results, but "working hard and sticking close to it, tells the story." [33]

A large $1,000 trophy was offered by the W. K. Kellogg Company of Battle Creek, Michigan to be known as the National Corn Trophy for the best single ear of corn. Mr. Kellogg also gave newspaper advertising costing him $75,000.[34] The various states were encouraged to relate their exhibits to those lines especially adapted to their own localities.[35]

The situation was well in hand by July. Funk wrote to Directors R. A. Moore and G. I. Christie that difficulties seemed to be fading in both Iowa and Oklahoma; that the agricultural interests were holding their own with Omaha and possibly with outside interests. This success was in no little degree due to the fact that wise leadership was exhibited by Funk himself. He was responsible for no reply by Omaha papers to articles in Iowa newspapers.[36] Funk wrote Director C. P. Bull that harmony prevailed all along the line. Sturgess was designated as the general manager without any formal appointment.[37]

The trip made by Sturgess to see Professor Bull, Campbell, J. J. Hill, L. W. Hill and Mr. Bass of the Great Northern Railroad in Minnesota during late July produced results. The conference brought an agreement by J. J. Hill to give $2,500 in gold and in supplemental premiums in the territory covered by the Great Northern Railroad. Mr. Hill also agreed to speak. The Great Northern Railroad was to be responsible for an exhibit costing $5,000 or to be shown adjacent to the small grain sections with the company paying $800 for the space. Furthermore, the company agreed to carry all exhibits free along its lines to the Exposition. Sturgess and Bull made plans to make the small grain section of the Exposition one of its leading features. Hill's cash premium offer and exhibition of products along the line of the Great Northern were offered with the understanding that they appear in conjunction with the small grain competitive exhibits. Some of the important features of the grain section were the milling test, showing of the bleaching process, market inspection and grading of grain, as well as the manufacturing of cereal food products. Calls were also made on the Washburn, Crosby and Pillsbury people. The millers were willing to cooperate. Mr. Sturgess proceeded through Montana and Washington. Here he found that Mr. Hill had sent advance word urging cooperation with the Exposition.[38] Space was held for displays from California and Mexico.

Information from Sturgess to W. O. Paisley, assistant general manager also sent on to President Funk, suggested the use of moving picture materials from the United States Agricultural Department. He was working about one week to ten days ahead of the agent for the Chicago Exposition. Contacts with Secretary Wilson proved advantageous in this respect. The Interior Department was also contacted through Secretary Ballinger.[39] Covered glass pictures and moving pictures were both instructive and interesting. C. P. Bull, responsible for obtaining Hill and Shaw to speak, felt that Sturgess saw the necessity for the agricultural interests to be thoroughly represented in the Exposition. Bull took over supervision of the small grains division, urging the University of Minnesota to send an exhibit. Bull corresponded directly with Funk in order not to "cross any wires." [40]

Professor C. P. Bull was appointed to obtain an exhibit showing the home economics of wheat. Leaves of absence from their positions at the University of Minnesota were granted to him and to his assistant, Miss Inez Hobart. The milling interests of the Twin Cities became interested. Baking and gluten tests were among the demonstrations. This was a forward step in showing differences in the quality of grain. The content of gluten was as important in those days as that of protein in later years. James J. Hill became so interested in the show that he personally wished to add blue and white ribbons to all prizes won by grades of wheat. The board of directors decided this was a too highly personalized designation of merit.[41] Their efforts were bent toward making the Association one of general cooperation.

Funk decided to send tickets for the Exposition to J. J. Hill, his son, and a Mr. Bass, writing each a personal letter.[42] He wished to prove to J. J. Hill that there was more back of the movement than merely the Omaha interests. Funk believed that Hill joined forces with the Corn Association because he saw possibilities in the organization for Hill. The fact that Hill confined the granting of his $2,500 premiums to within fifty miles of his railroad reinforced Funk's interpretation.[43] He thought Hill missed the word *National* in the title. President Funk was of the opinion that this method insisted upon by Hill made the premiums of importance only to the "Hill Syndicate." [44] Stevenson called attention to the fact that trophies should be given in the name of the National Corn Exposition since the latter was a purely local organizational title. The Kansas Wheat Trophy and the Colorado Oat Trophy and the Wisconsin Barley Trophy were in the process of completion. Governors were appointing state commissions to cooperate with efforts to send displays to the Exposition.[45] Sturgess attended the Trans-Mississippi Congress in an effort to secure good men for the program.[46] Funk was greatly encouraged by the reports from Messrs. Sturgess, Bull, and Moore. He returned from Chicago in August after a visit with leading businessmen. All of them expressed the opinion that an agricultural exposition of this sort was one of the finest things that had been projected, fully equal to the International Livestock Exposition.[47] There were indications that at least twenty six states would participate and that the railroads would provide cars for carrying the exhibits free to Omaha.[48]

E. G. Montgomery enclosed a clipping on the National Farm Land Congress which he feared was "in a way covering the work we have been proposing for the National Corn Association." [49] Difficulties were apparent by October. Funk was of the opinion that Mr. Paisley was ignoring the N. C. A. and that their meetings might also conflict with those of the American Breeders Association.[50] This difficulty was solved by an adjustment in programs.

Funk thought the so-called National Farm Land Congress under the auspices of the Hearst interests indicated a pure and simple political move and might have resulted from one of his own conversations with a confidential friend of Hearst. He also thought that Hearst was looking for some popular movement to square himself with the farmer. On the other hand Hearst might also be one of those who recognized the possibilities and necessities for such a movement at this time. He also believed that the Hearst interests would be interpreted as political and therefore could not hurt anything that would be done in Omaha. Hearst might help along the cause.[51]

The *World Herald* of Omaha set the tone of emphasis and significance in an article entitled "Big Men, Big Show, of the Great Big West," appearing in the Sunday edition November 26, 1909. It pointed to the fact that upwards of 100,000,000 more bushels of corn were expected in production in 1909 than in 1908, with increases in wheat and oats also predicted. The article continued:

Here then lies the fundamental wealth of the nation, the royal household of agriculture, with Corn as King and wheat, oats, barley, rye and hay as members of his court. Stack the enormous wealth producing capacity of this royal family up against the comparatively puny output of gold and silver, the annual totals of any individual line of manufacture, anything you choose, and it will easily display itself as the biggest thing in America, bigger than Niagara Falls, Joe Cannon, New York City, President Taft, the Tariff, or the Standard Oil Trust Capitalized at 6 percent, the forces responsible for the enormous output, represent an investment equivalent to sixty billions of dollars in trade.[52]

The purposes of the Corn Exposition were described as (1) to increase output, (2) to elevate the general standard of the farm; a big show backed by big men, production of big things, specialized yet comprehensive.

The names of James J. Hill and his son, Louis W., were listed first among those prominently connected with the Corn "Show," with James J. Hill described as one generously donating to the premium list and addressing the Exposition. The American Breeders' Association, Society of Agronomists, Missouri River Navigation Congress and the Midwest Retailers' Association were scheduled to hold annual meetings during the corn Exposition.

Exhibits from Departments of the United States Government shown at the Alaska-Yukon-Pacific Exposition were brought to Omaha. James Wilson, president of the American Breeders Association and Secretary of Agriculture was an enthusiastic supporter. Willet M. Hays, Assistant Secretary of Agriculture, spoke to the farmers. Gifford Pinchot, Chief Forester of the Department of Interior, was also on the program. The Mexican Government took a more active part than in 1908, sending Zeferino Dominguez with 100 Mexican farmers. This delegation appeared with the hearty approval of President Diaz. The Mexican National Band played during the two weeks of the Exposition.[53]

Those directly and intimately connected with production of corn included E. D. Funk of Shirley, Illinois described "as one of the most noted, progressive and model farmers of the country"; and Professor

P. G. Holden, the "Seed Corn Evangelist." [54] Local Omaha business-men were also included. The Funks were represented as wishing to put agriculture on a proper basis, especially since they held 25,000 acres valued at $150 per acre. Land, they believed, must earn a reasonable percent.

Advertising and publicity were given the Exposition by the railroads, by the Kellogg Company and by newspapers. The Western Newspaper Union supplied its subscribers, 4,500 county newspapers, with an article each week for thirteen weeks. Illustrated stories were printed by big metropolitan newspapers from New York to Portland, Oregon. The Hearst Newspaper Syndicate contracted for four special feature articles sent to hundreds of papers. Additional city, county, daily and weekly publications were on the mailing list.[55] The complete program was varied and interesting.[56]

E. D. Funk recorded in his *Diary* that Professor S. Scribner of the United States Department of Agriculture said it was the best and first Exposition he had ever seen open on time and complete.[57] President Funk, however, believed that insufficient credit was given to agricultural interests on the opening day. Omaha seemed to him to be taking all the credit.[58] Twenty-five State Agricultural College and Experimental Stations finally presented displays.[59] One account states that twenty two Departments of Agriculture were represented with seven more included in Railroad displays. This total was an increase over twelve exhibits for 1908.[60]

The National Corn Association became a corporation during the Second Omaha Exposition in 1909. Eugene D. Funk also became president of the corporation. The articles of incorporation provided that business could be carried on in any state or territory. The capital stock of $150,000 was divided into 600 shares of $25 each. The purposes of the Association were to improve and encourage agricultural methods; to hold and to assist other organizations in holding fairs or exhibitions of products of the soil and other items pertaining to agriculture; to collect facts and other matter that may be of interest and to cause the same to be published; to hold national and other farmers' conventions.[61] Fearing that other interests might assume the name of the organization, all haste was made to gain incorporation May 3, 1910. A telephone call was put through to Pugsley, who in turn called the Secretary of State in Nebraska who arranged for the filing of the papers on a Saturday.[62]

The address of J. J. Hill, delivered on December 9th, caught the attention of many. Some thought that the promoter of the Great

Northern Railroad was more interested in the expansion program of his railroad and with grains and grasses along its route than with the national emphasis upon corn. Few doubted that he saw with his usual drive and vision the significance of such an association. With his typical enthusiasm he placed his stamp of approval upon the activity. He spoke twice. In an address to the Commercial Club he talked about "Political Economy, Social Science and Civil Government." [63]

In his speech before the Exposition December 9, 1909, Hill spoke first of corn and its probable increase in amount. He believed that exports had fallen because demand as well as production had increased at home. After speaking of production in the corn-producing states, he turned to the problem of the world's food supply. Hill was definitely of the opinion that this country could not feed the population which it would have within a few years if it did not change its agricultural methods. He pleaded for reclamation and conservation. Hill also thought that the production of wheat was not keeping up with increase in population and consumption per capita. He then pointed to falling agricultural exports for a period of thirty years. [64]

This Second Exposition held at Omaha early in December 1909 was considered successful by its president, Eugene Funk. He wrote Professor Davenport about their "movement that has been so successfully undertaken towards agricultural education in a national and we might add international way." Fifteen states were represented with their exhibits from agricultural colleges. [65]

When E. D. Funk returned home from Omaha, William Jennings Bryan was on the train. He was highly complimentary to the president of the Association but did not realize Funk was from Illinois. In the course of the conversation, Mr. Bryan proceeded to explain to this veteran corn-breeder how to develop corn having high and low oil and protein. Funk let him tell his story. The next morning Mr. Bryan asked to hear more, finally realizing that Funk could inform him about the subject. [66]

Samples of American grain and hundreds of pictures from the show were sent back to Russia by Julius Rosen, a government representative from the Czar, who came to Omaha to see how they grew corn out in the real corn country. [67]

The illness of LaFayette Funk, Sr. came as a surprise to Eugene, Sr. on December 10th in Omaha. Mrs. Eugene Funk arrived on the eleventh as did the sad news of the tragic death of Isaac Funk, II. Mr. and Mrs. Eugene D. Funk, Sr. arrived in Bloomington a few days later. [68]

The Fourth National Corn Exposition was held in Columbus, Ohio. During the year 1910 arrangements were under discussion between the general manager, George H. Stevenson, and the president of the National Corn Association, Eugene D. Funk. The selection of Columbus as the site was a difficult choice.

Worried because of his father's slight paralytic stroke in January, 1910 and unwilling to borrow more money to aid Stevenson in Columbus, E. D. Funk was hoping that plans would crystallize by some other methods.[69] Campbell, who had aided with the Second Omaha Exposition, became an employee of the Great Northern Railroad. Minnesota expected to have its own Conservation Congress and efforts were made to select Mr. Campbell as publicity man. This might have given the Hill interests control within the state.[70] C. P. Bull recalled the experiences of difficulty between agricultural and commercial interests at Omaha. Funk revealed to his friend, C. P. Bull, that Omaha interests wished to have the Exposition return another year; Cincinnati and Indianapolis were also interested. He also understood through Campbell that J. J. Hill was anxious to have the meetings in St. Paul. Funk added:

I know your position in this matter and it is unnecessary to discuss it from our standpoint, that the National Corn Association, would be a thing of the past & should not connect up with this sort of a combination.[71]

Bull answered that he tried to discourage the choice of St. Paul until later.[72]

After one exposition in Chicago and two in Omaha several alternatives were possible; to remain in Omaha, to move east or south or to choose a northern location. An entirely different type of program was eventually followed when Columbus, Ohio was selected for the fourth exposition.

CHAPTER XV

Columbus, Columbia and Dallas

EXPERIENCES at Omaha influenced plans for the fourth Exposition at Columbus, Ohio. The Corn Association assumed the entire financial obligation of the Exposition. Heretofore the cities had guaranteed a fund, thereby assisting and controlling certain phases of the management. In addition to money obtained through stock subscriptions, a promotional fund was also established.[1] President Funk emphasized in his March 1910 letter to the directors of the Association the cooperative spirit of the last three years and gave credit to Secretary Stevenson. He called a meeting at Columbus April 29th and 30th.[2]

Some criticism meanwhile arose because of delays in paying for prizes won at the second Exposition held in Omaha.[3] Some dissension in the Indiana ranks was finally smoothed over after Funk explained some of the problems inherent in management devolving upon Stevenson at Omaha. In the course of the explanation he described the situation at Columbus. He believed the cities of Indianapolis and Cincinnati would not be suitable places to hold an Exposition at that time. People in Toledo would offer a guarantee fund. Stevenson visited there but was informed of their hesitation because of a telegram from Omaha describing the leaders of the Association as "poor company" to be avoided.

Louisville, Kentucky offered $30,000 but the idea was to place Louisville in much the same position as Omaha so they decided to return to Columbus. The president and secretary of the Columbus Commercial Club, however, refused to allow a hearing before their board. Nevertheless influential men in the city and state became interested. State Fair buildings were made available free of charge, thus saving about $40,000. The Governor of Ohio was interested as well as the corn farmers, together with the State horticulture secretary and agricultural and livestock groups. Funk noted that the Association assumed the financial responsibility only insofar as funds allowed; if they went broke they lost only that which each stockholder subscribed, because the stock of the Association was paid up and non-

185

assessable. Those who subscribed the guarantee fund ran the risk of losing. If there were any surplus the amount was to be divided equally between the Association and the subscribed guarantee fund.[4] Manufacturers were lukewarm on allowing premiums, saying that often they were sold at half price. Funk also noted that Stevenson was making a personal and financial sacrifice, working for the Association only for actual living expenses and clothes besides personally subscribing $1,000 to the guarantee fund with $800 already paid.[5]

W. M. Hays, Assistant Secretary of Agriculture, manifested interest in the forthcoming meeting at Columbus. He stated that it was possible that plans could be made under which the American Breeders' Association and the National Corn Association could cooperate. He was also interested in the idea earlier discussed with Funk to make the N. C. A. a national agricultural association.[6] Funk was hopeful that Nebraska and Indiana could continue to participate at Columbus. He believed that the Easterners were now delighted to think that Westerners, Southerners and Northerners were willing to meet on a common ground. Remembering his college days in New England, Funk believed that with agricultural education as the main feature at Columbus, they would in fact have formed a National Agricultural Association that would work from ocean to ocean and from lakes to gulf.[7]

Funk wrote that Stevenson, Stull and he, himself, were practically financing the Columbus Exposition outside of the 43 shares of stock sold. Stevenson had put in more time and money than anyone else and would be paid for his time and work.[8]

The Agricultural advertising representative from the *Kansas City Star* became interested in the Exposition. W. E. Richardson of Lord and Thomas, Chicago, who handled about all of the agricultural advertisements for his company, promised to see that every agricultural paper in the land as well as many local papers supported the movement. Although he told the men that there was no money available for advertising, he believed that if Lord and Thomas "waked up," all other agencies in the country would have to follow.[9] Fred McCulloch who knew both the Ames and Des Moines, Iowa groups was ready to work for an exhibit at Columbus.[10] Even on Christmas Day, 1910, problems relating to borrowing money in order to open the Exposition were apparent in Funk's thinking.[11]

The *Prairie Farmer* urged all to get their corn exhibits ready to attend this valuable affair designed purely on educational principles for the Betterment of Agriculture. All grains were to be exhibited.[12]

Advertisement and advance notices of the Corn Exposition held at Columbus, Ohio in 1911 took the usual form of a picture of the "Corn Girl" in Indian costume. The caption under the picture read:

Old King Corn that wealth-producing old Soul, will be formally crowned, sceptered and enthroned soon. The time will be the first two weeks of February and the place will be Columbus, Ohio. His virtues in the field, in the ear, in the shock, on the cob, in the can, in the mouth, in the form of meat and in myriad other forms will be sung, chanted and printed during the coming National Corn Exposition.[13]

Among the attractions listed on the program were lectures and demonstrations in "Homemaking." [14] Recognition of one hundred boys from the South, who raised the best corn crop during the preceding year, was an interesting emphasis at this time. They were to have the opportunity to exhibit ten ears each at the National Corn Exposition, January 30th to February 11th, 1911. Forty-six thousand boys belonged to corn clubs in the southern states. The Southern Commercial Congress, cooperating with the United States Department of Agriculture, paid for the transportation of exhibits of 100 most successful boy corn raisers to the Exposition grounds.[15] Recognition of the South brought a suggestion before the Columbus meeting from President Finley of the Southern Railway that Columbia, South Carolina would be the best location for the following year.[16]

More than thirty-five states were expected to send exhibits to Columbus. Twenty-five state agricultural colleges and experiment stations were to present scientific exhibits. North Carolina was to emphasize the cotton industry and its soil work. The Federal Department of Agriculture brought its famous exhibit in two large furniture cars. This exhibit had recently returned from an international exposition at Buenos Aires.[17]

The program included speeches by the Governor of Ohio, the Mayor of Columbus, President Funk and General Manager George H. Stevenson on the opening day, January 30th. January 31st was National Live Stock Day; February 1st, American Breeders Association Day, in charge of American Breeders Association; February 2nd, National Dairy Day; February 3rd, National Corn Day, with speakers, P. G. Holden, Iowa; C. S. Williams, Ohio; W. J. Spillmore, U. S. Department of Agriculture, with the National Corn Banquet in the evening; February 6th, address by Governor Penneville of Delaware, "The Farmer is a Statesman"; February 7th, opening of National Life Conference, speaker, Dr. L. H. Bailey, dean and director of the New York Agricultural College of Cornell University and ex-chairman of the Roosevelt Country Life Commission. The winter two-ring circus, band concerts and moving pictures provided by the Government were among special entertainment features.[18]

Funk's pre-Exposition statement was as follows:

We are bringing this national agricultural Exposition to the state of Ohio not with an idea of exploitation or the booming of some foreign lands but to present the latest practical demonstrations of agricultural research.

The formal opening of the Columbus Exposition was attended by a salute of twenty-one guns, supplemented by the playing of the national airs on the Trinity Church chimes. President Taft was expected to deliver an address on the closing day.[19]

An article by Frederick Haskin about this National Corn Exposition summarized the preliminary advertisements and information by stating:

This Exposition is the fourth annual event of its kind in America, but it is the first exhibit that has been financed and managed by the corn growers themselves. Heretofore the cities in which the shows have been held have assumed the responsibility. Now the growers with the co-operation of the American Breeders Association are aroused to the advantage of creating a national interest in bettering the quality and yield per acre of America's greatest crop.[20]

Haskin noted that the corn crops for the year ending December 1910 were valued at more than one and a half billion dollars on the farm; "a crop which aggregated more than three billion, one hundred million bushels, or nearly four and a half times as many bushels as the yearly output of wheat." Three days of the Exposition were to be devoted to sessions of the American Breeders Association. Scientists, according to Haskin, estimated that through the breeders' art, 10 percent may be added annually to value of plant products, "This would mean an increase of more than $150,000,000 in our annual corn crop alone." The work of W. M. Hays, Assistant Secretary of the Department of Agriculture, was pointed to when he was at the agricultural station in Minnesota. After estimating the wealth that an increased corn crop would mean to the farmers, he called attention to:

One of the leading figures at the Columbus Exposition will be Eugene Funk, President of the Exposition and the largest individual scientific grower in the world. Mr. Funk is the head of a famous family of corn growers and breeders whose holdings comprise more than 25,000 acres in Illinois, 9,000 of which are devoted to the cultivation of corn. He and his brothers have been interested for years in the work of propogating a hardier and fuller grained ear of corn. What he will have to say at the Exposition will be followed with the keenest interest by his associate corn growers.[21]

On all sides of the main building, booths 14 x 25 feet and in some instances larger ones, were allotted to the several colleges. The inner walls of each booth were covered with a deep wine-colored cotton cloth forming a rich background. Twelve feet in front of each booth, elevated ten feet from the floor, was a continuous mural painting depicting the agriculture of each state. Charts, pictures and crops illustrated the work of each college. Illinois presented a series of tubes filled with corn oil, showing the gradual gain in per cent oil which a strain of corn made under selection. The gain in starch content was shown by a similar device. Advantage of using phosphate rock on Illinois soils was also shown.[22]

President Taft arrived in Columbus from Washington at 1:45 p. m. February 10, 1911. After a brief parade through the city he motored to the Fair Grounds where he spoke in the crowded auditorium which had a seating capacity of more than 4,000. He made a direct appeal to the American farmers on the issue of Canadian reciprocity, declaring that reciprocity with the Dominion would not injure the American farmer. It would be a benefit rather than a detriment to agricultural interests. The greatest argument, he continued, for its adoption was the fact that it would unite two kindred peoples living together across a wide continent, in a commercial and social union to the great advantage of both.[23] According to this account, Taft said: "Such a result does not need to be justified by a nice balancing of a pecuniary profit to each."

He declared that it could not hurt the corn producer, for "The American farmer is king and will remain so, reciprocity or no reciprocity." With reference to wheat he argued that the domestic price is governed by the world prices and that the sending of any part of Canada's surplus through the United States instead of through Canada to be milled or to be exported without milling would not perceptibly or materially affect the price; proximity to markets would continue to have advantage in price of farm lands. Three hundred members of the Ohio Corn Improvement Association immediately adopted resolutions condemning the proposed reduction.[24]

Later in the evening, the President attended a banquet given at Ohio State University by President Thompson and officials of the Exposition. He spoke briefly on the subject of phosphates and the status of the dispute between the United States and Germany over

American potash mine contracts. According to the newspaper account, he said:

Within the past few months I have directed the withdrawal of millions of acres of lands known to contain phosphates to prevent their acquisition by private capitals. The time will come when American farmers will need them. We have no power to forbid exportation or to charge a duty on exports, but if the government owns the resources it will be possible for the government as the lessor, to control the product.

He narrated the story of the American contracts for the product of phosphate mines in Germany and the difficulty the Department of State was having in negotiating the deals.[25]

In order to assume the obligations from the Columbus Exposition, a draft for five thousand dollars on note executed by E. D. Funk, G. W. Stevenson, C. P. Bull, E. G. Montgomery and C. W. Pugsley was obtained.[26] After closing the Exposition in Columbus, Stevenson, Funk, Bull, Pugsley and Young turned immediately to the problem of locating the fifth exposition.[27] Decision was not immediately forthcoming. Stevenson was negotiating with C. P. Bull, Stull and the J. J. Hill interests in Minneapolis during April.[28] One-fourth of the guarantee fund had been pledged there within a few days.[29] Secretary Stevenson felt that:

We had to allow receipts from Exposition to be applied on expense but we will be in position both Bull and I feel certain, to get cash here, to meet balance of deficit $500 note at Springfield, $1,000 note at Bloomington and something to Mr. Stull. Don't worry, we have been having a stormy time all right, but the sun has begun to shine again. We really ought to be used to storms by this time.[30]

Funk reported that Columbia, South Carolina was inquiring during the negotiations at Minneapolis to determine if a decision had been reached.[31] Apparently Funk was a little discouraged. He had written Mr. Stull that he agreed they could not continue to sacrifice both time and money; had better lose what they had put in rather than risk more.[32] Finally Stevenson and Bull came to the conclusion that Minneapolis was not the place because they would be subjected to delays.[33] He and Bull, therefore, telegraphed the people in Columbia, South Carolina, that Minnesota interests failed to make good their promises.[34] Stevenson asked Funk for $600 or $800 to settle up Columbus accounts.[35] Funk wrote Bull that if they did not hold another show to try to make up some of their loss, the total deficit would be about $12,000.[36] Mr. Stull, uncle of George Stevenson, agreed to advance another $1,000.[37] Pugsley sent a $500 note for signature and Bull was also asked to raise the same amount.[38] Fred McCulloch again complained because he did not receive his premium money from Columbus.[39] One of the directors inquired why the last note was for 8 percent when the others were at 6 percent. Funk wrote Pugsley:

So far as I am personally concerned I have arranged to take care of the $5,000 note at the State National Bank, Bloomington, Illinois and have so far paid $2,500 on the face of the note and interest. So I don't want you boys to be worrying about the amount. I will take care of it some how, and then if the Association can sometime pay me all right, and if not I'll charge it up to profit and loss and experience. One thing I will never feel ashamed for having lost that amount and more for the good of the cause. The only thing I regret is that we have not all of us more that we could stand to lose and be in a position to push the good work faster than we dare do at the present.

I some times feel that when one is trying his best to do what is right that there is some Almighty power somewhere that tends to guide his footsteps, and I can not help but believe that this same power whatever it is, is slowly but surely helping us to unravel some of our difficulties. It was a deep disappointment to me that we were unable to put on another Exposition this coming winter at Minneapolis and yet I am beginning to see now that even tho we should have gone there this year, unless it would have been under the most favorable circumstances, we would have been worse off than we now are. The more I think of it I am becoming convinced that our stamping ground should lie, for a few years, at least, in those sections where there are forces to take into consideration soil fertility and crop rotation and the more economical methods of agricultural pursuits rather than antagonize the land booming and railroad interests in the newer country. Sooner or later, parts will also be obliged to look our way but you know it is awfully hard to get even ten men out of a hundred to stop and think of the possibilities for tomorrow. My opinion is that nine-tenths of the people never consider over one year ahead, and a large majority of this number live entirely in the present and never consider the future at all. And as I believe the people down south are going to appreciate our efforts more than the Northern and Western people possibly could at this present time.[40]

Funk added that Will Young and he held a note for $500 which Young raised and they did not ask the other directors to sign. Funk was willing to sign a similar note with Pugsley if the latter would agree to take care of it in the same way that Funk was assuming responsibility for the $5,000 in Bloomington.[41] He added:

Then if each of you and Young and Bull would take care of $500 apiece. Stull the $3,000 that he has put in, including promotional fund, Stevenson with about $2,000 and I with $5,000 borrowed and $1,000 in promotional fund we will have about wiped out the Columbus indebtedness.[42]

Pugsley wished all transactions to be on the same basis and expressed the opinion that Funk was taking care of more than his share and that possibly Mr. Stull was doing the same.[43] He was willing to put in the $500 if others were responsible as outlined above.

C. P. Bull was in accord with Funk's ideas. He observed a $40,000 deficit at the Minnesota State Fair and with the next year in prospect a total of $75,000 in the hole. He was also of the opinion that an Exposition at Minneapolis-St. Paul would have failed if undertaken in opposition to "certain interests which are prone to boom western lands." He added: "If our bunch can survive the life of a few whom we might mention and one man particularly, who enjoys carrying people westward to sand areas, I feel sure that our cause will be a winner in the end." [44] He also speculated on the advantages of a circuit in the South and staying "relatively" in the eastern part of the Mississippi Valley for the next ten years or so.[45]

Funk was particularly hopeful that Secretary Stevenson would explain to those responsible in Columbia, South Carolina that it was financially impossible for the directors of the National Corn Association to assume responsibility for a Fifth Exposition. He added:

And since it has cost us years of experience and personal sacrifices of time besides money to obtain the universally good will and standing that we have with Agricultural Colleges and other agricultural organizations, we feel that we are entirely justified in offering this experience and influence to offset the financial backing for the Exposition at Columbia.[46]

Funk believed that those closely connected with the National Corn Association would work all the more if there were some indication that they might receive their money for previous years' expenditures, provided there would be a surplus after bills were paid for 1913. He suggested to Stevenson that the sum of $15,000 included money advanced, individual notes, a few unpaid bills, a few unpaid premiums and subscription stock.[47] Funk wrote:

You know about what these amounts are and in order to not have it appear that there was the usual cry of 'rake off' and 'graft' should there be any money to pay back with at the close of the Exposition. I would for my part much rather it be known now where we stand than later on.[48]

The president, Funk, urged incorporation with some sort of understanding and statement in the transaction of turning the subscription list over to the National Corn Exposition Company. This method would enable the business side of the operation to understand the purpose of the National Corn Association in operating for the "Betterment of Agriculture."

Bull, in Minnesota, observed: "Our greatest difficulty in promoting our cause is to get the people to think in the right channels. Once this is accomplished, we have no trouble. In our future work we should see to it that we make an educational propaganda first, then follow this with our business proposition." He also noted that land shows such as the one being held in Minnesota under the direction of W. A. Campbell, formerly of the *Omaha Bee* were now better understood by the people as Land Show schemes undertaken by promoters.[49]

Funk advised R. A. Moore that a $40,000 guarantee fund was raised at Columbia, South Carolina. If any net profit remained after expenses, the National Corn Association was to receive all left over to reimburse those who subscribed to the Columbus Exposition.[50] Funk told Pugsley that he was forced to mortgage his own farm in order to meet obligations.[51] He repeated Bull's warning that the "friends" who blocked the Exposition at Minneapolis might be operating in the South.

The Fifth Exposition was held at Columbia, South Carolina. The guarantee fund of $40,000 from South Carolina, including an appropriation of $10,000 from the legislature was attractive. Funk, together with three or four members of the board of directors, personally guaranteed the expense of the Exposition. Funk's part was nearly $7,000.[52]

An estimate of attendance at previous expositions included 1908, a total of 95,897; 1909, total of 118,503, and at Columbus 41,867. The lower number at Columbus was explained by the fact that attendance was almost entirely from agricultural communities without cooperative support from the Commercial Clubs and lack of publicity in Columbus. Funk stated: "We will never again accept an invitation to present our Exposition in any place, unless we can be absolutely assured of the co-operative spirit from the city, commercial clubs, press and railroads that go to inspire both the citizens and the rural population to the extent that they may be led to realize that the Exposition is put on for no other purpose than for their benefit and that it is worthy of their attendance."[53]

According to Funk's thinking, agriculture, "the foundation and vital organ of this country's welfare," was rapidly drifting toward vast areas of abandoned farms. Southern Illinois in "Egypt" was typical of his description. He concluded: "It is part of the business of the National Corn Association to disseminate scientific knowledge not only for the present generation but also to provide for the future, that those who follow us may live."[54]

The Columbia, South Carolina Exposition also fell short a few thousand dollars, but the amount was taken care of by Columbia groups, "who have said that they would have gladly met a much larger loss rather than not have had the Exposition." [55] The Columbia Exposition began January 27, 1913 with the following six feature days: South Carolina Day, National Live Stock Day, Farmers' Union Day, National Education Day and Boys' Day. One thousand winning Corn Club Boys were expected from all parts of the South.[56] The U. S. Department of Agriculture sent three carloads of exhibits representing every phase of its activities. This was described as the best and most comprehensive exhibit ever made by the United States Government.[57] Secretary of Agriculture James Wilson, and the Committee on Agriculture in the House of Representatives attended the Exposition on Boys' Day. This was the first time the committee as a whole had accepted an invitation to attend as follows:

The Committee will welcome this opportunity to view the National Corn Exposition as an institution dealing with the fundamental agricultural problems of the nation, and also the excellent opportunity to get in close touch with the more advanced work of various State institutions.[58]

One of the striking features was a painting extending entirely around the main hall. The canvas was nine feet wide and nearly a sixth of a mile in length. It was divided into more than fifty separate panels. Landscapes typical of the states whose exhibits stood below with other scenes were completed after two and one-half months' of work.[59] The mural decoration by E. T. Sprague was described as the longest painting of its kind in the world, larger even than the famous French painting, "The Battle of Gettysburg." The main building, known as the Steel Building, was compared in size to Madison Square Garden in New York and to the Coliseum in Chicago. This main building was erected for the Exposition.[60]

Among the speakers were Sir Horace Plunkett, noted leader of Irish agricultural reform, and Walter H. Page, editor of *World's Work.*[61] Twenty-seven states were expected to present displays.[62] All exhibits were housed under one roof.

E. D. Funk in his opening address explained how the Corn Shows began, referred to Mr. Fursman's leadership and the long years of activity. He emphasized the following:

We have nothing to sell and there is nobody here to tell you of a Utopian land where he wants you to go. Not a railroad or a land company is allowed an exhibit in this building to exploit any particular section of this country. Some people say 'Why not? They will bring in revenue.' Yes but we cannot risk anything which might overshadow or detract from the agricultural and educational features of the Exposition. What we are trying to show you is how to grow two blades of grass where only one grew before. All the exhibits are practical. They are not installed until they have been proven so.[63]

The *State*, local newspaper in Columbia, South Carolina declared that an Exposition which is fundamentally educational was unusual. A progressive Exposition idea had been developed where vital topics were handled in more than a mere array of exhibits. The idea was applied to a better rural citizenship.[64] Miss Mabel Carney, director of the Department of Rural Schools at Illinois State Normal University, delivered an address on "Making the Most of the One Teacher School." [65] Mr. Clark of the United States Department of Agriculture was so impressed with the educational features of the show that he thought it should be permanent and sent from city to city. He believed that the land shows have their place but that "This movement is particularly interesting to people after they have gotten to the farm and does not make any attempt to move the farmer to the city or to any other section of the country . . . But if you can reach no more than 500 leading representative men of their respective communities in this manner and let them take back and put into practice . . . the principles . . . it would be of more ultimate benefit than if the gates passed 20,000 a day." [66]

The Corn Show was held over for a week. February 14th was designated as Negro Day and turned over to the Negroes of the state.[67]

Mrs. LaFayette Funk and DeLoss arrived February 5th and on the 9th with Fred Rankin, Harvey Sconce and E. D. Funk, they departed to Florida to see lands there.[68]

Some effort was made to bring the Sixth Corn Exposition to Rochester, New York.[69] The final choice, however, was Dallas, Texas where the contract called for $15,000 in cash and 25 percent of the net profits to go to the Association. C. P. Bull, who was secured as the secretary on leave of absence from his position at the University of Minnesota, made a tour of all of the states except New England, visited the heads of the Experiment Stations and secured thirty seven exhibits. This total was the largest secured in the history of the Expositions.[70]

Coates P. Bull was a scholar and student of the soil who had investigated and experimented until he found corn that would mature early in Minnesota. He brought twenty-two years of personal experience in practical and scientific farming to this position. As a graduate in the Department of Agriculture of the University of Minnesota in 1901 he was appointed to the staff of the University of Illinois. He returned to the University of Minnesota and received a fiscal year leave of absence, July 1913–14, from the University in order to take the position as secretary of the National Corn Association during the Dallas Exposition. He had previously organized the Minnesota Crop Improvement Association. As one of the founders and continuing member of the board of directors for the N. C. A., both his interest and contribution to the overall organization proved to be invaluable to the organization. His long friendship with President Eugene Funk, which did not terminate with the Dallas meetings, can be traced to the days of silo building on the Funk farm.[71]

Gene Funk's life was, indeed, a busy one. He told C. P. Bull that he would not attempt to make excuses for not writing promptly: "my wife says I don't loaf, so that ought to be enough. I find that I don't have half time enough to accomplish what I am both called upon to do and what I would like to do. Some people you know have a happy faculty of turning out a lot of work in a seemingly very short time. But I never have been able to reach that gait." He suggested that he would try his best to "crawl off somewhere in a fence corner and scribble a few lines for the Southwest papers, but remember I am no press agent so you will have to fix it up when you get it." [72]

His usual day at the office involved four or five visitors to see cattle or corn on the farms. A visit from a high school class required a talk on corn breeding. Time was consumed in parts of Kansas and Missouri where no corn was raised in order to introduce good corn. Finally at the end of the day Funk wrote, "Everybody is gone home; it is late and I want to go to the country." [73] One of the mottos was, "Keep consistently plugging and results are sure to follow." [74]

An evaluation of the Expositions up to 1913 led Funk to say: "It is true, mistakes have been made; who knows of any enterprizes attempted where mistakes have not been made? This is human nature and it is often more easy to make a mistake than to avoid the same. I am not apologizing, I merely want it to be known and facts will come out some day, that the National Corn Association stands for a principle that is most vital to the Agricultural interests of this entire country, and its mission will have been proven most likely at the close of the coming Exposition at Dallas. Already we have the assurance of Experiment Station Exhibits from over thirty states and a signed agreement with, I think the last report was, twenty-eight." [75]

Difficulties arose in the problems of management at Dallas. Funk declared, "The same proposition is being presented to us now that

Jones had at Omaha and Shamel had at Chicago. For my part I would rather make the fight to continue to control the management under guidance of the executive committee as originally agreed upon, or if this cannot be done, propose to them that if they do not feel that we are capable of handling the Exposition (and they have said they wanted us to handle it for them) and tell them that we would rather withdraw entirely, so far as active management is concerned." Funk wished to hold Dallas to its contract and lend support in securing the college exhibits. If this did not follow, then out of justice to themselves they must inform the college men who might withdraw exhibits if the Association lost control, "for they will remember our Omaha experience." [76] He concluded: "Let us be lenient in allowing Dallas to get all the glory that they are entitled to and let them have their say-so in amusements, but I don't see . . . how the Exposition can be conducted with two managers under the same roof." [77]

A firm but conciliatory letter from Funk to C. W. Hobson, president of Dallas Chamber of Commerce, outlined the problem of management. He concluded:

From the first National Corn Exposition in 1907 the Directors of the National Corn Association have adhered to the above matter (Betterment of Agriculture) in its broadest sense and for this reason alone this body of men stand today as one. Not one of the officers can be accused of having tried to take advantage of, or attempting to secure personal gain or notoriety on account of their official position. It is true, we have had to fight our battles, in order to keep certain outside interests from creeping in and attempting to destroy our cause and our organization as well as to obtain personal gain but we could not secure the cooperation of thirty-seven states for one minute, if we allowed anything of the nature to creep in.[78]

In answer to a request for a Funk Bros. exhibit at the Dallas Convention, he answered:

I must look at all sides and my final analysis has been that it is best for the National Corn Association that its president, under the circumstances, does not enter into something that would give cause on the part of any one for criticism . . . to be conspicuous by our absence would be the best policy.[79]

He wrote along the same line to C. P. Bull, "I was told there was some (criticism) at Omaha. That is why we did not appear at Columbus and Columbia. I don't want to do anything that would give cause for a single person to even insinuate that I ever had the Exposition or the Association to boost me or my company. You will all agree that I have always fought against anything of the kind and so long as my name

Sixth National Corn Exposition

FAIR GROUNDS, FEBRUARY 10-24, 1914, DALLAS, TEXAS

Organized under the direction of the National Corn Association

NATIONAL CORN ASSOCIATION

E. D. FUNK, PRESIDENT, SHIRLEY, ILL.
E. G. MONTGOMERY, VICE PRESIDENT, ITHACA, N. Y.

DIRECTORS:

WM. STULL, OMAHA, NEBRASKA.
C. W. PUGSLEY, LINCOLN, NEBRASKA.
W. H. YOUNG, ATHENS, ILLINOIS.
R. A. MOORE, MADISON, WISCONSIN.
V. M. SHOESMITH, LANSING, MICHIGAN.
G. I. CHRISTIE, LAFAYETTE, INDIANA.
L. B. CLORE, FRANKLIN, INDIANA.
E. D. FUNK, SHIRLEY, ILLINOIS.
C. P. BULL, ST. PAUL, MINNEAPOLIS.

NATIONAL CORN EXPOSITION

PRESIDENT HENRY EXALL, DALLAS, TEXAS,
PRESIDENT TEXAS INDUSTRIAL CONGRESS.
VICE PRESIDENT E. D. FUNK, SHIRLEY, ILL.,
PRESIDENT NATIONAL CORN ASSOCIATION.
VICE PRESIDENT J. J. ECKFORD, DALLAS, TEXAS,
PRESIDENT TEXAS STATE FAIR BOARD,
VICE PRESIDENT WM. STULL, OMAHA, NEB.,
DIRECTOR NATIONAL CORN ASSOCIATION.
TREASURER C. W. HOBSON, DALLAS, TEXAS,
PRESIDENT DALLAS CHAMBER OF COMMERCE.
SECRETARY-MANAGER C. P. BULL, ST. PAUL, MINNEAPOLIS.
SECRETARY NATIONAL CORN ASSOCIATION.

STATE VICE PRESIDENTS

ARKANSAS	MARTIN NELSON.	FAYETTEVILLE
COLORADO	ALVIN KEYSER.	FT. COLLINS
DELEWARE	A. E. GRANTHAM.	NEWARK
INDIANA	G. I. CHRISTIE,	LAFAYETTE
IDAHO	W. H. OLIN,	BOISE
KANSAS	W. M. JARDINE,	MANHATTAN
LOUISIANA	W. R. DODSON.	BATON ROUGE
MARYLAND	NICHOLAS SCHMITZ	COLLEGE PARK
MICHIGAN	W. F. RAVEN,	EAST LANSING
MISSISSIPPI	C. W. GLOTFELTER	WATERVILLE
MISSOURI	C. A. COBB,	AGRI'AL COLLEGE
NEBRASKA	T. R. DOUGLASS,	COLUMBIA
NORTH DAKOTA	T. A. KIESSELBACH.	LINCOLN
OKLAHOMA	J. H. SHEPPERD.	FARGO
OHIO	O. O. CHURCHILL.	STILLWATER
PENNSYLVANIA	D. W. GALEHOUSE.	WOOSTER
TEXAS	F. D. GARDNER.	STATE COLLEGE
TENNESSEE	A. M. FERGUSON.	SHERMAN
VIRGINIA	FRANK D. FULLER.	MEMPHIS
WASHINGTON	LYMAN CARRIER,	BLACKSBURG
MONTANA	IRA D. CARDIFF.	PULLMAN
OREGON	F. B. LINFIELD.	BOZEMAN
SOUTH DAKOTA	H. D. SCUDDER,	CORVALLIS
	A. N. HUME,	BROOKINGS

Dallas, Texas

appears as president, I want to continue along those lines and not allow a loop-hole for criticism, if I can help it." [80]

Funk felt that the Dallas Exposition, under the management of C. P. Bull, would be of great importance to agricultural and experiment station men. There were proposals for a series of morning meetings devoted to the interests of the men in charge of college exhibits. Exchanges of ideas and practical demonstrations from thirty-seven agricultural experiment stations resembled a post-graduate school. He added, "The exchange of original ideas of research work is the means of progress in every line of business and to have all this going on at an Exposition where the work is brought out in graphic form and demonstrations, it seems to me is approaching the meat of things in the right direction." [81]

The New England states presented an exhibit representing all of the eastern colleges. There was to be almost a complete showing from agricultural colleges west of the Mississippi. Funk noted, "This year will have about accomplished the original thought of the organizers of the National Agricultural Exposition. Last year at Columbia, South Carolina, the Exposition presented to the southeastern states such an awakening for agricultural knowledge as they had never dreamed of, and our directors chose Dallas for a similar purpose this year for the southwest. The affair has grown until but few cities can entertain the Exposition . . . Dallas Chamber of Commerce, the Texas State Fair Board and Texas Industrial Congress have signed an underwriting of $100,000 to insure the expenses of the Exposition." [82]

Future policy was necessarily under discussion. Two questions were formulated: (1) Shall the movement for the Betterment of Agriculture with an Exposition have a permanent location? (2) Can the Congress of the United States be appealed to for an annual appropriation to allow the Exposition to become an annual event? [83]

Funk was hopeful that A. G. Leonard of the Union Stock Yards, would attend the Dallas meeting. He reminded him of the fact that Illinois was the only state represented at the Exposition in Chicago (1907) while thirty-seven were scheduled for Dallas. He informed Leonard that the "little" corn show had grown to a National Agricultural Exposition embracing not only exhibits from the agricultural colleges but all of the products of the soil—corn, wheat, cotton, oats, tobacco, potatoes, flax, sugar cane, etc. Congress granted a government exhibit covering 12,000 feet of space. Leonard was told:

We are anxious to have a representative body of Chicago men some of these who took an active part in promoting the first National Corn Exposition to see at first hand, not only the growth of the enterprise but the possibilities of further development and I know of no one to whom I could appeal to at this time to help bring this about than yourself. I would especially like to have E. E. Conway, Charles Stevens and Harvey Wheeler accompany you and any other gentlemen you saw fit to invite to go in a special car and visit the Exposition at Dallas.[84]

Before the Exposition opened some effort was made to pay Funk part of the money he had previously borrowed for the work.[85]

The Sixth Exposition was well advertised to include grand opera, aviation flights and balloon ascensions, band music, circus and bronco busting and a Texas inter-collegiate track meet. Among the attractions were the National Grand Opera from Canada, Anna Pavlova and ballet of 85 Russian dancers, a Hawaiian theatre, the tango performed by eight couples, a show of 23 ponies. A collection of pictures from the Dallas Art Association and from the Busch and Lowell collections appeared.[86]

Words of greeting by Eugene D. Funk pointed to the fact that seven years ago, when the National Corn Association was organized, the Expositions were chosen as a method to bring the best products of the farm and the scientific means of their production to the public. Progress was somewhat slow because the farmer himself did not take kindly to the scientific "book farming." By 1914 this attitude was changing. Farming was becoming one of the most scientific, honorable and profitable of all professions. He added: "The Betterment of Agriculture, that we and our posterity may live better, is attracting the attention of thoughtful men and women everywhere." He believed that a great agricultural epoch was under way.[87]

The Kellogg trophy was again offered.[88] An exhibit sent by the United States Department of Agriculture occupied something over 16,000 square feet of floor and nearly 400 square feet of wall. This display was to be taken to San Francisco as part of the Panama Exposition. Space allowed at Dallas was much larger, so the display was far better in Texas. It was valued at $19,000.[89]

The Canadian Grand Opera with soprano Marie Rappold thrilled the audience. The performance of "Samson and Delilah" in French and "La Giocanda" in Italian was especially appreciated. Mlle. Pavlowa, with her partner L. Novikoff, presented an excellent program. Although the auditorium was not completely filled, the attendance was estimated at 4,000 persons.[90]

Addresses were delivered by Governor Eberhard of Minnesota and by S. J. Robbins, the Secretary to the Canadian Ministry of the Interior.[91] The American Society of Agronomy, the American Breeders Association and the National Southern Highways Association held conventions during the Exposition. Group meetings of Texans held during the two weeks included: Corn Growers' Association, Swine Breeders, Texas Horticultural, Farm Demonstrators, Industrial Congress and Dairyman's Association.[92] Colonel Henry Exall, president of the Texas Industrial Congress was president of the Exposition; Mr. C. W. Hobson, president of Chamber of Commerce in Dallas was treasurer of the Exposition; Judge J. J. Eckford, president of the State Fair of Texas was second vice president of the Exposition.[93] Colonel Frank Holland, of *Farm and Fireside* was instrumental in bringing the Exposition to Texas. Miss Briggs was an excellent publicity manager and Mrs. Flippen managed the Women's Day with Dr. Anna Shaw and Carrie Chapman Catt on the program.[94]

The Texas Cotton Growers' Association was concerned with the problem of marketing their product. W. H. Olin of the Agricultural College at Boise, Idaho, Professor R. A. Moore of Wisconsin, Professor C. W. Pugsley of Lincoln, Nebraska, Professor E. G. Montgomery of Cornell, and Dr. L. H. Smith of Illinois were among those speaking on Corn Day.[95]

"Northers" arrived in Dallas simultaneously with the Corn Exposition. The attendance was cut at first because of five days of disagreeable weather. Then the people of Dallas turned out in force. Activities at the race track held them spellbound in presenting frontier sports of broncho busting, when some of the best riders of the Southwest performed.[96] Mr. Frank Hale and Miss Signe Patterson claimed to have been the first to introduce the original Tango Argentina into America. They also presented a novel form of the national Brazilian dance and danced the Hesitation and Patterson Walk. They were advertised as appearing directly from Ciro's in Paris.[97] The political upheavals in Mexico kept Señor Dominguez from appearing.[98]

The Dallas Exposition was not a financial success. Mr. Funk attributed the difficulties to a number of reasons. The Association kept well under its estimated budget. Severe weather kept the attendance for the two weeks' period down to 43,000. A member of the Commercial Club in charge of entertainment and amusement features spent about $50,000 which endangered the finances of the show because of the small attendance. The Exposition stood to lose $58,000. This situation, Funk felt, would reflect on the Association.[99]

The Dallas *Sunday News,* however, pointed out that the Exposition brought many valuable lessons to thoughtful citizens. This publication asked, "Will the supply of our own food products ever fully meet our demands?" Every individual who could do so was urged to produce a vegetable garden.[100]

After the Dallas Exposition, the future of the Corn Association, and the entire movement it stood for, weighed heavily on its president's mind. A letter to Eugene Davenport at the University of Illinois revealed Funk's concern. He believed it was foolish for the men who had sacrificed time and money to continue. The new Armory Building at Urbana seemed to be a most appropriate place for holding a strictly educational show. He wondered if the exhibits from various agricultural colleges might be held there next winter during the Farmers' Short Course. This idea would eliminate completely any commercial part of the Exposition, "for which we have all been striving for a number of years." [101]

Difficulty resulted in settling the financial problems from the Dallas Exposition. The officers of the Association thought they had an iron clad contract, but C. P. Bull found it necessary to remain after the sessions. He endeavored to gain a final settlement in April. The Chamber of Commerce delayed in making payment to the Association.[102] Settlement was arranged in May 1914 with final cost of about $2,000 to the directors.[103]

E. G. Montgomery was among those who thought that the Corn Shows ought not to be continued although he was not adverse to the possible location for one year in New York. He believed the Grain Show did not carry general interest and that the educational exhibits did not make strong enough appeal to the crowd. Amusement features cost more than the total income. He asserted that many large national shows struggled at the beginning but in some cases had heavy financial backing enabling them to succeed. The National Dairy Show, according to Professor Montgomery, was a financial failure for the first three years, until a professional promoter was obtained to handle the business end of the Show. The chief difficulty in the case of the Corn Shows was the problem of financial backing since no large commercial interests were directly affected enough to back it in a legitimate way. Manufacturers of the farm products were widely separated from the producers.[104]

War and the San Francisco-Panama Exposition interfered with any contemplated activities in 1915. New responsibilities claimed Mr. Funk's attention. The National Corn Association remained alive but dormant until a reviving spark pulled it out of a lethargy at the time of the World's Fair held in Chicago in 1933.

The historical and agricultural significance of the Six National Corn Exhibitions must be placed in proper perspective. Many have disposed of the corn carnivals, shows and state fairs as dens of iniquity, especially when judged by the amusement concessions found on the ever-present midways. A superficial glance at the foregoing contemporary materials relating to the purposes of the directors of the National Corn Association impresses the reader with their sincerity. It is true that there were often differences of opinion between the officials of the Expositions made up largely of businessmen from the locality involved and the representatives of the Association proper. These differences were largely based upon differing purposes engendered by pride in local accomplishment and the contrasting national purposes and viewpoints of the agricultural leaders. It would be difficult to say that no benefits were derived from the educational and scientific displays, lectures and emphases of these exhibitions. It would be closer to the truth, probably, to point to the fact that the National Corn Expositions from 1907–1914 admirably filled a real need in bringing cooperative information to a rural population. These were not the days of radio and television. Dissemination of ideas by the group method was almost a necessity. The National Corn Exhibitions brought together for the first time in the history of American agriculture the best in scientific accomplishments of the various state experiment stations and departments of agriculture. In one sense they marked the beginning of cooperative activities. The efforts of the board of directors, the various state vice presidents and the officers of the National Corn Association cannot be overlooked in estimating the contributions to a progressive period in agricultural knowledge. E. D. Funk, Sr. provided the leadership, enthusiasm, perseverance, and judgment to enable the National Corn Association to work continuously for the Betterment of Agriculture.

PART FIVE

The Changing Times

CHAPTER XVI

The Company and the Farms
1913–1920

A VISITOR TO FUNK BROS. SEED CO. in 1912–13 could have entered the main warehouse and walked through one of the first and largest seed drying bins, past the germinator and through large store-rooms. One room contained large glass cases of the ten average ears used in breeding work since 1901. The Funks picked corn before there was danger of frost and when corn reached maturity. Experience taught them about drying corn by artificial heat. This knowledge was applied in the construction of a dryer to reduce moisture content from 35 percent to 10 percent in three days without injuring germination.[1] Quick artificial drying held the germinating power at maximum strength, thus contributing increases in yields per acre. The seed corn at this time was stored in warehouses with temperatures never below 40 degrees Fahrenheit.[2]

Careful selection of corn sold on the cob was made with germination tests for each ear. Shelled corn was treated in the same careful manner. It was passed along from hopper to mechanical "butters" and "tippers" in order to remove irregularly formed kernels. Grading followed, so that corn would drop uniformly from the planter.[3]

Germinators were large enough to handle hundreds of bushels of corn at a time, marking an advancement over earlier methods. Previous methods had employed a large baking pan approximately two inches deep, ten inches wide and fourteen inches long. Folded canvas attached to a wire was suspended over this pan. Corn kernels were then placed in the bottom of each fold. Water in the pan kept the kernels moist. Another method, known as the "rag-doll," utilized strips of muslin about one foot wide and five feet long, marked in three or four inch squares. Ears were numbered to correspond with the numbers of the squares. When the squares were filled with kernels, the cloth was rolled up and the ends tied securely. The "doll" was placed in a container to keep it moist for five to eight days at above room temperature. These ideas were replaced by sand or sawdust trays to hold the moisture. The marked cloth was placed over the tray as before to designate the correspondingly numbered ears. These trays were placed in a germinator heated by steam pipes. Sufficient moisture was sprayed onto the cloth each day. Improvement was sought by boiling the covers or by daily supplies of fresh sand or sawdust. During the winter, sand covered with a light sprinkling of lime acting as a fungicide could be used. Temperature in the room was maintained at 85 to 90 degrees by steam pipes which passed around the room. No corn was shipped out that did not germinate 95 percent or better.

The fertility and productiveness of the land were increased by stable manure. Chicago was one of the best sources, and this supply was for the first time employed in large quantities on central Illinois land. Shipments were made in 40 ton cars through the summer months from May to October. During the first year shipments averaged about four cars per day. Large stockpiles were established at Funk's Grove and on the farm of E. D. Funk. Clover was used in rotation of corn, oats, and the clover was plowed into the fertilized soil.[4]

At LaFayette's farm in the northeast corner of the estates there was a large crib filled by a grain elevator driven by work horses. An observer could travel across 200 acres of virgin blue grass to the next farm. Here an unusual silo contained steam cooked silage. Little was known about this subject. After filling the silo in the ordinary manner steam was admitted in perforated pipes previously laid under the bottom in octagonal form some distance from the wall. Live steam passed through the silage during the night. The next day the additional filling was treated in the same manner. The entire mass was cooked for several days when the silo was filled. The result was a slightly darker silage which did not readily spoil. Although this feed was for cattle, horses also were said to eat and relish it. This experiment was carried on for a few years.

The tenant system included some cash renters and some who farmed for half the crop. Approximately 250 men were employed on the entire estates. During the winter months less than half this number were retained. The tenant houses were well kept and attractive. The recently organized Ben Funk School was attended by the children of both tenants and owners.

White Leghorn hens were raised in quantities on the Lyle Funk farm located east of McLean. Twelve incubators required 4,300 eggs to fill and demanded the attention of an expert. The brooders and heating arrangement were automatic. Eggs were furnished during the winter at 50 cents per dozen in the crate to the Blackstone Hotel in Chicago.[5] The chicken business of Lyle Funk attained national and international recognition. Toulouse geese were also available. The egg farm covered about 1,000 acres. In 1919 Lyle Funk stated that the farm was perhaps the largest of its kind in America. The incubators would hold 22,000 eggs and he could brood 15,000 chicks at once. The breeding and laying houses accommodated 5,000 Leghorns and 1,000 geese. The Leghorns were line bred, not inbred. Their value as layers was stressed, and not for show. Lyle Funk founded the egg farm in 1899 and in 1909 came to the conclusion that Single Comb White Leghorns were a more desirable breed for egg production. The International Strain of Mammoth Full Blood Toulouse Geese was established in 1910.[6] The French Government in 1922 conferred on Lyle the *Chevalier du Merite Agricole*.

Charles A. Funk maintained forty-two head of Guernsey cows. The University of Illinois cooperated with the dairy in the matter of milk tests and feed recommendations. The cows received a ration of gluten and cob meal in proportion with corn silage and clover hay. The milk was sold wholesale in Bloomington. Guernseys were also the dairy cattle on Deane Funk's farm. One feature of his farm was a 700-foot round barn with a silo in the center.[7]

Arthur Funk raised 1,800 pigs a year. The farrowing home was 16 by 200 feet with pens on the north side for thirty sows with the feedway along the front or south side. The front was made up of doors which opened to let in the sunlight. A water hydrant stood in the center. After a few days the sows were moved four at a time by crate wagon on low wheels to pastures, with pigs in a box behind. This method solved the difficulties of trying to drive a sow to pasture. One hundred houses for two sows each were cut from home timber. These were placed in the pasture. These houses without floors were easily moved from place to place. The sows were kept in groups of ten, each having a large pasture with water fountain, medicine box and an acre patch of rye. Water was supplied by a reservoir on high ground Each pasture had a concrete feeding floor with an automatically filled water trough and a self feeder. The pastures were seeded with clover and other grasses. When the rye became too large it was plowed under and rape was sown.[8] The hogs remained in the pasture until the corn was mature enough to "hog down," which was about the middle of August or first of September. Most of the hogs were fattened by "hogging down the corn" thus saving the labor of husking and handling the corn. Cobs and manure were left on the land. Prevention of cholera was a great problem. All dead pigs were burned.

Lawrence P. Funk developed on his farm the largest hog nursery in America. His decision to manufacture and market the remedies which made the Funk Hog Farm famous marked an important step in the hog industry. He was in 1919 the largest hog raiser in Illinois. On these farms, known as the "Garden Spot of the Corn Belt," his advice and remedies followed the pigs from before birth to maturity.[9] "Pig guns" were owned and used by the McLean County Better Farming Association in Illinois against hog worms. The "shells" or pills were originated by Lawrence P. Funk, and he generously turned over his discovery to the association. After September 1918 this treatment was available for all hog growers.[10]

The fame of the Funk Farms extended beyond the boundaries of the United States. A member of the D. I. Andronescu family of Roumania who was interested in plant breeding and dry farming visited the Funks in 1913. C. P. Hartley, in charge of corn investigations for the Bureau of Plant Industry of the United States Department of Agriculture introduced him as a representative from the Roumanian Government in the following manner:

He has read in European literature of your corn breeding work and is desirous of seeing for himself what you are doing and how you are doing it.[11]

An agreement to sell the *Farmers Voice* to the *Prairie Farmer* negotiated in July 1913,[12] as well as the sale of some oil properties at Chanute, Kansas for $15,000 aided in paying off some of the indebtedness.[13] Sale of stock and bonds in the Springfield and Northeastern Traction Company by both LaFayette and Gene brought $3,030 apiece.[14] These transactions relieved Gene of some responsibilities at a time when the National Corn Association was consuming time and money and when his attention was again turned to the affairs of the seed company.

When LaFayette and Jacob, the two remaining brothers of the eight sons of Isaac, reminisced about their younger days, they often talked of the old cattle trail to Chicago. On September 8, 1913, LaFayette, Jake, Deane and his son Donald undertook an automobile trip that brought back more vividly the old memories. They managed to follow the old trail to Joliet with little trouble, although the original stopping points were not too definitely located. On the second day they drove west of the Des Plaines River along the old route, arriving at the Union Stock Yards about eleven o'clock. Jake and LaFayette returned by train while Deane and his son returned with the car. A century of transportation changes had erased the historical landmarks of earlier economic enterprise.[15]

Mr. and Mrs. LaFayette celebrated their fiftieth anniversary on January 13, 1914. There was no formal reception, but neighbors from the countryside and many friends from Bloomington called.[16] LaFayette observed his eightieth birthday on January 20th. Three months later he met with an accident when his horse fell with him.[17]

A noteworthy event occurred in the annals of the Funk family when a portrait of Isaac was admitted to the Illinois Hall of Fame at the Illinois College of Agriculture. LaFayette's family, Eugene D. with his wife, LaFayette, Jr., Eugene, Jr., and Elizabeth attended with some twenty other descendants of the pioneer. About a thousand people attended the ceremony from over the state. Elizabeth drew the flag from the picture. Gene wrote, "Let us hope that no descendant of Isaac Funk ever does anything that will give cause to bring shame on this illustrious man." [18]

Eugene and Deane Funk became more interested in the Florida project. They talked with Fred Rankin again and with Messrs. Sconce, L. Burns and a Dr. Finch. Ultimately the Illinois men said they would go into the arrangements if Eugene thought the proposition a good one. They would join if he did. Gene, however, refused to take part without convincing his father that it was the right thing to do. He wished to have his approval before going ahead.[19] LaFayette and Deane made a trip to Barstow, Florida to look over the land.[20] Gene and Deane finally agreed to invest about $5,000, and James Melluish, an engineer from Bloomington, agreed to take over some of Gene's stock.[21] The total amount due by April 1st was $18,-575.41. Gene's share was $1,741.44 and Deane's $870.72 [22] on the first payment toward 15,000 acres of muck land in Polk County, Florida. Jim Melluish started to Florida April 15 to begin a survey of the area. His report was very favorable.[23] The first payment was made with the proviso that the company also receive some railroad lands—about 5,000 acres in addition. Gene became interested in the problems of organization and in the advisability of having a representative in Tallahassee who knew leaders in the state assembly. The Lake Fanny tract was also under consideration, but the Illinois group wished to hold decision in abeyance on this tract in view of the possibility of the railroad land.[24]

DeLoss Funk was with J. G. Melluish when he cross-sectioned the Lake Fanny tract.[25] Finally Mr. Sconce advised the acceptance of the agreement without the railroad land which he thought would come through anyway.[26] The drainage bill passed the Florida Legislature, and organization of the company with the possibility of inclusion of the Lake Fanny district was underway. The location of the branch of the Sea Board Airline railroad continued to be important.[27] The corporation was known as The Peace Valley Farms Company. Decision was made to organize a stock company known as the Poinsettia Park Company in the Lake Fanny tract.[28]

The Peace Valley Farms Company was made up of eleven stockholders, with a capital stock of $200,000.[29] The Peace Valley Company held 15,162.28 acres of muck lands. There were 14,117.84 acres within the Peace Creek Drainage District.[30] The first payment by September 1, 1913 was to amount to $43,464.88.

The Poinsettia Park area itself was once part of the Inman Estate. It claimed about one and a half miles of shore line to be landscaped by Professor Major of the State University of Missouri, one of the foremost landscape gardeners.[31] The park was composed of 600 acres with massive live oaks, palms and pines. It was located on the high lands of the most beautiful lake regions in Florida, fifty miles inland from Tampa, two miles from Florence Villa and three and a half miles northeast of Winter Haven. The altitude of 210 feet above sea level and the many surrounding lakes enabled the owners to boast of immunity from frost for citrus growing. Ten lakes were located in the area.[32]

The Peace Valley Company progressed although there were delays in 1915 in the drainage program. Native Floridians had not previously seen perfect drainage of the muck lands and were often skeptical of results. Demonstration of the wonderful results to be obtained in growth of vegetables on this soil helped to create interest. It was hoped that the drainage district could be completed within a year. The constitutionality of the drainage act was confirmed by the State Supreme Court. Bonds were advertised for sale by the company. Current expenses were a continuing problem.[33] E. D. Funk inquired again about the completion of the drainage ditch in 1916. He was glad to make a note of some money in the treasury at that time.[34]

The Florida Development was not the only organization claiming attention. Eugene was president of the Illinois Live Stock Breeders Association in 1915 and a member of the Advisory Board of the Agricultural Experiment Station at the University of Illinois.[35] He became president of the Chester White Breeders Association in 1916.[36]

Another memorable occasion for the Funk family occurred July 9, 1915, when the Funk Farms Picnic was held under the auspices of the Funk Bros. Seed Co., *The Prairie Farmer* and the McLean County Better Farming Association. Ten thousand people attended, and over one thousand automobiles were parked through many acres of land.[37] The registration book showed people present from almost every town within a fifty mile radius of Bloomington. Three men from Missouri came especially to tour the farms, and there were five from Ohio, several from Iowa, one from Canada and a party from Wisconsin. Dr. C. G. Hopkins of Urbana arrived from South Dakota with his father and brother. A delegation of fifty farmers from Livingston County would have been three times larger if the weather had not discouraged some. About 300 arrived from Springfield and vicinity. Four hundred railroad tickets were sold from Bloomington to Funk's Grove during the day. Several sleeping cars were brought down from Chicago the night before.[38]

The first automobile tour began at 9 a.m. The lead cars were numbered and each carried an American flag on the front. Five churches were represented with tents to furnish noon dinner. Barrels of ice water were set a few rods apart. Auto dealers from Bloomington were ready with tires for the unfortunate. The autos going in and out of gates resembled busy ants going about their work. Many questions were asked about the work on the farms. The large scale operations interested the men, some of whom were observed trying to count 700 brood sows on an alfalfa pasture. The women admired the beautiful farm homes.

C. V. Gregory of the *Prairie Farmer* was chairman for the day. A speakers' platform was arranged in the Grove, canopied with red, white and blue decorated with oats and wheat sheaths. Seats were made of logs and planks. D. O. Thompson gave the welcome. The chief speaker for the occasion was "Uncle" Henry Wallace, editor of *Wallace's Farmer*. He stressed the point of trying to overlook the things not believed in common in country areas in order to work unitedly for a broader conception of rural life. This could be attained after more work on the part of those who pioneered in certain fields. Wallace was especially impressed with the Ben Funk School. He emphasized social life in rural districts. He urged the building of a dependable race of men upon the prairies.[39] He continued by warning that when the European War was over, production of food would be increased. Here on the Funk farms were men who had learned to bring out the wealth of the land. He added:

I am not here to boast about the Funks, because their work shows for itself, but it is a privilege for you to see not merely one kind of farming, but almost all kinds of farming carried on by the application of brains. . . . Brains applied to the problems of agriculture is great, but I tell you a greater thing to see than that. It is to see a family working together for one great purpose, and that purpose the betterment of human conditions, the development of the soil.[40]

President John W. Cook of De Kalb Normal College gave the dedication upon the erection of a great boulder to the memory of Isaac Funk. A bronze tablet listed the names of Isaac and his wife Cassandra as well as the descendants of the second generation. Assistant Secretary of Agriculture Carl Vrooman, from Bloomington, gave a short talk. Eugene Funk thanked the crowd for interest and their kindness toward the Funk brothers.[41] All in all it was a great day at Funk Farms. The memorial boulder with its bronze plaque can still be seen on the site of the cabin where Isaac Funk settled on the edge of Funk's Grove in 1824.

Eugene, Sr. wrote after the celebration:

We have just passed through one half or twelve years of the "Dream" and I am well pleased with what has been accomplished. I realize that the next twelve years will require equally as diligent study and if anything more careful guiding. . . .[42]

LaFayette fell again on the ice January 19, 1916, the day before his eighty-second birthday, breaking his right hip. He was helping to put up ice as he had done for many, many years.[43] As a consequence he was unable to attend the International Live Stock Exposition, the first he had missed since the first show in the Old Exposition Building on the Lake Front.[44]

Efficient cost accounting methods for farm management interested the Funks. E. D. considered the initiation of the system on the Funk Farms as "one of the best if not the best thing that we ever did." [45] A series of reports would prove very valuable. Frank Pearson advised Funk that labor and wages appeared to be better on larger farms.[46] Another Funk Republican Barbecue was held October 20, 1916 at Funk's Grove.[47]

There was criticism during the year of a five percent increase on livestock rates in Illinois granted by the State Utilities Commission. Frank Funk was the only member of the Illinois Commission who voted against advancing rates. E. D. Funk thought that the railroads had based their claims on figures compiled prior to 1914 and disregarded subsequent years of prosperity. The livestock interests also had benefited, he said, but nevertheless every cattle feeder was losing money with corn at about $1.50 per bushel. It was a question how long this prosperity would continue. If railroads would reduce rates when livestock prices dropped, then profits would be willingly shared.[48]

Interest in Rotary International was uppermost in Gene's mind in April 1917. He was a charter member of the Bloomington group and deeply interested in the organization. He had difficulty in deciding whether to attend the A. S. T. A. at Detroit or to go to Atlanta for the Rotary Convention.[49]

The seed company was continuously active. At a stockholders' meeting, November 29, 1913, Deane Funk was again elected president, an office he had filled from 1908. Frank Funk was again elected for one year to the board of directors. Eugene D. Funk was also elected for one year. Dwight and Lyle W. were returned to the Board for two years and Lawrence P. for three years. Eugene D. Funk was again chosen general manager, a position he had held since 1908. At a meeting held in 1914, Deane was re-elected to the presidency. Two of the older generation, LaFayette, Sr. and A. B., attended this meeting, as did Arthur, DeLoss and Charles A. Funk.

Yet difficulties in the corn breeding work still troubled Eugene D. Funk, and during the war years he turned again to search for the answers.

CHAPTER XVII

The Enemy in the Dark

EUGENE FUNK WROTE that he first realized in 1913 that corn breeding work was seriously hampered by unknown diseases. Company records, he said, revealed some trouble as far back as 1900. When the Illinois Corn Breeders had discussed corn breeding problems in the 1890's there had been some expression of ideas about the best types of corn. This association of eighteen men decided on the rough type of corn as the ideal one to produce in the Corn Belt. The score card which they produced was worked out with the ideal ear having the following points: (1) cylindrical, (2) carrying this type from tip to butt, (3) well covered at both ends, (4) with deep medium rough wedge shape kernels. Then these men undertook to grow strains from all varieties in their possession that would measure to this ideal ear. In this period of corn growing history there were seven recognized varieties as standard for the Corn Belt: (1) Reid's Yellow Dent, (2) Leaming, (3) Boone County White, (4) White Mine, (5) Riley's Favorite, (6) Golden Eagle, (7) Champion White Pearl. Some of the older men may not have had the academic and scientific training of the younger generations but they possessed an uncanny instinct born of experience and practical application of their knowledge. James Reid of Delavan was one of these with practical experience in corn breeding.

Reid favored the smooth type at this time, but he was overruled. The Funks had also been growing a fairly smooth type but in order to cooperate with the majority they adopted the rough type.

When Funk recounted this story at Columbia, Missouri in 1922, he said that large acreages on the Funk farms made it possible to carry on work with all of the standard varieties. It was possible to select strains and carry them along for four or five years with big yields. He discovered that strains of rough type corn would "go all to pieces and fall down in yield to less than average farms in the neighborhood." Funk could not then understand the loss. Often he became so discouraged that it seemed advisable to give up the business.[1]

Gene Funk said little but he did not completely accept this idea.

216

He decided to experiment in order to test the relative value of different types of corn. He selected seven types of the same variety, Leaming, securing one lot from E. E. Chester of Champaign and the other from J. H. Coolidge of Galesburg. These seven types ran from extreme smooth to the extreme rough types. Funk explained at Columbia, Missouri that these types were planted in separate rows, usually one half acre to each type. He carried the experiment on for seven years. The smooth type in the corn from the Chester farm outyielded the rough six out of seven times. The smooth type from the Coolidge farm outyielded the rough five out of seven times.[2]

When this evidence was presented at the annual meeting of the Illinois Corn Growers at Champaign in 1909, Gene Funk described the result as a "near riot." About the only person in the audience who agreed with him was Mr. Reid, who danced around saying, "I told you so; now I am going home and tend to my own knitting." [3]

Problems in the entire program of corn breeding demanded additional attention. At Funk Bros. Seed Co. the germinators were giving trouble, or at least they were thought to be at fault. Thousands of dollars were expended to obtain a satisfactory system. All kinds of patented arrangements were secured as well as home made germinators and disinfectants. When a few kernels from single ears were placed in a square on the germinator, kernels here and there would show mould. Some of these would germinate 100 percent. Consequently they paid little attention at first to the mould, especially when the corn germinated.

At a meeting of the Illinois Corn Growers Association held January 19, 1912, Eugene D. Funk again spoke on "Some Results from the Ten Years of Corn Breeding." His interest in corn was apparent in his introduction when he expressed his appreciation for an opportunity to talk about "the most wonderful of all American products—Corn." The little kernel was capable of growing to a height of twelve feet or more in ninety days, reproducing itself over 1,000 fold during the short season. Gene believed that the American farmer of the Corn Belt scarcely realized the possibilities in and necessities for corn breeding work. He was able to reproduce before this audience almost verbatim the speech he had delivered in St. Louis on October 8, 1904 during the World's Fair (the Louisiana Purchase Exposition) before the Congress of Experiment Stations and Colleges of Agriculture on *Commercial Corn Breeding*. His ideas had not changed regarding the smooth type of corn. After quoting at length from the 1904 speech he concluded with another of its statements:

Personal experience has proven to us the above facts for some of our *highest yielding strains* of *Corn to-day* are *anything but ideal ears from the standpoint of the score card.*[4]

Gene Funk then called attention to a striking and practical demonstration of ten years' work along this line exhibited in eleven glass cases. He added:

For ten consecutive years we have carefully put away in a hermetically sealed can—a bushel of Leaming corn representing the seed selected for planting on about 100 acres. Each of these ten ear lots represents the seed selected for planting in their respective years and so these are not the ten best or the ten poorest but as nearly as possible a true representation of the whole.

He pointed to the difficulty in determining the exact increase in yield. The average yield in 1902 was sixty-two bushels and in 1911, eighty five bushels. This comparison in itself was insufficient, because as Funk remarked, the soil in 1911, where improved was better than in 1902. An entirely *different type* of the same variety was prominent in the breeding blocks for highest yields. Here selection was governed by *type* gathered from the highest yielding rows and by comparison with *type of mother ear*. Ten ears were then selected from Funk's Gold Standard Leaming and Funk's Yellow Dent. Funk said:

It is most striking that both varieties show a tendency towards the same type of corn and neither of them conform to the present score card of our arbitrary selection of type for a perfect ear.

The general increase had been about fifteen bushels to the acre.

The speaker referred to lists of several hundreds of names and to copies of letters from those who had planted this seed. These letters came from practically all of the corn growing sections of the world, from New Hampshire to Texas in the United States as well as from Ontario and other parts of Canada. Increases ranged from five to twenty or more bushels per acre from planting the high yielding strains.[5]

He recalled the emphasis on the smooth corn from the seven-year experiment with seven different types of corn within the same variety in the 1909 speech referred to above. Funk also believed that farmers were demanding too large an ear for a seed ear, thus producing corn of late maturity. Large ears were not necessary to a bumper crop. Gene Funk advised corn breeders to strive for a medium sized ear on a maximum number of stalks.[6]

This was the general situation on June 10, 1913, when young James Ransom Holbert, then a student in the Purdue College of Agriculture, arrived to work for the experienced seedsman, Eugene D. Funk. His summer salary was $26 per month.[7] He lived in Eugene Funk's home near Shirley and soon became an accepted member of the family circle, where his piano playing endeared him to the large family of children. The long discussions with E. D., Sr. about corn during and after the evening meal were a real inspiration to the young student.

When James Holbert first arrived he asked E. D. Funk for some practical experience. Funk recalled, "I sure gave him what he asked for. I first put him in the hay field and on the corn plows, later on an old planter wheel, dragging between the corn rows to form a dust mulch. We found Mr. Holbert to be above the average student." [8]

During his work on the farms in the summers of 1913 and 1914 the young student sought a direct method of fixing desired characteristics in a new strain of corn. He discovered that the corn families developed by Eugene Funk were "remarkably well fixed in characters." [9] These "families" were selected by close (line) breeding as explained in chapters VIII and IX. The elder seedsman requested Holbert to "breed a better strain of corn that any we have ever produced." [10] This was one of the biggest assignments that could have been made to a young student. The work of E. M. East and G. Shull, begun about 1905 and publicized in 1909, had attracted the attention of Holbert back on his Indiana farm. Mr. Funk also knew of the work. The discussions in those days of 1913 and 1914 when the world was on brink of the First World War were among the significant steps in the History of Corn Breeding. They also talked about Funk's corn families and of the fact that Funk had done inbreeding in 1902. No direct evidence of inbreeding on a commercial scale, except as related above in chapter IX, has been found in the early Funk corn breeding materials. However, the story of experimental work in inbreeding corn was related in later years by E. D. Funk to James Holbert.[11]

Eugene Funk also revealed in 1936 that by planting during 1904 the seed from a given ear in one row which was detasselled, and then planting the seed from an unrelated ear in the next row left tasseled, the result was seed of marked vigor. He also added significantly for the record, "about this time [1904] some experiments were also conducted by fertilizing the silks of a given plant from the pollen produced on the same plant." [12]

It has already been shown that P. G. Holden's work in inbreeding at the University of Illinois was discarded. The Funks accepted the general belief that inbreeding was harmful in their large scale commercial work. They knew, however, that the close relationship within the corn families did preserve desirable characteristics to a marked degree. They stressed the idea of pedigrees obtained through de-tasseling and hand pollination in the earliest years of their work. Yet they were constantly on the alert for information leading to improved corn able to withstand the diseases described by Gene Funk as "Enemies in the Dark." He knew he had been fighting them for twenty years.

Funk Bros. Seed Co. can claim a close connection with the chain of events that brought about the experimentation of Professor E. M. East in Connecticut. After East left the University of Illinois he requested some of the seed used in the experiments of earlier years at the University. H. H. Love had been an assistant to Dr. Graham for the Funks at Wesleyan in Bloomington during the chemical analysis program. It was largely through recommendations of Funk, Holden and Graham that Love became a professor at the University of Illinois. When East made his request for inbreds from Illinois, it was H. H. Love who sent the seed to him. H. H. Love declared in 1957 that these were from Leaming Yellow Corn, and that he shelled this corn off himself from inbreds he and East had experimented with at Illinois.[13]

As stated above, the important work of Professors East and Shull became known about the same time. Both of these men were botanists who were chiefly interested in genetics.[14] Gene Funk received a significant letter dated January 17, 1914 in answer to one he sent to G. H. Shull who was then in Berlin, Germany. The letter is interesting enough to quote:

Your letter and catalog describing the methods used in your seed corn production have been duly received and I am much obliged to you for them. Your catalog will be very useful to me in preparing for the address which I am to give in June.

I am glad to note the growing interest in pedigreed seeds; the excellent results obtained by the use of your seed corn has undoubtedly had much to do with this development. I can well understand therefore your feeling that a change of teaching on your part might jeopardize the gains already made. On the other hand, I think this side of the question can be over-emphasized. According to my view it is not the method which you use but the name of Funk Bros., that has become impressive to the intelligent farmer and if you should find by careful experimentation that some form of direct hybridization will give higher yields with better quality, and so forth, than your present methods, your statements to this effect would be accepted by your constituents quite as readily as they now accept your statements regarding the value of intelligent selection on the basis of performance records in the ancestry.

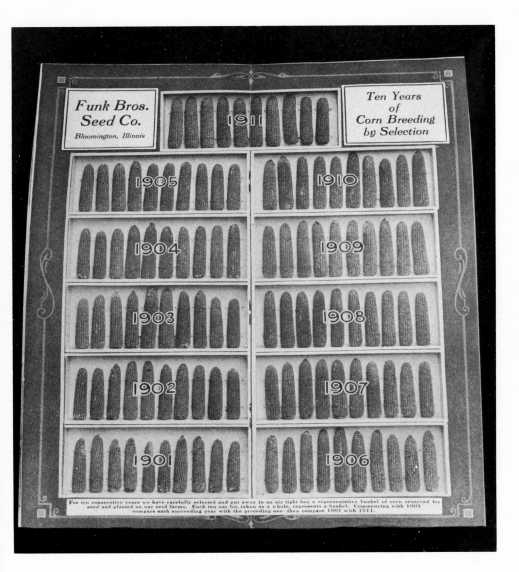

TEN YEARS OF CORN BREEDING BY SELECTION
For ten consecutive years we have carefully
selected and put away in an air-tight box a representative
bushel of corn reserved for seed and planted on our
seed farms. Each ten-ear lot, taken as a whole, represents
a bushel. Commencing with 1901, compare each succeeding
year with the preceding one—then compare 1901
with 1911.

Shull also commented that it would be disastrous to recommend growing crops from hybrid seed before convincing themselves that this was the answer. He said that the Funk establishment was on such a sound foundation of high esteem among corn growers in America that "you could afford at least to carry out some fairly extensive experiments to test the value of hybridizing methods." He also thought that Funk owed it to himself and to his constituents to undertake experiments along this line, guided as always by the "purely practical consideration of securing the largest possible yields." [15]

James Holbert wrote Funk from Purdue during the spring of 1914 that time was passing rapidly. He was already anticipating the next summer's work in Illinois and wondering how much corn, oats and wheat there would be. He hoped to be of more value on the farm "with the two-row cultivator and so on." He called Funk's attention to an article that he had written in the March issue of the *Purdue Agriculturist* concerning the tractor in Indiana. He hoped that Funk would not have too much criticism.[16] Funk answered that he expected Holbert to be of much more value after the winter of study, adding, "We are all anxiously awaiting until the time comes for you to appear in blue overalls again." He also informed him that Wash Barker had been made foreman on his farms.[17]

During the month of September 1915, James Holbert returned to Funk Bros. Seed Co. to continue his work in corn breeding at $100 per month. In the meantime Gene Funk came to the conclusion that the root system of the corn plant needed as much attention as the stalk or the ear. "In other words," he wrote, "there was more underground that we did not know than there was above ground that we did know." Holbert was asked to study the root system of the corn plant. The first assignment from Mr. Funk included finding a way to correlate what could be seen on the germinator with field performance and to find some method of eliminating diseases on the germinator and in the corn fields.

Before starting to work for E. D. Funk in the fall of 1915, James Holbert helped to make a cereal disease survey in Minnesota where H. K. Hayes, a student of East, was in charge. From the study of wheat rusts Holbert became "convinced that careful plant selection on the basis of big numbers was an indispensable step in any crop breeding operation." [18]

When young Holbert arrived he was again invited to stay in the home of the Funks. There he learned to appreciate the fine contributions of Mrs. E. D. Funk and the characteristics of the eight lively children. He helped with detasseling in ear to row corn breeding plots where odd rows were detasseled in one half of each plot of approximately 100 rows; in the other half even rows were detasseled. Discussions at the dinner table revealed that Mr. Funk was acquainted with men all over the United States who were engaged in corn improvement work. Holbert was impressed by statements previously made about smooth corn by Funk.

According to Holbert's later recollection, he and Funk during that first fall of his employment decided that the original standard was "good sound ears on standing stalks with ears at a convenient height and surrounded by other good plants." This objective was described as exceedingly difficult if not impossible of accomplishment, but they persevered to secure the kind of seed qualities they desired. Selections were made in what Funk considered the most important strains of Funk's Yellow Dent and Funk's Ninety Day, Leaming, Silver Mine and Bloody Butcher. The plant selected ears were not numerous nor did they qualify for entries in corn shows; there was not a rough ear in the group except an occasional Funk's Ninety Day. Holbert wrote:

> At that time I was very grateful for lack of comment, for I couldn't see very much myself to get excited about excepting that I was very conscious that I had worked long and hard on this difficult assignment. Also that there was great need for improvement. This Mr. Funk never let me forget. Nor did he ever express doubt that some day, some how, this improvement would be accomplished.[19]

These plant selected ears were cleaner, and more vigorous in germination tests, than better appearing ears selected at cribbing time from the elevators. These were included in the ear-to-row test plot of more than 1,000 ears the following spring [1916], with the best appearing ears from the thousands of bushels that came into the seed house in Bloomington. Ears used in this study passed the tests for vigorous germination and freedom from disease on the germinator. Some good show type ears were also included.[20]

When studying at Purdue, Holbert learned of E. D. Funk's report on rough versus smooth corn, referred to above, and he had also studied Shull's "Composition of a Field of Maize," delivered before the American Breeder's Association.[21] At first Holbert hoped that large numbers "without continued reselections from the few highest yielding rows, with only relatively small numbers to start with, would minimize the depressing yield on the inbreeding resulting from these previous attempts." Holbert stated in 1956 that from a large ear-to-row test field of ear rows in 1916 which filled a forty acre field only nineteen qualified as being good enough for breeding purposes.[22]

An interesting and significant event in connection with those nineteen ears occurred when James Holbert and his assistants finished gathering all of the varieties and strains from the breeding blocks in the fall of 1916. They then asked Gene Funk if he could pick from the seven varieties the rows that had grown the highest and the lowest yields. Gene Funk immediately did this, to the surprise of the young men. Funk asked them to open the old cans containing the types of ears that withstood the seven years' test, when the smooth type outyielded the rough type. Comparison of the types from the crop of 1907 with those of 1916 proved them to be identical. "Here was conclusive evidence," Gene Funk wrote, "that there was connection between *type* of corn and prevalence of the root disease, as well as correlation between type and yield." [23]

On the next day Funk announced plans to report that "smooth ears for seed were superior to rough starchy show type ears." Funk recognized that the public accepts new ideas slowly. He advised proceeding carefully, taking local agricultural leaders and neighbors into their confidence.

The problem of determining the highest yielding types of corn attracted the attention of the Better Farming Association in McLean County. Members gathered at the home of E. D. Funk one blustery afternoon in November 1916. Gene Funk and James Holbert explained their ideas about the high yielding types.[24] One of the interested listeners, A. J. Bill, farm editor of the Bloomington *Pantagraph,* reported that the facts would be accepted slowly but the truth was bound to prove out pointing toward a *type* yielding better than other types. He added: "A *type,* understand, not a variety or strain of corn, but a type in the different varieties, probably in any variety." [25]

Dave Thompson, the McLean County adviser, was also greatly impressed and regarded this first public announcement as epoch-making for the entire country. Funk explained the old ideas of the Illinois Corn Breeders Association and the score card ideal. He stated that he had explained his ideas to a few people—"On one occasion to the Corn Breeders Association in 1909 at the University, and again at the National Corn Show at St. Louis, 1904." By the last he no doubt meant the Louisiana Purchase Exposition. The evidence bears out the truth of his statement. Funk also said that he had never spoken of the problem in McLean County.[26]

Dave Thompson said that it would be difficult not to believe the results because they had been carried on in as careful and conscientious a manner as at any Experiment Station.[27] According to a contemporary account, Holbert explained that after he had worked for a year with 1,000 mother ears of corn, he and Funk without previous discussion of the problem found that their conclusions were the same.[28] From Holbert's 1,000 rows of corn there were eighty high yielding rows with the most obvious characteristic being a smooth ear although the mother ear was almost always rough or medium rough. The average ear was nine and three quarters inches long. Seventy-five percent of these ears had only sixteen rows, some eighteen and a few twenty thus differing from the twenty two to twenty-four row corn that had been advocated. The kernels were about a half-inch long.[29] Dave Thompson believed this to be the most fundamental piece of work in corn investigation ever accomplished, and was all the more impressed that the answers and investigations were to be found in McLean County.[30]

James Holbert later revealed that of the 100 mother ears 50 percent were Reid's Yellow Dent, from thirty three strains; 100 ears of Silver King; 92 ears of Boone County White; 100 ears of Bloody Butcher; 100 ears of Leaming from three strains and 100 ears of Ninety Day, making a total of 999 ears. The object was to find the type of corn in all varieties and all strains that would yield the highest. Half of each mother ear was saved in planting the thousand ears. The reserve was to be planted in the plot of 300 ears to be developed by hand pollination from similar high yielding corn. Another 100 ear experiment was tried in 1917.[31]

Four accounts of the subsequent significance of work by Holbert in producing Utility Type Corn called 176A are interesting. One of these appeared in 1920 in an article in the *Florists Review* regarding corn improvement in Bloomington:

In 1918 Funk Bros. Seed Co., advertised the Utility Type for the first time. It included ten of the most disease-resistant strains maintained for twenty years or more by Mr. Funk and twenty new strains developed by Mr. Holbert. It was called 176A. In 1921, the Illinois Crop Improvement Association recognized the advantages of the new type and conducted the first Utility Type corn show at Galesburg.[32]

The *Catalogue* for Funk Bros. in 1923 in describing Strain 176A reads as follows:

In testing thousands of ears of corn on the germinator during the winter of 1915–16, a few ears were found which were much superior to all others. They produced clean, healthy, vigorous root systems. Next season their yield in the experimental plots far outclassed all others. These superior ears were of Funk's Yellow Dent variety. They were the origin and foundation of Strain 176A.[33]

Another statement describing this same process appeared in 1940 in the twenty-fifth anniversary booklet of the company:

The fall of 1915 found Holbert back at the Funk Farms. Without waiting for the next growing season he went to work. From the great seed fields of Funks Yellow Dent he plant-selected several thousand ears. The best 1200 of these were shelled and put in envelopes. Half of the seed was put into ear-to-row tests in the standard techniques. Holbert, though, found that from 1200 ears a mere two dozen were the outstanding yielders. Uniformly medium dent and all out crosses of line bred "corn families" in the Funk's Yellow Dent variety, these 20 ears formed the foundation of Funk's 176A Yellow Dent, which, introduced in 1917, far excelled any variety established by prior methods.[34]

These activities marked the beginning of study for the young scientist on the relation of physical appearance to field performance in open pollinated corn. From nineteen top performers came a very important contribution to the acceptance of Utility Type Corn and eventually to good germ plasm for future Hybrids. Holbert related the procedure many years later [1956] as follows:

Some of these 19 performers came from plant selections from several different farms owned and operated by different members of the Funk family. Mr. Funk informed me that some of these men had been keeping their corn separate and distinct for a considerable period of time and for that reason, he was anxious to have it tested separately. Others came from ears selected from a number of other different strains of Funk's Yellow Dent.

As years passed Holbert came to regard his accomplishment as singularly significant. From the bulked remnants of the nineteen performers there was planted a small plot on the east edge of Funk's Grove the following year. Results were good despite severe frosts. This smooth type corn came to be known as Utility Type corn. After some discussion with the company's manager, H. H. Miller, who recognized the commercial value of this good appearance and performance, it was agreed to call it 176A. This development pointed the way. Holbert noted in 1956 that "From this variety have come directly and indirectly more widely used inbreds than any other single open pollinated variety with which I am familiar." He also pointed to the fact that from this new seed, Mr. St. John, then stationed with the U. S. D. A. at Purdue, developed Inbred 38–11. The important work by Holbert is further described in Yearbook 1936 of the United States Department of Agriculture.[35]

It can be readily seen that the early work in highly selected corn on the Funk farms also contributed to Holbert's findings when he verified the earlier conclusions of E. D. Funk in regard to smooth corn, and produced 176A. Probably E. D. and his cousins were closer to the real secrets of the corn plant than they knew.

The experimental plot for 1917 was located on the Lyle Johnstone farm near Bloomington. There were 156 rows of corn, each from a separate ear of corn; each row was 74 hills long with three kernels to the hill. This plot was a Better Farming Association project directed by County Adviser Dave Thompson.[36] Lyle Johnstone was president of the Association. The three years of work already done by James Holbert under the direction of Mr. Funk proved to be invaluable.[37] It had been determined that there were different kinds of damage to the kernel from moulds which might also harm the stalk. When Carl Vrooman, Assistant Secretary of Agriculture and a long time resident of Bloomington visited the warehouse of the seed company, he was shown the corn germinator by Gene Funk. Funk explained the trouble that had arisen in testing corn which eventually led to the discovery of the effect of the mould.

James Holbert explained his work in studying the moulds. He found it necessary to set up standards for the terms he used. Kernels of corn showing every shape, characteristic or diseased condition were glued to boards. They could be distinguished by a code term. Hours of study and exhaustive work produced these standards. Different kinds of fungus disease affected the kernels in different ways. Germinating corn seedlings were preserved in alcohol in jars to show the status of injury. Sometimes the tap root was destroyed. Typical kinds of injuries were visible in ten glass tubes. If the germinating seedling lived, the fungus or rot would follow up the stalk as it grew, finally destroying or reducing the ear.[38] Hundreds of ears were kept on hangers. They were numbered and results were recorded. Half of the ear was kept in a tight tin can. Holbert also candled the kernels of corn. This process was a kind of x-ray in order to determine content of starch or oil. Here then was the beginning of investigations that were of tremendous significance to the Corn Belt of the United States.

Eugene Funk appealed to the Farmers Congress meeting in Peoria during September 1917 for assistance in influencing Congress to make an appropriation for this work. As he spoke he answered a running fire of questions from men from all parts of the continent. He admitted that:

I talk corn in my sleep. It is my deepest thot and 20 years ago I thot I knew more about it than I do now. We are only beginning in the breeding of corn.[39]

The test that the Better Farming Association was following so closely on the Lyle Johnstone farm emphasized the fact that yield from healthy plants was continually important. This test also favored smooth type corn. Vigor in germination was only part of the secret of strong corn. This corn might also carry disease that would reduce the crop.

James Holbert believed that the results of this test plot should be checked with results for two succeeding years. Then, he felt, he would have valuable data for practical corn production.[40]

The day at Lyle Johnstone's farm was a memorable one. Dave Thompson acted as master of ceremonies and brought the corn to the rack where James Holbert weighed it while DeLoss Funk recorded the weights. E. D. Funk put a sack over his shoulder and helped. Lyle Johnstone and others participated in this important event.[41]

Those first years when James Holbert worked so hard on the difficult assignment from E. D. Funk, Sr. became especially significant in the development of the company and of better corn. In addition to the findings with regard to smooth corn, other important ideas were in the process of crystallization. Holbert found during his summer vacation work for Mr. Funk that a number of the corn families developed by Funk were remarkably fixed in characters. "So nearly pure were these line bred families," he stated, "that they exhibited many characters which breeders have subsequently learned emerge only after three or four years of direct inbreeding." Holbert made a number of crosses in Funk's Ninety Day families. At the same time in 1916 he made thirty self-pollinations in Funk's Ninety Day and Funk's Yellow Dent. These inbred lines were combined into experimental crosses with the resulting Funk's 329 as an outgrowth of these hand pollinations between the linebred families. This work was described in 1940:

It was the first variety ever established by controlled pollination of two families. Neither family was inbred as closely as is done in self-pollination, as it is practiced today, but they have been purified to a remarkable degree by a long period of line breeding. Funks 329 outyielded its parent strain,

Funk's 90 Day, by 20 bu. per acre and showed vigor and uniformity that was for the period truly amazing.

Another interesting experiment occurred in 1915. Holbert and E. D. Funk, Sr., completed a cross of three varieties, Leaming, Funk's Ninety Day and Funk's Yellow Dent. The three line-bred families produced a "Tribrid" which was sold in 1916 as the first hybrid corn ever marketed commercially. The word hybrid at that time did not refer to the single cross and double cross recombinations in general use today. But the lines in this "Tribrid" were not inbred sufficiently, so Holbert turned again to his inbreeding and to further testing. It must be remembered that the word hybrid describes any result of cross breeding.

Holbert produced some good looking inbreds by 1918. He planned ahead to the planting of a field in 1920. All went well the first season in 1918, "and the inbred ears were multiplied by hand pollination to further enough seed for an isolated breeding plot of two acres in 1919. Into this two acre plot went the two inbreds in alternate rows." The summer was hot and dry—and the pollinator failed. Only enough single cross seed was produced to plant 20 rows of the field that was planned to be forty acres. But these few rows of hybrid single cross produced corn that was greatly admired. Many predicted that it would sweep the Corn Belt, but few paid any attention to the drought stricken nubbins from which the crop came. The pollinator parent of this first hybrid went "the way of thousands of weak inbreds that perished for every strong one that has survived." [42] The other inbred was famous *Inbred A*, which was continuously used in good hybrids all over the country.

Looking ahead a few years, it can be noted that a double cross hybrid known as "Pure Line Double Cross 250" was sold commercially by Funk in 1922. It was later described in Funk Bros. Seed Co. catalogues and was followed by Funk's Hybrids 365, 517, 220 and 206 and many others.

An additional accomplishment during these years immediately preceding the entrance of the United States into World War I resulted from Funk's realization that the germinators must be watched carefully. As has been noted, Gene Funk suspected a hidden enemy. Holbert wrote in 1955:

> . . . We hardly knew where to start except to record behavior on the germinator and to follow through on performance in the field with hundreds and thousands of individual ears. Different degrees of vigor in germination and on the germinator also were recognized and recorded.[43]

Usually but not always vigorous seedlings free from disease on the germinator were selected. Holbert wrote:

As we might well have judged from what we now know, and didn't know then, results were not always consistent. Some ears slightly diseased on the germinator were better in performance in the field than some that had an unusually clean bill of health on the germinator.

The young scientist and the veteran seedsman became convinced that they were on the trail of something valuable in the improvement of the corn crop. The fancy show ears, carefully selected from thousands of bushels of seed corn, were consistently inferior on the germinator in both vigor of seedlings and freedom from disease. These findings "shocked" Jim Holbert during that first year 1915–16. He prized his official corn judge's certificate and therefore thought that he should vindicate its principles. Possibly something was wrong with his tests. So he included the fancy ears in his field tests to determine results. But the so-called show type had no better comparative record in field performance. Severe frosts during the last weeks in September created problems.

The country was at war in 1917, and good germinating seed was essential to the general welfare. All regular germinator facilities at Funk Bros. Seed Co. were in operation. Extra tables were left outside the heated germinator room. The seed corn situation was serious enough to influence Governor Lowden of Illinois to appoint a Seed Corn Administrator. Eugene D. Funk, Sr., was chairman of the Advisory Committee.

Holbert continued to check the germinator tables before they were read off. Usually good results were marked so that corresponding ears could be saved. By this method several hundred good germinating ears were accumulated. They lacked "uniformity and eye appeal." E. D. Sr., paid little attention to them, and Holbert did not blame him. But he also conducted some special germination studies in a small room next to the big heated germination room. Temperatures fell at night in this room to 60 degrees or below while they remained about 70 degrees Fahrenheit during the day. Results were slower here than in the heated room, but differences in behavior were more distinct, and disease infections showed up that were not observable under higher temperatures.

An article by R. A. Moore of the University of Wisconsin was known to Holbert relating how Moore had used an ice box as a germinator. He decided to run a repeat germination test in the cooler room on the good ears from the heated room. This eliminated some of the ears that had passed the first test. Several bushels of good seed resulted. Holbert wrote in 1955, "In terms of present understanding, that was a first rate modified cold test." [44]

This seed was sent to Frank Moberly, a valued friend of E. D. Funk. Moberly preferred to plant corn during the first weeks of May. From this seed he planted the first field in McLean county in May 1918. Other fields were planted with ear tested seed as good as that tested in the warm germinating room. But because of the frost, seed was not so good as usual and by the middle of May demands arrived for seed to replant. Frank Moberly, however, declared that he never had a better stand and asked: "Say, what was that seed you gave me?"

H. H. Miller, general manager for Funks, immediately sensed the importance of this corn and its valuable characteristics. From the Moberly field Funk Bros. selected some seed which was given the special germination test. Mr. Funk had become aware many years before that shellers sold better than craters. Shellers were not from the show corn as were craters or ear selected corn. Smooth seed ears were merchandised as shellers. He had become aware that they had a good bright appearance. This in general was the appearance of the Moberly corn. Now Holbert had proved for himself that some scientific selection was producing good appearing seed that had excellent qualities in field performance.

In another instance he had proved that acid phosphate on recently plowed virgin soil northeast of the residence of DeLoss Funk, where an ear to row test was planted, did not cut down on disease although it increased yield. There was one exception—a strain from the farm of Charlie Funk—which was satisfactory on light soil. Increased fertility of soil did not help. Many years later some hybrids responded in the same way.

Vital questions became apparent, and according to Holbert, writing in 1955, they included:

1. Just how far can open pollinated corn be moved and still give good results?
2. Would smoother, heavier ears give the same benefits in other open pollinated varieties as they did on Funk Farms and in McLean County?
3. How important were these corn diseases, anyhow?
4. What control measures could be recommended for these corn disease problems that were whittling away at the nation's corn crop?

With these important years of work behind them and a nation now at war, both E. D. Funk, Sr., and James Holbert were called upon for participation and advice. Holbert, as Mr. Funk always said, was "loaned" in 1918 to the government. A Federal field station was located on the E. D. Funk farm, where the young scientist undertook to find some of the answers. His position with the United States Department of Agriculture enabled him to work with well qualified men from this department, from Purdue University and from the Universities of Illinois and Wisconsin.

During the years 1917–18 Eugene Funk, Sr., also was contributing effectively as a member of the Food Commission appointed by President Wilson with Herbert Hoover as chairman. These were the formative years. The following decades brought continued difficulty and an economic depression, but also opportunities for experimentation, experience and expansion.

CHAPTER XVIII

War and Price Fixing · 1917–1919

EUGENE FUNK was engaged in important research work on corn during the years 1914–1918. His interest in the development of the seed company is apparent from the record. Events of pressing national significance led to the declaration of war by the United States on the side of the Allied Powers in April 1917. The price of grain, especially of wheat, became a problem not only to the farmers of the country but also to the Allies. Eugene Funk as president of the National Corn Association attained national recognition. He was among the agricultural leaders chosen to represent the farmer's point of view during the Wilson administration.

Wheat as a basic food has considerable economic and psychological importance, especially in time of war. Any rise in its price influences prices of other cereals. As an index of living for the poorer economic groups, the price of bread affects more consumers than price rises in other foods.[1] An increasing price level for wheat and flour occurred in a twelve month period ending June 1917. Net exports ending June 30, 1917 of wheat were 45.6 percent over the average of the three pre-war years. There was only a carryover of 55,918,000 bushels, the lowest amount since 1909.[2] A rapid rise in prices occurred from the first of February to the middle of May 1917 when the price was nearly three times as high as twelve months before. During June and July prices were well over twice the level of the same months in 1916. Wheat sold at Chicago May 1917 at $3.45 per bushel with the consumer paying for flour on the same basis, whereas the Department of Agriculture had estimated the average price received by the farmer for his 1916 crop at $1.44 per bushel.[3]

Poor crop prospects indicated lessened supplies in the United States and Canada in addition to little or no production in other countries, and this situation helped to push up the price. Uncontrolled buying in American markets by representatives of Allied and neutral countries contributed to the spiral. Mr. Julius Barnes said wheat and wheat products had become munitions of war.[4] Consumers tried to stock up. Jobbers, dealers and operators speculated. The public

232

paid well for panic but the farmers received little benefit from the high prices.[5]

The Chicago Board of Trade stopped trading in May futures on May 15, 1917 and forced settlement of outstanding contracts at $3.18 per bushel for the May contract when cash wheat sold for $3.45 per bushel. Similar action for July and for September futures on outstanding contracts brought prices to $2.75 and $2.45 respectively. The American marketing system fell "like a house of glass." [6]

A Committee on Grain Exchanges in Aid of National Defense together with one representing western exchanges conferred with Herbert Hoover who had recently returned from Europe. A tentative plan was submitted recommending among other ideas direct governmental control over transportation of foodstuffs; also the fixing of a price for wheat and its maintenance without change for the entire crop year. These recommendations outlined many policies later implemented by the Food Administration. Representatives of the wheat milling industry were also consulted. A letter from ten representatives of this trade recommended a Food Administration and Administrator as well as price fixing. The millers tried to stabilize their own industry under a committee of nine appointed by Mr. Hoover.[7]

The Lever act, providing for the control of food, was not passed until August 1917. Meanwhile wheat prices at the principal interior terminal markets approximated $3.00 per bushel. Herbert Hoover announced his plans regarding wheat flour and bread August 12, 1917. Among these ideas was the proposal that the President should appoint a Fair Price Committee to determine a fair price for 1917 wheat.[8] The Food Control act guaranteed a minimum price of $2.00 per bushel for the 1918 wheat harvest, but this did not apply to the 1917 harvest.

Eugene D. Funk was asked by Hoover to attend a preliminary meeting in June 1917 in Washington, D. C. Funk was inclined to oppose price fixing of any kind before hearing Hoover's analysis but he changed his views after looking over the situation.[9] This request from Herbert Hoover to proceed to Washington settled the question of attending either the Rotary meeting in Atlanta, Georgia, or the National Seed Trade Association convention in Detroit. Funk, when he left for Washington, was also concerned about the exemption from military duty of those engaged in seed production and distribution. Funk believed any man who was capable of carrying out the intricate business of the seed trade or of plant breeding could never be called a "slacker." He should rather be classed as one of the true patriots for working day and night to preserve for future use the seeds which go into the ground to produce the food to feed and clothe the world.[10] There were expressions of approval when Funk's appointment to the committee became known.[11]

After Funk's return from Washington he immediately sent out a form letter of inquiry to farmers through county agents regarding their ideas of a fair price [12] for wheat in the event of the passage of the Lever act. Replies from Indiana and Illinois indicated that the average price for 1917 wheat should be $1.87½ per bushel.[13]

Funk received a wire from his good friend, William Stull, a banker of Omaha, Nebraska, regarding his survey of conditions among farmers in Illinois and Iowa, August 30, 1917. His ideas were further described in a letter on the following day. After a 600 mile trip, Mr. Stull concluded that grain wasted because of lack of labor was most discouraging to the farmers. He believed that the minimum price should not be less than $2.75. Conditions were worse than Stull had thought before he undertook his trip. Of the 2,400 farms observed, two tractors were at work in the fields although the general opinion seemed to be that every fifth farmer had at least one or two tractors. He wrote that those who believed that the farm was out of debt with plenty of stock were in error. Total personal property and permanent improvements on an average farm in the Corn Belt were not equal to the mortgage on the land. Stull pointed to the fact that oil went up from $1.70 to $2.00 per barrel. Before the war oil sold from 45 to 50¢. Oil men said that the increase was not on account of increased cost of production but to further development in order to meet demands. Stull felt that the production of agriculture needed the same kind of help.[14]

Funk became a member of the Committee of Twelve appointed by President Wilson after the passage of the Lever act to fix the price of wheat for the 1917 crop. This committee was made up of three college professors, one economist, one representative of a farmers' organization in the South, one from the cooperative elevators of Iowa, an ex-president of the Chamber of Commerce, one representing the Grange, two from Labor, one from telegraph and telephone groups and one real Farmer. E. D. Funk remarked that some said they were farmers during the discussions but he was the only one actually residing on a farm.[15]

Eugene Funk presented his point of view August 28, 1917 before the committee. He said that he had tried to forget himself and think

of his country first, and referred to the fact that he was not certain
what group he represented on the committee. For some twenty years
he had tried to teach the doctrine of cooperation along conservative
lines in agriculture, principally through conducting agricultural educational expositions.[16] He noted that at one time he had experienced
the dominating influence of large corporations. He also declared that
he favored constructive organization, but was fearful of "radical
farmers." Funk added: "Frequently this class of men are the loudest
talkers and the greatest calamity howlers. However, nature is so
constituted that a man who will lambast and rave over the poor
downtrodden farmer, merchant, miner or laborer will be able to
secure an audience on almost any corner, while the man who is trying to teach cooperation, education or advancement will more often
entertain the smaller audience." Funk asked for peace and harmony
during the war. He spoke of the willingness of the farmer to sacrifice
anything within reason. He referred to the fact that at one time
farmers would have accepted $1.85 a bushel for the 1917 wheat crop.

The explanation continued with reference to the price of cash
wheat from July 1 and during August at $2.25 to $2.50 per bushel,
Chicago. Funk reported a conversation with Mr. Griffin, president of
the Chicago Board of Trade, who said that if it were not for the rumor
of $2.00 per bushel as a fixed price, wheat would be selling at $3.00
or more per bushel. Despite this rumored price of $2.00 the posted
daily reports of Chicago markets showed cash wheat in Chicago from
$2.23 to $2.32 per bushel, while No. 1 hard wheat sold at $2.30 per
bushel.

Mr. Funk also pointed out that farm boys had been drafted since
July 1st although harvest—threshing of wheat and oats—was less than
half finished. The farm labor situation created a real problem. Because of scarcity of labor some farmers were changing their plans
and were talking of less wheat acreage. Funk believed that the price
of $2.25 would satisfy the great majority of farmers and influence
them to increase acreages. He reviewed the general situation in which
the farmers found themselves, concluding:

I am placing $2.25 per bushel as a fair price for the crop of 1917 wheat,
fully realizing as I do that the price is 50.8 percent above the average
price for wheat for the past three years, but at the same time I realize
that it is asking the farmers to accept at least seventy-five cents per bushel
less for their wheat if they were allowed to have an open and unrestricted
market.[17]

There were real problems to be encountered in the fixing of the

price for 1917 wheat. Funk's account of the discussions was published in 1919 when he led a plea for organized agricultural groups,
especially in Illinois. According to this account, sessions were held by
the committee day and night for two weeks. He felt keenly in 1917
the fact that he represented no particular organization of farmers.
He realized how much the farmers needed a spokesman. Men knew
that Gene Funk would not shirk such a responsibility.

Believing that he was at liberty to speak about the situation after
the war was over, Funk told how he had favored at first a price of
$2.25 for wheat. He preferred to go up instead of down on the price.
Funk told of a threatened strike from Maine to California within 30
days during the crucial discussions. His description follows:

> You could have heard a pin drop. Nobody seemed to dare to open their
> mouth. We were cowed, there wasn't any question about it. Some of the
> biggest men in the country were there and they sat as though they were
> statues. I did not know what to do myself. I expected some of the agri-
> cultural colleges, men who had studied the situation all their lives, would
> be able to answer such a demand. I expected some of the business interests
> would answer. I waited for them to answer. I expected the economist who
> had studied the situation would be able to answer. Not one spoke. I know
> the beads stood out on my head. I saw it on others. It was a strike in this
> country right when we were getting into war. What would it mean?

Then Funk leaned back in his chair, saying to himself, "Funk, you are
a foolish man, but if nobody else will say anything, maybe you had
better." He knew that he represented no one in particular, but his
listeners did not know the long chance he was about to take.

Turning to the gentlemen Funk asked in the name of agriculture in
the United States that it be recorded that agriculture was now reply-
ing in the same way it had been spoken to. He asked permission to
accompany the gentleman who would send telegrams to his organizations regarding the strike. Funk said that he also would send telegrams that would include the other man's message with his own statement. Then he repeated that he intended to advise farmers to store
their goods in their cellars; to put away enough food to last indefinitely; to lock their doors and refuse to put any grain or food or
livestock on the cars to be shipped to any point until the strike was
called off. Then Funk asked: "Now who holds the key to the situation?"

This was a moment in history charged with tension. Gene Funk
seized the dilemma by the horns. He spoke for agriculture in a
moment of need. Support came almost immediately from the repre-

sentative of the National Farmers Union. Agreement on price resulted. Funk's account in 1919 read:

In the next few minutes an agreement was reached and it was the difference, gentlemen, between revolution in this country and compromise on wheat.[18]

This incident is reminiscent of the speech of Isaac Funk in 1863, when he spoke for his section of Illinois against the Copperheads. His words received national acclaim. His grandson also spoke well at a critical moment.[19]

Ten years later the events of the price fixing days rose again for consideration by the American public. Their revival belongs to the 1928 Presidential campaign. E. D. Funk was called upon at that time to recall the sequence. His memory served him sell. He remembered that he was the second man called by Hoover to Washington regarding the possibility of price fixing. Funk wrote: "Yet he, Hoover, expressed himself as being opposed to price fixing and he proposed to avoid it as far as possible." [20] According to Funk's account, Hoover should receive neither credit nor criticism for the deliberations and findings of the committee's decision for the price of 1917 wheat. Hoover procured the rooms on the sixth floor of the old Albany Hotel where the sessions were held. He appeared before the committee on the first day and outlined purposes and duties. The committee said Gene Funk did not see Mr. Hoover after that first day. Herbert Hoover corroborated this statement in 1955.[21]

According to Funk's account in 1928, the price fixing committee was handicapped from the beginning by "certain interests that demanded of us to find a price that would permit the consumer in the east to obtain a loaf of bread that would not cost him over five cents." The investigations of the committee disclosed that five cent bread could not be purchased even if farmers grew wheat gratis. Funk added "We were then confronted with a demand and a threatened strike in all of the ship yards and army munitions plants in this country, if we would not set the price of wheat at $1.87½ per bushel." [22]

As a member of the committee of twelve to set the price of wheat for 1917, Funk received letters, he said, stating that if he appeared in a certain district a convenient rope and limb of a tree were waiting for him because they had not obtained $3.00 wheat.[23] Funk believed they were lucky to receive $2.20 at that time.

Affairs in Washington were not the only responsibility of Eugene

Funk while his country was engaged in war. There he recognized the national and international problems of agriculture especially during war times. There were also difficulties in the central Corn Belt. Funk became chairman of an advisory committee to the State Board of Agriculture in Illinois. The seed corn situation throughout the Corn Belt was precarious. Funk's knowledge was based upon a personal mailing list of over 60,000 of the best farmers in Illinois, Iowa, Minnesota, Wisconsin, Indiana, Ohio, Michigan and Kentucky. A careful survey in Illinois alone showed a shortage on January 22, 1918 of about 40,000 bushels. It was Funk's opinion that seedsmen could not begin to handle the problem. He inquired about Federal assistance.[24] The State Council of Defense and the State Department of Agriculture told the Advisory Committee to proceed. One more responsibility was given to Eugene Funk. As chairman of the committee he was in charge of looking after, purchasing, and distributing 400,000 bushels of seed corn for Illinois. The seed houses were practically sold out. This meant that corn would have to be taken largely from cribs.[25] The price of seed corn was fixed at $5.00 per bushel.

While Funk was in Washington during March 1918, he received a telegram from the Secretary of the Advisory Committee in Illinois asking that he request the Secretary of Agriculture for a million dollar appropriation from seed stock funds to the Illinois Seed Corn Administration to buy up a reserve of seed corn.[26] Funk replied that some help would be forthcoming, possibly for 50,000 bushels.[27] Funk was one of three members on seed corn for the Agricultural Advisory Committee. The entire appropriation available up to March 26th for emergency purchase and sale of seed was only $2,500,000. The Department of Agriculture was thus limited. An urgent deficiency act, passed March 26, carried an appropriation of $4,000,000 for the emergency purchase and sale of seeds.[28]

By June 1st the seed corn campaign was nearly completed. The assistance of the U. S. Department of Agriculture, the State Agricultural Administration and the State Council of Defense, backed by fifteen Chicago banks, procured sufficient seed corn for a prospective big crop.[29] Funk was also on the Executive Committee of the Illinois Live Stock Association in 1918.

An official notification of appointment to the advisory body for the Department of Agriculture and Food Administration was received by Eugene Funk March 2, 1918.[30] As a result of accepting this appointment Funk spent considerable time in Washington working on these perplexing problems. He served on the sub-committee on livestock and was appointed Chairman of the seed committee mentioned above. During these deliberations Funk thought that the interests of the farmers were often placed in jeopardy.

Prices for grains and livestock during the first world war were dependent upon many factors. The European Allied countries secured much of breadstuffs, feed, fodder and some fats, meats and sugar from overseas sources. These supplies were practically cut off except from the United States. Difficulties were apparent. This was especially true after the U. S. ships were needed to convoy troops. Consequently, in the weeks before America's entry, the Allies tried desperately to secure supplies. They organized their buying under a single head in an endeavor to dominate the market, and agricultural problems developed in the United States. The American farmer could better sell his crops because of the European demand and cease to grow animals. Therefore, production of animals rapidly decreased. With the wheat crop failure in the U. S. in 1917, the situation was difficult. These were the problems at the time the United States entered the war. The Food Administration was faced with these problems. Frank M. Surface saw the challenge as one to bring exports not only up to the pre-war normal of around 6,000,000 tons of food per year but also to increase the supply to upwards of 20,000,000 tons annually. This would enable the U. S. to replace the inaccessible markets and to feed the allied populations and armies. In order to accomplish this, allied demands were to be shifted to animals rather than feed. The total would be greater if American agriculture concentrated on production because concentrated foods were more easily shipped. Surface described the situation: [31]

The Food Administration had to set up price levels that would be just and that would stimulate American and Canadian farmers; it had to secure a decrease in consumption and to create agencies that eliminated the vast speculation and profiteering by middlemen then in progress.

Shortly after the war began in 1914, an increase in demand for pork products arose. Numbers of hogs on farms at the beginning of 1914 were less than 59,000,000, rising to 67,760,000 January 1, 1916. Higher prices contributed to heavier marketing. Inroads on breeding of stock occurred in the early part of 1917 when the higher prices continued to prevail. When the Food Administration was inaugurated in August 1917, it was estimated that the number of stock hogs was below 60,000,000. Requests were mounting from the Allies.[32] The situation was not a simple one. Wheat and corn prices in 1917 rose, but prices of hogs and pork did not increase to the same extent as the grains.

By August the ratio between price of corn in leading corn and hog states and the Chicago price of hogs fell to 8.6, the low ratio for several years. This meant that 8.6 bushels of corn equalled the price of 100 pounds of live hogs at Chicago. Under the best conditions, the ratio of 11 or 12 bushels was required. Farmers, therefore, found it more profitable to sell corn than to feed it to hogs.

Mr. Hoover recognized the situation. He and Secretary of Agriculture Houston called a committee of the American National Livestock Association. Members believed that the situation would continue unless producers could be convinced that market price would cover cost of production and a fair profit. This point of view was supported by the National Swine Growers and Swine Growers of the Corn Belt.[33] After several meetings in September and October 1917, Mr. Hoover informed Secretary Houston that as a result of the conferences he believed it would be possible to get the packers to maintain a price for hogs related to price of corn. His plans were expanded to include the appointment of a committee consisting of seven men to investigate the cost of producing hogs:

John M. Evvard, Chairman	Ames, Iowa
Lawrence P. Funk	Bloomington, Illinois
N. H. Gentry	Sedalia, Missouri
W. A. Williams	Merlow, Oklahoma
J. H. Skinner	LaFayette, Indiana
Tait Butler	Memphis, Tennessee
E. W. Burdre	Herner, Nebraska

The committee's recommendations included the comment that hog production for ten years ending 1916 at the ratio of 11.67 bushels of corn to 100 pounds of hog equalled little if any profit. The normal number of hogs was 65,000,000. The supply was 60,000,000 at the time of discussion. They believed that the equivalent of at least a ratio of 14.3 bushels of corn for every 100 pounds should be established in order to stimulate production 15 percent above normal. To prevent premature marketing of light unfinished pigs and of breeding stock, a minimum emergency price for good to select butcher type hogs of $16.00 per 100 pounds was to be established on the Chicago market. To stimulate production of swine for the next year they recommended establishing of a ratio to become effective February 1, 1918.[34]

A statement by Joseph C. Cotton formulating the basis of Food Administration toward hog prices was issued November 3, 1917. It embodied the following: Prices so far as they could affect them would not go below 15.50 per hundredweight for average of packers' droves on the Chicago market. This statement was not a guaranty backed by money. It was not a promise by the packers, but it was a statement of intention and policy of the Food Administration which meant to do justice to the farmer.[35] There was some question whether there was power to maintain the policy.[36] Mr. Hoover knew one of the major problems was the supply of fats. It was recognized by the Food Administration that this minimum price for hogs was not a guaranty backed by money, but a policy to be maintained so far as the control of allied and government buying would permit.

A proclamation from President Wilson, October 8, 1917, required that meat packers among others would be required to secure a license from the Food Administration as a condition for doing business after November 1, 1917. Profits were limited to "fair and reasonable" returns.[37] The ratio appeared to work as long as the price of corn remained relatively stationary. William Stull wrote to E. D. Funk December 24, 1917 that he had received a copy of a report on hog prices as related to corn prices, made by the commission appointed by Mr. Hoover. Stull thought the findings correct but believed they should be immediately effective instead of waiting until February 1, 1918. He noted that packers held the prices down through a monopoly of the market, buying hogs at prices that resulted in a loss of 4-6 bushels for every 100 pounds of pork sold. Stull attended the Farmers' Congress, which he believed was controlled by commercial interests. Few members ever had a copy of this report. He believed it should have been distributed.[38] Again on January 2, 1918, Stull requested copies of the October 27, 1917 report.[39]

Surface pointed out that the November 3, 1917 announcement of the policy to stabilize the price of hogs resulted in checking prices. Time, however, was required to increase the supply. Hogs were being held back on farms to consume the soft corn from the 1917 crop. From November 1917 through January 1918, hogs marketed were light for the season of the year. From February 1 to May 1, 1918, the number of hogs killed under Federal inspection rose to 14,305,000 or 17 percent more than the corresponding months of 1917. The total export of pork and lard in March 1918 was almost double the amount exported in any previous month. But difficulties in transportation increased cold storage holdings of packers.[40]

Rumors of cessation of war began to circulate in August and September 1918. It was realized that low-priced corn in Argentina and South Africa would be thrown on market. A price decline for corn in the U. S. occurred between July and October 1918 of from 25 to 40 cents per bushel.[41] If this were incorporated in 13–1 ratio, declining prices for hogs would occur. A heavy run of hogs made it difficult for packers to maintain prices.[42] The influenza epidemic affected home consumption.

The Agricultural Advisory Committee, especially the Livestock Committee, was kept informed. At a meeting of the subcommittee September 25, 1918, the continuation of the 13–1 ratio was recommended.[43] A special committee of the subcommittee composed of Eugene D. Funk, John M. Evvard, John H. Skinner, A. Sykes and N. H. Gentry recommended that the Food Administration should at once announce its intention to maintain the minimum price of not less than $15.50 continuously during the war.[44] A special meeting was called in October by Hoover, and representatives of the swine industry were included. The committee abandoned the 13–1 ratio. Eugene Funk was among fourteen producers—four representing the Food Administration, two from the Department of Agriculture and twelve packers—who were in attendance.[45] The packers agreed not to purchase hogs for less than following minimum during November: Daily minimum $17.50 per hundredweight on average of packers' droves; no hogs except throwouts defined as under 130 pounds, at less than $16.50 per hundredweight. The average of packers' droves to be average of total sales in the market of all hogs for a given day based on Chicago.[46]

Funk recalled ten years later the problems of the Advisory Committee regarding the price of hogs at the ratio of 13–1 to the price of corn.[47] He declared that Hoover insisted that the packers maintain the price of $15.50 for hogs and if they did not the entire packing industry would be taken over. This was after it was proven to and approved by the Advisory Committee that it was impossible to maintain the 13–1 ratio of the price of corn to 100 pounds of hogs when the price of corn reached $2.00 per bushel. The price was placed at $15.50 and afterwards advanced to $17.50.

Funk recalled also that the buying power of surplus meat was concentrated in the hands of one man representing England, France, Belgium and Italy. He refused to place additional orders until a compromise was reached. Up to this day hogs had advanced to $18.50 per hundredweight. Funk wrote: "I plainly saw that we had better take a loss of $3.00 per hundred than to run the risk of a slump that would run five or six cents decline." Funk and his family had 8,000 hogs on hand ready for market.[48]

Gene Funk honestly believed that the dip would have been greater if they had not accepted the $15.50. The committee sent out to Iowa, including Lawrence Funk and Nick Gentry, found it took thirteen bushels of corn to produce 100 pounds of pork. This committee presented its findings to the twenty-four men on Hoover's Advisory Committee. This Advisory Committee knew it had no authority to make a guarantee. The members were instructed to plan for a ten-year war.[49]

Funk also recorded that before the price was decided upon, and unknown to Mr. Hoover or to the committee, the packers shipped a lot of their surplus fat pork to England in order to clear their cellars. The Englishman in whose hands purchasing was placed took advantage of crowded yards, slaughter houses and cellars. He refused at first to buy. The committee saw that if he went out of the market for a week or ten days as he threatened, the hog market would go to pieces. Finally he agreed not to get out entirely, but to take pork on a basis of $15.50 as the minimum price.[50] Mr. Hoover then invited the seventeen packers to Washington.[51]

Funk recalled ten years later that the Advisory Committee later appointed in 1918, made up of twenty-four farmers, had almost daily conferences with Mr. Hoover. This was the committee that decided on the minimum price for wheat in 1918 and on the ratio 13–1 as the price of hogs. This was the time when *Wallace's Farmer* criticized the procedure.[52]

An account of the difficulties encountered was recorded:

I vividly remember one of those trying days when Mr. Hoover stood before 75% of the packers throughout the United States and told them in very plain words that he would give them just ten minutes to decide as to whether or not they would continue to maintain their part of the program or the Food Administration would be compelled to take over the entire packing industry.[53]

A copy of resolutions from the Agricultural War Board in Illinois adopted October 18, 1918 was sent by Eugene Funk to Herbert Hoover. These resolutions referred to the nationwide appeal to farmers to increase pork production with the understanding the price ratio would guarantee them a fair profit; to the average price of $18.00 for hogs at Chicago for October as at least $1.00 per hundredweight below the 13–1 basis; and to the failure to mention the 13–1 ratio as a serious breach of faith.[54] A copy of a letter from Herbert Hoover to Samuel Insull, chairman of State Council of Defense for Illinois stated:

. . . as to the purpose of these resolutions I wish to say that their interpretation of the thirteen to one formula is entirely contrary to the promise made by the Food Administration and even of the interpretation given by the Producers in Conference last month in Washington. I cannot entertain the suggestion of bad faith of this administration nor do I believe such a suggestion will be entertained by any single one of the gentlemen who have attended the conference including Mr. Funk, to whom you refer.[55]

Lewis Straus enclosed a copy to Funk of an editorial from the *Boston Evening Transcript,* October 28, which accused the committee of raising prices of pork to consumer. Straus said "The fact that we catch it at times from both producer and consumer is a pretty good evidence of impartiality." [56]

Eugene Funk was appointed as a member of the Special Committee on Agriculture by President H. A. Wheeler of the United States Chamber of Commerce in August 1918.[57] The committee had as its immediate task an investigation of the so-called Non-Partisan League, which accused "Big Business" of dealing unfairly with agricultural interests.[58]

The problem of the December price for hogs immediately arose. Funk received an inquiry from Snyder Powell of the Food Administration saying that hog men believed over-shipments during the latter part of November would be prevented if December price were the same as for November. The price should be immediately announced.[59] Funk disliked any change in arrangements already made that might bring dissatisfaction, but said that he would agree to raising lightweight hogs to 150 pounds.[60]

These situations in Washington impressed Funk with the lack of organization among farmers. He knew that he spoke for no strong farm organization when he acted as a farmer member of these committees. Realization of this situation influenced him to support W. G. Schmidt and C. V. Gregory in giving what may be described as the final convincing argument at the Peoria meeting leading to the formation of the Illinois Agricultural Association. Three other important events followed the war years: the organization of the Farm Bureau in Illinois and other states, the introduction of the Grain Show at the International in Chicago, and the reorganization of Funk Bros. Seed Co.

During the troublesome war years, Eugene Funk realized that his company would of necessity undergo some change. At a meeting in January 1917, it was agreed by the cooperating cousins to assume debts to themselves of $34,918.26. Eugene D. Funk assumed the largest amount of $12,344.74 and Deane cancelled a debt of $8,997.47. Other amounts were under $5,000. All accounts of individuals with the company were to be settled. Real estate for the time was deeded to Lawrence Funk. This action marked the termination of the company in its original form.[61]

For many years members of the third generation maintained accounts with the company. This cooperative effort proved advantageous as an ingenious idea for focusing cooperative interest within the ever-growing branches of the large family. Faced by an agricultural economy adjusting from the impact of the First World War, many of the cousins, with their diversity of interests and responsibilities for their own families, believed the time had come for change.

Scientific problems needed solution. Corn breeding experiments required more attention. Eugene D. Funk continued his abiding faith that results could be obtained. Officers of the company resigned at a meeting held January 17, 1918. The number of directors was reduced to three. Eugene D. Funk, DeLoss Funk and H. H. Miller, the new manager, were elected to these positions. They also became the new officers as president, secretary and treasurer respectively.[62] E. D. and DeLoss acquired 140 shares of stock held by other members of the family. Funk Bros. Seed Co. was now in reality directed by two Funk brothers, sons of LaFayette Funk.

PART SIX

A Spokesman from the Corn Belt

CHAPTER XIX

Through the Years, Eugene D. Funk, Sr. and Family at Home

DURING THE THIRD DECADE of the twentieth century, Eugene D. Funk, Sr. reached his fifty-fifth birthday. The twenties brought many trials and tribulations as well as increasing responsibilities. There was always the retreat from the city to home and the comforting realization that his family of eight children, four boys and four girls, had enjoyed the advantages of growing up in the country. During the middle years of his life his dark hair and mustache showed a slight greying tendency. Despite business problems there was usually a twinkle in his very blue eyes. As he greeted people with a smile, his manner indicated a shy and unassuming person, yet there was firmness in his attitude and voice conveying the impression that he meant what he said. His eldest daughter Gladys wrote, "His temper rarely showed, but its flash was one you did not want to kindle again." He stood about five feet eleven inches and kept his trim figure to his later years, walking with a firm, quick step that took him directly about his business. His tanned complexion indicated that he spent almost all of his time out of doors. He possessed a polite manner reflecting his dignified home training and a flavor of eastern schooling. Gene Funk always described himself as a "country boy" and never sought again to move to the city.[1]

As Mr. and Mrs. Funk thought back to their decision to move to the South place and to complete their new home in 1907, many memories crowded across the years. When the large frame house was finished, a decorator from Chicago made it a beautiful and comfortable place. The family of six increased to eight in the first four years of occupancy, and the home was managed with the help of two country girls, one to cook and one to clean. The older children soon learned to help one another and to look after the younger ones. The seventh child, Ruth, arrived in August 1907 only a few months after the family moved into the new home. Mrs. Funk later remarked, "A house is not a home until children have been born into it." [2] The last of the eight

children, Mary, was born in 1910. Gladys, as the eldest of the children, always assumed the greatest amount of responsibility. Realizing
that her mother could not be everywhere at one time, she washed
many a face and curled many a ringlet. This same sense of responsibility continued into later years when she often rose quickly to the
defense of her brothers and sisters. The children missed their helper,
Fugii, who had returned to his homeland in Japan. With the aid of
the two women, Gladys had more time for her favorite pastime, horseback riding. She helped to drive the sheep, hogs or cattle, and rode
with Grandfather LaFayette as he looked over the fields and livestock. His was a familiar figure when he set forth with his hoe over
his shoulder as fair warning to any courageous weeds that reared
their unwanted heads.

When it became difficult to obtain efficient help in the country
and financial problems pressed during the twenties, Mrs. Funk again
resumed the duties of cooking. "Liffy," as Elizabeth was known, made
cakes and other desserts. Gladys cleaned the house and kept it
straight. All of the children, boys and girls, helped with table and
dishes. The young men who came from the University to learn practical farming did their share.[3]

The new home, later called "The Outlook," impressed the children.
There was ample room for the entire family to gather in the spacious
living room. An electric bell system was an intriguing method for
notifying the help on the second or third floor that they were needed
below. Gladys recalled many years later that the building of this new
home had been almost a family enterprise:

> The new house was an interesting project from the night Father took
> us all to the new plot and set stakes by the North Star. I felt the heavens
> had a part in it. Dad could inspire one with a dream or an idea in which
> he had faith. Perhaps that is one reason he could accomplish so much,
> and always with his hard work and plans things became a reality. It was
> never he who gave up but others who lacked his clear vision who faltered
> now and then.[4]

The children grew to realize that much of The Outlook came from
their mother's "inlook," for her devotion to her family and her consistent belief that they would do the right thing profoundly influenced
their lives. The house was set upon a slight rise in the rolling prairie
land. Gladys summarized it:

> Surrounded by fertile fields of clover, alfalfa, swaying fields of wheat
> or oats and tall corn rows reaching for miles and miles. Different fields
> of 60 to 300 acres squared off and edged with osage orange hedge fences

or sturdy posts and strong wire. Weeds and bluegrass kept trimmed by the roadside, yet wild roses and strawberries bloomed and fall goldenrod, asters and ironweed gave proof that the meadowlark had nested and found shelter. . . . Horizons boundless except by the skyline.[5]

Gate posts of native stone, bordered by a spirea hedge pure white in spring, gave wide entrance to a two-acre lawn as a setting for The Outlook. A Y-shaped gravel driveway circled the house. A tulip tree bloomed white near tall oaks by the front entrance. Close by the house stood a redbud tree. Wisteria vines circled some of the fourteen pillars of the brick and concrete porch on three sides of the house. A screened porch on the east provided a restful eating place in the summer and a comfortable place for conferences. The south and west porches were open under a slate roof. The front entrance was in the center of the south side. A large front door held a square-paned glass. This door led to a tiled vestibule and to another door opening into the front hallway.[6] To the right an interesting collection of canes, long the pride and joy of Mr. Funk, could be examined.

Mrs. Funk often quoted poetry to describe her love of the country and to express her welcome to the many visitors who came to her home. She saw the tall straight lines of corn stretch far away until in the distance they seemed to touch the sky. She urged her friends to remain away from the crowded cities where hurry and worry prevailed. A long summer day in the country was her remedy for urban strife and toil. Rest, calm and quiet were just rewards for those who lived on the farm.[7]

In the large living room to the left of the front entrance, the long fireplace against the west wall was always a center of attraction. Pictures of corn by the famous artist Montgomery were fittingly placed above the mantle in later years. Windows were hung with yellow curtains in a waffle weave. Walls were buff Japanese grass cloth, and brown and green rugs covered the floors.

The library to the right of the main entrance was shelved with glassed book cases of walnut fence rails, originally from the Grove, presented to E. D. and his bride by Mr. Duncan Funk many years before the house was built. Down the hallway a large dining room was paneled with four foot high light honey locust, also from the Grove. Beams of the same wood crossed the ceiling, providing effective decoration.[8] The side walls between the panels were covered with light blue grape decorated wallpaper. The ceiling was painted blue gray. A large glass lightshade, inlaid in blue, tan and green was suspended above the light wood table. A long sideboard of the same wood stood against the wall. The table seated ten and could be lengthened to accommodate eighteen as was often required. For large gatherings, an additional table of the same size was brought in, so that a total of thirty-six could enjoy hospitality and friendship in the room. Mr. Funk always carved at the table. Good manners were early taught and always demanded at table. Back of the dining room, a spacious kitchen was located at the rear of the house with an entrance to the east. Acetylene gas light fixtures added a truly modern touch during the early years of occupancy.[9]

Although Mrs. Eugene, Sr. affiliated early with the Presbyterian church in Bloomington, it was difficult through the years while bringing up a large family to maintain regular attendance. The children were baptized into the church. Fond memories remain of early Sunday school attendance before 1907 in the McIlvain school and later at the old white church in Funk's Grove, where services were conducted by ministers of different faiths on succeeding Sundays. The family often held picnics in the Grove on Sundays. Gene, Sr., who treasured moments of quiet and peace in the timber, often looked over the trees on these afternoons. He read his paper near Timber Creek and as was his custom smoked his favorite cigar.

This could be a significant occasion for the family when the wild flowers were beginning to bloom. Hepaticas, trillium, dutchman's-breeches, jack-in-the-pulpits and violets were all watched carefully. Mrs. Funk knew when spring flowers were in bloom. Whenever she spoke of this to the children they knew that they would be off on a searching expedition. This recognition of the beauty of Mother Nature especially in the Grove has long been a cherished custom of the entire Funk family. From their early activities came the intention to preserve the natural appearance of the timber and to protect the flowers. Such a plan was often in the thoughts of E. D. Funk, Sr. When the carpet of bluebells covered the bluffs above the branch of Timber Creek as it wound its way back of the church in the Grove, the sight was one that called the Funk family again and again to view the soft, eerie effect, especially as the sun sank in the west. The sunlight during the warm summer days as it penetrated the new green leaves of an early spring reminded one of the yellow to be found only in a Rembrandt painting. Deep in the Grove there was a solitude and a calm that bespoke the sermons in Nature. Gene Funk, Sr. kept this deep religious recognition of the wonders of Nature as a guiding principle throughout his lifetime. He was not a regular attendant at

Mr. and Mrs. Eugene D. Funk

Eugene, Jr.   LaFayette   Eugene D. Funk, Sr.   Paul   Theodore

NORTH

Funk's Grove
Elevator → O

Church and
Cemetery Area

University of Illinois
63-Acre Tract

G. M. & O. RR.
Also Route 66

Aerial View, Funk's Grove area where virgin timber still stands.
The University of Illinois Natural Forest Area outlined.
Presented to the University in 1950 by the Funk Family.
Some trees with diameter of 4 to 5 feet estimated 500 to 700 years old.
Here students conduct botanical studies.

Funk's Grove Church, erected 1864-65, open to
any denomination. Supervised by members
of the Funk and Stubblefield
Families—who represent the Funk's
Grove Cemetery Association.

Across from the church is located the
outdoor chapel, erected 1956, attended by
thousands of people each year.

State Husking Contest, November 7, 1930, on Eugene D. Funk Farm

Eugene D. Funk Family, 50th Wedding Anniversary

church but one could never describe him as anything but a reverent man. His quiet and easy manner both on the farm, with his family and associates inspired confidence and respect.

E. D. Funk, Sr. often related the story of his Illinois oak sapling to his children. This sturdy tree, rooted deep in the timber of Funk's Grove, towered high above all others like a sentinel. During one of many visits to Florida, Funk had witnessed the burning of a number of pine trees. Funk believed that the owner intended to create a "Nebraska town" in this area, and such destruction moved him deeply. When the same man from Florida visited him later, Funk showed him the towering oak and explained how much it meant to him. The presentation must have been effective because in his last hours the Florida visitor later talked to his son of "The Illinois Sapling." [10]

Mrs. Eugene Funk quoted on many occasions the comment of Theodore Roosevelt: "A mother who raises a family is greater than a general in the army." She was widely known throughout Illinois for active participation in both agricultural and literary groups and was affectionately called "Mother Funk" by all who visited the Farms.[11] She believed implicitly in her children and always recognized their good points and traits; consequently they tried to overcome weakness to gain her praise. If they disappointed her now and then she praised their accomplishments and they responded to her expectations.[12]

Discipline in the family was provided by E. D., Sr. The presence of eight lively children produced noise that could not always be ignored. As the large rooms rang with their laughter and play, his even-voiced "Let's quiet down" never needed repetition. When he said "That's enough now" as he picked up his paper to settle down in his black leather chair in the living room, all was quiet. Other vivid memories of this family group include Fourth of July picnics and displays of fireworks held at a different Funk home each year. There were always enough youngsters to form teams and groups to play baseball, croquet, horseshoes, duck-on-the-rock or tag on any large front lawn.[13] At E. D.'s place a tennis court was available for week-end parties of visiting cousins or for guests who came from town. Generally it was a case of the more the merrier. Many a time there were fourteen or fifteen guests for dinner. Often it was necessary for the cooks to bake bread every other day.[14]

Eugene D. Sr. inspired his children with the wisdom of dreaming a little in order to set their course by an objective worthy of accomplishment. His wife contributed an appreciation for the surrounding beauty in nature and in literature, especially in the poems she loved to quote. Through the years the new home continued as a center of activity, and it became a meeting place for agricultural leaders from all parts of the United States and from foreign countries.[15]

Mamie Funk was a gracious hostess, and some of the best-known names in agricultural circles were counted as her welcome guests. Many an important question affecting the future of an agricultural program was discussed from the extraordinary vantage point of the comfortable top of the wood box in her large kitchen. The children were trained to assume their individual responsibilities when groups came to view the experimental work on the farm. Food was always plentiful, and numbers rarely disturbed the family. The first Home Bureau meeting was held at her home under leadership of Clara Bryan. Mamie Funk became interested in Home Bureau work and was later president of the local group. Her interest in the League of Women Voters and in the D.A.R. continued into the later years of her life. Gene Funk was not a little surprised that his charming wife could assume so well the responsibilities of leadership within these groups. Her love of literature and poetry had won for her a cherished place on the program of the History and Art Club of Bloomington. She was often asked to repeat her poems for the group. Her favorite poems, running to the hundreds in number, were committed to memory as she ironed, rocked the latest baby, churned or picked potato bugs from the vines. This appreciation for poetry was part of that literary interest during her college days back in Oregon. Over the years her selections served to emphasize the wide range of her interests. Her love for poetry may have been inherited from the Bryant side of her family.

Memories of early trips include the visit to Oregon in 1901–02 and the trip to Florida in the winter of 1905 when Mr. and Mrs. E. D. Funk with six children visited New Smyrna, Florida. The two older children attended a private school there. They learned to ride bicycles on the crushed shell streets and made trips to the beach and up the river. These events remained long in their memories and were often relived in the telling.[16]

All of the interests of the family, however, did not center in the home. Deeply aware that their children should have educational advantages, both Mamie and Eugene Funk, Sr. became interested in the consolidated school movement. They contributed their ideas, energy and leadership to the Ben Funk School constructed in 1911–12. Mrs. Eugene D. Funk served as a director for this school for twelve years. She was followed by her son, LaFayette, who became president of the board for the next seventeen years and was president of the board four years at Heyworth. For many years she was consulted regarding programs and policies. Her children attended this school along with those of neighbors and tenants. They wrote for the school paper. The Ben Funk School early became a model in the area. Seven districts in Funk's Grove Township were brought together.

When Eugene D. Funk was in Nebraska at the Omaha convention of the National Corn Association, he and P. G. Holden took the opportunity to visit a consolidated school. The University of Illinois had published a bulletin in 1904 tracing the movement from Massachusetts under a law of 1869 which became operative in 1874. By 1904 twenty states had adopted the idea. The first consolidated school in Illinois was at Seward in Winnebago county in 1904. A superintendent's report for Indiana in 1900 reported 181 wagons transporting 2,599 children in 51 counties.[17] Certainly the grant of land from Ben Funk and the leadership contributed by many of the Funk family in the establishment of the Ben Funk School was a forward step in the development of the consolidated school movement in Illinois.

Later the children lived in Bloomington during the week while they attended University High School on the campus of Illinois State Normal University. The boys played football. LaFayette was captain in 1916. Gene played fullback in 1917. They made many friends in town, where they attended dancing classes and parties. Gladys attended I. S. N. U. for one year after going to Frances Shimer College in northern Illinois. She later attended National Park Seminary in Washington, D. C. Elizabeth attended Washington University in St. Louis and also enrolled at National Park. The boys all attended the University of Illinois. Ruth specialized in art at the University of Pittsburgh. Mary attended the University of Illinois.[18]

While the eight children were growing up, young University students came to help with the scientific programs. They learned to understand and to appreciate the family solidarity. Some of these young men lived in the new home or at the South place. Among them were Curt Rehtmeyer, James Holbert, Du Bois Marquis and Frank Pearson. Rehtmeyer was in charge of the pedigreed sheep and hogs. He also helped Mr. Funk with the buying, selling and showing of stock in many states. He loved the large family of children, read stories to them, taught the boys to box or took them off to Heyworth on Saturday to the old swimming hole on Kickapoo Creek, ending with a banana split in town.[19] These were indeed happy days. He would discuss plays with "Mother" Funk or help Mr. Funk with correspondence and business problems. He was offered a position with the company, but his personal interest in Gladys led him to seek his fortune elsewhere, only to return when she finished her schooling.[20] During the evening, after the discussions about corn, "Jim" Holbert would play the piano and Du Bois would bring his violin. The strong young voices filled the air and it was not unusual for Mr. E. D., Sr. to join with the group. One of the fondest memories of his children is being taken to their grandmother's home, "over the hill and far away," to the tunes of familiar operas sung by their father.

James Holbert recalled the enthusiastic discussions regarding the practical problems relating to corn during these days. His many conversations with Mrs. Funk deeply impressed him. He remembered with gratitude her kindly interest in the years before he established his own home in Bloomington. His loyalty and responsibility to the Company were in no small part due to the continuing influence of his early associations with the family.

A persistent guiding principle in the lives of the E. D. Funk family was the desire to contribute to the betterment of the whole group. Possibly the early dream of E. D., Sr., to bind the diverse families of the third generation together, was responsible for his continuing emphasis on the idea of cooperative responsibility in his own family. He did not demand that his sons and daughters follow any set pattern of training or line of responsibility. Yet it was expected that from their heritage, opportunities and understanding of the problems, and by following their own initiative, they would find a place and contribute substantially to the general scheme of things. Over the years it often appeared that they were growing up slowly. This may have resulted in part from not being given definite areas of responsibility early in their lives. But there were no "bent twigs" in this family. There was indeed a feeling of responsibility on the part of the four sons which appeared in the twenties when they realized that their father needed their help.

Conferences held on Sunday afternoons became customary, when E. D., Sr. exchanged ideas with his sons and charted the next steps in the development of the business. Gladys often attended these meetings. She, in fact, helped to initiate the idea. Realizing that her brothers often hesitated to offer suggestions until they were requested, and that her father was waiting for them to speak up, she arranged opportunities for discussion. The custom has remained part of the procedure of the four Funk brothers. As children they were not commanded to act, nor were they given full rein in the modern method of self expression. They were expected to learn how to express themselves diplomatically if they were to be heard. Gladys wrote, "We stood on our own feet, but we stood, and most of the time we knew why or we boiled inside until we knew how to express our case. The quick Funk temperament of generations was there; but it was, as a farmer would say, 'A field disked over,' as far as our family was concerned." [21]

Gladys was married August 23, 1917 to C. A. Rehtmeyer, who was established in Chicago in the automobile sales business. Their wedding occurred in the spacious living room, with the family in attendance. Mary and Ruth were flower girls. Elizabeth was at the piano, accompanying Du Bois Marquis on the violin. The scene reminded all of the happy days of their childhood. Almost immediately the army called the young husband to duty near Washington, D. C. Gladys remained at first near home, with occasional trips to Washington, where her father was working with the Food Commission. Later she lived there, and Elizabeth attended National Park Seminary. LaFayette, Jr. entered training for the Navy while at the University of Illinois, and Gene, Jr. also was in uniform on the same campus, obtaining S.A.T.C. instruction. After the war Gladys and her family were in Chicago and then moved to Pittsburgh where they established a successful automobile sales agency.

"Aunt Bert," sister of Mrs. Eugene Funk, was a welcome visitor during vacations from her position with the Railway Express in Kansas City, Missouri for some twenty-five years. Her love of art produced oil paintings of the Grove, church and timber.

Marriages in the family occurred with rapidity during the twenties. LaFayette, Jr. married Cleda Otto on July 23, 1919. They built a home across from the Funk farms processing plant, preferring to live in the country. After Elizabeth's church wedding in Bloomington to Robert McCormick in 1923, she and her husband moved to Gibson City, but returned to Bloomington in later years. Gene, Jr. married Maeotta Divelbiss in July 1925 and established his home in Bloomington. Three years later Ruth's wedding took place in the beautiful setting of her Grandmother LaFayette's flower garden near the fountain. Theodore and Elizabeth Holmes were married in 1928 and made their home in nearby Normal. The youngest daughter, Mary, whose wedding took place at home, became Mrs. Lester Ahroon in 1935 and lived for some time in Washington. Paul is a bachelor.

Fortunately for Eugene, Sr., his four sons recognized his need for their help in the middle twenties. They took their places in the operation of the farm and the seed business. Increasing responsibility devolved upon them as their father undertook many tasks requiring absence away from home during these years. LaFayette managed the farm from 1919 to 1927. During the difficult decade of the twenties his knowledge of farming problems enabled him to assume greater responsibilities. Later, as a director of the seed company, he gained considerable practical experience in the business of construction, enabling him in later years to assume supervisory responsibility in the organization. Gene, Jr. worked summers for the company while attending the University of Illinois. After 1925 he worked continuously for the company, learning every phase of the business under the able instruction of H. H. Miller and his father. Although the demands were many, the skills and information he acquired were of immeasurable help to him in later years when he became president of the company. Paul traveled for the company in the years when it was making the transition from a mail order house to a wholesale business. The contacts he established as a member of the Funk family engaged in selling proved beneficial in later years. Theodore took over the responsibility of farm management after 1927, during the difficult years of financial pressure. His businesslike methods and his recognition of the value of increased emphasis on livestock proved to be unusually successful.[22]

Mrs. Eugene D. Funk was chosen as one of the twenty Master Farm Homemakers in the nation and one of five from Illinois during 1929. The movement, less than two years old in March of that year, sought to bring a belated recognition to countless farm women and to celebrate their steady progress.[23] A short biographical sketch of Mrs. Funk included reference to her belief in providing recreation for the children at home. Illustrative of this idea was the pool table in the attic belonging to the boys of the family.[24]

In a speech over WLS in connection with this award during the Homemaker's Hour, she spoke on the subject, "What it Means to Be a Master Homemaker," saying:

I am one of several hundred women who have been so honored. It is not so much what we have done but that we represent a type of modern homemaker.

For many years Mrs. Funk continued to attend yearly reunions of her Illinois group and gained considerable pleasure in the national meetings of this group. She believed that such recognitions gave dignity to life on the farm. With her constant emphasis on the home as the center of life she recalled how her children had gone almost every week on picnics to the woods from the time early spring flowers appeared to late summer when purple asters and goldenrod bloomed.

She also recalled how in 1936 Bill Braid taught the boys to play polo. The field was located north of the house. Hired men, boys and some older men from McLean joined the teams. E. D., Sr., often tried his hand, much to the delight of the onlookers. All of the Funk children loved horses and learned to ride early.[25] The entire family were accomplished riders. They early acquired their own horses. This was especially true of the boys. At one time sixty head roamed the pastures including mares and colts, and eight or nine Palaminos.

Mrs. Funk never relaxed her belief that the country is the only place to live, especially when there are boys and girls to bring up. She was of the opinion that her own children gained a tenacious grasp upon strong traits of character that would bring them the richest returns in their everyday lives.[26]

At a Farmers Institute meeting held in Galesburg, she led a discussion after the main speaker had enlarged upon the role of homemaker as a profession. Mrs. Eugene, Sr. turned to her favorite topic, "Home," describing it as a place to work and "a place of love and relaxation . . . an abode of sympathy and understanding, a place to take all one's troubles and a place to leave them." She added that in her own life, "lived so much within the four walls of home, which might tend to give a narrow view, I have felt the need of going far afield for inspiration to the master minds of the ages. How beautifully the poets see this old world of ours!" She quoted from Edna St. Vincent Millay the poem beginning, "Oh, world, I cannot hold thee close enough," saying that Miss Millay saw the world through rose-colored glasses. She added her own statement, "And sometimes we need them." She chose selections from Walt Whitman and from Robert Browning, two of her favorites, and closed with one from John Burroughs.

The wide choice of poems committed to memory by Mrs. Eugene D. Funk Sr., brought beauty and inspiration to her friends and to her children. She realized that happiness does not come for the asking but is often the reward for a difficult task well-done. She often told her children and her grand-children to ask for strength equal to their responsibilities.

By the decade of the twenties the children of Eugene D. Funk Sr. were ready to assume their places in the operation of the Farm, the Company and community activities. During these years E. D. faced many problems. His friends suggested his name many times for national appointments; he received deserved recognition in the seed· business. He continued to speak effectively for the farmers always considering himself one of this group.

As economic difficulties arose to plague the United States Eugene D. Funk did not cease to search for methods to improve corn and for new cash crops to help the farmers in the mid-west.

CHAPTER XX

Appointments and Appointees

AFTER THE EXPERIENCES of World War I Eugene D. Funk, Sr., accepted additional responsibilities and was accorded considerable recognition by his contemporaries. His leadership was evident in three areas: (1) as a spokesman for agricultural interests (2) as a leader in the American Seed Trade Association and (3) as one of the pioneers in the processing of soybeans and in the introduction of commercial hybrid corn. Although these activities occurred simultaneously through the decade of the twenties, each carried a clear thread of continuity thus forming important chapters in his life. The first two have been combined in the following account. The third is discussed later under the development of the seed company. During this interesting decade Frank Funk was a member of the national House of Representatives. Again in the history of the Funk family of McLean County as in the decade of the 1890's the same two branches of the family received recognition by their participation in the affairs of the nation. They continued the proud tradition of the past by contributing effectively to the present in order to prepare for the future.

Eugene D. Funk participated as a member of the committee on resolutions at a meeting of farmers from the states of Indiana, Illinois, Missouri, Michigan and Iowa, Nebraska and Ohio held in October 1919 at Indianapolis. Recommendations included a ten-hour day in all productive industries "because shorter hours would reduce the amount of production and increase the high cost of living." There was also a suggestion for a league for all industrial organizations to determine controversies arising among them and for enforcing industrial peace. Funk was complimented for the position he took on these subjects.[1]

The University of Wisconsin recognized the "eminent services of Eugene D. Funk in improving a great cereal crop and in devoting time and energy to the upbuilding of American Agriculture." This testimonial was presented February 4, 1920, on recommendation of the College of Agriculture. Eugene Funk was a leader in all agricultural groups.

261

Early in 1920, after two conferences with Herbert Hoover, J. G. Brown of the Indiana Farm Bureau from Monon, Indiana was inquiring from E. D. Funk regarding Hoover's chances as a candidate for the Presidency on the Republican ticket.[2] Funk answered that when he left for Winter Haven, Florida, where he spent the winter, he promised to do all that he could for "my friend and fellow citizen, Frank O. Lowden. I called on a number of Southern leaders and with only one exception they were for Lowden." While at Winter Haven, Funk received a telegram from the *New York World* asking his views on Herbert Hoover for President. He did not answer for publication because he knew that Hoover was not a Democrat. Later he learned that the *World* supported Hoover regardless of politics. Funk, in his acknowledgment of the letter, referred to his great admiration for Hoover and to his experience in working with him during the War. If Hoover were nominated over Lowden from Illinois "you will learn of one man from this state volunteering to stump this or any other states in his behalf and I will be proud to have the opportunity to tell of some of the personal acts of Mr. Hoover of which but very few people know, and so far as I know have never been published." [3] He felt that he would be classed as "two sided" if he were to come out for any other than Lowden. He added, "He also would make a great President and I would not say so if I did not know him." Then he stated that he never would have brought Lowden before the meeting of the Farm Bureau in Chicago if he had not believed him a man for agricultural people. Funk wrote that he and Harvey Sconce brought Lowden over to their meeting from a room where he was speaking to soldiers. Funk stated that Mr. Lowden did not know of their meeting. Funk's idea of a proper candidate for the Presidency was a business man who knew something about agricultural problems. He believed that Lowden and Hoover were alike in many ways.[4]

When Funk was invited to attend a meeting in New York April 8, 1920—apparently in support of Hoover—he refused, saying that he believed that Hoover would not wish him to change from his support already announced for Lowden. He then wrote Hoover directly, enclosing his answer to the invitation. He excused his absence on the grounds of being president of a company attempting to finance a machine to husk corn on the stalk with the annual meeting occurring April 8th.[5] He explained that he promised to support Frank Lowden not only because he was his friend and from Illinois, but also because like Hoover he was "fearless and tied to no clique, gang, or backed by no particular interest." [6] A copy of his Peoria address was enclosed, thus recalling the days of wheat price fixing. Funk was asked by Harry Wheeler and Robert Stevenson in Chicago to join the Hoover movement. He again explained his position, saying, "Mr. Hoover fully concurs with me."

Lowden was never at any time assured of the nomination, but his political position was important as the support for both Leonard Wood and Hiram Johnson increased. Many factors contributed to turn the choice of the nominating convention to Warren G. Harding of Ohio.[7] Funk supported his party's choice.

Following the November election of Warren G. Harding to the Presidency, Funk wrote Brown informing him that during the summer and at fall fairs a number of men had urged him to allow his own name to be presented to the President-elect as a possible appointee for the position of Secretary of Agriculture. He stated that his reply had invariably been that he believed the office should seek the man; that he had never sought political or other honor. He was aware that full support would be necessary "during the evolution of the New Agricultural Era that is now in the making." He asked Brown for a frank answer as to whether he should give any consideration to the matter.[8]

The McLean County Farm Bureau adopted resolutions unanimously calling attention to the eminent qualifications of Eugene D. Funk of McLean county as a "dirt farmer." The eleven reasons for his appointment to the secretaryship outlined in these resolutions were described by the *Pantagraph* as not overdrawn. The editorial continued:

His record as a practical farmer, his understanding of the problems of the farmer, his original research work calculated to increase the yield of grain and to eliminate grain disease, his invaluable service to the state and nation as an always active member of innumerable national and state boards having to do with farming and livestock interests, his "international as well as national version of the place and relations of agriculture to all other industries and occupations," his constant square dealing which has gained him the respect and confidence of farmers every where—all these attributes and accomplishments mark Eugene D. Funk as the best fitted and the logical man for Secretary of Agriculture in the Harding cabinet.

A significant concluding paragraph declared that there was something more than these personal qualifications involved, namely that the great Corn Belt of Illinois—the richest purely agricultural region in the world—was entitled to highest honors occasionally in the Federal Department of Agriculture. This Bloomington, Illinois newspaper stated that Iowa was a great agricultural state also, but that fact did not entitle it to a monopoly on the office of Secretary of Agriculture. The article stated that "Tama Jim" had been secretary from Iowa for sixteen years. The secretary in 1920 was also from Iowa.[9]

President Harding's administration did not heed the request. Henry C. Wallace from Iowa was appointed to the position. Funk, himself, wrote that he had known the new secretary for many years. He was also intimately acquainted with his father who visited him shortly before his death. The elder Wallace gave Eugene Funk, Sr., credit for bringing him before the public in Illinois at the Farmers Institute when his paper was at a turning point in 1894–95.[10]

Funk took no part in advancing his own name for consideration. He recognized the difficulties immediately inherent in the selections when he heard of the appointment to the Secretaryships of Commerce and Agriculture. The animosity between Secretaries Hoover and Wallace owing to the stand taken by the latter in his editorials during the war would not, in Funk's opinion, lead to harmony in the Cabinet.[11] He commented:

Both men are in the habit of having their own way and neither likes to give in to the other. Hoover knows he was right and had the unanimous backing of our committee. Wallace did not stay long enough in the conference that was called to Washington in October, 1918 to learn the main facts of why the 13.3 ratio could not be maintained and he has continued to put the blame on to Hoover through editorial after editorial in his paper. Of course, this was good stuff for his subscribers to read, and in truth was pretty good politics but you and I know how Hoover feels about it. Fortunately there are only a few of us who know the facts.[12]

In view of later interpretations of the strained relations between Secretaries Hoover and Wallace during President Harding's administration this comment by Funk is interesting. Funk believed that the misunderstanding between these two men began before their respective appointments occurred. As J. H. Shideler points out, the differences continued throughout the administration and were accentuated by the belief that the Department of Commerce encroached upon the operating responsibilities of the Department of Agriculture.[13]

There was no lessening of responsibilities and demands. A letter from Congressman Frank Funk referred to E. D.'s possible appearance in 1921 before the Joint Commission of Agricultural Inquiry. Frank Funk was a member of this commission. E. D. wished to remain at home until after threshing, but in the meantime he set about obtaining information.[14] He also sent notes to Secretary of Agriculture Henry C. Wallace and to Secretary of Commerce Herbert Hoover asking for conferences.[15] He wrote his old friend Dave Thompson, now with the Illinois Agricultural Association in Chicago, asking for an interview on his way to Washington.[16] He appeared before the Joint Commission appointed by Congress during June and July. The Joint Congressional Commission of Agricultural Inquiry referred to above was created by Congress in June 1921. Frank Funk of Illinois, Ogden Mills and Peter Ten Eyck of New York, with Hatton Summers of Minnesota and Sydney Anderson of Minnesota, were selected from the House of Representatives. The Senate members of the commission were Lenroot of Wisconsin, Capper of Kansas, McNary of Oregon, Robinson of Arkansas and Harrison of Mississippi.[17]

Late in the year 1921 E. D. Funk wrote to Secretary of Commerce Hoover at the request of many members of the American Seed Trade Association regarding relief work in Russia. Grains were requested from farmers in the central West to be sent both to Russia and to the Near East Relief. Funk favored sending garden and farm seeds by members of the A. S. T. A. He remarked that farmers of the Middle West were not financially able to contribute as they had during the war and immediately thereafter. He said, "Corn is selling as low as 16 cents in Nebraska (I have heard of some selling as low as 9 cents in the Dakotas) and 30 cents in Illinois at a cost of about 58 cents per bushel to produce the crop. Thousands of farmers are facing bankruptcy. Last year a great many landowners either extended credit or cancelled the tenant's share of the rent. Now both landowners and tenants are facing a serious situation.[18] Secretary Hoover replied that it was indeed "a lot of gall" to ask the American farmer to contribute to any charity for anybody, anywhere, at that time. He thought possibly the government would find it possible to purchase grain to ship to Russia, thus relieving two groups at once. The gift corn campaign resulted in the passage of the Russian Relief Act, December 22, 1921.[19]

Secretary Wallace also requested E. D. Funk to participate in the Agricultural Conference called in Washington, January 23, 1922 to consider present and future agricultural problems.[20] Funk attended with two or three hundred other men.[21] Invitations were issued to 439 [22] including farmers, representatives of cooperatives, farm organizations, agricultural journalists, educators and economists, experiment station directors, industries, bankers and congressmen. The real "dirt farmer" appeared to be in the minority. President Harding opened the conference saying that legislators could probably only give the farmers a chance to organize and help themselves.[23] When the executive department called its conference, it was interpreted as an answer to the growing strength of the "farm bloc" in Congress.[24]

Sydney Anderson, who was chairman of the joint commission, reported to the Agricultural Conference in January 1922 regarding the conditions uncovered by the commission. He commented on the rapidity with which all the familiar features of a business cycle were condensed into the two and one half years following World War I. He thought there had never been a time when more public misunderstanding occurred of the fact that the conditions were world wide, growing out of a long period of economic and political dislocations. According to his view, it would be a long time before that continued economic stability described as "normalcy" could be reached. He stated that President Harding recognized this by calling together the conference. The Congress had recognized the problem by creating the commission. The purposes of the commission were to investigate the agricultural situation and to report upon remedial measures. The work of the commission was divided into the following parts: The agricultural crisis and its causes; credit, particularly agricultural credit; transportation; marketing and distribution. Reports on the first and second topics were made before the conference opened. According to Anderson, data for the last two topics was in the process of compilation.[25] M. Benedict described the analyses of the commission as essentially correct but far from satisfying to farm leaders who sought quick action.[26] Delegates to the conference listened to summaries of agricultural conditions throughout the United States. A. Sykes from Iowa analyzed the problems in the Corn Belt, declaring that in forty years of farming he had never seen the farmers' purchasing power reduced to such a level.[27]

Eugene D. Funk was listed as a "farmer" in the group of men attending the conference. He was appointed chairman of a subcommittee under the general division of Committee No. 6 on Crop and Market Statistics. The subcommittee dealt with farms and market statistics. This subcommittee recommended a number of methods whereby the United States Department of Agriculture could improve its informational services. A summary of the conclusions of the subcommittee included (1) collection and publication periodically by the U. S. D. A. of information showing prices received by producers for crop, livestock and live stock products; prices for classes of farm lands and their total value; prices farmers pay for hired labor, seed fertilizers, machinery, equipment and supplies; wholesale and retail prices of principal agricultural products by classes and grades at important market and consuming points; (2) price factors to be published periodically; (3) analysis, correlation and interpretation of data to be presented graphically; (4) statistics from foreign countries should also be made available; (5) there should be Congressional appropriation to enable greater cooperation with the International Institute of Agriculture at Rome; (6) appointment of Agricultural Attache to foreign nations; (7) more adequate dissemination of information by the U. S. D. A.; (8) commendation for the voluntary crop reporters in the United States; (9) the U. S. D. A. should publish frequently reviews of commodity conditions; (10) dates and details of questionnaires should be decided by administrative departments; (11) there should be higher salaries for statisticians concurred with recommendation of joint commission to enlarge the statistical services of the U. S. D. A.[28]

Several points of view were presented during the conference. A group minority advocated price fixing with the major discussions occurring in committees. It was recommended that the idea receive further study. George N. Peek, a delegate, also offered a remedy, now endorsed, for fair exchange value of farm products. However, there was a recommendation that Congress take some action. Congressman Frank Funk elected to the House in 1920 with a plurality of 24,878 votes was a member of the subcommittee on transportation in the Corn Belt.[29] When the report of the committee on transportation was presented, W. H. Stackhouse, representing manufacturers of farm implements, offered a resolution from the floor condemning wage scales of labor. Shideler stated that there was no evidence of any plan by anti-labor industrialists to use the conference for their purposes. Samuel Gompers spoke at length.[30] E. D. Funk commented on the circumstances as follows:

We had quite a time down at Washington. Mr. Gompers again tried his tactics of attempting to dictate to the super advantage of those he represents but he barked up the wrong tree this time. At one time he had a goodly number of the delegates with him, but he spilt the beans by attempting to go too far and it was an interesting sight to note how quickly the crowd changed against him when they fully realized the object of his plans.[31]

The international situation appears to have been given some consideration. An academic economist, Clyde King, is quoted as commenting that the committees gave attention to world problems. The known opposition of the President evidently prevented a resolution requesting American participation in a conference at Genoa.[32]

The depression of 1921 gave impetus to the analyses of the joint commission. The national conference was to provide some kind of national approval for the recommendations of the commission. At least there was an awareness of farmers' problems exhibited by the administration.[33] Funk could see no appreciable relief for agriculture before the next summer, but he believed that Mr. Hoover was doing all possible to secure export of grain to the foreign countries.[34] He declared in February 1922 that the farmer had been hit harder than ever before and that even on the most fertile lands of Illinois, 90 percent of the farmers would be obliged to borrow. He added, "We are hoping for better days, and if they don't come in spite of thunder, every blooming other industry will be drawn into the whirlpool with us." [35] If things were not better he would be obliged to call all his children home from college.

Congressman Frank Funk undertook a trip at the request of the Secretary of Agriculture, who asked him to bring home a report on European conditions. One of the stipulations was that Funk pay his own expenses. In a speech before the Young Men's Club, July 1922 in Bloomington, Illinois, he reviewed situations in France, Austria, England, Scotland and Germany. The falling value of the mark, attitudes of the German people and the Treaty of Versailles were commented upon by the speaker. Cancellation of the war debts and reparations were also discussed. Funk was expected to present a formal report to the Secretary of Agriculture before the Congress met in December 1922.[36]

The agricultural situation continued to worry Gene Funk. He observed in March 1922 that there had been a rise in the grain market but about 90 percent of the farmers were borrowing money to pay taxes. Many were bankrupt. There was a late season with rain throughout the central West. Oats were not planted and the seed corn situation was bad. He wrote: "We are running our germinators to capacity and throwing out from 20 to 50 percent of diseased infected seed corn." There was a short pig crop which he attributed more or less to diseased corn. He believed that farmers would not listen or realize their difficulties for at least another year. He added, "I wish we had the old 'Exposition' going so we could demonstrate some of these things." [37]

Appointments to the Federal Reserve Board were always of interest to the farmers, especially when the question of credit might be involved. This question also arose in early 1922. J. R. Mitchell of the Reserve Board advised Funk in March that the bill amending Section 10 of the Federal Reserve Act increased the number of appointed members on the Board from five to six. This provision had passed the Senate. He described the activities of the Board and expressed himself as pleased at any prospect of Funk's appointment as the agricultural member of the Board.[38] Funk's old friend George Stevenson thought the Farm Bureau would have to become active in order to secure the amendment. If it passed, Funk would have a good chance for the appointment.[39] Funk received many letters from friends, but desired to remain silent. Funk continued to be inactive in his own behalf because of his original belief that the job should seek the man. Public honors, he insisted, should come unsolicited.[40] His good friend Frank I. Mann met with President Harding and at that time urged his appointment. About this time the President inquired if Eugene Funk were the husband of a Mrs. Funk who had made many political speeches. Mann advised him to the contrary,[41] and informed Funk that he had better clarify the matter. Fred Rankin then wrote to Senator McKinley on behalf of Funk, saying that he had known Gene Funk for years and knew that his friends were the ones urging him to seek office. He described Funk as conscientious and unselfish in public service "and has probably given more time without any recompense to public service work than any other man in our agricultural group." Rankin added Gene Funk stood high in all agricultural councils in Illinois and in other states.[42-47] N. H. Owens of *Farm, Stock and Home* pointed out that Funk combined knowledge of and sympathy for farmers' problems with successful business operations.[48]

Appointment was delayed until after the November 1922 election. Funk advised Mitchell on November 23, 1922 that he was certain that he expressed the views of a large percent of the farmers of the central West when he said, "Things in general seem to be moving slowly in Washington and that the farmers are doing a lot of thinking." Although there is some question as to whether this letter was posted, the ideas were certainly indicative of Funk's thinking and of his clear insight into agricultural problems. In the copy found in his files he remarked that he had so informed Senator McCormick before the election in 1922. The results showed that he "was not far off the scent." Funk advised thinking seriously of 1924.

He emphasized the fact that the transportation situation for both grain and livestock was in deplorable condition. Farmers were in a mood to listen to any argument and to blame the administration.[49] Funk did not receive the appointment to the Federal Reserve Board.

Milo D. Campbell of Coldwater, Michigan was appointed to the newly created position. His death, however, occurred within a few months, leaving the position vacant. Friends of Eugene Funk urged him to come out in the open at this time for the appointment. His good friend C. P. Bull of St. Paul, Minnesota was interested in the situation. Funk finally addressed a communication to Secretary Hoover upon the insistence of Senator McKinley during a meeting in Champaign, Illinois. He merely advised Hoover that the two senators from Illinois were supporting him. He did not ask Hoover's support because he did not wish to put into words his reasons for willingness to serve on the Board at this time. Generally speaking, he thought that he could serve agricultural interests to their advantage.[50]

Information arrived indicating support by eleven United States Senators and seven livestock associations from western states with more to follow from Montana and California. Funk realized that he was not too well known in the East. He informed Mitchell of the situation.[51] Senator M. McCormick described Funk as coming from "the greatest family of farmers and corn growers in Illinois"; as an organizer, manager and president of Funk Bros. Seed Co. known all over the Union, "and furthermore is a bank director." He said he knew of no man better fitted for the place than Eugene Funk.[52] Funk reminded Owen T. Reeves of the Corn Exchange National Bank in Chicago that Chicago banks were favorable to his appointment the previous summer but the matter had been handled "by you and others and I had nothing to do with it." He hoped, however, that the support could be revived.[53] He told Senator McCormick that "I am not enough of a politician to know just how to manage this campaign but am going to leave it largely to you and to Senator McKinley." [54] He advised A. G. Leonard of the Union Stock Yards of the situation [55] and then wrote to Secretary Wallace in much the same manner as he wrote to Secretary Hoover—not with the expectation of active support, but to inform him in case the President consulted him.[56]

The situation soon changed. Senator McKinley advised Funk on April 18, 1923 that he had no desire to withdraw his recommendation but had understood from Fred Rankin that Leonard was not a candidate.[57] He was then in receipt of eight telegrams asking for A. G. Leonard's appointment with one signed by C. V. Gregory of the *Prairie Farmer* and another by W. H. Thompson, president of the Illinois Agricultural Association; one from Carlton Trimble, member of the executive committee of the I. A. A., as well as from other members of this committee. The Senator feared the practical result of having two candidates in the field.[58] Funk replied that he doubted that Rankin knew of Leonard's candidacy and that he himself had learned of it by accident one day during the previous weeks when Leonard himself asked Funk to withdraw his name. Funk told Leonard that had he known a week or so before he would have considered the request but could not now do so. Funk recognized two factions in the Farm Bureau set-up, so believed that one faction attempted to bring Leonard forward in opposition to another candidate, Mr. Cunningham. He added: "Thank goodness I have nothing of that sort hanging over me." He referred to many years spent attempting to coordinate various agricultural interests with other activities. He also deplored the actions of those who would ruin the Farm Bureau movement by introducing politics saying, "For this reason I have not sought the endorsement from any state Farm Bureau associations." [59] He had a talk with the president of the American Farm Bureau, Mr. Bradfute. They were in accord. The president would not support any one person.[60]

Funk wrote to De Witt C. Wing of the *Breeders' Gazette* that he greatly appreciated what he and many others had done for his candidacy.[61] He realized, however, from the beginning that the President was not inclined to recognize Illinois on account of political reasons, "as I told those who first insisted on my allowing my name to be presented." Funk believed that the best had happened as far as he was personally concerned. He preferred to remain at home with his family and had only considered the matter because he thought he might help agricultural matters along.[62]

He was also interested in the Christmas 1923 number of the *Gazette* because it contained an article by Frank O. Lowden on "Grain Marketing." He stated to Lowden in reference to the article:

I am more glad than ever that we had our conference before I had an opportunity to read your article, for now it is not necessary for either of us to waste words in explaining how nearly both of us agree on all of the fundamental principles of the great question.[63]

He also referred to how Mr. Mehl changed his mind about Mr. Lowden as one opposing the U. S. Grain Growers Organization.

Freight rates were reduced, but this effort did not prove to be the first answer to the farmers' problems. A national wheat conference was held in June at Chicago during 1923. Conservative groups predominated, with Anderson who was president of the Congressional

Joint Commission as chairman. Then the Farm Bureau called a conference July 23–24 of the same year. Again those who were instrumental in this action were more concerned with long range planning and development of cooperative marketing. Aaron Sapiro, attorney for several California cooperatives, spoke. The conference through a committee of seventeen brought forth a plan for the establishment of the United States Grain Growers, Incorporated in the spring of 1921, with a ratification conference in April of 1921. The Grain Growers Incorporated grew out of the Sapiro movement stressing "cooperation American style." He advocated centralized producer cooperatives entering terminal markets to take over grain selling, warehousing normally handled by commission merchants, line elevator companies and others.[64] What came to be called "administered pricing" was to replace normal procedures of shipping major farm products to large competitive terminal markets at prices determined by the interplay of supply and demand in those markets. Surpluses were not to depress prices but would be held off the domestic market and would be sold at whatever price they would bring, probably abroad.[65] This organization was said to have included representatives from nearly every farmers' organization. G. H. Bustafson of Farmers Union was named president and W. G. Eckhardt, director of Grain Marketing Division of Illinois Agricultural Association became treasurer. Internal dissension broke out almost immediately. The grain exchanges were displeased and the membership campaign lagged.

Mehl was the secretary to the first set of directors who saw and protested against the quarrels and internal disorders as well as the extravagance of the board. Funk said he had been drafted as a member of the new board, starting with a bankrupt situation and the loss of confidence. Mehl's office door was directly opposite the elevator door. Those who might have helped often walked swiftly by. Funk felt the American farmer would follow leaders when the leaders show that they are "on the square."

During December 1923 he inquired of his cousin, Congressman Frank Funk, who was reelected in 1922 with a plurality cut to 6,224 votes, about the merits of the McNary-Haugen bill. He understood that the President and Secretary Wallace were not in agreement about the bill. Legislative proposals during the early 1920's emphasized more direct action. Outside the Congress, George N. Peek and Hugh S. Johnson advocated a two-market system with the producer absorbing his share of the loss. Wheat growers were having considerable difficulty. The first McNary-Haugen bill drawn up by

Charles J. Brand, former chief of The Bureau of Markets, was introduced in 1924. Five McNary-Haugen bills came under consideration 1924–1928. The central idea was to provide for a government export corporation to buy up the specified agricultural commodities and bring up the price in domestic markets to the "ratio price." The Farm Bureau Federation did not support the plan. In January 1924 an amended McNary-Haugen bill was introduced providing for an export corporation. The House debated the bill in May 1924, and it was defeated. Peek became president of the American Council of Agriculture. Efforts were made to gain favor for the plan in the election of 1924. President Coolidge, however, was unfavorable to the McNary-Haugen idea. He did appoint a commission November 7 after the election.[66]

Eugene Funk had also heard in a confidential way that Secretary Wallace was going to leave his position. There was a request that Funk get in line for the job. Senator McKinley and Mr. Hoover were reported to be favorable. An old school friend, one of the leading judges in Boston and a friend of President Coolidge, circulated a pamphlet describing Funk's activities together with mentioning him for the Secretaryship. Funk did not know of this activity until he received one of the circulars. In reply to one letter he answered:

The position you are asking me to consider, should the opportunity present itself, is one of tremendous responsibility. Whoever accepts such a position should feel that he has the cooperation and confidence of those he represents and in a general way also the public confidence. Of course, he cannot expect to please everybody.

Funk believed that something must be done to place agriculture on a parity with other commodities. He thought that cooperative marketing was acceptable in theory but would take years to apply. He also considered the various nationalities composing the farm population as a deterent to cooperation because each wished to judge for himself when and where to market his own product.

E. D. took the opportunity in 1924 to advise his cousin, Frank, regarding the political situation at home. It looked as if the Democrats had helped nominate Republican Len Small for Governor in order to return to the support of their own ticket at the election because they knew that many Republicans would not support Small. He thought Small would not carry McLean county on a Republican vote. Many people had asked him to tell Frank not to line up with any faction but to come home and meet all on an equal footing. He advised, "Saw wood and let the other fellow do the fretting." Then he asked Frank for advice on what action he should take. His boys could run the farm; the seed company was well organized, and he could spare the time to make his living at something else and perhaps save the farm for his children.[67]

E. D. Funk became a member of the Advisory Committee on Agronomy at the University of Illinois in December 1921, an appointment he held until 1944.[68] During the same month he received a letter from his old friend, E. G. Montgomery, then with the Bureau of Foreign and Domestic Commerce. Montgomery referred to a communication from the Illinois Manufacturers Association asking for someone from the Department of Commerce to be present at a joint meeting of manufacturers and farmers the following January in Chicago. He requested information from Funk.[69] The latter answered that he also had received an invitation but was leaving soon for Florida with his mother. Personally he expected nothing from the meeting but "windjammering and perhaps a few resolutions in order that the newspapers may make it appear that the poor (?) farmer is being thought of." He reminded Montgomery of their experience in 1908 at the Great Northern Hotel when "certain interests" attempted to influence them when they "tried to show our brother farmers a way to prosperity." [70] He recalled that he recently had had the opportunity to tell a few of the younger generation now striving for the "Betterment of Agriculture" how true it was that history repeats itself, adding: "To you and to some of us it *is* a bit of history." Funk reiterated that what was needed was a leader in Agriculture. He referred to Farm Bureau problems. He also informed Montgomery that when in Lincoln, Nebraska recently he paid the dues for the National Corn Association —so it still lived! [71]

Personal difficulties, largely financial, troubled E. D. during the decade of the twenties. His father's estate, while a substantial one, nevertheless necessitated borrowing to meet the inheritance tax levies. He wrote his cousin, Congressman Frank H. Funk, to inform him that the papers had been sent to Washington. He and his brother De Loss had borrowed $4,000 more to pay both taxes and interest only the previous week. Gene wrote that borrowing to pay taxes and interest often suggested "another of the Funk estates that will be placed on the market before long unless something happens with our agricultural conditions and that very soon." [72] When labor on the farms demanded $45-$50 a month plus board, E. D. wrote: "We just cannot compete for labor against the high wages of the hard road, garages, and factories in general." [73]

The economic plight of the farmer in the Middle West was of continuing concern to Gene Funk. During the spring of 1924 he brought to the attention of Secretary of Commerce Hoover the poor prospects for the corn crop. This situation occurring after three years of difficulties would spell more misery for the farmer. He spoke of his four sons who worked like beavers: "I can see them going through a period of gradually slipping and losing interest in the farm . . . I have no argument with them when they say, "Dad, you cannot mention another occupation but what we can make more money, less hours and less hard work than farming." Funk regarded this as a typical situation among farmers.[74] Funk, himself, experienced severe financial strain during these years when his own farm income was often channeled to support the seed company. Heavy mortgage obligations and current expense brought agricultural problems into sharp focus for the Funks.

Secretary Hoover answered that he was not so despairing of the future for agriculture. He based his encouragement on the growth of the population and the practical absorption of agricultural reserve areas. He thought that within ten years we might be a food importing country. He added, of course, that this might not occur if there were interruptions such as panics and slumps.[75]

Problems arose with the Grain Growers Association and its relationship to the Grain Marketing Company organized in 1924. The formation of the Grain Marketing Corporation occurred July 28, 1924 with Gray Silver as director. It went out of existence in the summer of 1925. This corporation was to serve as a channel through which several of the largest terminal grain elevators in Chicago, owned by Armour, Rosenbaum and others might be acquired by the Bureau on behalf of the cooperative wheat marketing associations. The concerns would purchase $4,000,000 worth of stock in the company to finance it for one year. An equivalent amount was to be sold to farmers. The season was prosperous but the farmers bought only a small portion of the stock. Neither the Illinois Agricultural Association nor the Indiana Farm Bureau Federation supported the idea. Mr. Lowden predicted its failure.[76]

Calvin Coolidge was elected President in November 1924 in his own right after completing the term for Warren G. Harding, whose death occurred in August 1923. Strikes, the Red scare and the political scandals of the Harding administration occupied the headlines. Yet agricultural leadership was aware that economic difficulties affecting the farmers had not been solved.

The question of the selection of a new Secretary of Agriculture again arose when Henry C. Wallace died during the campaign in 1924.[77] Frank O. Lowden, when urged to accept the position, informed Funk that he was going to disappoint him again because he thought he could be of more service to agriculture out of the department than as a member.[78] J. G. Brown of Monon, Indiana also was suggested for the position by J. D. Harper of the National Live Stock Producers Association.[79] Brown was described as a lifelong friend of Herbert Hoover and as standing high in the councils of President Coolidge. He might possibly be opposed by grain and livestock interests, but not so seriously as some other candidates. At this time Funk stated that he wished to remain neutral, knowing that requests for suggestions from the Farm Bureau and other associations only gave the President time for consideration. Everyone knew that all organizations could never agree on any one man.[80] Funk had learned by experience. He also expected some "wire pulling" at the coming meeting of the International. After a long conference, when Funk begged Lowden to accept the Secretaryship, he realized that Lowden had no idea of participating in the Coolidge administration.[81]

The grain marketing situation continued to cause difficulty. After some discussion with Mr. Keefe of the Grain Growers, in an effort to get Bernard Baruch to come to Chicago, it was decided that E. D. Funk and Mr. Cowles, secretary of the Illinois Agricultural Association should journey to New York. Funk wrote:

We made the trip, but as I told Mr. Baruch, since I had paid my own expenses for almost thirty years in trying to work out some of the problems for the Betterment of Agriculture, I would not at this time make exceptions to the rule by placing myself under obligation to anyone; so I spent a week, stopping off for two days at Washington and two days in New York.[82]

He intended to report on the meeting verbally soon after Mr. Legge returned from Europe. He enclosed a copy of Baruch's suggestions to the Committee for consideration; "He wrote and rewrote several times and gave me final draft just as I left him the second day. Read it carefully. I think you will recognize that he devoted no little time and thought in expressing his views of what he wished to have presented to the committee." Funk also stopped in Washington to secure, if possible, direct information as to the administration's reaction and feeling toward the Grain Marketing Company and said "While most of what was told me was confidential, I will be glad to relate to the committee." He added:

I might say tho that my trip East brought out the fact that the U. S. G. G. Committee is, if rightly and carefully conducted, in a position to accomplish more for the future of American Agriculture than some people ever dreamed of. An opportunity is presented at this time to amalgamate the political interests of all parties together with finance and large commercial interests toward one common cause of trying to solve some of the problems for Agriculture and we will be slackers in our duty if we do not take advantage of the opportunity to act as an unbiased jury that may help to bring about this crying need.[83]

After he listened to discussions from all angles and observed from an outsider's point of view Funk could find only one missing link to ultimate success: "An Agricultural Moses must be found somewhere, somehow, around whom all of these great interests are seeking to throw their entire strength and influence." Funk believed that the administration, financial and commercial interests were now willing to accept and to work with such a man, "provided the various factions in agriculture will throw aside personal and petty jealousy and unite with them for the common good of everybody." He had noticed that 95 percent of the leading business men in commercial circles came from the farm, "and yet when we find ourselves in need of a real leader in Agriculture, there are few men who can qualify." [84] Mr. Legge was expected home in January and then would work with the committee.

Early in January, as chairman of a committee of the U. S. Grain Growers, he wrote Alexander Legge about returning from the recent conversations with Mr. Baruch relative to the merits and demerits of recommending to the members of the U. S. G. C. that they become members of the Grain Marketing Company. Funk asked Legge for another meeting of the committee with him.[85]

Almost a month later a telegram from Herbert Hoover asked Funk to come quietly to Washington.[86] Funk left on February 4th for the Hamilton Hotel in Washington, D. C. He saw President Coolidge three times while in Washington, including breakfast with him at 8 o'clock on Saturday, February 7th. On the same day Funk wired his son, E. D. Funk, Jr., "Favorable but not definite announcement." By the 12th his friends were commenting on a *Chicago Tribune* article.[87]

Funk wrote the same day:

The President called me to Washington last week and I had a conference with him. It was quite a surprise as there had been no effort on my part to bring about such a meeting. He told me he had called me on his own account without any political petitions or endorsements. I don't know what he is going to do. The matter is still up in the air.[88]

The *Tribune* asserted that either Eugene D. Funk or William M. Jardine could receive the Farm portfolio: one, an Illinois farmer; the other a Kansas agricultural college "prexy." The article described Funk as one of the greatest practical farmers of the country, from a family of farmers famous throughout the Corn Belt. The article remarked that he was a cousin of Congressman Frank Funk; that he was educated at Yale and had spent a number of years in post graduate work in German universities; that he was a keen student of agricultural economics and that it was his views "on this phase of production and distribution" that attracted the favorable attention of the President. Although the *Tribune* claimed a little too much in the way of training at German universities, their enthusiasm for a native son of Illinois pitted against a college President may have been the reason.

William M. Jardine was a member of the President's Agricultural Conference then in session in Washington. The Kansas delegation in Congress had endorsed J. C. Mohler for the Secretaryship, but on February 12th rescinded it. They now unanimously backed Jardine. Jardine outlined views before the Senate Committee explaining recommendations of the Agricultural Conference. He stated that agriculture was passing through a normal post-war crisis from which recovery was certain.[89] The *Tribune* noted that Mr. Jardine underwent a stiff cross-examination at the hands of the committee. After he described the conference recommendations dealing with "orderly marketing," Chairman Norris insisted that an "emergency program" was needed. Senator Kendrick (Dem. Wyo.) asserted that the conference report "erred" in placing the blame for the farmers' situation, and Senator Norbeck (Rep. S. D.) complained of the "absence of any reference to causes." [90]

According to the *Tribune*, Dr. Jardine began his career as a cattle puncher in the Big Hole basin of Montana. At 20 he went to Utah Agricultural College. He went to Washington in 1896 and became assistant U. S. cerealist in charge of grain work in the western half of the country. Four years later he became director of agronomy at Kansas State and its president in 1918.[91] A. J. Weaver of Nebraska was also mentioned for the position.[92]

The *Pantagraph* noted that midwestern agricultural interests might object to Funk because he was the choice of Herbert Hoover. According to this article a pledge had been made during the previous campaign to the Republicans of Iowa. This admission came following the announcement that Herbert Hoover, Secretary of Commerce under Harding, had been offered the agricultural post. A midwestern group fighting the program of relief recommended by the President's Agricultural Commission made no concealment of the fact that neither Mr. Hoover nor anyone who might be considered as his candidate would be satisfactory. This claim or pledge came as a sensational climax to the struggle developing over the control of the Department of Agriculture and over alleged encroachments by the Department of Commerce on the Department of Agriculture. These encroachments, according to the *Tribune,* were denied by Mr. Hoover.[93] This newspaper also claimed that the opposition of farmers' organizations to the proposed legislation advanced by the President's Agricultural Commission was so firmly cemented that suggestion of the name of Eugene Funk of Illinois did not meet with their approval. The article continued with the idea that objections to Mr. Funk by Midwestern Farm Organizations was based on the fact that he was considered too close to Mr. Hoover. They claimed that Mr. Hoover was the chief opponent of their export corporation plan. The Farm Bureau severed its connection with Gray Silver, the Washington representative, who was a close adviser to the President's agricultural conference.[94]

Gene Funk finally telegraphed President Coolidge that since his return from Washington he had learned of the telegrams and letters sent to the President. He stated that he had nothing to do with this activity. He had requested people to refrain from such action.[95] The Presidential secretary advised him that the President appreciated the wire and fully understood the situation.[96] Almost immediately the selection of Dr. Jardine as Secretary of Agriculture was announced. Mr. Hoover said in 1955 that President Coolidge offered him the appointment but that he refused. He added, "I recommended both Mr. Funk and Jardine to Coolidge. I told him I thought Mr. Funk was a more experienced administrative mind and asked the President to see him. Senator Capper played a large part in this picture." [97] Funk's wire of congratulation and offer of assistance followed.[98]

On the same day, February 14th, W. W. Burch of the *American Sheep Breeders* from the Union Stock Yards praised the Centennial catalogue of the seed company, adding: "We hope Gene Funk is made Secretary of Agriculture. The Funk family has done more for agriculture in the Midwest than any other influence." Judge Homer Hall wrote on the same day that although the two U. S. Senators from Illinois had not endorsed Funk, a word from Senators Deneen and West might help. He described Funk "as an exemplary man," and said, "In fact he is one of the best of the Funks and you know there are a number of good Funks. He is not making any active canvass for the job. In fact he has insisted that no special efforts be made for him." Hall pointed out that Funk was not engaged in factional politics; that Iowa had had the position for some time and Illinois deserved the position; that he did not know of a single objection. Strong forces were operating in the political arena.[99]

Funk sent word to Secretary Hoover:

May I take this opportunity to thank you for all that you have done for me. Perhaps after all, it is best. Let us hope so anyway. I know where your heart is relative to the success of American Agriculture. I intend to see that others become acquainted with the facts as well.[100]

He also informed his good friend Dave Thompson of seeing President Coolidge three times during his brief stay in Washington, at lunch and at breakfast. He recalled that "we went over many things and I left him with every assurance that I would be asked to return, but politics are politics and the other fellow overbalanced me at the last minute. Anyhow my hands are clean and I would rather be where I am than have the position if I had to resort to work which is against my principle." [101] At his last conference with the President he had been led to believe that the President was going to ask an Illinois farmer "to carry on with some of his agricultural ideas," but evidently the "political gang" was too strongly entrenched.[102] Funk declared that he wanted nothing of such a position if he had to resort to political intrigue to obtain it. After relating the same account to "Charlie" Funk, he added that Senator Capper, the Senate whip, got busy at the last minute.[103] He was also of the opinion that his last telegram to the President, sent when he sensed that something was happening, had some influence. He had told the President to do what he thought best "For the Betterment of Agriculture." This, in effect, was a kind of a release from any implied Presidential promise.

In his letter to N. H. Gentry he wrote:

I am really glad that he decided to appoint the other fellow. I know that a general shakeup was due in the Department and some of those who would have to go have been friends of mine for years and it would have been a difficult and painful undertaking to have had to ask for the resignation of so many men.

Funk hoped that Secretary Jardine would make a clean sweep of dead timber and clear the atmosphere of petty jealousies there since World War I.[104]

In a letter to James O'Donnell of the Bloomington *Bulletin,* Funk expressed his appreciation for the printing of a signed letter from Herbert Hoover setting forth his own views for American agriculture. He especially appreciated this because of his belief that people had been led to think that the sympathy of the Secretary of Commerce was not with the farmer.[105] In this situation he thought that a real injustice had been done:

I have been in a position to study and know Herbert Hoover as well as any man in America. I was closely connected with his activities during the war in the Food Administration. I have held several interviews with him since then. I know his ambition is to try to bring about the amalgamation and cooperation of agriculture with commercial activities insofar as it is possible and practical to accomplish. I know that he has and is now sacrificing his own interests for you and for me and for the producer and for the consumer in order to make the United States of America the best country on earth in which to live.

Modest in the sense of seeking publicity for himself he has suffered on account of publicity given out by those who are jealous of his activities and ability to analyze a situation as it usually is.

Funk was sincere in his continued devotion to Hoover. He believed that his training as an engineer influenced him to seek facts before acting; that like others he could make mistakes; that he refused the appointment as Secretary of Agriculture in order to be of more value to agriculture as Secretary of Commerce. He stated that he worked sixteen hours a day for his country.

Political alignments and leadership in national and state politics were undergoing many changes. It was increasingly difficult to determine the pressures and the economic forces influential in producing decisions. Eugene Funk, Sr., brought a wealth of information and understanding of agricultural problems to the decade of the 1920's. He never sought political recognition, but at the same time he did not avoid responsibility. He gave generously of his knowledge and he participated actively when called upon. Like his great grandfather, his father and his uncles, he spoke courageously for the farmer. He always described himself as one of this group. He knew instinctively when their welfare was in jeopardy.

CHAPTER XXI

Problems and Persistence

EUGENE D. FUNK BECAME president of the American Seed Trade Association in 1925. His election to this important office was a mark of distinction and respect. Funk Bros. Seed Co. had been a member of the association since 1902. The choice of Funk, who had been vice president during the preceding term, was made in part because of his leadership in national agricultural affairs and because of his wide acquaintanceship in governmental circles. The election of Funk was a departure from the usual selection of a garden seedsman. The seed trade faced problems in the middle twenties and sought the strongest possible choice for the Presidency. Funk had been brought before the association as early as 1921, when he delivered an address in St. Louis entitled, "Latest Developments in Corn Breeding." [1]

At the time of the 1921 speech E. D. Funk was torn between an invitation to attend a reunion of his class at Yale University and his feeling of responsibility to say a few of the things that were on his mind. He referred in his address to the cooperation that his company had received over the years from the government and the universities, as well as to the inspiration from the excellent papers heard during the meetings of the association. He admitted that he had profited greatly when some member had the courage to offer criticisms to the group. At this time he called its attention to the alarming problem of corn diseases.[2]

When Funk accepted the presidency he recalled that his first attendance occurred during the presidency of Jesse Northrup, a person "who gave to us an inspiration to try to do the best we could, not only for ourselves but for our country and our association, and particularly for the younger men of the association." Funk hoped to be able to do the same for others.[3]

The American Seed Trade Association in 1925, with the Wholesale Grass Seed Dealers, was made up of members who handled commercially over 70 percent of the flower, garden and farm seeds.[4] Funk referred in his presidential address to the necessity for a national agricultural program. His chief emphasis was upon cooperation with state experiment stations and with the U. S. D. A. He drew upon the examples of such cooperation on the Funk Farms to support his ideas. He again stressed the need for the preservation of soil fertility and attention to the problem of standard farm lands. Professor W. L. Burlison from the University of Illinois spoke on the subject, "Agricultural Experiment Stations and their Relation to the Seed Trade." During 1926 Funk appeared on the program of the Seed Marketing Conference to speak on "The Seed Requirements of the Modern Farmer." W. A. Wheeler of the U. S. D. A. was in charge of these conferences, where problems of seed certification were discussed.[5]

The third McNary-Haugen bill was introduced in 1926 and lost May 21 in the House by a vote of 212 to 167. Against this background, Congressman Frank Funk formulated his ideas on the agricultural problem.[6] He did not speak at length on farm legislation until January 29, 1926, when he called attention to some of the hard times experienced by farmers of the Middle West, particularly in the Corn Belt. He stated that in his own district, located in the heart of the Corn Belt, 80 percent or more of the people were engaged in or were dependent on agriculture. He added: "Two of the five counties in the United States producing the largest annual value in agricultural products, McLean and Livingston, are a part of the district which I represent." He said the Corn Belt farmer was not asking for any new or different legislation from that already enacted for the benefit of other lines of business—only for a square deal. He believed that benefit conferred on one class of business should also be available to others. Then he added that whenever 40,000,000 people engaged in agriculture requested legislation to stabilize and place their business on an equality with others, they met opposition. Objections of "economically unsound," of "innovation" and of "sets aside rules of supply and demand" were then heard.

Referring to Lincoln's famous statement about a nation unable to exist half slave and half free, Funk claimed that farmers of the Middle West insisted that the people could not exist one-half protected by legislation and one-half unprotected. He said the farmers of the Middle West were in earnest in demanding relief, as was shown by resolutions unanimously adopted by the Illinois Agricultural Association, by the Illinois General Assembly and by the Corn Belt Committee of the American Council of Agriculture in sessions in Des Moines, December 21–22, 1925, and by the conference at Des Moines, January 28, 1926. He asked unanimous consent to print these resolutions as a part of his remarks. They follow his speech in the

Congressional Record. He referred to the many solutions for the farmers' problems, including Secretary Jardine's reported statement, "The best way out is for the farmer to work out his own salvation, that the farmer must help himself." Funk answered that the nature of the farming business prevented this type of solution because farmers were not organized to control prices as other industries were. He also referred to the speech of President Coolidge before the Farm Bureau, December 7, 1925 suggesting that the most important legislative aid would come through the creation of cooperatives. Funk said the farmers did not object to this, "but every practical man knows that it will take at least a generation or two before this idea can be put into effect." He interpreted the various legislative remedies [7] as of possible aid. Restoration of the purchasing power of the farmers' dollar Funk believed would provide the greatest remedy.

Congressman Funk stressed the fact that prices paid for farm products were far below those of other commodities. This was true, he said, because "the so-called natural law of supply and demand has been arbitrarily set aside by legislative action and results in the establishment of prices by trusts and combinations. The tariff laws kept out goods from other countries where labor costs are far below that in America." Funk recognized the situation in 1926 when he said:

In other words, The farmer buys on a protected market but he produces a surplus of grain in excess of domestic requirements. The price he received for this surplus established the price of grain consumed in America.

Yet he believed it was in the best interests of the American people to produce a surplus. He added that food producers should not be forced to accept world prices for food consumed in this country because of a surplus. He believed the surplus was an insurance policy to all for sufficient supplies each and every year.

Referring to the protective tariff system as of great benefit to the farmer, who had a protective tariff for practically all his products, Funk observed that protective tariffs did not raise prices for articles in surplus over demands for domestic consumption.[8]

He also expressed the hope that an export farm crop corporation would be authorized by the Congress, controlled by the Federal Government. Farmers could not restrict their output as the industrialist when business was poor. He closed by saying that he could see no hope until Congress disregarded precedent and by "setting aside the so-called laws of supply and demand" would enact direct legislation to raise the income level of the farmers as it had legislatively protected the income of other groups.[9]

At home in Bloomington, Illinois, Eugene Funk appreciated the kind words of Congressman Henry T. Rainey from Carrollton, Illinois regarding an address before the Illinois Manufacturers Association. He explained to Rainey that he could not refrain from referring to the committee to which they both had given considerable time. Regretting that the committee had not been able to get out a final report, he said, "Perhaps it is just as well, as conditions seem to be going from bad to worse and what we say today is obsolete tomorrow." [10]

Discussion of the "deplorable condition" of agriculture was uppermost when visitors from other states arrived at the offices of the Seed Company. An unidentified visitor from Ohio called upon ex-Governor Fifer and Gene Funk. Funk wrote Frank Lowden to ask if he would meet with a group composed of Fifer, who did not attend; Mr. Hoke Donithen of Marion, Ohio; Mr. Joe Hutzell of Fort Wayne; R. S. Woodrow of Toledo, formerly of Illinois, and Funk himself. The party was to assemble in Bloomington the night before and proceed the next day to Oregon, Illinois, home of Mr. Lowden. Funk explained: "It was thought best to have this conference at your home so as to avoid any possibility of publicity in any way." [11] Lowden wired that he would expect them to arrive any time between April 14 and 20, 1926.[12] Funk replied that they would leave on the following Saturday, the 17th, with six in the party.[13] Lowden then advised that he had received a similar letter from Harvey Sconce and suggested inviting him to join the group.[14] A week after the meeting Funk told Lowden that the men from Ohio and Indiana were greatly pleased with their discussion. They stayed in Chicago over Sunday "and planned a quiet campaign for the immediate future. All agreed that they had received from you a broader view of the whole situation and realize now as they never had known before of the seriousness of the agricultural conditions and inevitable results if something is not done, and they are more convinced than ever that you are the one to lead the procession." According to W. T. Hutchinson, biographer of Lowden, this action by Funk supported by ex-Governor Fifer from Bloomington apparently spearheaded the early efforts to influence Lowden in 1926 to undertake a well-organized and well-planned political campaign for the Presidential nomination in 1928.[15] Funk reported that he attended the state Republican convention in Springfield, where he talked to a few of their immediate friends. All said that they would attend any preliminary meeting that might be called. Funk realized that Lowden would be away in June 1926 and that it was a long time until June 1928. He recalled that Donithen told him that Harding's campaign was arranged two years in advance of the convention by about fifty men in Ohio. Funk asked Lowden:

Conforming to your wishes, would you think it advisable to have say twenty or twenty-five men from Illinois meet here at my home sometime before you sail for Europe and would you be willing to meet with them? It need be known only to those who are invited. Delegates of farmers often come here to see our seed corn plots and it need not lead to any suspicion as to what the meeting is for. You of course to set the date to suit your convenience. Also will you have any special friends that you would like to have present.

He added that he had read Lowden's article appearing in *Worlds Work* in October 1925.[16] This article recommended a modified McNary-Haugen proposal. Until the appearance of this article few knew that Lowden had supported the equalization fee some six months before as it was brought forward by Congressman Dickinson. Peek and Lowden both backed this proposal.[17]

Funk also informed Dean Davenport that "our bank" has over $10,000,000 loaned on farm mortgages in this (McLean) county; the third county in the United States, "and not a dollar of the principal was paid this year."[18] He declared that he had "never come out in the open in active politics, but it begins to look as though something has got to be done to place a man in the Presidential chair who has some knowledge of the farmers' conditions west of the Allegheny Mountains." He told Davenport, whose summer home was located in Woodland, Michigan, that they were working quietly for Lowden. He asked about the situation in that state. He added, "We do not care to make any announcement before the fall elections, but Ohio and Indiana are telling us they are ready to join Illinois in placing his name before the Republican convention two years hence."[19]

Congressman Frank Funk spoke in favor of immediate farm relief legislation, in the House on Saturday, May 8, 1926. After three or four days of discussion on the pending bills, he thought that the membership of the house would have been fully advised as to the seriousness of the situation of the farmers. But that very day in the House restaurant a man from the Atlantic seaboard said that there was no farm problem. Funk said that he could not speak for the rest of the country but he was going to speak for his own district; "I represent a district in central Illinois in the heart of the Corn Belt, where the bulk of the land produces corn, and I speak for the Corn Belt farmer."[20] He declared himself to be one who supported the Haugen bill. He represented 5,000 members of the Farm Bureau, the total membership in the five counties of his district. Three out of five farm bureaus had requested him not to vote for the Tincher bill because they regarded it as an inadequate makeshift. This bill provided for the establishment and government recognition of cooperative societies. Funk believed that it would take a generation to get farmers identified with such groups, and that it could not be administered by government in 50 years. He supported the Haugen bill because the corn farmers needed immediate action. This Congress faced the most serious crisis since the war.

Congressman Funk believed in a balanced industry. He would vote for the Haugen bill as brought in, but thought that the equalization fee for each product should take care of the loss due to the surplus in each crop. He stated that he would vote for the subsidy of $350,000,000 or $375,000,000, but opposed requesting it. He then announced that a subsidy did not frighten him. He was amazed at those men of intelligence who argued that the farmer was in difficulty but interpreted legislative remedies as interference with laws of supply and demand. These men also described the proposition as economically unsound or remarked that Adam Smith did not teach this in his elementary treatise on economics. F. Funk said that 40,000,000 people who were engaged in agriculture could not understand why they were not entitled to the same legislative benefits as other groups. Frank Funk then referred to his seven years as a member of the Illinois State Public Utilities Commission under two governors, not as a lawyer, but as a farmer. He turned to his present colleague, Governor Yates, from Illinois also in the House, for corroboration:

I can see greater interest in the business and the production of food for the public, and I claim, therefore, it is charged with even a higher interest by the government and by the State than is the property of the utilities corporation. I can do without my telephone—I can walk home—I can do without gas—but the people of our country cannot do without food, nor can anyone else.[21]

Word came to Gene Funk that administrative policy was to turn everything concerning agricultural legislation over to Mr. Hoover, and that President Coolidge, "seeing the trend of things," was grooming Hoover for President. It was suggested that Funk communicate with Secretary Hoover and urge some immediate helpful program, since he was the only man who could influence President Coolidge to listen. Seven or eight thousand telegrams sent to Hoover might help. If Lowden would call on Mr. Crissinger, governor of the Federal

Reserve Board, he would receive interesting and useful material.[22]

Funk wrote Lowden referring to a recent visit with Governor Fifer and his grandson at Lowden's home and to Lowden's trip to Elkhart. He informed Lowden of the confidential information he had received.[23] This was received before Lowden sailed for Europe on June 5. He was encouraged by the fact that the people of the country were beginning to realize that there was a farm problem, even if legislation was not forthcoming.[24]

E. D. Funk was of the opinion that the emergency would be eased by taking care of a small percentage of the surplus farm crops and finished live stock products immediately. The average manufacturer, banker or merchant could forsee the possibility of political and internal strife if something were not done to relieve the situation.[25]

The House of Representatives rejected the Haugen bill by a sectional rather than a partisan vote and pigeonholed the Tincher bill.[26] By November 1926, E. D. Funk could say to Lowden that it looked to him as if the path was opening for a "straight shoot" to the White House.[27] Lowden answered, thanked E. D. for calling his attention to an article on the *Corn Borer,* and expressed appreciation for the kind wishes. He added, "Hope that our paths will cross soon. When are you to be in Chicago again and for how long? Or are you likely to be coming this way at any time in the near future?" [28] Funk answered Lowden, saying he would be in Chicago about January 13th at the time of the executive committee meeting of the A. S. T. A.[29] Lowden answered that he had nothing special to talk about but added: "It is always refreshing to have a visit with you." He designated three days of the following week in January when he would be at the Blackstone in Chicago. He hoped they would meet.[30] Funk held to his dates, the 13th and 14th of January, at the time of A. S. T. A. meeting, saying that if Lowden were in the city he would be glad to arrange a conference.[31]

Eugene Funk, farmer, appeared in Chicago at a hearing of the Business Men's Commission on Agriculture, described as an independent body of inquiry and recommendation appointed jointly by the National Industrial Conference Board, Inc., and the Chamber of Commerce of the United States. In talking with industrialists and bankers in the large cities of Washington, Chicago and New York, Funk found them uninformed about "farmers'" problems. They usually thought of the farmer as an ignorant person. Funk believed the farmer was as well informed as many city dwellers but isolated because he had no group activity. Funk pointed out that 82 percent of the men in *Who's Who* were once farm lads, and that in large cities 95 percent of the leading men had begun as farm boys. If farm boys moving to cities were supplanted by imported labor, peasantry was possible. Funk said that no other group could think of living for seven years unable to receive for commodities the price of their production. Funk feared that these conditions would produce Bolshevism in the cities. With abandoned farms, lack of production and high prices, the farmer stops buying, the manufacturer no longer produces goods and hunger results in the cities. Hungry men become desperate. He described the unprofitable occupation of farming in terms of cost accounting. On the average, the farms paid only hired man's wages to the operator and 5 percent interest on a value of $115 an acre for land and buildings. Real estate value varied from $115, one half of pre-war valuation, to $60 an acre.

Questions followed his explanation. When he was asked about fair tests of farming, he observed that operators of dairy farms could cut down more easily than grain farmers. He knew of no way to estimate demand. He thought the surplus was only temporary. In McLean County 90 percent of farmers borrowed money to pay their taxes. He also commented on the taxing system as it affected land, livestock, grain and equipment. When asked what remedy he would provide, Funk answered:

I think the Government should form an agricultural policy to perpetuate America for all time. It is just as vital as the protective system, if not more so, since it is food that we are more dependent upon we should protect the soil by fertilization, by crop rotation, by reforestation.

He described the McNary-Haugen bill as the best remedy thus far proposed.[32]

On February 19, 1927 Funk was impelled to wire Secretary Hoover as follows:

Hundreds of thousands of our best farmers are already broke. Many more are on the ragged edge. This morning's paper carries two full pages of closing out farm sales. The purchasing power of the farmer is rapidly approaching naught. Our merchants are curtailing orders. Farmers are not renewing orders for farm seeds. Interest and taxes cannot be met. We must not allow ourselves to misunderstand this critical situation. In order to save our country, our agriculture and the Republican Party and perhaps ultimately avoid Revolution within the ranks of unemployment in congested centers, in my judgment there is no alternative under the circumstances than to permit the McNary-Haugen bill to become a law.[33]

The *Pantagraph* stated that the same wire was sent to President

Coolidge. Funk believed that if Coolidge vetoed the measure, it was because he was misinformed and had no personal touch with people who knew the actual situation, although he had close contact with the group that opposed the measure. "That is natural for a New England man," [34] said Funk.

Funk informed Lowden in March that he was leaving for Winter Haven, Florida and would try to talk with a Mr. Genon of the Internal Revenue Office and a Republican bellwether. Funk asked if there was anyone he should see there between March 22 and April 4. He asked if there was anything to be done in Illinois.[35] In May he was answering inquiries about Lowden by saying that he had known him and his family for twenty-five years; that everyone considered that he was one of the best Governors Illinois ever had; that he had brought unity out of chaos with good business policy. He described Lowden as a fearless fellowman who spurned dictation but was open to reason. He believed that he thoroughly understood the agricultural situation, realizing that something must be done about the equalization programs, thus permitting at least one-third of the population to share on equal terms with the other two-thirds.[36] In Florida Funk saw Judge Walker, an attorney in Edwards County, who thought it quite possible to secure six out of the eight delegates for Lowden.[37] Lowden expressed thanks and hoped to see Funk in the near future "and go over things with you." He had placed Walker's letter in the hands of friends [38] who were interesting themselves in the matter.[39] Meanwhile Walker was hopeful that if anything were discussed with him it would be done soon.[40] The judge was coming north, and Funk advised Lowden that he would not act unless Lowden suggested action. Lowden advised that this matter was being handled entirely by Omer N. Custer of Galesburg, Illinois and Clarence F. Buck of Chicago. "I shall refer it to them," he said, "I do appreciate your kindness." [41]

C. F. Buck informed Funk of a visit to Lowden from Governor McMullen of Nebraska, predicting resolutions similar to those from Indiana; of a visit from W. L. Stockton, president of the Montana Farm Bureau with a committee having similar resolutions. W. R. Hearst stated that Coolidge would be unable to overcome a third term prejudice. Then he pointed to the fact that he had written Buck about the matter but had received no reply.[42] On the next day Funk answered, indicating that he had been in Detroit for two weeks. He expressed Walker's disappointment in not seeing either Lowden or Buck, adding:

I telephoned the Governor that the Judge would be in Chicago and I had intended going up to Chicago to sit in with this conference but the Governor did not give me encouragement that he cared to meet Judge Walker and I did not insist to push this matter.[43]

He said, however, that when he was in Florida he had tried to feel out the situation for Lowden as he had done in 1920. He believed that Florida was rapidly becoming a Republican state. There were two factions in the Republican primaries in the South: Those who would hold office under the present administration and those who would go with a winning candidate.[44]

Lowden thanked Funk for a copy of his interview in the (Cleveland) *Plain Dealer*.[45] Funk informed Lowden of what he had written Buck and said that he himself refrained from having further correspondence with Walker.[46] He remarked that if Lowden and Buck would indicate what was best to do, he would act accordingly. Buck had remarked that he knew Walker very well. Lowden replied:

I cannot tell you how greatly I appreciate your kindness and I am sure you will find that Senator Buck will handle this matter in accordance with your views.[47]

Funk departed for two weeks in Michigan, Ohio and Indiana to inspect the corn borer area with the Agronomy Advisory Committee [48] of the University of Illinois. The candidacy of Herbert Hoover gained momentum in 1927. Lowden was reluctant to announce his candidacy and to empower his campaign manager to act.[49]

If Eugene D. Funk recognized that Lowden's chances for the nomination were encountering difficulty, there is no record of such a reaction in his available papers. Nor is there any indication of wavering loyalty to the man from Sinnissippi whose candidacy he had urged and implemented.

While leadership demanded time and attention, and responsible spokesmanship became necessary, agricultural difficulties increased. Political leadership was under close observation, and legislative remedies were under consideration. The election of 1928 aroused interest because of the agricultural problems and the choice of candidates for the Presidency by major parties. Funk played an active part in the campaign of 1928.

CHAPTER XXII

Confidence Amid Confusion

E. D. FUNK FIRST WAS INTERESTED in the candidacy of Governor Lowden for the Republican nomination in 1928. Funk's friend, Herbert Hoover, also became a potential Republican candidate. He continued to support his first choice as in 1920, but also learned that Hoover's position on price fixing during the First World War was being questioned. Funk's knowledge of the events of 1917–18 impelled him to speak during the 1928 Presidential campaign.

Choices of nominees in 1928 presented problems for both major parties. Frank Lowden, supported by many midwestern farm leaders, was not acceptable to some eastern leaders. Moreover, there was a split within the Republican ranks in Illinois, with Mayor Thompson of Chicago controlling one group. There was also growing support for the nomination of Charles G. Dawes, a not-too-distant neighbor of Lowden. His selection probably would have pleased some Coolidge men, since he would draw support from Lowden. The Hoover boom was noticeable in early 1928. If Eugene Funk was confused by the turn of events, there is nothing to prove it in his correspondence. He was aware, however, that it was difficult to obtain positive statements from Lowden or from his campaign manager.[1]

When the challenges to those who participated in the price fixing activities of the period of World War I appeared, there was little that Eugene Funk could do except tell the story as he recalled it. He was one of the few who could speak about those wartime actions. As the repetition of the 1918 story continued, Eugene Funk urged Secretary Hoover to make clear his ideas about agriculture in 1928.

The Kansas City *Star* referred to the many statements about the responsibility for the war price of wheat since the introduction of the McNary-Haugen bill. Some leaders in public addresses blamed Herbert Hoover, U. S. Food Administrator in 1917–18. Many inquiries about Hoover's connection with this wartime problem influenced the Star to send to headquarters for information. Mr. Hoover was charged with arbitrarily and unfairly holding down farmers' profits for the benefit of England. Dr. Garfield, chairman of the commission approved by President Wilson to determine the price of 1917 wheat, contacted the living members of the committee. Fortunately Garfield had preserved the basic data. He stated unequivocally that Mr. Hoover had nothing to do with the matter other than to urge President Wilson to protect the American farmer. The surviving members of The Committee in 1928 were Mr. Charles Barrett, president of the Farmers Union; L. J. Taber, master of the National Grange; E. D. Funk, President of the National Corn Association, and W. J. Shortbill, Secretary of the Farmers Cooperative Elevator Association. These gentlemen signed the document agreeing with Mr. Taussig and Chairman Garfield.[2]

The signed statement declared that the occasion for establishing a fair price arose from the fact that the Allied Governments had consolidated their buying agencies into one agency and through this power over the surplus controlled the price of American wheat the moment that exports of new crop began. Allied buying agencies thought they should not pay more than $1.50–$1.80 for the wheat. They advanced the idea that there was abundant wheat in the Argentine and in Australia at prices ranging from $1.25 to $1.50 per bushel. Furthermore, they had fixed the price for their own farmers at about $1.80 per bushel. Their reason for purchasing American wheat was to free allied ships from long voyages thru the southern hemisphere to carry American crops. They felt they should not pay in excess of these prices. Garfield and others claimed that President Wilson appointed the committee directly and the commission declared the price of $2.20. Congress fixed the 1918 price at 20 cents less, or $2.00 per bushel. Mr. Hoover, according to the statement, was not a member of the commission and took no part in its deliberations or conclusions.[3]

E. D. Funk sent a copy of the signed statement prepared by Dr. Garfield regarding the price fixing situation to C. J. Gross, president of the Piatt County Farm Bureau at Monticello, Illinois. He told Gross of the samples of letters coming to his attention. Funk urged Secretary Hoover to give an interview about agricultural relief and future development which would help to clear the atmosphere throughout the Middle West and Southern states.[4] Funk's answer to C. J. Gross was semi-confidential, with a request to be so treated until after the National Republican Convention.

Funk was caught as in 1920, because his two friends, Lowden and Hoover, were again leading candidates in 1928. Both men were "close friends of mine," and for this reason alone, he said, "I have the best of reasons for not being drawn into the whirlpool any further than it is absolutely necessary at this time. Both are good Presidential timber and I will be glad to take my coat and shirt too, off to help elect either man President." Nevertheless, he felt Hoover was accused of things for which he was not personally responsible.

According to Funk, Congress had authorized a minimum price for the 1918 wheat crop of $2.00 per bushel, "and Mr. Hoover requested me to find out as best I could what the farmers in the wheat growing districts would be willing to accept for their 1917 crop of wheat." All of the replies from over 40,000 farmers averaged about $1.87½ per bushel. As Funk said, "That was the average price the farmers themselves were willing to take for their unharvested wheat in June 1917." Then, he continued, sometime in August came notification that from a list of forty names submitted to President Wilson, Funk was chosen with eleven others to make a detailed study of the cost of production to determine a fair price for the 1917 crop.

Funk also recalled that he was later, a member of the Advisory Committee for both the Agricultural Department and the Food Administration. This committee and subcommittee working on problems for 1918 had almost daily conferences with Mr. Hoover during eighteen months. Funk said often that they did not agree "but I have no recollection nor do my notebooks record any occasion where we did not iron out a common understanding and agreement of proceedings." The Agricultural Advisory Committee agreed with Mr. Hoover that the ratio price of 13 to 1 on the price of hogs could not be maintained when corn reached two dollars per bushel and when England, France, Belgium and Italy all concentrated their buying price in the hands of one man who refused to go above a certain price on fats and pork products.[5]

Then Funk straightened out more chronology: "It was at this point that Mr. Henry Wallace, afterwards Secretary of Agriculture, and Mr. Harding crossed swords with Mr. Hoover. Now it so happened that Mr. Wallace was also a close friend of mine, and I knew Mr. Wallace at that time better than I did Mr. Hoover. But Mr. Wallace did not then (and I don't think ever did) understand the real situation. Mr. Wallace was not a member of the Advisory Committee and he was not in touch with the inside information that the committee held." Funk stated, "I felt then and feel now that Hoover tried to play the game square." He added that he believed that it mattered little in 1928 to the average farmer what had gone on during the war. What he really wanted to know was what would happen to him and his family in the very near future. Then Funk believed that Hoover would make a gross mistake if he did not come out with an open statement on the current agricultural situation. Funk believed that the situation was so acute that nothing could prevent its becoming a national political issue because the Middle West was in no mood to be trifled with.

Funk left for Washington at the invitation of the president of the U. S. Chamber of Commerce, to meet the first week in June with the Federal Reserve Board. He asked Mr. Hoover for an interview.[6] At this interview, as Funk later said, he advised Secretary Hoover that he was supporting Lowden. It is well to keep in mind that this meeting occurred in the early part of June 1928. Mr. Hoover stated in 1955, "I knew of his preference for Governor Lowden as the candidate and respected his reasons." The circumstances later causing the withdrawal of Lowden left the way open for Mr. Hoover's nomination by the Republican convention in June 1928.[7]

Funk was concerned about propaganda circulating in Illinois during early July. He told Hoover that he could help "squelch" some of it, "If you will send me a personal letter stating your views on agriculture." He asked for three copies of the same letter, signed by the nominee; one to send in answer to letters; one to carry in his pocket to show to farm leaders as he met them. Hoover replied that it seemed necessary to "all of us" to hold up "our agricultural statement" until the acceptance speech was made early in August.[8] He stated that he would do his best to demonstrate a sympathetic attitude toward the agricultural problem. On the next day Funk answered, enclosing a letter from Mr. Hastings in Georgia reflecting similar reactions, together with clippings from Illinois. Funk added that he knew most of the local leaders, some of whom were under obligations to him. He believed that he could handle without publicity some of the propaganda that would affect the outcome of the election in the Middle West. If critics were allowed to continue, he said, "They will spill the beans in Indiana, Illinois and Iowa in my judgment."[9]

Funk said it was no longer important to him in 1928 whether Hoover was a Republican or Al Smith a Democrat, but the main question was who could best fill the office.[10] A meeting in Cedar Rapids, Iowa, was attended by Hoover. Funk returned home confident that Hoover would help struggling farmers.[11] He also wrote to C. P. Bull about the meeting in Cedar Rapids when delegates from twenty-two states assembled in the interest of agriculture. Again he referred to the serious statements made by Herbert Hoover at the meeting. Funk requested a list of Republican farm voters in Minnesota and three clippings from *The Minneapolis Journal* entitled "Peek's Politics Termed Personal."

Later in August 1928, Funk was given the responsibility for organizing Republican agricultural interests in the states of Indiana, Minnesota and Illinois, where results seemed doubtful. He was relieved of the Minnesota assignment in September.[12] Funk's plan of organization included the following: (1) Calling together influential men regardless of party or organization as a voluntary agricultural movement; (2) Quietly presenting factual information about Hoover; (3) Supplementing party organizational activity already underway; (4) Approaching men like Brown of Monon for lists of farmers instead of deans of agricultural colleges as Republican Headquarters had suggested. Funk preferred to talk personally with people he knew.[13]

Funk also tried to clarify another misunderstanding from the days of price fixing for wheat during World War I. The differences of opinion between Secretaries Wallace and Hoover during Harding's administration have already been noted. Funk wrote the last of August that he had an appointment with Henry A. Wallace, September 7th "to try to get him straightened out in the matter of the unfortunate situation he is laboring under, which dates back to the date when his father and Mr. Hoover became estranged during the war." [14] He told C. V. Gregory of *The Prairie Farmer:*

> Confidentially, I am going to try to get Wallace straight on the long standing and unfortunate situation during the war between his father and Mr. Hoover, which has caused ten years of editorials in *The Wallace Farmer* that a few of us know are unfounded, and probably I am the only one that knows the real facts and I am going to tell young Henry the best I can, the facts because I was present at the time that the disagreement occurred between Mr. Wallace and Mr. Hoover.[15]

A letter came from Wallace on September 11th. Funk wired: "Letter just received will see you Peoria Wednesday." [16] Although it is not clear when Funk talked with Wallace, he did write Samuel Guard on November 8th that Wallace visited him after the Cedar Rapids meeting and spent the day with Funk, who commented:

> His visit cleared up a number of things both for himself, and for myself as well, for of course there are always two sides to everything.
> He admitted that what I had to say to him was entirely new to him and I am glad for his sake . . . if for no other reason . . . that he left here with a different viewpoint of the time when the first misunderstanding

took place between Mr. Hoover and his father. His recent editorials have shown me the results of our conference.

Funk added that some day he might have the opportunity to clear the atmosphere with Hoover. He was surprised how often a mole hill could grow through misunderstanding into a mountain among the best of friends.[17]

Funk said that party platforms always dealt in generalities; if the Democratic platform intends to say that it favors the equalization fee, then "Mr. Smith plainly and emphatically states that he is opposed. Mr. Hoover is also opposed to the equalization fee." He told Mr. Bull that he, (Funk) also had supported the equalization fee until he received Hoover's private opinion on the matter.[18] According to Funk, on three separate occasions Hoover as Secretary of Commerce asked for a conference with the administration and Congressional leaders as well as agricultural leaders with a view to getting together on legislation. His requests were refused. With the contest now between Hoover and Smith, Funk preferred the former.[19]

Funk's activity during the campaign included the preparation of a pamphlet about Hoover's participation in the price fixing days of 1917–18. J. Oglesby informed him that his story was ready for distribution of 400,000 copies September 24, 1918.[20] After being relieved of the responsibility for Minnesota, Funk turned energetically to the problems in Illinois and Indiana, saying that many farmers were undecided and intensive work would be necessary.[21]

One thousand copies of Funk's *Pantagraph* article regarding Hoover were forwarded to J. G. Brown in Indiana at Republican headquarters in Indianapolis.[22] Funk declared that although he realized that Illinois was organized in "pretty good shape," nevertheless the farmers had to overcome Democratic majorities in Peoria, Chicago, East St. Louis and Springfield. He asked for 1,000 copies of the article, for 500 automobile stickers and lapel buttons as well as thimbles. He believed that county precinct men in all congressional districts were organized.[23]

In answer to a personal and confidential request from Renick W. Dunlap, Assistant Secretary of Agriculture, who promised to keep Funk's replies confidential, he wrote that for ten years people had been criticizing Mr. Hoover far beyond what the man deserved. It would take hard and active work at this point to overcome the situation. He believed that some were willing to listen to facts rather than rumors. He also referred to consultation with leading agricultural men, to attendance at a number of small meetings resulting in the formation of the careful campaign for October through Indiana, Illinois, Iowa, Minnesota and Nebraska. These groups were composed of volunteer members independent of the regular political organization including many of Funk's old friends in the National Corn Association. He feared if eastern leadership were placed in the Presidency there might result a deep cleavage between East and West because of agricultural difficulties. He also stated:

> I know I am saying in the above a whole lot and I would not make these statements in any public way but I do know what the undercurrent is among farmers throughout the Middle West, how they talk in their own homes and their own fields, because I deal with about 65,000 of them every year, and if they are not allowed to have their industry brought about on equality with other industries, I dislike to think of what the future might be.

He also realized that many who would vote for Mr. Smith were simply ready "for a change." He also believed that Hoover would win, but it would be one of the hardest fought campaigns for many years.[24] Funk stated that the method of organizing the farmers was intended in no way to conflict with regular state and county organizations but to supplement their work.[25]

Early in October he participated in meetings at Rantoul, Homer and Champaign and was convinced that the "doubting Thomases" were coming along in good shape.[26] Funk agreed to be in Virden, Greenville and Pana, with a couple of days in Senator Flagg's district. There had been about 250 in attendance at Tolono. The county chairmen were running short of circulars. He suggested to Oglesby that they also receive the Republican literature and that congressional committeemen receive the same. He quoted Henry D. Heise of Joliet as saying that the circular was the complete answer to the story being spread by the Democrats in that part of the state. Phil Haner was organizing the Taylorville district.[27]

Funk's old friend Frank Fulkerson of Jerseyville referred to Funk's pamphlet, "The Republican Party and the Farmer," "Hoover Saves Hog Prices" and "Prices Under Hoover and the Food Administration." Frank Fulkerson told Gene Funk that he was indeed surprised to find "how far from grace one of our early-day members of one of the first organizations of our own state in behalf of farming has fallen. You (meaning Funk) certainly fell from an airplane when you fell for Hoover." [28]

Funk's fairly long explanation to Fulkerson included reference to the nominating convention at Kansas City in June 1928. Funk had tried his utmost to secure the nomination for Lowden but he said "it was simply hopeless—The East were 100 percent for Hoover and so were a great majority of the southern delegates. We here in the Middle West did not have a corporal's guard toward securing the nomination of Mr. Lowden." [29]

L. J. Tabor came to Bloomington to see him about the constant reference to the price fixing issue in the campaign. Funk also wrote his old friend Gentry that Coolidge had done great harm to agriculture, because with his New England background he did not understand the agricultural problems in the Middle West. Funk also thought his advisers did not "want him to know the real situation." He repeated that Mr. Hoover had imparted the information "strictly confidentially," that "last winter" he attempted three different times to beg Coolidge to call a big conference with the congressional committees and real farmers, but that the President had turned him down. He reported to Gentry that Hoover was not for the equalization fee in the last McNary-Haugen bill. Hoover had asked Funk if he remembered the trouble during the war with the packers and millers. Hoover then pointed to a joker in the bill which he thought would place agricultural interests in the hands of the above-mentioned organizations. He felt that even those who were backing the bill would soon regret it. Funk continued to believe that 99 percent of those who were against the man neither understood him nor the situation.[30]

This question of possible misrepresentation on the price of wheat during the war became so pressing that Funk wrote L. J. Tabor, master of the Grange, on October 22, 1928 that he had had a conference with Mr. Hoover at his residence. He reported that Mr. Hoover felt that the committee should prepare another statement to meet any continued misrepresentation or new statements so that he could be fortified with necessary material. Tabor enclosed a statement for Funk to approve saying:

You will note that I tried to make the conditions exactly as it occurred and to keep the statement in harmony with statement issued which we signed on October 18 of last year. I have included a short statement and one just a little longer. Am perfectly willing to sign either one or both of them and leave it to Mr. Hoover which one should be used, if used at all.[31]

Funk signed both statements. He told Tabor that as far as Illinois was concerned, the problem was being cleared. He felt that Hoover would carry the state without any doubt, "Our farmers have accepted my statements as facts." [32] He also wrote Hoover that he had heard from Tabor and again repeated that he believed they were winning

Illinois against false statements regarding the price fixing information.[33] Will T. Carlson from Greenville, Illinois in Bond County wrote that the Democrats were on the run after Funk's speech in the court room. The speech was to be "poll-parrotted" throughout the county, with local papers publishing the speech.[34] Encouragement also came from Montgomery County.[35]

During the last week of the campaign the Volunteer Agriculture Republican Committee for the State of Illinois informed as many farmers as possible. Funk also urged his friends to influence the doubtful voter.[36] He took care of his own expenses for the past two weeks, telling John Oglesby that the bill was not high. He donated the time and then "sponged off his friends." He had already spoken in Logan County at Emden and Chestnut; in Tazewell County at Eureka and would go to Kendall County if necessary. C. P. Bull advised that Minnesota appeared to be safe for Hoover by October 26th. Funk urged his congressional district leaders to keep going during the last week of the campaign.[37] He was able to wire his friend Herbert Hoover on November 7th, "Good and faithful servant, you deserved it."[38] Hoover stated in 1955 that Mr. Funk was "a great support in the campaign."[39]

A. R. MacKusick of Boston again brought up the question of Funk's appointment as Secretary of Agriculture. Funk again stated that he would make no personal effort. He believed that any man who would undertake the position at this point would need almost public support. Any man who would seek the office and support from friends and polititians would thereby defeat the purpose he should have in taking the office. As always he believed that the position should seek the man. Therefore, it was up to his friends, not to him.[40] Later he told MacKusick about his campaigning in southern Illinois and sent him copies of the article that was so often reprinted. He estimated that he had spoken twice daily for about a month during the campaign. "We carried all the precincts in a Democratic section in Illinois that had never before gone Republican."[41] The McLean County Farm Bureau was active in his behalf again. This is an interesting statement in view of the claims of George N. Peek who by this time had gone over to the Democratic party with the nomination of Herbert Hoover and the loss of the McNary-Haugen equalization fee idea. Congressional supporters of the McNary-Haugen idea, however, including McNary and Haugen, Brookhart, Dickinson and others, supported Hoover.[42]

Under the guidance of Peek, independent agricultural leagues were formed in Ohio, Indiana, Illinois, Missouri, Iowa, Wisconsin, Nebraska, Minnesota, the Dakotas and Montana. Peek learned that it was difficult to isolate a specific issue in a Presidential campaign. Gilbert Fite points out that Mr. Hoover had an abundance of capable campaigners. Among them Senator Borah effectively assaulted the equalization fee.[43]

The following counties in the entire state of Illinois returned Democratic majorities: *Monroe, Perry,* Clinton, Effingham, *Franklin,* Gallatin, *Macoupin, St. Clair,* Union and *Wabash.* Of these, six had returned Republican majorities in 1924 and 1920 as italicized. The following counties returned Republican majorities after being Democratic in 1924: Pike, Brown, Greene, Jersey, Jasper, Schuyler, White, Hamilton and Jo Daviess. In all other counties returning Republican majorities, there was a comfortable margin of over 1,000 except in Cass, Scott, Washington and Williamson. The Republicans had scarcely any difficulty above the 39th parallel and carried the southern part below this line except in eight counties. The Republican majority in Cook County was reduced to 95,780 in contrast with a majority of 462,832 in 1924.[44]

After hearing over the radio December 13th that Frank Lowden would support Hoover, Funk wrote to Lowden as follows:

I was in Washington last June—the week previous to the convention in Kansas City on Committee for the National Chamber of Commerce—and while in the city I called on Mr. Hoover as I had always been in the habit of doing. I learned from him direct his views on agricultural problems. I had in my pocket a telegram asking me to come to Kansas City to help to try to nominate Frank O. Lowden. Hoover knew that I was for you and I am greatly disappointed we were not able to rally sufficient force to bring about your nomination. After the nomination certain interests as well as certain individuals undertook to poison the thoughts of the public with such malicious falsehoods about Mr. Hoover, of things that he did and did not do during the war which I personally knew were wrong for as you know I was with Hoover during the eighteen months that he was Food Administrator.

He explained that when John Oglesby and the National Republican Committee asked him if he would try to counteract these statements, he felt that it was his duty to do so. He also informed Lowden that a number of agricultural organizations had passed resolutions asking for the selection of someone from Illinois as Secretary of Agriculture. His own name had been mentioned "absolutely unsolicited" and without his previous knowledge. Then he urged Frank Lowden to accept the position; he offered to withdraw quietly and throw all of his influence to his good friend. He almost implored Lowden to accept:

You have the opportunity now, Frank, to be the real leader of our Agricultural cause that we have cherished the hope for many years. I believe Hoover realizes that he needs you and if you will allow us to use your name we will do everything we can to show him that you are the one man who the farmers as a whole will accept as their leader. You can do more for Agriculture than anyone else at this critical time. The Cause is the thing now. It is bigger than any individual but some individual must lead. There are a lot of men who might be President but there are very few men who our American farmers have the confidence to rally round and support with the attempt to place Agriculture where it rightfully belongs. You are the one at this time who can swing the pendulum in the right direction.[45]

He also informed the McLean County Farm Bureau of these ideas.[46] However, the *Seed World* reprinted a *Pantagraph* article and the picture of Funk, referring to him as a possible Secretary of Agriculture.[47] Resolutions went forward from the Illinois delegation in Congress including Senators Deneen and Glen [48] and from the Illinois Farmers Institute. But the selection fell to Arthur N. Hyde.

An effort to estimate whether the stream of history would have been changed appreciably if Eugene D. Funk had risen to the Secretaryship of Agriculture in the decade of the twenties seems impossible. Yet the man himself represented something during the era that was lost to that position in the scramble to find the answers. All would agree that leadership in the important post of the Secretaryship from Illinois in the central Corn Belt was overlooked during this decade. The practical farmer was disregarded in official appointments. Funk's analyses of agricultural situations were usually accurate and his ability to measure the farmers' reactions was unquestioned. Often, however, his faith in his "friends" blinded him to their obligations under the demands of "practical politics." Once recognizing the direction of events, he played his continuing role without complaint or criticism.

After the inauguration of President Hoover's administration, Funk Bros. Seed Co. was engaged in developing markets for soybean seed in Illinois (See below, Chapter XXVI). There is every reason to understand why agricultural groups in the Middle West could support the Republican Party and its general position on the tariff. Knowing that a surplus crop such as corn was not in a position to be helped by protection, leaders realized that the comparatively new crop, soybeans, needed every encouragement. Since E. D. Funk was one of the pioneers in establishing the soybean processing business in the Central Corn Belt he was deeply interested in the situation. He urged his friend, Charles L. Meharry of Attica, Indiana to write his Congressman, Fred S. Purnell. Funk told Meharry that he had an old friend in Washington looking into the soybean meal and oil tariff situation. Funk feared difficulty without duty on soybean oil.[49]

E. D. Funk was host in 1930 to 25,000 to 30,000 corn husking fans on the Funk farms. He was introduced by Dave Thompson, former McLean County farm adviser, then on the staff of *The Prairie Farmer* "as the foremost corn breeder in the country." Frank Moberly, president of the McLean County Farm Bureau and Floyd Keepers, editor of *Prairie Farmer,* were also there. The *Pantagraph* airplane circled overhead as thirteen huskers matched their skill and speed for 80 minutes in what was described as "the greatest of all Illinois corn husking contests." Thousands of parked cars lined up, but one of the main attractions was thirteen matched teams of fine Percheron horses supplied by McLean County breeders and farmers. The exhibit was described as the largest since the days when Bloomington-Normal was known as the Percheron breeding center of the United States.[50]

Renewed interest in the old National Corn Association brought a reunion in 1930. Of the original organizers, promoters and workers, twenty-six indicated their intention to attend.[51] This effort was the result of a meeting at the International in 1929 of E. D., Sr., C. P. Bull and W. H. Young, Fred McCulloch and Kruger of Wisconsin. After a dinner they spent the evening talking over "old times," with the result that they decided to hold a reunion during the International in 1930. Only seventeen arrived: Clore, Stone, Winters, Rankin, Mosher, Olin, Young, Ten Eyck, J. A. King, Kruger, Mumford, Sconce, Wheeler, Maxey, McCulloch, D. Thompson, E. D. Funk. Sconce, as a director of the World's Fair for 1933, issued an invitation to the old association to take charge of the grain exhibit during the exposition in the fall of 1933.[52]

Correspondence between Funk and Fred McCulloch revealed that Sconce had not consulted Leonard and Heide of the International. They felt that the old Corn Association was trying to take the show away from the International. Funk sent word to Heide and Leonard that such was not the case. Moore was of the opinion that the old association should "die a natural death," and that the Crop Improvement Association ought to succeed the old National Corn Association. Funk suspected that Moore had talked to young Holden at Madison and that accounted for P. G.'s silence. Funk added, "So far as I am concerned I don't give a rap who puts on the show and I don't intend to force the issue that would get our old N. C. A. into a squabble with any of them." He reminded McCulloch that Sconce voluntarily made the offer and that he (Funk) would not proceed without a clean slate with expenses furnished.[53] Funk also wrote Sconce regarding an article in the *Drovers Journal* the day after the reunion. Funk felt that if the International offered cash prizes and the World's Fair only medals, the result would be obvious.[54] Funk delayed action until a thorough understanding could be brought about between the World's Fair officials and the International Live Stock Hay and Grain Show.[55]

The newly elected directors of the old Corn Association included C. P. Bull, W. H. Young, A. L. Stone, Fred McCulloch, Dave Thompson, L. M. Vogler, Val Kuska, W. L. English and E. D. Funk.[56] No officers were chosen at this time.

Ground was broken for the Agricultural Building at the New World's Fair Grounds on Friday, May 20, 1932 for the Century of Progress on Northerly Island. Chas. S. Peterson, vice president of A Century of Progress, presided. A pageant in four parts dramatized the development of American Agriculture from oxen-drawn plow to tractor-drawn gang plow. The first period was illustrated by Dr. A. W. Bitting in charge of foods of the Agricultural Section, who drove a team of Connecticut oxen harnessed to an old wooden plow built in 1750, loaned by A. Watson Armour of Chicago. The second period was illustrated by Frank I. Mann, pioneer farmer of Gilman, Illinois, who drove a span of mules hitched to the old original wood beam steel bottom plow, known as the walking plow. It was the first plow manufactured in the first plow factory of William Parlin of Canton, Illinois in 1847. The third period was illustrated by Eugene D. Funk of Funk Farms. He drove the champion Clydesdale horses to the original sulky plow introduced more than sixty years ago in the United States. The fourth period was illustrated by Harvey Sconce, who drove an International Harvester gas tractor.[57]

Charles Boyles from Chicago commented on Funk's activity in obtaining a million dollar corn loan through Intermediate Credit Bank. He added, "I appreciate of course that this whole movement is the product of your brains and activities." [58]

E. D. Funk continued to talk to groups throughout the state. He was not very popular with some at the State Fair in 1931 as a result of urging farmers to vote for Hoover in 1928. In a speech to the Illinois Brotherhood of Threshermen in March 1932, he referred to some of the problems of Illinois in relation to responsibilities of farmers mentioned in his 1925 talk to the I. M. A. He spoke of the significance of the plant breeder, showing how Iowa Oat 103 came to be selected. He summarized by emphasizing the importance of adaptation to environment and of resistance to disease in grain crops.[59]

Funk was not downhearted. He spoke over WBBM April 9, 1932 in what he described as "one of the most wild-eyed campaigns" ever witnessed. He supported the candidacy of Omer M. Custer for Governor. Lowden also supported Custer.[60] Other activities included appointment to the Agricultural Committee of the Illinois Manufacturers Association on September 8, 1932.[61]

During the late twenties and early thirties Funk was engaged in important agricultural development for his company. Depression years slowed activity and created problems, but progress in expansion of soybean acreages and hybrid corn were under way.

CHAPTER XXIII

Depression Years

DURING THE DEPRESSION year 1933 Eugene D. Funk described the plight of the farmer to his industrial friends, urged consumption of grain by new methods [1] and participated in the programs provided by the Democratic administration. The decade of the twenties emphasized as never before in the history of the country problems confronting agriculture. Throughout the years, Eugene Funk spoke for the Corn Belt farmer, faced economic difficulty himself and sought new and improved crops for the future. As he looked squarely at depression he also realized that these same years were potentially advantageous for the company.

At a meeting of the Agricultural Committee of the Illinois Manufacturers' Association held in Chicago, January 13, 1933, E. D. Funk, a member of the committee, admitted that 90 percent of the farming community recognized the need for relief but did not approve a Farm Board. He also noted that farmers were compelled to curtail expenses. Many were grinding wheat and corn on the farms and converting their raw material into food products. He advocated some aid with as little new legislation as possible. He believed farmers would not agree to restriction of production. He reported that there were 4,000,000 acres of farm land in Illinois which had never been able to produce crops at prices above cost of production. This land was low in fertility. Much of it was rolling and should go into forestry for the benefit of future generations. Illinois could reduce taxes on all fallow land and make it an inducement to curtail grain production. He spoke of a tract of land owned by his family consisting of 3,000 acres originally forest land. The taxes on this tract were $2.30 per acre. All except 1,200 acres were converted into crop land in order to pay taxes and other expenses.

Funk suggested that Illinois induce farmers to restrict their production by reducing taxes on land planted to legumes. Fallow land producing weeds lost fertility. Such land should not be taxed as long as the owner planted it to clover or alfalfa and plowed the legume crops under. The *Chicago Tribune* referred to a plan relieving high taxation on all fallow land. Illinois Revenue laws, however, would not permit exemption of fallow land: if planted to legumes exemption might result. A committee was suggested to work with Mr. Funk.[2]

Eugene Funk presided at a committee meeting of the same group February 10, 1933 when Mr. Beshers explained his plan for grain alcohol. Tentative drafts of bills to be presented by Congressman Hull (16th District) and Hall (17th) were discussed. Funk also presided at the March meeting. Representatives who were interested from Standard Oil attended. The possibility of securing a market for corn in the depression years 1932–33 increased interest in grain alcohol.

A demonstration for the use of grain alcohol in automobiles occurred at Yorkville in Kendall county, Illinois, November 1932. J. J. Groetken of Aurora, manufacturer of fuel products, made these tests.[3] Paul Beshers of El Paso, Illinois, as an early advocate of grain alcohol, presented a radio address on the subject over radio station WLS in Chicago, January 9, 1933. His plan was originally sponsored by the Lions Club of Gridley, Illinois and later by the same organization in Peoria. He and his sponsors believed that this plan contained the elements of a good farm relief program. Its specific terms included:

that all petroleum products which have a gravity of 36 percent Baume, or above, that may be used as fuel in internal combustion engines, shall be adulterated 10% by volume with ethyl alcohol made from agricultural products grown within the United States. Ethyl alcohol can be made from any or all agricultural products.

This country uses approximately 17 billion gallons of fuel yearly which comes under our definition, 10 percent of which would be 1,700,000,000 gallons which is the amount of alcohol we will need to make from your products. Translated into corn this would mean a market for approximately 689,000,000 bushels.[4]

Alcohol made from corn was among the most publicized ideas for consuming grain. The editor of the *Chicago Drovers Journal* January 26, 1933 printed the ideas of the Standard Oil Company of Indiana to the effect that the alcohol in all foreign countries being used as a blended motor fuel was manufactured locally, usually by government subsidized monopoly. In these countries gasoline was usually imported, subject to high duties. Alcohol was therefore cheaper in countries having no petroleum supplies. Cars in foreign countries also had motors and fuel systems different from those in the United States. This statement of Standard Oil declared that various proposals in the United States to this end had all fallen flat because of technical and economic obstacles. This report also pointed out that alcohol can be made cheaper from other materials than from excess farm materials.[5]

Despite this discouraging note, the *New York Times* noted editorially, March 8, 1933 that in nearly a score of countries alcohol was mixed with gasoline. The editorial said, "Why not introduce the practice here? Legislate a little alcohol into every gallon of gasoline and the farmer would pay off his mortgage, we are told." The Corn Belt could become the Promised Land if admixtures ran from 2 to 20 percent. This newspaper added that there could be no question that alcohol would be a good fuel for automobiles if engines were designed to burn the product. The 2 percent did not cause trouble but a falling off of efficiency occurred when proportions rose to 10 or 20 percent. Then a significant observation followed:

Aside from these economic and engineering considerations the chemist would question the soundness of alcoholic farm relief. The alcohols are so obliging. The most obliging of all is ethyl alcohol—the kind distilled from grain. Almost anything that can be made to ferment will yield it. Fruits, potatoes, vegetables all are good raw materials, and so is wood. It might be expected that the petroleum refiners would lift their voices in protest. Instead they reserve a cheerful silence. For petroleum can be "cracked" to yield ethylene from which the synthetic equivalent of ethyl or grain alcohol can be obtained. In 1931 some 8,000,000 gallons were produced and sold in a highly competitive market.[6]

A "Beshers' Plan" governing body was formed at Gridley including W. E. Froelich, Lions Club president; J. R. Heiple, vice president of the Gridley State Bank; E. E. Kaufman, clothier; State Senator L. C. Sieberns; S. H. Ravenacht, farm owner and headquarters manager; B. L. Andrews, insurance; Mr. Beshers, Philip Hayes and C. C. Kingdon, all from El Paso. From Bloomington were included John W. Rodgers, Jr. president of the Association of Commerce; Eugene D. Funk, chairman of A. of C. Agricultural Committee and Campbell Holton, wholesaler. From Peoria were included James Dacem, president of the Lions Club, George Bosham and Henry Naw.[7]

Eugene Funk was active in bringing the Beshers Plan to the attention of all who were interested. He recalled the demonstration of the model converting grain to alcohol sent by the U. S. D. A. to the Corn Association meeting in Omaha during 1909. He rode in a 1927 automobile with 10 percent blended alcohol with common gasoline. The test showed two additional miles per gallon over ethyl alcohol.[8]

By 1933 he declared that agriculture stood squarely up against the wall and "if we are forced to push that wall over we will surely drag everything else through." [9]

Four bills came before Congress endorsing the mixture as an aid to agriculture. Oil company officials, however, predicted that the fuel would raise costs to the consumer from 2½ to 4 cents per gallon. Representative Dirksen from Illinois furnished ten gallons for the car of Secretary Wallace. Dirksen said in April 1933 that 500,000 gallons of the fuel had been sold in Illinois and that much alcohol had been shipped to Iowa, Nebraska and Kansas for blending.[10]

Frank Gillespie (Democrat) described his seventeenth district of Illinois as the "richest lands on earth" where the farmers were reduced to bankruptcy because of 7 cent oats, 10 cent corn, 3 cent hogs and 4 cent cattle. He declared that the bill to help the farmer and the nation by introducing agricultural purchasing power "is the most important bill that will be presented to the Congress." He sponsored the Beshers Plan in H. R. 1744. Sec. 2 stated, "It shall be unlawful for any person to sell motor fuel in the United States unless at least 10 percent thereof by volume is alcohol manufactured from agricultural products." [11] Gillespie closed his speech before the House with the words, "We are at Armageddon and fighting for the Lord; for Justice. The farmer's cause is a holy cause." The speech was printed in the *Pantagraph*. Congressmen Hall of Bloomington and Hull of Peoria favored similar plans [12] before their terms of office expired March 4, 1933.

Disillusionment resulted when people became aware that the distilleries in Pekin and Peoria made alcohol from blackstrap molasses rather than from Illinois corn.[13] What was believed to be the first fuel of its kind offered to the public anywhere in the United States, however, was on sale at Farm Bureau filling stations in the Peoria area at 3 cents above untreated gasoline.[14] Senator Shipstead of Minnesota gained the approval of a resolution asking the Secretary of Agriculture to investigate the possibilities of using alcohol manufactured from corn as a motor fuel.[15] The report from the Department of Agriculture giving approval to the principle of blending alcohol with gasoline was received by the Senate Committee on Agriculture, May 10, 1933. This report was described as more favorable than previous answers sent out by the Department.[16]

According to the *Pantagraph* May 4, 1933, Congressman Gillespie was of the opinion that an Illinois Congressman from Chicago on the House Agricultural Committee who was only faintly interested in the proposal had been apathetic toward it. The Senate was also said to have sidetracked the Beshers movement in May 1933.[17]

The information for the press released May 8, 1933 by the Department of Agriculture declared that manufacture of alcohol from farm products would be an aid in taking care of agricultural surplusses and stablizing markets; that most gasoline engines then in use appeared to be able to handle a 19 percent alcohol gasoline mixture without adjustments and without much change in mileage per gallon of fuel; that the use of 10 percent of alcohol would add 2⅗ cents a gallon and utilize 560,000,000 bushels of corn and 112,000,000 bushels of barley. Although the consumption of gasoline might be reduced at first the resultant rise in farmers' buying power might increase use of automotive machinery and gasoline thus offsetting in part the increase in costs of blended fuel.[18]

As early as March 18, 1933 E. M. Dirksen (Republican) registered a protest on behalf of independent oil companies in his home town of Pekin. He charged Government competition with private business in connection with marketing "highball" gasoline, a fluid containing 10 percent denatured alcohol. The federal authorities gave the farmers' cooperative oil company permission to sell the new fuel, but it was charged that they denied the same privilege to the independents. Dr. James Doran, fuel commissioner of industrial alcohol, said that further permits were not granted because the Pekin project was experimental. Independent dealers wanted to take part in the experiment.[19]

The *Prairie Farmer* stated that of 712 Illinois customers using the 10 percent alcohol gasoline blend motor fuel, 430 reported an increased mileage over regular gasoline of 2.66 miles per gallon. Three customers reported average mileage decrease of one mile per gallon. Others did not report. Five hundred and seventy-nine favored this fuel because it improved starting; 678 found increased power, and 683 reported generally improved motor performance.[20]

A Beshers National Economic League was formed at a meeting of the Bloomington Association of Commerce of Bloomington in January 1935.[21] James Gray, Clyde Huddleson of Normal and S. H. Rivenacht of Gridley were named as a committee to edit and publish a circular. The suggestion that the Federal Administration include the alcohol gas program in its agricultural adjustment administration plan was made by 1,000 delegates at an alcohol-gas mass meeting held in Bloomington, February 11, 1935. James Gray was general chairman. Members of the sponsoring committee represented the Bloomington Association of Commerce, McLean County Farm Bureau, Illinois Agricultural Association and the Alcohol Motor Fuel Association.[22] Alcohol was produced at a plant in Atchison, Kansas in 1936.[23] Unfavorable factors discouraged efforts to consume corn.

E. D. Funk, Sr. was "drafted," as he said, by President Franklin Roosevelt with eight others to represent Illinois in the N. R. A. campaign and also as a director of Regional Credit Corporation. He added, "I am a blamed fool for being on any of their committees, but what is a fellow going to do? I did not ask for any of the jobs but was told I was drafted to serve." [24] Funk accepted voluntary codes with one exception, "Where the labor union is attempting to get in a position in order to be able to dictate to industry as to the personnel of its employees, regardless of efficiency or loyalty, and forcing the employer to help support a lot of 'walking delegates,' saddled with authority who practically would tell you how to run your business." He added that in signing the President's tentative code, "We wrote a reservation on that point." After returning from a meeting with the Governor of Illinois and eight others appointed by the President to represent the state on the N. R. A. he believed that Illinois would cooperate to the utmost to bring about relief and cooperate with the President.[25]

Funk, Sr. had his doubts about curtailment and never agreed with "surplus propaganda" before or during 1933. He believed that lack of confidence and depressed agricultural prices had more to do with the situation than anything else. However, he was fearful that:

mental action on the part of the grain trade in general to discredit if possible, the Administration, and that feeling has more or less reflected into the speculative element. Naturally the Corn Products and other manufacturers are taking advantage and they are not going to bull the market alone altho I have been told by sons of them they wish the price was higher, as a high market is better for their finished product than a low depressed market.

At Bloomington, Illinois through the Association of Commerce the President and the Secretary of Agriculture were asked to set a price of 60 cents per bushel to the farmer for this year's crop (1933) if he agreed to cut his acreage 20 percent for 1934. They also asked Governor Horner to call a conference of other Governors with commercial and agricultural interests from other states. The purpose was to let Washington know that the Middle West had its "back right up against a stout wall and something must be done to relieve the situation." Funk thought that 50 cents for Number 2 corn, Chicago, did not mean much after costs of freight, commission and other charges were deducted. He added:

What the farmer needs now is for the commercial interests of this Middle West to realize that they too must help and get behind a united effort that will save all our hides, otherwise there will be another year of wail and woe, foreclosures and bank failures.

The N. R. A. is getting away ahead of the agricultural hounds and our merchants cannot sit with added expense indefinitely without the farmer coming to town and able to purchase his necessary requirements and at the same time pay off part of his indebtedness. Labor will not have an opportunity to work. It seems to me it would be much better to start circulating money raised from crops and fat livestock than to distribute all of it through the welfare and what is rapidly developing into a dole system.[26]

With all of these problems confronting agriculture, E. D. Funk, Sr. tried over a period of two years to work out some system whereby the Funk Bros. Seed Co. could qualify for a loan from the Reconstruction Finance Corporation. Efforts to explain the connection between the company, the land and the experimental work carried on over the years did not gain the desired results. Mortgages on the land plus the desire of bond holders to foreclose added to the deep concern of E. D. Funk through these difficult years of the depression. Added to these disturbing factors was the knowledge that hybrid corn was on the threshold of Golden Years and that soybeans were greatly in demand.[27] With tight credit from the banks Funk scarcely knew where to turn at a time when opportunities were the best in many years (see chapters 26, 27 and 28 below). As late as June 20, 1935, E. D. Funk thought the R. F. C. loan might materialize. Such a loan was never forthcoming.

Funk attended the Chemurgic Committee in 1935 at Detroit and encouraged the formation of a Midwest Council, comparable to that in New England.[28] By the middle of 1934 E. D. Sr. was writing his old friend Fred McCulloch at Hartwick, Iowa that he was still a Republican but was willing to give the Democrats a chance. He said he had no patience with throwing stones when all were grasping at straws and was signing The "Corn-Hog proposition" as a temporary solution, "a permanent solution has yet to be initiated." He added:

I also feel that Henry Wallace is sincere and honest and his sympathies are for agriculture. I happen to know that he has had a hard battle to fight almost alone and against great odds and powerful influence so I have learned not to believe all that I read in the newspapers which at times would appear that Wallace was backing something which he really is not doing.[29]

He finally wrote to Secretary Wallace regarding the status of his farms.

Henry, I have just got to have some sort of relief so as to satisfy the bond holders. They know as well as the appraiser that our land is worth at least $150 per acre. The present loan averages about $155 per acre. We have most of the bondholders committed to take a 20% discount right now if we can get the cash, but they are also pressing to take the land and about 700 acres has already been taken.[30]

Two days later, an article by "Farmer" E. W. Rusk, farm adviser in Coles County, Illinois, appeared in the *McLean County Farm and Home Bureau News* written after he visited the Experimental Corn Plots in September 1934 which were continuing on the Funk Farms. He commented on the significant scientific information received from Doctors R. J. Holbert, senior agronomist U. S. D. A. and Earl G. Sieveking, soil and crops specialist at Funk Bros. Seed Co. This project was described as a great cooperative undertaking by the agricultural colleges and experimental stations of several states. As he closed his comments Rusk wrote:

In closing this short story about the highlights I saw in a visit to Funk farms, I desire to pay special tribute to the man in whose heart and brain developed the realization of the need for and plans to carry on this great work so beneficial to mankind. My hat is off in profound respect and deference and in admiration for the sturdy, progressive pioneering heart and soul and wise mind of the real man—scholar, farmer, animal husbandman and practical benefactor—because of his great interest and participation in the greatest corn breeding work of the age. My hat is off to the Honorable Eugene D. Funk—your friend and mine. Blood—good breeding—will tell in both corn and man.[31]

Efforts were continued in 1935 to secure financial aid on the basis that if the farms were lost the cooperative work would have to be discontinued. Funk in commenting said he did not know where the work could be taken if they ceased operations, adding, "It is not only expensive but requires years of toil and patience." On the other hand, he noted that there was a certain fascination and reward from the fact of pioneering and giving "our best efforts to assist our brother farmers to a better agriculture." For these reasons he hoped to be able to continue and if possible to perpetuate the work for future generations.[32] E. D. Sr. explained that the mortgages were necessary because of excessive inheritance taxes and assessments on bank stock. The land was assessed at $450 to $550 per acre in 1920. The amount of the loan was reduced to $25,000. March 1st, 1935 was the deadline for payment. Some land was taken over by some bondholders and others were insisting that more land be deeded to them. Some land was surrendered by warantee deed rather than have foreclosure procedures follow.[33]

With these worries Funk continued his usual participation in many activities. He attended the Detroit Farm-Industry-Science meeting, May 1935. Funk and James Gray represented the Bloomington Association of Commerce.[34]

In 1936 Funk was apprehensive about a third term for President Roosevelt, fearing that a revolution of a kind was in the making. At Indianapolis about 1922 or 1923 he recalled saying, "We were facing a bloodless revolution." He added, "Our grandchildren must not be blamed if in their day they repudiate this tremendous debt that is being saddled upon them." He advocated the drafting of the Republicans for Frank Lowden for the Presidency. Funk had presented to the annual meeting of the National Chamber of Commerce in Washington, a copy of resolutions. Many, he said, were adopted.[35]

An association of lasting significance in the development of the seed company began following a letter from Funk's friend, H. G. Atwood of Allied Mills, now in Chicago. He informed Funk that George M. Moffett, president of Corn Products Refining Company had expressed satisfaction in producing a crop of Funk's Hi-Bred Corn in Maryland. Atwood suggested that Funk write him.[36] Out of this association came an interesting sequence of events (see chapter XXIX). By 1937 Funk informed his friend J. A. McConnell, manager of G. L. F. Exchange, that his corn and soybean programs were now covering states from Nebraska to Maryland.[37]

Adjustments after World War I had created difficulties for those following chiefly agricultural pursuits. Changes in the world position of the United States often occurred without realization by the great group of people. The vision of some leaders also was unusually dim. Old political ideas and economic principles did not always provide immediate remedies for underlying problems. Eugene Funk always sought to analyze the difficulties confronting agriculture. He supported those men he believed to be speaking with the interests of agriculture in mind. He was not always aware or informed of pressures exerted upon candidates or officials from other parts of the country. During this confusing decade he and his associates advanced agricultural interest in many field seeds and especially in extensive acceptance of soybeans and hybrid corn.

By 1940 E. D. Funk, Sr. could spend his usual winter vacation at his home in Winter Haven, Florida where he continued experimentation with corn and other crops, with a definite interest in improving a tomato variety. As the years crowded along he could view with satisfaction the years that had passed. His life was filled with advantages, pleasures, opportunities strangely complicated by problems and difficulties that would have discouraged a man of lesser courage. Events already recorded from 1920 to 1940 are closely tied to the development of Funk Bros. Seed Co. expanding under his direction as president. If there was any one center of his interest outside his family and his hope to contribute to the Betterment of Agriculture it was to lead the company to the production of the best products he could bring to the American farmer.

PART SEVEN

Not the Largest but the Best

CHAPTER XXIV

The Company, Leadership, Personnel and Policy · 1918–1944

THE ORIGIN OF Funk Bros. Seed Co. as a family enterprise was the result of the planning and initiative of Eugene D. Funk, Sr. The idea was so ingrained in his thinking that after the reorganization in 1918 he continued to speak of the "family company." During the early years Gene Sr., received considerable recognition for his leadership in agricultural and civic activities and was known widely for his contributions to the seed trade. Policies for his own company were initiated, tested and accepted during these formative years. His basic philosophy of life and his attention to integrity and honesty, often reflected in the ideas of various members of the Funk family, found early and repeated expression. He initiated and continued the policy of recognizing capable and responsible personnel by promotion within the company. As the company expanded, more important assignments were made to long-time employees.

Eugene Funk, Sr. often said that an organization can be no better that the people who work in it. He was among the first to emphasize the individual contributions of his employees. The crowded years 1918–40 revealed the extensive and demanding activities carried on by this remarkable man. His interests outside the development of the seed company indicated the kind of recognition and respect he had been accorded through one and one-half decades. The energy of the man, his understanding of agricultural problems, his concern for the welfare of the farmer and his wide acquaintanceship are testimonials to a busy and active career. Along with these responsibilities, assumed partly because of the developing company, he carried the burden of directing its growth during a period of agricultural difficulty and of depression economy. The development of the company paralleled the events already discussed during the twenties and thirties. Each of the major departments in the company underwent interesting and complicated growth providing interesting chapters in themselves. Eugene D. Funk, Sr. always provided a directing hand.

319

E. D. Sr. came to the office regularly to take care of his correspondence and his many appointments. Visitors from all over the country came to talk with him. His associates recognized his concern for farmers and their problems. When yields were down and prices low he thought that it was his personal responsibility to try to help to remedy the situation. His judgment was respected and his counsel sought. On occasions he displayed the typical Funk characteristic of sternness. He was forceful, fair, thoughtful and considerate of the people with whom he came in contact. Often when he gave the appearance of indecision, those who worked with him knew that he was trying to weigh all sides of a question.[1] Although his manner was kindly, few chose to cross him at the wrong moment.

He practiced the democratic ideas that he advocated in the company described by him as a "family organization." His employees recall that he knew them and spoke to them whenever he happened to meet them. He was accessible for conferences and welcomed comments. No battery of secretaries kept him from talking with people he liked so well. Employees were expected to keep busy. Mr. Funk always seemed to see at a glance what was going on when he walked through the office or warehouse.

The offices of the seed company in the twenties were located in a two story frame house near the site of the present office building. The managerial and bookkeeping departments were on the first floor. Mr. Funk occupied the second floor where Dr. J. Holbert also had a desk while he continued his employment with the United States Department of Agriculture.

Eugene Funk was described as one of the most likable people and as a perfect gentleman who did not wish publicity, with an integrity typical of the Funks. Employees were pleased when Mrs. Eugene Sr. knew the names of all the employees. E. D. Sr. summed up the purpose of the organization when he said, "It is not necessary to be the biggest organization in the Seed World, but the best." Funk would give people responsibility and time to carry out the assignments. The elder Funk emphasized the necessity for maintaining good will in the business operations. Funk always looked ahead, saying, "We will be in business 100 years from now." Employees admired the impersonal attitude that E. D. Sr., maintained toward his employees. There were no favorites, or friends who had access to him after hours that others did not have. Yet he was always friendly, interested and kindly but there was a dignity and a reserve in his dealings with employees. These characteristics created confidence.

With the reorganization of the company in 1918 H. H. Miller who had arrived the preceding October became general manager. The many activities of E. D. Sr. called him away from the office as the preceding chapters related. Able assistants were depended upon to carry forward the developing business. Miller's previous experience included work at the Guelph Agricultural College in Guelph, Ontario, Canada. He was also associated with Albert Dickinson Seed Company in Chicago for many years. His early associates in Bloomington remembered him as an able and well-liked administrator who dealt fairly and firmly with the personnel. His knowledge of field seeds and his ability as a shrewd and successful buyer often proved to be the difference between profit and loss during the trying decade of the twenties. He worked well with E. D. Sr. Older employees recalled that it was sometimes difficult to determine whether one or the other proposed an idea for the overall program. Miller was interested in the problems and work of each individual. Each Saturday the sales group in later years of his management would come together for a meeting. He would ask what had happened in their territory. After their comments he in turn would tell them what he knew about their situations. He was never aloof. Associates described him as a keen trader with a good sense of values. He was able in training others by allowing them to learn to avoid difficulties and to solve problems. Often he covered for their mistakes.

Miller was a quiet and thoughtful person with a businesslike approach to problems. He would ask a pertinent and penetrating question and in turn provide a thorough answer. When he planned improvements he estimated what he wanted and the amount to be spent. Then he expected results. When new activities were to be undertaken he was often heard to inquire, "How much might we lose by this action?"

The office force in 1921 in addition to the president and the general manager included an elderly gentleman, Howard Leaton, who acted as bookkeeper and cashier for approximately twelve years before Miller's arrival. Newton Crosby replaced Leaton as bookkeeper and Rachel McIntyre was employed as a secretary and billing clerk. Margaret Schertz was added to the force as a secretary in September 1921. Ernest Radley was employed in February 1922 and Vaughn Dunbar came to the office in June 1922. At this time these three people with Mr. Miller were the only "office help." Sons of E. D. Sr. have also participated in the company's activities for a comparable length of time. Of the sons, Eugene Jr. while at the University of Illinois worked for the company during the spring of 1921 and following summers through 1924, learning almost every phase of the operations by actual participation. Possessed of a pleasing personality, likable and friendly, Gene Jr. became a full time employee in 1924. He attained experience in all general office work with wages at $25 a week. He often acted as buyer and salesman on the road. After experience in the office he assumed responsibility in the warehouse, working as a laborer and eventually becoming a foreman. He was deeply interested in soybean operations. With the appointment of Bradley as manager of the Taylorville plant, Gene Jr. assumed additional responsibility in soybean operations with the help of H. H. Miller, J. A. Waring and later Harold Abbott. Gene Jr. became secretary and director in 1932 and president of the company in 1944.

The eldest son of E. D. Sr., LaFayette, managed the farms until Theodore assumed this responsibility. A large portion of the open pollinated and later of hybrid seed corn was produced on the Funk Farms under the supervision of LaFayette. His work included all operations of planting, harvesting and sorting the seed corn from 1918 until he relinquished the management of the farms to his brother. He also acquired a practical knowledge of construction enabling him to contribute effectively to the expanding nation-wide research program in hybrid corn after he became a director of the company in 1937. He early supervised some of the hybrid corn planting in the Missouri Valley of Iowa. After purchase of the foundry at Belle Plaine, Iowa, he was responsible for the remodeling, construction of storage bins and new metal drier. He also planned the construction of both the small and large driers at the Funk Farms and the expansion of the plants at Mason City, Illinois; Traer, Iowa; and Rockville, Indiana. He and Howard Reeder accommodated the needs of the expanding business with efficient building and procurement of adequate equipment. Their advice has been sought for construction in Mexico, Italy, Spain and Argentina. LaFayette is also well known as president of the Mid West Federation of Mineralogists. His interest for a decade in collecting rocks, minerals and gems earned him an expert's knowledge and recognition as a qualified "Rock Hound" and lapidary. His informed and interesting lectures have been in demand before seed company groups and others throughout the State of Illinois as well as Indiana and Iowa. Hundreds of visitors came to the Funk Farms from all over the United States and even from foreign countries to view his valuable collection. This collection is one of the most outstanding in the United States.

Margaret Schertz, who was confidential secretary to Eugene D. Funk, Sr. during his presidency of the company, assumed the same duties for Eugene D. Funk, Jr. when he became president in 1944. Her knowledge of all office operations, general information regarding files and understanding of the growth of the business has made her a most valuable employee. Even-tempered and calm, often in the face of lost papers and forgotten appointments she has maintained a kind of protective barrier against too great disturbance in the executive office. Her attention to continuous work, her courteous and admirable office demeanor have earned for her the respect of all who visit the executive office.

Paul Funk traveled extensively through Illinois for the company during the years when the transition from a mail order house to the wholesale business was under way. Many of the contracts established in this area proved of lasting value. He built confidence by the methods he employed as a representative of the Funk family engaged in sales. Although illness prevented his continuation in the active work of the company his interest in developing sales programs is reflected in his later contributions as a director of the company. He was also interested in the Mid West Laboratories established by E. D. Sr. His membership in the Illinois Society of Farm Managers and Rural Appraisers has been maintained over a long period of years.

When Vaughn Dunbar first came to the office he began as a stenographer in general office work helping with bookkeeping until Mr. Crosby departed. Dunbar took complete charge from 1922–45. He learned to appreciate the sincerity and helpful attitude of E. D. Sr., and recognized the family atmosphere. This same sense of appreciation was extended to all of the family, especially to Mrs. E. D. Sr., who knew all the employees by name. Before Research Acres became the focal point for large gatherings, it was not unusual for those who visited the plant and the farms to see field days and demonstrations to be entertained on the large front lawn at the E. D. Funk home near Shirley. Visitors gathered under the trees. Employees of the company were always invited to attend. A philosophy for handling credit matters developed during these early years. Dunbar tried to put into practice the idea that "Credit is man's confidence in man." Common sense coupled with the belief that a large percentage of people are honest became his guiding principles. Mr. Miller recognized this valuable approach in contact with farmer customers. As the credit department grew with the expansion of the business his work became largely supervisory, often requiring travel away from the home office.

Another of the oldest employees, Ernest Radley, came to the company in 1922 as a billing clerk. During thirty-five years of service with the organization he remained in this department also acting as traffic manager. He acquired a valuable knowledge of freight and traffic problems over the years when orders were sent directly to farmers by local freight, parcel post or express with few carload shipments. With the development of the soybean mill after 1934 and with added need for transit applications in all departments, his responsibility became a time consuming one. Pressures in the seed business during the time of rush orders in the spring require long hours trying to determine the most direct routes for shipments. Long and strenuous hours were often and consistently contributed by Radley. No assignment proved too small or too large for him.

This group composed of Eugene Funk, Jr., LaFayette Funk and Paul Funk of the Funk family together with Dunbar, Radley and Margaret Schertz remain active in 1958 with thirty five to forty years of continuous service to their credit.[2]

Earl Sieveking while at the University of Illinois worked for James Holbert during the summers of 1924–25–26–27. He held a B. S. degree from Purdue (1920); M. A. degree from University of Missouri (1922); and a Ph. D. from the University of Illinois (1928). His work came to the attention of Funk Bros. Seed Co. as much of it was done on the Funk Farms. He became a permanent employee of the company in 1928. Sieveking, formerly of the Illinois Soil Survey and the Agricultural College in the University of Illinois, was engaged to undertake a new plan of work in 1928 related to the development of seed corn. He was employed by the company as a soils and crop specialist. Thus an effort was made to link corn breeding work with scientific studies of soil conditions as in the days of C. G. Hopkins. H. H. Miller, general manager, advised that it did little good to develop superior strains of seed corn if they were planted in depleted soil. He anticipated the development of special types of corn for fertile soils and others for poorer soils. Miller thought seed corn was like dairy cows in that both breeding and feeding were essential for best results.[3] It was believed that Earl Sieveking was the first man in America assigned to the task of connecting soil studies and seed corn breeding on a commercial scale.

Sieveking also looked after the breeding plots including all steps through the sale of seed corn to the customer. He knew breeding operations as they existed at that time. He also carried on the testing and experimental programs. Other phases of the activity such as

Old Office Building, North East Street

Old Office Building, West Washington Street

New Office Building, West Washington Street

Aerial View, Funk Bros. Seed Co., Bloomington, Illinois

Research Center, Bloomington, Illinois

production of foundation seed and commercial seed production were not only new to him but to everyone else interested in the product. During these early days of his employment he became active in setting up the Associate Grower program which has become an integral part of the company's system of expansion. He recalls that when he first arrived at the company, Double Cross Hybrid 250 had been produced and sold for a few years. A few acres were produced in 1928. The future of hybrid seed corn seemed assured although it was new. Eugene Funk and his manager, H. H. Miller, were aware and confident of its future. They also realized that its production involved special practices, as compared to open-pollinated corn. Research, testing and the production of foundation seed were essential, with special production fields to be planted and cared for throughout the season.[4] His long years of able analysis entitled him to qualify for added responsibilities as the years passed. His incisive mind and direct statement as well as objective observations have made him a valuable employee.

J. M. Davison or "Red," as he is better known to his associates, joined the company during these early years in 1926 in charge of warehousing records. Following this assignment he worked as a laborer in field seed and soybean departments. He transferred to a position as field seed and hybrid corn salesman. In 1941 he became a hybrid corn salesman on the road, rising to assistant sales manager for the Bloomington office in 1946. As sales advanced he was placed in charge of hybrid seed corn sales in Illinois, Indiana and Michigan territories. Fourteen district sales supervisors eventually came under his direction. Each supervisor had from 70 to 114 dealers working for him as the business expanded. When he first came to the company he was not so certain that he would remain. He was impressed when Mr. E. D. Sr. personally explained in this manner some of the work. "Now I want to tell you about the characteristics of Funk's Great American Oats." The family atmosphere in the company, the feeling that an employee "belongs" is of the greatest importance in his thinking. Many a time Mr. E. D. Sr. walked quietly alongside and commended in some manner his observance of an extra piece of work well done. The willingness of the Funk boys to help when something was needed did not go unobserved by employees. This fact in itself helped to cement the regard that the older employees felt through the years for the entire family.[5] This early policy of training and advancing capable and loyal personnel continues to be uppermost in the thinking of management. In the seed business the "know how" acquired by long years of experience in buying and selling can only be gained by actual day to day experience in the operations. These four men are good examples of the way the policy is put into practice.

Harold Goodwin was first added to the staff in 1924. He remembered well the day he was hired by H. H. Miller, who often did exactly what he was expected not to do. At first Miller informed the young applicant that there was no position for him. Goodwin then recommended a friend for the only vacancy. As he was about to leave Miller called to the foreman who was soon saying, "I can always find a place for a good man." Later Miller gave the original position in the office to Goodwin. He left in 1926 but returned to the Company in 1929. As Goodwin himself says, he learned the field seed business "from an expert," H. H. Miller, who after several years said to his apprentice "You might as well sign those letters as Manager of the Field Seed Department." This was indeed direct and high praise. Those who work with Goodwin describe him as having almost a sixth sense about markets and trends. He believes that Good Will is an essential requirement in good business.

James Holbert returned in 1937 to active employment after his work with the U. S. D. A. Office space was provided for Holbert by Funk during the years 1918–37. When the young scientist returned to the company he became vice president and director of research for hybrid corn. With the death of H. H. Miller in 1942 he was appointed general manager, a position he retained until his death in 1957. Over the intervening years he built a powerful research department and a national research program. He helped young scientists to learn and to develop their own ideas. He possessed an unusual quality of enthusiasm enabling him to bring renewed interest to his research personnel. He was thoroughly convinced of the quality of the products he had worked so closely to produce. Such knowledge gave him the courage to convince others. He also learned to transmit this information to the farm groups. At first it was difficult to translate the terminology of the scientific world into everyday language, but "Dr. Jim" stayed with the assignment until he mastered the technique. Farmers came to know him as "Doc" as they spoke to and of him with respect and admiration. The title in its full meaning of academic accomplishment brought him recognition in the world of the scientist as well as fellowship among those who profited by the results of his technical ability. He also gained the respect of his competitors in the commercial world. Competitors from both large and small companies counted on him for a fair and businesslike response to their questions.

James Holbert never spared his own strength and energy. His enthusiasm for the growth of Funk Bros. Seed Co. was his very life and indeed he gave it unsparingly. He was often heard to speak of the deep satisfaction gained from his association with E. D. Funk, Sr. and of the influence of the older man upon his thinking.[6]

His own scientific training and interest enabled him to recognize the necessity for an atmosphere in which young scientists could work and grow. He had the teacher's skill of asking an additional question to enable the questioner to find his own answer. But he could give a close answer himself and add something more in concrete fashion. He has been described as a great scientist, a great teacher and a great organizer in the field of hybrid corn development.

Harold Abbott came to Funk Brothers in 1935 after thirty-six years of experience with Albert Dickinson of Chicago, where he had risen to a vice presidency from office boy. As early as 1900 he gathered samples of field seeds for Paris exhibits and for Buffalo in 1902 and supervised a corps of men at the Louisiana Purchase Exposition in 1904. In 1903 he started a division, now known as Formula Feeds, for Albert Dickinson. He was one of few men giving time to the blending and mixing of feeds. Soon he devoted all of his time to this work. Abbott's position with Funk Bros. was manager of the soybean division. Under his capable and well informed supervision orderly and efficient merchandising prevailed. Abbott maintained his Chicago residence, remaining in Bloomington only during the week from Tuesday through Friday. In this way valuable contacts and information were readily available. His busy office with two or three Chicago telephone connections operating at the same time suggested his activity. Abbott brought knowledge and left "know how" with Gene Jr., whom he loves as his own son, with Mac Convis and Ralph Savidge and later Delmar Walker. Abbott is highly respected and recognized in the world of soybeans and seed trade. He has served in many organizational offices and has acted as a balance wheel in the Funk organization (See Chapter XVI). Harold Abbott possessed to a remarkable degree the ability to inspire confidence in those who worked with him. This confidence increased as contemporaries recognized his competence and understanding of all operations. A friendly and thoughtful manner endeared him to his associates. Long hours of intense work and study enabled him to attain these characteristics of leadership. His friends are widely distributed throughout the United States at all levels of organized business activity. He is described as considerate and with a reputation for integrity and honesty.

"Rusty" Laible graduated in 1920 from the University of Illinois. From 1921–25 he worked in the Department of Animal Husbandry, receiving his M.S. degree in 1925. From 1925–28 he acted as county adviser in Greene County, from 1928–31 in Marshall-Putnam, and from 1931–37 in McLean County. He joined Funk Bros. in 1937 and became agricultural director of sales for the Bloomington office and chairman of the information and advertising committee for all units. He has also been assistant secretary of the board of directors and became vice president and a director in 1957–58. His ability to explain and discuss farm problems in clear, concise and understandable manner has made him a valuable employee. His comprehensive knowledge of agricultural methods gained from actual experiences enabled him to talk the farmers' language. As a consultant and administrator his contributions to the development of the overall program are constantly apparent in the day to day operations.

Quality seed required adequate storage facilities. These requirements demanded certain kinds of construction. The most important problem was to merchandise equipment to save labor and develop methods for eliminating losses without injury to the product. Over the years Howard Reeder recalled many times the sound advice given to him as a young man by E. D. Sr. When he sent Reeder to Indiana to look up a customer who had complained about a two bushel order, the elder Funk said: "Remember if you're honest you will always be in business." Reeder gave the customer a fair and frank answer to his complaint, and subsequently the customer sent in a 100-bushel order year after year. On another occasion when discussing construction of a storage bin, E. D. Sr. said: "My boy, when you don't have a good foundation, you don't have a building, and whenever you don't have a foundation for your business you don't have a business."

Competence in the field of construction also was developed as the business grew, especially in the hybrid seed corn division. Howard Reeder started with field seed in 1936. He worked for John Howard until 1937–38 when he was sent to the Normal plant as a supervisor. Reeder acquired two years of engineering training at night school and worked closely with LaFayette Funk, eldest son of E. D. Sr. They supervised construction as the nationwide and foreign research program of Funks expanded. His assistance was greatly appreciated by agricultural leaders of Mexico. Among the chief centers of expansion are processing plants at Funk Farms, Normal Plant, Mason City, Illinois; Belle Plaine and Traer, Iowa; and Rockville, Indiana.

LaFayette Funk and Reeder have contributed effectively in expansion programs for Associates.

Lewis Falck came to the Iowa branch of Funk Bros. Seed Co. in 1935, working until 1938 with Fred McCulloch Seed Company, an early associate of E. D. Funk, Sr. Falck recalled a trip to Research Acres where he first met James Holbert who said, "Young fellow, I believe you and I will get along all right together." This statement influenced Falck to remain with the organization.

The expansion of the Iowa branch of the company has shown steady growth from 1936 forward. Falck was permanently employed by Funk Bros. in 1938. Falck recalled specifically the influence of E. D. Sr. and his statement "Not the biggest company but the best" as an idea repeated throughout dealer meetings. Iowa corn was at first brought to Mason City, Illinois for processing. Finally it was decided to locate the Iowa branch in Belle Plaine. The foundry at Belle Plaine was purchased in 1940 and the first metal drier was installed in 1941. A plant was established at Traer in 1947 continuing the steady expansion in the Iowa-Minnesota territory.

Lewis Falck gave credit to James R. Holbert for the ability to spark the personnel to action. Holbert was so convinced of the superiority of his product that he inspired his followers. Falck stated, "I don't believe there has ever been anyone more universally respected for his ability with hybrid corn than Jim Holbert." Lewis Falck's contribution has also been of marked significance. He has built the Iowa-Minnesota division into an effective operation in a highly competitive area. He has contributed leadership of an unusual quality in the Associate Group and on the committee of advertising and information.[7]

The personnel of the Iowa division is also composed of many long time employees. Their contributions have been of lasting importance in implementing the overall Funk program. Initiative and enthusiasm have been among their valuable characteristics displayed under the able direction of Lewis Falck. Those who work with Falck appreciate and understand his direct approach to difficult problems. He does not hesitate to state effectively his ideas and attitudes. This is a quality in leadership respected by the management of Funk Bros.

Leon Steele began his employment with Funk Bros. August 1940. At the age of ten in 1925 he had worked for James Holbert as water boy with the U. S. D. A. Each succeeding summer he was employed in the warehouses and field laboratory. He attended Illinois State Normal University in 1935, graduated in 1940 with a B. S. degree from Illinois Wesleyan and has followed graduate work at both I. S. N. U. and the University of Illinois. After finishing college he was employed as a corn breeder with Michael Leonard Seed Co. He returned to work with James Holbert at Funk Bros. in 1940 as research assistant, then served as manager of the research department until 1953 when he was appointed associate manager of research. He easily assumed the responsibility as director of the Funks G research division at the death of Holbert in 1957. He projected the entire program along the well laid plan of the developing research initiated by his father-in-law, James Holbert. His close association and long years of apprenticeship under Holbert's direction have provided a valuable continuity in the research department. Steele is respected by those who work with him. His analyses of scientific data indicate a thorough grasp of procedures. His explanations are easily understood by all groups visiting the Research Center and Research Acres.

Others also qualified in the fifteen year classification by 1958 include Elias W. Rolley, Mac Convis, Theodore Funk and Wesley Wilcox. E. W. Rolley was a self employed public accountant from 1921 to 1938. In this capacity he was engaged in accounting work for Funks, preparing the year end audits from 1923 to 1938, later prepared by Alexander Grant and Company. From 1939 to 1942 he prepared the monthly statements, and became a full time employee in 1942. His thorough knowledge of insurance problems, tax matters and accounting systems has made him an efficient and able comptroller for the company. With the expansion of the company the financial judgment of E. W. Rolley and Gene Funk, Jr. proved to be a constant bulwark against the sometimes zealous efforts of those who would spend easily. One of Rolley's chief contributions throughout the years began when he and E. D. Sr. decided in the fall of 1943 to sell preferred stock and assume a mortgage in order to provide working capital for the expanding operation. In the later years, Rolley and Gene Jr. have worked as a financial team.

Theodore Funk has been closely associated with the company, especially since his graduation from the University of Illinois. As the youngest son of E. D. Sr. he assumed responsibility for the management of the farm in 1927. His businesslike methods and interest in cattle feeding gave him recognition. He became a leader in many livestock organizations: director and vice president 1947–53 of Producers Live Stock Credit Corporation of Chicago; director of National Live Stock Producers Association 1946–53, director of Chicago Producers Commission Association 1938–53, vice president 1946–47 and president 1947–53. In later years he has often acted in an advisory capacity on agricultural problems as a member of the Commodity Credit Corporation Advisory Committee (1953–57) to the administration in Washington, D.C. Like all the sons of E. D. Sr. he assumed his share of responsibility. Although he maintained his home in Normal, his days on the farm often began at daybreak. He became a director of the company in 1943 and contributed effectively because of his wide knowledge of agricultural conditions. As a director and treasurer of the First National Bank of Bloomington he knows the financial problems of the Middle West.

Mac Convis had also known of the Funk family for many years. He regarded it as a distinct honor to work for the company. He remembered invitations to chicken dinners at the Funk Farms, the poetry of Mother Funk and the *esprit de corps* within the family. From 1936 to 1943 he worked for Herbert Moore in the grain brokerage business. He first worked at Funks evenings during 1943, and later was employed full time. He was closely associated with Harold Abbott, who knew every angle of soybean operations. Convis recognized Abbott's ability to teach others. At first Convis purchased soybeans for milling purposes. When Abbott retired he then became responsible for sales of soybean oil and meal. He had become a thorough student of purchasing, processing and merchandising soybeans. His interest in civic activities has gained for him recognized position in the community. At one time he acted as assistant probation officer. He is a supporter and leader of group activities within the company.

Versatility is one of the major qualifications for executive employment at Funk Bros. Wesley Wilcox filled this description. Formerly experienced as a cashier and vice president of the Normal State Bank his assignments with the company have been responsible and varied since his employment in 1943. He served as executive assistant to James Holbert, was placed in charge of personnel and later acted as an assistant to R. J. Laible in supervising sales from the Bloomington office. He has been treasurer and secretary for the Funk information and advertising committee. No assignment proves too difficult for him to assume.

Although only top administrative personnel have been individually mentioned, others are also efficient and loyal employees. Space does not permit description of their valuable contributions.[8]

Eugene D. Funk, Sr. was among those fortunate enough to hear some of the good things his friends and neighbors said about him.

During the last four years of his life 1940–44 their tributes and honors expressed widespread respect and esteem.

Friends and neighbors joined to honor Mr. and Mrs. Eugene D. Funk at the Ben Funk School in 1940. A plaque was presented by Frank Moberly, one of a committee of six who organized the party. A large bouquet of roses was presented to Mrs. Eugene Funk, Sr. O. V. Douglas read a list of some twenty-seven achievements by Eugene Funk, Sr.[9] This list included almost all of the events that crowded his life. Frank Moberly said that he had lived all of his own life since his birth in 1886 on Funk land as a neighbor of Gene Funk. He has been a leader in everything progressive and is known as one whose word is 'as good as his bond.'" [10]

H. H. Miller, general manager of Funk Bros., described E. D. as a man of vision, courage, independence and integrity "whose life was rich with friends and associations, vibrant with opportunity, experience and leadership." Dave Thompson, an old friend of Farm Bureau and *Prairie Farmer* associations, stressed the Funk lands and home as patterns of country living with the greatest of Gene Funk's contributions—his family—now carrying on the fine traditions of the Funk family in Illinois. Former Governor Frank Lowden wrote:

Gene during his long life has been a leader in every movement for the betterment of the American farmer and American farm folks. I have often said I have known of no one who has contributed more in a practical way to the great progress agriculture has made in the last half century than Gene Funk. And in all this Mrs. Funk has been a perfect helpmate. They both have my admiration and affection.

Eugene Davenport, for many years the dean of the Department of Agriculture in the University of Illinois, wrote with the knowledge of the work of Eugene Funk, Sr. as follows:

Gene Funk has always led the movement for better crops. There is no influence stronger in this direction than the research program of Funk Bros. Seed Co. Any one can go along with the crowd but to lead in pioneering takes both vision and courage and Gene Funk is liberally endowed with both these valuable qualities. In the language of the Arabian, may his shadow never grow less.

Among the tributes were four from the sons of Gene, Sr. LaFayette recalled that since his childhood his father always seemed to know what might be expected of tomorrow. He had planned how to correct errors and had been willing to lend a helping hand to others who shouldered heavy problems. In the eyes of his eldest son, Eugene, Sr., appeared always to embody the pioneering spirit enabling him to try to improve on the work of others or to develop new methods:

Normal, Illinois, Plant

Mason City, Illinois, Plant

Funk's Grove Grain Elevator

Belle Plaine, Iowa, Plant

Rockville, Indiana, Plant

Traer, Iowa, Plant

You have taught me to have an interest in community work and face public problems with a public spirit, to do what one believes to be fair and just, to look upon both sides of a question, to plan for future development.

Gene, Jr., described his father as one devoted to his family, friends, business, welfare of his community and nation; one unselfish with time for counsel and with a constant view to the future. Gene believed his father to be afraid of nothing; not stern but able to stand his ground well. Gene knew that his father had often been alone in his thinking but "undaunted he stands." He concluded:

A lover of children who could have all the clean fun and make all the noise they wished. To have lived these many, many happy days with him has been a real inspiration. No American family has had at its helm a more faithful or truer Dad.

Paul also said that his father seemed to know what was expected of tomorrow and planned his work for future problems in farming, financing, seed breeding, production, advertising and selling. Paul knew that his father had long planned for "the best institution of its kind in the country." When his ideas appeared to materialize E. D., Sr., often stated that no business is any better than the personnel of the whole organization. He believed in the fine qualities of the people who were associated with him in the company.

Theodore recalled that when he was a youngster, men often said, "Whose boy are you?" He replied proudly, "My Dad is E. D. Funk." It became a lasting inspiration to try to live up to their expectations when they added, "So you're one of Gene Funk's boys. Well, son, you've got a mighty fine father."

Men from many walks of life described Gene Funk as one who had helped and inspired them to achieve some of the good and desirable things in life. But these four men, his sons, knew the man they spoke of far better than any others. As Theodore remarked, the understanding look, a few quiet words of counsel, encouragement, help, fairness and ability to see more than one point of view and an uncompromising desire to see worthwhile tasks done right continued over many years to inspire those sons of E. D.'s to carry on as their father would wish them to do.[11]

Honors came again to Eugene D. Funk, Sr., when his portrait was presented to the Saddle and Sirloin Club of the Union Stock Yards. Over two hundred persons attended the banquet and witnessed the ceremony. The Funk family now held the distinction of having pictures from three generations in the famous Gallery of the Saddle and Sirloin Club, said to be the largest in the world devoted to a single industry—Agriculture. Thirty-five years ago Funk Bros. Seed Co. of Bloomington exhibited the Grand Champion car lot of cattle at the International Livestock Show.[12] The portrait of Eugene Funk was presented by P. G. Holden, accepted by C. E. Snyder of the Club, unveiled by Fred McCulloch and John T. Smith. Mr. Snyder recalled how the fire at the Stock Yards in 1934 destroyed the former gallery. Since that time all former portraits were repainted to provide the pictures of the leaders in agricultural achievement.

The chairman of the event was Dave Thompson. Statements were made by O. J. Sommers, Dr. W. L. Burlison and James R. Holbert. Agricultural men from several states as well as many from the staff of the seed company attended. P. G. Holden quoted from Dean Swift: "Whoever makes two ears of corn or two blades of grass grow where but one grew before deserves better of mankind and does essential service to his country than the whole race of politicians together." Holden declared that Eugene Funk had accomplished this to the extent that there was not a city or country home that had not felt the impulse of Mr. Funk's work. He added:

In all of my associations with Mr. Funk, I never knew him to measure success in terms of dollars, but rather in terms of service to others, to humanity. . . . Eugene Funk seemed to live and act as though he were living for a thousand years. No person can live well who does not live in the hearts and souls of humanity. The warm and sympathetic blood of the heart, coursing through the veins is vastly more powerful than the cold critical eye of the intellect.

Holden recalled how Gene Funk's idea to have an international hay and grain show back in 1906 had been turned down by the livestock group; how Holden, Funk and Fursman had decided to proceed with their own show, and how many years later the two events were united following World War I. He also referred to Gene Funk's desire to have the Funk Farms contribute to the good of humanity: "We are but tenants upon them for a few short years. They belong to the world, to the generations that come after us." [13]

C. P. Bull was pleased to think of Gene's picture among the many notables who have done so much for Agriculture, "But none I feel certain as much and in so broad a field as Gene." [14] Edward J. Dies, of the National Soybean Processors Association said: [15]

We may rake the records of midwest agriculture without finding a more sterling and inspiring character than Gene Funk. He is not only brilliant but downright lovable.

CHAPTER XXV

Field Seeds

ONE OF THE PURPOSES of the founders of Funk Bros. Seed Co. in 1901 was to secure and to distribute only the best seeds available. Early experiments on Funk Farms revealed the wide interests and knowledge of Eugene D. Funk, Sr. The center of development in Funk Bros. Seed Co. is in the field seed department. This department has maintained a nucleus of operation in the area immediately surrounding Bloomington, Illinois and in the state of Illinois. The very nature of the field seed business controls its breadth and depth within the company. Its continuity provided a stabilizing and balancing relationship to the more spectacular expansions in hybrid corn and soybean operations.

The Funks and their capable assistants recognized that skilled knowledge in the field seed business is part of the "know-how" handed down from generation to generation. A recognition of this skill is in reality a badge of confidence won through the respect gained by generations who may have dealt with the same company. A glance across the United States revealed well-known family names of long standing managing the companies that deal in field seeds. Eugene D. Funk, Sr. gained during his lifetime high regard, as a reputable seedsman, from the farmers of the local area. Much of the strength of his leadership came from the confidence of these people. He had built well upon the foundations of esteem in which his father, LaFayette and his grandfather, Isaac, were also held. The present generation continues to build upon and to reap the harvest from confidence built in these past years. Any proper estimate of the field seeds department includes far more than its contribution in dollar volume to the total income of the company. It has been from its beginning an integral part of the Heritage.

Eugene D. Funk, Sr. realized the advantage in experimenting with oats, red clover and alfalfa during the early twentieth century (see above chapters X and XI). He cooperated with the United States Department of Agriculture whenever possible. He was especially interested in improvement of corn under field seed operations.

Eugene D. Funk recalled in 1941 that beginnings in the seed business were little more than cooperative efforts by the operators of the Funk Farms to keep the area they farmed free from any noxious weeds that were spreading across the Corn Belt. These problems arose because of unreliable sources for clover and timothy seeds. Scientific agriculture was awakening in those years (1892) when E. D. Funk, Sr., took his European tour. Mr. Funk always felt that too little attention was given to the improvement of pasture crops. He noted in 1941: "Even timothy, usually regarded as the minimum in pasture mixtures, did not simply replace the blue stem grass of my Grandfathers' day. When we entered the seed business, reliable known-origin timothy of 95 percent germination and free from weed seeds was hard to find." According to his statement, sweet clover did not "just move from the roadside" into the fields. There was much that the Funks learned about harvesting, scarifying and developing new varieties to make this legume a part of corn belt rotations.[1] He wrote that red clover was the first legume on Illinois farms. With decline in fertility of the soil there was greater difficulty in "catching a stand." Seed inoculation and varietal improvement helped to save this crop from extinction.[2]

The field seed department handled soybean seed, except for a few years when the soybean department directed and handled these sales and all other seeds except hybrid corn. A glance backward to 1904–05 reveals that in addition to "elevator corn, elevator oats," the items for sale through 1904–08 included crate and shelled seed corn, oats, clover, timothy, alfalfa, rape and two large classifications known as farm seed and garden seed.[3] The dollar value was as follows:

Fiscal Year	Crate Corn	Shelled Corn	Oats	Clover	Timothy	Alfalfa	Rape
1904–5	$17,510.72	$11,487.95	$ 5,701.65	$ 4,527.50	$1,106.30	$3,108.15	$1,113.78
1905–6	13,775.44	10,230.74	6,106.92	5,811.04	978.20	1,800.06	753.68
1906–7	9,950.56	16,853.20	10,299.10	8,822.79	2,433.02	5,800.64	450.14
1907–8	15,013.17	27,385.29	13,477.65	39,638.73	2,414.02	4,457.79	345.49

"At the turn of the century," said Mr. Funk, "We were engaged in hybridizing experiments. From more than 400 varieties of oats then on the market the Funks tested and found many duplicates. There were many others not worth propagating." It was at this time that Professor Norton and Charles Brand were stationed by the U. S. D. A. on the Funk Farms.[4]

Funk's Great American Oats were the result of this painstaking work done in 1903, 1904 and 1905. This variety was offered to the public in the Catalogue of 1908 by Funk Bros. after five years of testing and with comparative results showing higher yields than for other varieties on the market at that time. Mr. Funk noted in 1941 that older readers of the *Prairie Farmer* would recall that this seed "created a stir comparable to the recent reception given hybrid corn." [5]

The varieties of oats offered from 1903–1930 by Funk Bros. included the following changes:

Great Dakota, Silver Mine, Early Illinois were offered in the first of these years. Big Four, Early Champion and Gold Mine were added the following year. Early Illinois was dropped and a Swedish variety was added in 1906. Big Four, Early Champion, Red Texas, Silver Mine and Great Dakota were listed and Funks Great American was introduced in 1908, along with the listing of Silver Mine, Big Four, Great Dakota and Texas Red.

According to the catalogue 1909, Garton Bros., Ltd., of Warrington, England occupied the same position in England that Funk Bros. then held in America—"That of premier breeders of all varieties of field seeds." Mr. T. R. Garton came to this country intending to establish a branch. He was advised to see Funk Bros. and requested that they handle Garton Bros. Oats for the season of 1908. Representatives from Funks visited Garton Bros. at Acton Grange and Warrington, England in the summer of 1907. As a result of their contacts Funks offered Garton Bros. Oats. The management explained in 1909: "This is a radical move and a departure from our established policy of handling no seeds except those bred by us and grown on our farms." [6]

From 1910–16 the offerings remained much the same with the addition of Funks 60 Day. During the war year 1918, Iowa 103 was added along with Great American, Silver Mine and Funk's 60 Day. Another variety, Iowar, was introduced 1924–25. Minota was offered in 1927. [7]

The parallels in history between man's search for wealth and his introduction of known seeds for his better agricultural existence in new lands is a truism not always referred to or explained adequately in the history books. An example can be found in the migration of alfalfa from ancient civilization to eastern and western United States. Its development as a major forage crop resulted from its introduction into California during the middle of the nineteenth century. This plant spread eastward across the mountains to Utah where it met the Mormons; thence to Colorado and Kansas and Nebraska. By the turn of the century it had crossed the wide Missouri to Iowa and Missouri. Wendelin Grimm introduced to Minnesota in 1857 the variety known as Grimm alfalfa. A. B. Lyman called the attention of Willet M. Hays and Andrew Ross to the survival of this variety in 1900.[8]

The interest of the Funks in the extension of alfalfa into the territory east of the Mississippi River where hardiness became an important factor has been told. Alfalfa was reportedly seeded at the University of Illinois Experiment Station in 1871.[9] The total acreage of alfalfa in the United States at the turn of the century (1899) was just over two million acres. According to W. A. Wheeler, "In each of the next two decades it doubled the one previous, and in the third, fourth and fifth decades it increased one-seventh and one-eighth respectively over the previous decade." He also stated that one percent of the total alfalfa acreage was east of the Mississippi at that time. Fifty years later in 1909 it was over 40 percent in that area.[10]

There were controversies over the question of how Grimm's alfalfa secured its hardiness.[11] Nevertheless it continued to sell well, not only in the United States but also in Canada. Baltic was found during 1905 in South Dakota. A hardy variety known as Ontario or Canadian Variegated was obtained in Europe by a farmer in Welland County, Ontario in 1871. This variety was widely grown in Eastern Canada." [12]

There is no indication that the Funks were interested in breeding alfalfa, but they were especially interested in the growth of the crop in Illinois. E. D. Funk, Sr., recorded in 1941 that Professor Hansen sent to the Funks some of the alfalfa seed gathered when he made his trip in 1897 to Siberia in search of early alfalfas.[13] By 1909 McLean county produced only 419 acres.[14]

Alfalfa was listed by Funk Bros. as a general offering from 1903 to 1915. It was described as grown on non-irrigated Kansas soil in 1916; in 1921 and 1923 listed as Funks Dry Land Kansas Seed, and in 1923 Certified Grimm from South Dakota was also listed. The following years, 1924, 1925 both Certified Grimm and Canadian Variegated were advertised. Other varieties advertised in 1926 and 1927 were Northwestern Dry Land, Blackfoot Grimm and Dakota No. 12. The 1926 Catalogue described Canadian Variegated as similar to Grimm and said it was discovered by Dr. Colver, who brought it from Baden, Germany. The explanation was continued in 1927 stating that Canadian Variegated was a Grimm Type Alfalfa. The management used this description "because it explains in a brief way the character of growth or hardiness." They also quoted from a Canadian source not named but declared to be reliable as follows:

At the present time we can get no government experts to distinguish or pick out for us fields of Grimm from genuine Ontario Variegated. So far as we know there is absolutely no difference in root systems, stems, leaves, blossoms or hardiness between the Grimm and Ontario Variegated. Both belong to the Variegated type so that Ontario Variegated can certainly be classed as Grimm Type.

Funks stated that they could furnish genuine Grimm at a reasonable price; they grew Canadian Variegated almost exclusively on their own farms; advised continuation of the Kansas seed if it gave results and suggested Hardy Northwestern as first choice in common alfalfa seed.[15] However, the variety was dropped from the listing 1928 and 1929. With the coming of the Seed Verification Service, Funk Bros. participated and have continued to distribute seeds of known origin. They advertised as noted above Bee Hive, Dakota 12 and Montana Alfalfa of Verified origin in 1929.[16]

Named origins of alfalfa were first distributed. After 1942 named varieties for specific purposes such as Buffalo, Ranger and Lahontas were common. This change now accounts for approximately 35 percent of the total alfalfa seed produced with the larger amount from the far west, especially California.[17]

The catalogue for 1924 carried an announcement regarding H. H. Miller, general manager and expert in field seeds. According to this statement the management of Funk Bros. had followed his activities for many years before his appointment in 1918. H. H. Miller was a native of the eastern townships, of Quebec, Canada where he worked on his father's farm. Later he completed an agricultural course at Guelph, Ontario. Then he was employed for three years by the Canadian Seed Branch of the Dominion Government, at Ottawa. His experience in this position included seed testing, crop inspection and the establishment of the first seed testing station in the Canadian Northwest in Calgary, Alberta. He became identified with Albert Dickinson Seed Company about 1906 as its seed expert. While there he organized the first commercial seed testing laboratory in the United States. During his employment with this Chicago company he passed on millions of dollars worth of farm seeds every year to comply with the requirements of the various state seed laws. He kept in close touch with experiment station work and was active in directing seed legislation in more than twenty-five states.[18] He owned and operated successfully a farm of some 1100 acres. His early work was with legume grasses and forage crops. His addition to the staff at Funk Bros. complemented the major interests of E. D. Funk in corn.

Harold Goodwin, presently in charge of the field seeds department for Funk Bros., joined the company in 1924. He recalled the early training he received from H. H. Miller. At that time the company was operating chiefly as a mail order business. Catalogues and circulars were assembled during the winter months and were mailed out during the early spring. They carried detailed information about crops. Other informational media were not always available to the farmer. Few owned their own trucks. Roads were impassable in the spring of the year. Therefore they ordered a large percentage of their shipments by rail.[19]

Better means of transportation including improved roads changed the method of distribution in this business. Farmers could soon drive to the warehouse in Bloomington, Illinois without forewarning during the winter from a distance as far as one hundred miles to obtain seeds. Salesmen and distribution points soon became necessary. Later the trend toward the establishment of a wholesale business brought about shipment by rail or commercial trucks. Door to door delivery in the fifties became available in many areas with a Funk Bros. fleet of trucks.[20]

The long term policy of fair dealing in these more immediate areas paid off unexpectedly during the difficult years of the Great Depression in the late twenties and early thirties. Large insurance companies loaned money to farmers throughout Illinois. Many farms were taken over with no particular desire on the part of the insurance company to enter the farming business. This situation was especially true when these companies were located in the eastern part of the United States. Officials in some of these companies knew Mr. E. D. Funk, Sr. Soon their representatives appeared asking for aid in filling seed requirements. Funk Bros. furnished a large portion of the supplies needed by these companies. The source of this income was of considerable advantage to the seed company at this time.[21]

Forage crops best adapted to the northeastern quarter of the United States including Illinois are the following:

GRASSES: *Bluegrass,* Canada and Kentucky
             Bromegrass, Smooth
             Canary Grass, Reed
             Fescue, Chewings, Meadow, Red, Tall
             Foxtail, Meadow

Oatgrass, Tall
Orchard Grass
Red Top
Ryegrass, Common, Perennial
Sudan Grass
Timothy

LEGUMES: *Alfalfa*
Birdsfoot, Trefoil
Lespedeza, Korean, Common, Sericea
Clover, Alsike, Crimson, Ladino, Red, Sweet, Common
White [22]

Major problems are ever present in determining increased volume and sales of field seeds in the operation of a commercial seed company. Relative importance of the seeds, if it could be determined, would aid in estimating conclusions. According to Herr and Jordan, conclusions might be computed on a number of different bases such as (1) acres harvested for seed, (2) the acreage that the forage seed produced would plant. Purposes in planting the seed should also be considered. Measures differ when interest is in soil conservation or in land utilization.[23] Money value, however, has become an important factor from the standpoint of both the farmer and of the seed industry.

Five legumes are listed as recently grown in the area designated above including red clover, alfalfa, lespedeza, alsike clover and sweet clover with Kentucky bluegrass and timothy.

Factors influencing prices received by farmers together with seasonal price movements and marketing margins are of significance. Seeds increasing in importance and in value during recent years include common rye grass, crimson clover, ladino clover and tall fescue.[24] In the cases of red clover and alsike clover areas of seed production differ although areas of seed consumption may be the same. Red clover production remains in the Corn Belt but with an increased trend westward. Production of alsike is definitely toward the Pacific Northwest and California. The time of harvest may determine the difference, especially when the crop is used in rotation. Sweet clover has not shifted noticeably. Commercial production of alfalfa continues in the West with increased production in California. Changes in production of lespedeza are difficult to determine with leading producing states north of the Cotton Belt and south of the central Corn Belt.[25]

If it were possible to predict changes in acreage harvested for seed it would be possible to estimate with more certainty the total production of seed for a year. Factors influencing farmers in their decisions upon acreages are also important. Prospective yield, prospective price and last season's yields may influence them. Changes in acreage account for most of the changes in seed-crop production. Prospective yield and prospective price are influential but these factors are difficult to measure satisfactorily.[26]

A number of factors may influence demand for forage seeds and their prices, such as livestock numbers, crop rotations, gross farm income and often personal income.[27] Factors affecting supply include primarily domestic production inasmuch as foreign trade varies from year to year. Timothy is the only seed studied by Herr and Jordan exported in very large amounts but all seeds except lespedeza were imported in "significant quantities for particular years."[28] Carryover stocks of seed also play an important role. This is a difficult factor to estimate because data are limited before 1939. Since that time there is not an adequate analysis.[29] Seedsmen also know that certain seeds are competitive and therefore price them in relation to each other. Quantities of competing seeds are therefore also important.

In addition to the above problems in the field seed business there are certain varieties which differ in their adaptability to different geographic regions. As a consequence different price-making forces may be operative.[30] Alfalfas and lespedeza show these differentials. Price differences for other seeds may reflect surplus and deficit areas with transportation costs accounting for a large part of the differential.[31] The authors of the above analysis believe that the experienced seedsmen would reach these same conclusions from his own observations but also add that more data are desirable before drawing too definite conclusions.[32]

Experienced personnel at Funk Bros. Seed Co. agree with the above findings and that the seedsman must know what the carryover is from the preceding year, the production of each seed item he handles and the potential intention of the farmer's demand. They would add that prices for the past season are seldom factors in determining values for the current year. They look at climatic influences and watch these situations continually. Changes in supply can be quickly affected by these changes during a given year thus affecting price. The very unpredictable part of this factor, the weather, is in itself a variable. Prices will affect volume of purchase. Large inventories of seed and lessened demands affect price. New and changing legislation may also be a significant factor.[33]

Seedsmen of long established houses like Funks are guided in their operations and in their decisions on the purchase of seed by knowledge of price relationships over a period of years. This knowledge is obtained by long study and recognition of trends in price and quantity during different seasons. No two are ever the same. Factors that enter into their estimates of supply and demand are essentially the same as those described above. There are additional problems also because there is not always a well-defined farmer group producing seed each year. There may be a known number of acres planted for a given seed crop, but there is no guarantee that any certain amount will be harvested for seed purposes. This uncertain factor also has a bearing on sales. Certain areas could be classed as buyers in one season but might be sellers the next year.[34]

Although difficulties in determining farm seed statistics have been considerably alleviated by the work of the Agricultural Estimates Division of the United States Department of Agriculture, they have not been entirely eliminated. At first the work of this division was pointed toward the estimation of the annual volume of agricultural production by states and for the United States. As the country expanded, the work of the division increased. The crop reporting system grew with the nation so that estimates were made in 1957 for some 150 crops and livestock items. In addition to more than 500 yearly reports from the Washington office, there are also many reports released by individual states under a Federal-State cooperative program. The function of the Washington office is one of coordinating the various 41 field offices. The assignment to accumulate seed statistics is a difficult one.

According to S. R. Newell, Director of the Agricultural Estimates Division, U. S. D. A., "The coverage of vegetable seeds is of comparatively recent origin. Fifteen years ago no official estimates were available for vegetable seeds, and estimates of field seeds were limited to only the leading kinds, some of which in recent years are of declining importance as they are being replaced with new and improved varieties." [35] He stated that from 1936 to 1955 the reporting space for seed statistics doubled in the Yearbook of Agriculture. Statistics that were sufficient in one decade may no longer meet the situation in more recent periods. Added to this problem are the usual elements of statistical errors. Voluntary reporting is the basis for the collection of materials. The program is dependent on demands of the seed industry, farmers, dealers and handlers for basic facts to aid in producing, marketing and distributing seeds. Mr. Newell said:

Seed is basic to our whole agricultural economy. Seed is an important farm crop and a source of direct income to those who produce it. Seed is also a production-cost item to many more farmers . . . we need to know more precisely the total volume of production and domestic use.[36]

Rapidity in acceptance of new varieties and development of new legislative programs created a considerable lag in accumulating statistics not included in the program of the division. The problem of accurate forecasting of probable production of seed is dependent on factors such as the weather, price, pressure of farm work and labor supplies. The farmer can change his mind at the last minute.[37] The division depends upon what information is available at the time of making its estimates.[38]

Personnel of seed companies such as Funk Bros. need statistical information. They are dependent to a degree upon the services of the U. S. D. A. mentioned above and they realize that many improvements are needed to make the service more adequate. They also recognize that their own contributions of information possibly can be improved. For example, the United States verified origin figures, published monthly, do not include certified seed which are increasingly a large portion of the industry.[39] Monthly reports of imports about the middle of each month have proven very accurate. The members of the seed industry recognize that the problems involved in the forecasting seed production are continuingly difficult. Spokesmen for the industry emphasize the same uncertain factors selected by the United States Department of Agriculture including weather conditions and change of mind by the producer. Suggested improvements included interim reports. The industry also recognized need for information regarding certified and uncertified seed. Accurate and unbiased reporting on the part of the industries would help the overall reporting. There seems to be increasing recognition that cooperation between the A. S. T. A. and the statisticians of the United States Department of Agriculture and the Department of Commerce may produce a greater degree of efficiency in reporting field seed statistics.[40]

The experienced personnel of the commercial seed company will continue to be a significant factor in the operation of the field seed business. Their experience and "know-how" in estimating needs becomes the solid core of information needed in estimating the general situation.

The very nature of the field seed business requires experience in the processing and buying and selling of seeds. The degree of success in this operation determines the measure of confidence built up in the thinking of the consuming public.

Seed technology at Funk Bros. under supervision of James Barnes, includes the quantitative as well as the qualitative aspects of seeds in general. Quantitative analysis includes determination of the component parts; qualitative analysis "evaluates viability or field producing power by the use of germination tests under optimum conditions." [41] Results from these findings are guides to proper labeling of seeds in interstate commerce as required by law. They are also employed in "bulking and processing procedures of all major seed houses." The seed technologist becomes the eye of the seed industry. Seed technology, however, is a relatively new development in plant sciences employing botany, taxonomy, plant physiology, plant pathology, plant ecology, plant geography and plant morphology together with agronomy, chemistry, meteorology and archeology.[42]

The seed laboratory at Funk Bros. is a control laboratory and a pilot plant combined. Problems relating to purchases, sales, bulking and cleaning are considered in conferences with personnel concerned with operations. Under the capable management of Harold Goodwin, the members of the field seed division—Ward Alderman, Bernard Dahlquist, Richard Funk, James Barnes and Walter Elgin —determine the selection of seeds purchased and sold.

Customers send seed samples to Funk Bros. for purity and germination testing. Other services include soil testing, weed identification, surveys of poisonous plants, as well as preparation of many educational exhibits for fairs, seed schools and newspapers. Personnel maintain close cooperation with specialists from the University of Illinois and the Illinois Crop Improvement Association.[43]

Seeds of grasses which are light and chaffy are sensitive to light. They are placed on moist blotters in a germinator having light similar to daylight. Other seeds require high temperatures during the day and low at night. Such seeds as timothy, brome grass, wheat and rye are dormant at harvest time. These usually move rapidly in commerce. Therefore the seedsman must know how to test these by a "pre-chilling" process in a proper medium within a refrigerator just above freezing for about five days. They will show their plant producing power within six to twenty-one days in a regular germinator. This process is described as "breaking dormancy." [44] Seeds of oats, rye and soybeans are placed in pots filled with vermiculite, a mica product highly retentive of moisture, and then placed in germinators for a required number of days. Seedlings when removed can be evaluated as strong, weak, dead or diseased. Years of research have gone into perfecting these methods now so important to the seedsman and to the farmers.

The processor has acquired more responsibility to provide clean seed with the complete mechanization of harvesting operations. According to an article by H. Dean Bunch and G. Burns Welch:

Farmers and seedsmen are probably more "seed conscious" than ever before in the history of American agriculture, and it is only natural that growing numbers should come to recognize the value of high quality seed.[45]

According to W. A. Wheeler, little information is available in written form about seed cleaning equipment. Long established seed houses are hesitant to reveal all of the information regarding their processes. Seed cleaning equipment at Funk Bros. consists of clipper cleaners or "fanning mills," gravity mills, scarifiers, buckhorn and dodder mills with skilled operators, proper screens, wind blasts and controlled volumes to obtain best results. The skilled operators are as important as any one factor in the business.[46]

Progress in developing varieties, in forming associations and in educating through extension and commercial programs has increased. The job of providing clean seed has fallen to the seedsman. Therefore, adequate and skillfully used equipment has become necessary. When seed comes from the farmers' own bins there is no opportunity to apply labeling laws. False values can be attached to so-called "cleaned" seed if the farmers do inadequate work.

The management of Funk Bros. has encouraged its personnel to participate in local, state and national organizations. Their purposes have been to support worthwhile programs at all levels. These objectives have been part of their desire to contribute to the over-all welfare of American agriculture. Close attention to research on the part of this commercial company has enabled the organization to rise above the ordinary classification of a seed distributing company. Ward Alderman has served as secretary, vice chairman and chairman of the Junior Seedsman Division of the A. S. T. A. He has also been active in the Illinois Seed Dealers Association. Joseph E. Barnes has been active for many years in commercial and official seed analysis associations. He was at one time president of the commercial group. Harold Goodwin served for many years as director of the Illinois Crop Improvement Association and vice president and president of the same organization. He has also contributed to the International Crop Association. He also served as director, secretary, vice president and president of the Illinois Seed Dealers Association.

During his presidency the Illinois Seed Soil Science Clinics were started. During 1954 he was vice chairman of the Farm Seed Division of the A. S. T. A. and in 1955 helped to formulate plans for the first Farm Seed Division Industry-Research Conference. He acted as the first chairman of this project.[47]

Unwritten records of the now historic and justly famous Research Acres on Funk Farms prove that long before the naming of these acres there was continuous research, breeding, selecting and procurement of many kinds and varieties of seeds. Here new varieties were planted and checked against older varieties to prove their adaptation and performance before release. Samples of new alfalfas, oats, wheat, rye, soybeans, barley and other new experimental crops such as guar, castor beans and sesame were studied. Early in 1940 one of the most important introductions into Illinois agriculture was Pawnee Wheat. Barnes stated, "Farmers all over the state profited greatly from this introduction which was sponsored by Funk Bros. Seed Co." Annual test plots are conducted at Research Acres. Farmer customers secure first hand information on the adaptation of untried varieties and are thus protected against the high pressure salesman who may attempt to sell untried varieties at high prices. The policy of the company includes invitation to specialists from the universities to evaluate the research at these acres. The company also contributed financially to research carried on at universities. It can also be said that the personnel of Funk Bros. have given unstintingly of their time and knowledge in helping to solve the knotty problems that have confronted American agriculture.[48]

CHAPTER XXVI

The Miracle Bean

As a part of the field seed business, Funk Bros. sold soybeans for seed purposes as early as 1903. Information about the soybean was available because of the extensive travels in the Orient by William Morse when he was with the Bureau of Plant Industry in Washington, D. C. He was inspired by his co-worker, Dr. Piper who once described the bean as "Gold from the Soil." Eugene Funk was among the early advocates of increased planting of soybeans in the early nineteen twenties.

Shortages of oil during World War I required importation of oil from Manchuria. Interest increased in the expansion of the crop in the United States. The American Soybean Association was formed in 1919.[1] Eugene Funk was among those Professors, Growers and Processors who were pioneers in the early enterprise.[2] He established one of the first processing mills in central Illinois, urged farmers to adopt the soybean and helped to create a certain market in the late nineteen twenties.

Eugene Funk watched with growing attention a mill operated by George Brett and I. C. Bradley at Chicago Heights, Illinois. This mill processed soybeans in 1919 with an expeller plant. Beans grown by farmers in Indiana and Illinois were for the most part used as seed beans. Therefore, mostly cracked beans were brought to this mill producing only a few drums of low quality oil.[3] The seed beans were also of a low quality. Bradley and Brett therefore decided to obtain ten carloads of yellow beans from North Carolina and Virginia. Through the efforts of Otto Eisenschiml of Chicago four tanks of oil produced in 1921 were sold. He recalled that he distributed about 85 percent of the oil up to 1927 as far as the immediate area was concerned.[4]

One of the chief difficulties in the early soybean business was the lack of markets for both oil and meal. Bradley recalled peddling and exhibiting the meal to farmers in order to increase demand from the mill at Chicago Heights.[5] When he saw the possibilities of using soybean flour for edible purposes he sent samples to hundreds of pro-

348

spective purchasers. A. E. Staley established a mill in Decatur, Illinois in 1922 thus adding another cash market for soybean growers.[6] Despite this activity the business was only in its infancy. Problems increased. There was need for organization and orderly procedures.

E. D. Funk, Sr. described the coming of the soybean to the farming system of corn, oats, wheat and clover rotations in the Central Corn Belt as follows:

Once in a life time! Yes, only once in the annals of crop production has our agronomy experienced anything like the Soybean. . . . Oats fell in acreage before it. Corn and wheat were challenged as cash income crops. Even in the realm of soil building, it threatened established legumes.

At Funk Farms acreages were turned over to producing seed to meet the demand. Over 2,000 bushels of their crop were hand picked in 1921 to obtain every possible pound of pure merchantable beans for pleading customers. The soybean boom worried Mr. Funk in the 1920's. Illinois grew 16,000 acres in 1919. Indiana's acreage was too small to be included in the crop census. These two states by 1923 planted a half million acres. E. D. Funk noted that "somewhere in this mad rush seed production would catch up to demand. When it did would beans for hay, feed and fertilizer absorb the crop at continued profitable levels? We doubted it."[7]

Before Funks marketed their 1922 crop they were assured of the installation by the Staley Manufacturing Company of their soybean mill and extracting plant at Decatur, Illinois. After considerable urging by H. H. Miller and Eugene Funk, Jr., as well as Paul Cooper of Atwood, Illinois, Gene Funk, Sr. contacted Brett and Bradley. He decided to establish a processing plant in Bloomington in 1924. This important step was taken when the equipment including cracking rolls, two No. 1 Anderson expellers, cookers and filter presses were transferred from Chicago Heights to the Funk plant. The expeller method for extracting oil is a continuous screw process. The plants of Staley and Funk were the vanguard of an expanding soybean processing business in Illinois. Eugene Funk recognized the importance of locating a plant near the producers. He understood that the real significance of the entire operation was in uniting the seed business with the processing of the soybean. The undertaking was not only an important development in the industry but also a fortunate decision for Funk Bros. Seed Co.[8]

The problem of maintaining a constant supply of beans at the mill increased with insufficient production of beans sold at the milling price. Almost all of the grain was used for seed, for production of hay or for plowing under. Seed prices were usually from 50 cents to $2.00 per bushel higher than the processors were able to pay. The Funks purchased beans for processing during the fall months but their supply vanished before the following season. Only three, four or possibly six months of processing resulted during the year. Feed mills that normally purchased meal needed a year round supply to maintain their formulas. The basic problem appeared to be one of educating the farmer to his advantages in producing the bean and in using the soybean meal as a new protein feed.[9]

In planting early soybean crops it was customary to seed with a wheat drill, planting solid. They were harvested either with a grain binder, shocked or mowed and raked into piles, then threshed by a grain separator. Binders, wasteful because of the shattering of the beans, were soon discarded. When grain separators were used it was necessary to slow the speed of the cylinder and remove almost all of the concave teeth to prevent cracking. The difficulty of this harvesting method was not conducive to bean growing. Soon combines came into use. Frank Garwood of Stonington, Illinois, in 1924 owned one of the first, a Massey Harris. This method of harvesting was an incentive to soybean growers. Planting was also changed from solid seeding by wheat drill to spacing in rows 24, 26 and 30 inches apart. Later beans were planted in rows of corn-planter width. This allowed cultivation with ordinary corn equipment with fewer seed beans planted per acre. When planting with the wheat drill it was customary to plant one and one-half to two bushels per acre. When planting with the corn planter as in later years, 40-50-60 lbs. per acre became the general practice.[10]

While Funk Bros. were engaged in processing soybeans during the early years they also handled a large volume of seed beans. They endeavored to secure and distribute the better new varieties developed by the Universities, especially in Illinois and Indiana. These new varieties were grown for wider distribution among farmers. The combination of this seed business with the processing enterprise proved advantageous as E. D. Funk and his advisors had foreseen. Farmers were also interested to obtain higher yielding beans with higher oil content. These two facets of the soybean business continued as integral parts of the Funk program. Constant experimentation contributed to increase of yields per acre.[11]

Farmers, however, were slow to accept the new protein food. Those who grew beans believed they could grind their own product and utilize the whole bean. This idea was detrimental to the business because the feed produced soft pork. The entire program in developing the soybean business was experimental and dependent on an educational process. Several years passed before farmers realized the advantages of soybean oil meal. Manufacturers of feed were also slow to utilize the meal as a new protein feed because they were not assured of the demand by farmers for the product.[12]

During their first year the Funk processing plant operated for about five months using approximately 20,000 bushels of beans. The results for both Funk and Staley were financial losses.[13] Although Funk showed a profit during the second year he realized that the beans were low in both yield and in oil.

The first varieties included A. K., the Midwest, Ito San, Black Eyebrow and Manchu. The hay varieties included Virginia, Ebony and Wilson.[14] The Funks also found it necessary to peddle the meal in one, two and five bag lots to farmers in McLean and surrounding counties to acquaint them with the product. They also procured several carloads of Mammoth Yellow Soybeans from the Carolinas. These beans were low in yield of oil but produced good meal.[15]

The original operation in the fall of 1924 began with a capacity of 300–350 bushels per day. A third No. 1 type expeller was obtained in 1927. Two more expellers were added in 1929. With five No. 1 expellers there was a capacity of approximately 800 bushels per day.[16] Sales of the soybean department in 1923 amounted to $25,659.16 increasing to $386,350.55 in 1925 but dropped to $221,853.78 in 1926.

I. C. Bradley who came to the Funks as manager of their soybean mill stressed early in 1927 the need for diversifying their crop. He said that the soybean was entirely overlooked by those who argued against diversification. Soybean production, according to Bradley, could be increased a hundred fold without producing an exportable surplus.

Bradley recalled the existence of an oil milling business for twenty years extracting oil from every conceivable source. The situation was complex because soybean oil competed with other domestic and foreign oils. He was of the opinion that soybean production would not be overdone in the next twenty years. Among the arguments he advanced in favor of growing the soybean were the following: (1) It was resistant to the European corn borer; (2) It fitted into all rotations designed for corn borer control; (3) It reversed the flow of farmers' money into manufacturing centers with the oil going then to paint manufacturers and the meal eventually to dairy regions; (4) It could reduce the corn acreage; (5) It could be harvested with combine and other equipment; (6) Its increase would mean more efficiency for the processor; (7) Consumers of soybean oil and meal would give preferences to soybean products; (8) Soybeans utilized nitrogen from the atmosphere thereby not robbing the soil. He also stated that if and when the domestic demand could be supplied, tariffs could be inaugurated to protect the farmer. Farmers in Mc-Lean County were slow to grow beans in comparison with those in Champaign, Piatt, Macon and others in the Champaign-Springfield area. Freight charges could be saved if the beans were grown nearby.[17]

A second step in the expansion of soybean production was possible because of leadership in central Illinois. There was a need for meal on the part of the Grange League Federation organization of New York. The acquaintanceship of H. G. Atwood of American Milling Company of Peoria with James A. McConnell of G. L. F. on the one hand and with Funk Bros. of Bloomington on the other, facilitated a discussion of the problem. I. C. Bradley stated that he and Eugene Funk interested Atwood in an idea sometimes attributed originally to American Milling Company. It is fair to say that Funk and Bradley did as much to initiate the introduction of a guaranteed price as anyone.[18] Without Eugene Funk's initiative and knowledge of agricultural conditions a combination of cooperative leadership might not have resulted. H. H. Miller also provided able guidance for this program. It is also fair to say that without Atwood and McConnell the plan would not have succeeded. The American Milling Company placed in operation an unused factory in Peoria where I. C. Bradley helped to install machinery to remove oil and grind soybean cake into meal.[19] The decision of G. L. F. to buy meal for the New York milkshed created a wide market. A guaranteed price of $1.35 per bushel was offered up to a total of a million bushels in 1928 to 1,500 Illinois farmers for beans by Funk Bros. of Bloomington, by the American Milling Company of Peoria and by Cooperative G. L. F. Incorporated. The *G. L. F. Shareholder* stated that their organization realized that prospective supplies would be inadequate, and knew that a protein shortage would be costly to G. L. F. patrons. They, therefore, entered the agreement to secure a supply of protein with the dairy feed market as its primary outlet. The source was the farms of Illinois and the product was soybeans. The Illinois College of Agriculture, the Farm Bureau and the *Prairie Farmer* cooperated.[20]

The final decision regarding the guarantee for the 1928 crop was made at a meeting in Urbana of fifteen county farm advisers, representatives of Funk Bros. and of the American Milling Company. A committee of three was named to draw up the agreements.[21] I. C. Bradley commented many years later:

We solicited the aid of the late Mr. H. G. Atwood, President of American Milling Co., at that time, which later became Allied Mills, Inc. His first reaction was in this response . . . 'The farmers are our customers. His stock needs protein. He should produce it.' That was the 'Spark Plug' for the beginning of a new and great industry. He said we will take all of the meal your plant can produce.[22]

A. E. Wand of Staley's attended the Urbana meeting. He left with word that he would urge them to join but he apparently was not instrumental in gaining this action. However, Staley continued to provide a market for beans and was increasingly interested in the development of this crop.

The million bushel limit in 1928 was considered adequate. Only one-half that amount was offered to mills in the area during the previous season. The 1927 U. S. A. crop was 2,288,000 bushels. About three-fourths of this amount was used for seed and for purposes other than for milling.[23] The guaranteed price in 1928 of $1.35 per bushel was for No. 2 grade beans and was considered satisfactory by the farmers. Under the agreement, if the farmer negotiated to grow beans he was not compelled to ship to either of the participating companies if others offered higher prices.[24] Agreements for 1928 in order to stimulate production were made in terms of acres instead of bushels.[25] Strictly speaking, this announcement was a guarantee, not a contract.

J. A. Waring, with many years of experience in the grain business came to work for Funk Bros. in 1927. His duties included the purchase of soybeans. Waring handled the paper and contracts for the program in 1928 from the office of Funk Bros. According to his recollection most of these contracts of the three companies were mailed from the Funk office.[26]

The legume project of the University of Illinois during the season 1928 placed its chief emphasis on the soybean. This program was composed of two parts: (1) To standardize better adapted varieties through publicity and field demonstration; (2) To assist in supplying a satisfactory market for surplus seed and for beans of lower quality.[27] Professor J. C. Hackleman of the University of Illinois contributed effectively to the entire program by urging farmers throughout Illinois to accept and grow soybeans. The early processors recognized the importance of his contribution.

The three manufacturers also recognized in the winter killing of wheat that farmers needed a substitute crop. Oats did not present advantages and corn acreages were already too high. Farmers had decided advantages because of the

(1) Guarantee by three large companies who had reputations for doing what they promised with a good bank account to back up their guarantee.

(2) Elimination of speculation on a major farm crop. Beans went straight from farm to manufacturers.

An article entitled "Taking the Gamble out of Soybean Marketing" described how the 1928 guaranteed price was put into practice. Processors who bought and used these beans paid little if any more for this crop than in the past few years. The *Prairie Farmer* commented:

These are the net results of the first year's experience with a system of crop contracting and price stabilization that was put into effect this year by the principal users of soybeans and under which 90 percent of the soybeans grown in the state were handled.

Of the two greatest gambles in crop production, the weather and the market, one was thus removed. The three companies who used nearly all of the crop were interested for different reasons: (1) Funk Bros. for production of oil and meal from soybeans; (2) The American Milling Company for production of soybean meal and; (3) The G. L. F. Exchange as the largest buyer of soybean meal in the United States. Deliveries reached 650,000 bushels in Peoria and 350,000 at Funk Bros. in December when the million bushels were received.

Better varieties of beans were used: Manchu, a good yielder with a high oil content and the Illini which stood better than other varieties. Grading also was important. Probably 90 percent of the farmers were satisfied with the agreement. Nevertheless some were discouraged by weather conditions, others had difficulties with the elevators who received beans and shipped them to Bloomington or Peoria. Almost all of the elevator operators accepted the idea but some who were more speculators than service men made it unpleasant for the farmers. Handling charges by the elevators varied with higher charges for smaller lots of beans. In some communities farmers shoveled their own beans on the cars. The *Prairie Farmer* said in 1928:

The value of an experiment such as this soybean price stabilization program is that it is an example of what may be done with all kinds of crops with the proper organization and with a progressive point of view on the part of the manufacturers who use these crops. There are many farmers who would welcome something of this kind for all their crops and thus escape the market gamble in which they have been engaged all their lives.

The manufacturers were equally pleased. Gene Funk and H. H. Miller were quoted as saying they could afford to proceed with this kind of plan because known acreages under agreement enabled them to plan efficient factory operations. Arthur Heidrick of American Milling Company said it enabled them to expand their business. J. A. McConnell of G. L. F. was equally enthusiastic.[28]

The G. L. F. *Shareholder* commented that this soybean oil meal program "relieved a very tight situation on protein." The eastern farmer received his dairy feed at a better price while the farmers of Illinois received a certain outlet at a fair price. This same publication added:

But this project has more significance than its immediate benefits. It is a new development to find the dairymen of the east contracting for protein with the prairie farmers of the midwest and one that opens up a big vista of future responsibilities which were undreamt of before farmers went into business on a big scale.[29]

The *Prairie Farmer* noted in February of 1929 that the "Peoria Plan" as the 1928 Guaranteed Price was often called, continued in 1929. The American Milling Company, Funk Bros. Seed Co. and G. L. F. Exchange again offered the contracts to the farmers for fall and winter delivery. The contract price was to be $1.33 for No. 2 beans, f. o. b. Peoria or Bloomington for delivery by November 15 with an increase of one per cent per bushel every fifteen days until $1.38 was reached by January 15 to February 1. Each grade under No. 2 took a one cent discount; a one cent premium was paid on No. 1 Grade. This was actually a contract rather than a guarantee. The grower who signed a contract obligated himself to deliver the acreage at the specified price. Contracts could be obtained from the farm adviser or the local elevator.[30] Farmers often hesitated because they could not determine their total acreages. Many agreements in the previous year were not signed until June 4.[31] One source pointed out that the contracts for 1929 were specified in bushels and with a sliding scale in order to hold back delivery dates thus avoiding repetition of storage congestion as in 1928.[32] The original contract, however, leaves a space for the number of acres.[33]

Problems immediately arose. The idea of a Farmers' Cooperative was supported at meetings held in Champaign and in Monticello, Illinois. A subsequent meeting was held at Funk Bros. in Bloomington, March 19, 1929. A committee of six chosen at the Monticello meeting including Mr. Armstrong, Champaign County, Chairman; Mr. Richardson of Shelby County; Mr. Ellis, Moultrie County; Mr. McCormick, Douglas County; Mr. Probst, Macon County; Mr. Walsh, Piatt County; for the farmers and Farm Bureaus. From Funks there were E. D. Funk, Sr., H. H. Miller, I. C. Bradley, J. A. Waring and E. D. Funk, Jr., The first six represented the bean growers regarding the contract. Some agitation resulted because leaders of the Farm Bureaus thought that they had been overlooked this year in the contracting of the beans. Contracts were being sent out directly to the growers whereas in 1928 they were chiefly handled through the Farm Bureaus.

Mr. Armstrong said in Bloomington:

I am sure we appreciate to the fullest extent the pleasant relations and dealings we had with your organizations last season and it is not the wish of anyone to sever those pleasant relations, but we did feel that possibly—in view of the fact that there seems to be a little feeling between the Farm Bureau members and possibly the elevators—we might be able to smooth this over and resume the cooperation we had last year.

He spoke for the Farm Bureaus and their offer to service the 1929 contracts, by sending them to their members for a small remuneration to go to their associations. The committee also felt that growers would lose on the $1.33 price. If beans were held for $1.38 it would not be worth while to farmers to scoop them in and out of the bin. They also felt this new arrangement was more of a help to the elevators than to the growers. Armstrong stated that 90 percent of the growers would prefer bringing beans direct to the processor. They asked for last year's price and 2 cents per bushel to be paid to the Farm Bureau Association for contracting beans.

Eugene Funk, in his usually deliberate manner, asked a few questions. Did Mr. Armstrong mean 2 cents per bushel all season? Mr. Waring inquired if they could guarantee a certain quantity. Mr. Miller asked if the price would go to $1.35? Mr. Armstrong answered that their idea was to accept the contract as it was. Funk then said that he wanted to correct the impression that the price was lowered. He stated that it was raised.

Funk said regarding the cooperative, "Not at all if you will stop there." He then pointed to an article from the *Illinois Agricultural Record* referring to the Monticello meeting of March 14th reporting Harrison Fahrnkopf, director of grain marketing for the Illinois

Agricultural Association as helping to organize the "new bargaining association." Mr. Funk asked about the statement that "7,000,000 bushels will be sold through the Association and the purpose of the organization will be to maintain the bargaining power of the growers." He was interested to know the meaning of "bargaining." Mr. Armstrong and Mr. Richardson denied intention of the implied purpose.

Armstrong noted that by the suggested schedule the farmer could not receive $1.35 until December whereas in 1928 he could move the crop from his machine at $1.35 if he had No. 2 beans. He also pointed out that the farmers' acreages were governed somewhat by their lack of storage space. He also explained that since G. L. F., a cooperative, was buying the meal it seemed possible that a cooperative in producing the beans would be welcomed. Steps toward cooperative organization would be taken through the Illinois Agricultural Association providing they did not recommend a bargaining position.

Funk explained the processors' point of view. They asked for 1,600,000 bushels. This amount could be handled through the year but not all in one week or within a three-months' period. In order to pay $1.35 per bushel for beans there must be assurance of running the mill during the entire year. He said, "It takes a lot of elevators to handle 1,600,000 bushels of beans." He was of the opinion that there was a certain group of farmers who would sell early and a certain group that would delay. Last year twenty cars were on track one day at Funks and one hundred cars were received at Peoria in one day. Funk paid demurrage for two weeks at $5.00 per day per car. Arrangements for holding the beans off the market over a period of weeks was important to processors.

Funk said that J. A. McConnell was in Buffalo and H. G. Atwood was in New York with previous business appointments or they also would have been present. He agreed to report to them the two cent proposition but he could not act independently at that time. To prove his own interest in Agriculture he said:

Further than that to show you my interest in agriculture—I am not boasting about it—but I do represent a fair acreage of land as a family. My family connections represent about 50,000 acres of Illinois lands. Why shouldn't I be interested in agriculture?

Funk explained how demands in dairy districts had increased during the year 1928 thus providing an outlet for more meal. American Milling had also started to process beans and were also taking the meal from Bloomington. Thus the Funks were able to cooperate with them and with McConnell who was the G. L. F. representative of 20,000 dairymen in New York. When the price per ton per meal increased $3.00 the processors could raise the price on beans. Had McConnell said "no" at any time there could have been no added price to the farmers. He also explained that Atwood's influence as president of American Milling Company was back of the Champaign meeting. To a certain extent Farm Bureau and elevator men were represented in 1928. However, the elevator men were left out during the last meetings in 1928 chiefly because there were two groups. These were old line elevators and some new Cooperatives. Funk did not hesitate to say that he and his family had connections with both elevator groups. His brother and relatives were in one group and he, himself was vice president in another so "I know the ins and outs of that business." The elevator men asked to be included in 1929.

Funk believed it was evident that the beans had to go through the elevators. He also told the committee that the presidents and secretaries of both elevator organizations met at Peoria with representatives from the Farm Bureau, Dr. Burlison and Professor Hackleman, both of the University of Illinois. At this meeting the sliding scale of prices for 1929 was set up. There was some fear that more oil mills might be established if the open contract of 1928 were repeated in 1929. For that reason they decided upon a regular contract in 1929. There had been no suggestion to omit the Farm Bureau. Their thought, according to Funk's explanation was to help both the Farm Bureau and the grower. He also added that contracts were sent both to last year Growers and to the Farm Bureaus. It also appeared logical to send contracts to the elevator operators who often had a closer contact with some growers because the grain went through their hands. Then Funk said, "Perhaps we made a mistake and when this agitation came up we called a meeting and called that matter off just because you fellows in Champaign County did not want it. We thought we would eliminate all dissatisfaction."

Then with characteristic humor he said, "I am afraid, men, you are going to 'spill the beans' rushing at it absolutely from an agricultural standpoint and forgetting the manufacturing end of it entirely." He advised against doing what they had in mind. He stressed the newness of the processing business and the fact that all concerned were feeling their way. The time had not yet passed when G. L. F. could say "No." If this situation arose certain other offers of protein known to be in the hands of G. L. F. could be accepted. So far, Funks and Peoria had refused these offers. Then Gene Funk told these men that

Illinois was going through a very critical situation from the point of view of soybeans. He did not blame them for asking for all they could obtain, that was human nature; but he advised, "Do not ask for more now." He pointed to possible losses for the processors, declared that what the farmers needed was rotation of soybeans with corn and told them confidentially that other mills would take their processing plants where there were other supplies of beans if there were continued agitation.

Armstrong appeared to recognize the wisdom of this straight line of talk and declared that they felt the same way about the situation. His group realized that there were both visible and invisible forces at work. He had, however, some feeling against the old line elevators that had too much to say about the price of the farmers' grain. He believed they would be against any cooperative organization. Armstrong's idea in forming the Cooperative was to strengthen the industry.

Funk also explained that contracts with the elevators were decided upon in order to fix the price they would charge for handling the beans. Discussion revealed that contracts were sent to the elevators to establish a price for handling beans although no minimum charge was set. Armstrong interpreted the sending of contracts to the elevator as a possible weakening of the Farm Bureau. The processor, however, also had to think in terms of the problem confronting the elevator.

I. C. Bradley then explained how the price had been arrived at from the study of records at the University of Illinois. He again called attention to the fact they were dealing with a new crop.

After the various points of view were expressed Armstrong confessed that he was greatly impressed by the statements but continued to think that the requests of his committee were not unreasonable. Bradley pointed out that perhaps the great favor in 1928 was not that the Farm Bureau secured signers for the contracts but more essentially that any contracts were offered. These offers could be withdrawn at any time. The agreements increased the prices, as Waring added, from 1927 when beans brought only $1.10 per bushel.[34]

After some figuring Funk observed that a charge of 2 cents per bushel by the Farm Bureaus would add 66 cents per ton to the cost. He asked what they thought J. A. McConnell would say when asked to pay this proposed 66 cents per ton for meal. Bradley then said that what was a service to the processor was also a service to Farm Bureau members and after all that was the reason for the existence of Farm

Bureaus. Funk added that 66 cents per ton on a million bushels would equal $20,000. He could not decide the matter alone but would if they insisted, take the matter up with the American Milling Company and with G. L. F.[35]

About three weeks later Armstrong wrote a letter to American Milling Company stating that the Committee of Bean Growers finally decided to recommend to their County Farm Bureau "your soybean contracts for the 1929 crop" with wholehearted cooperation. He continued:

> We believe that a letter from you indicating the acreage desired accepting our proferred assistance will set the wheels of good will and cooperation into motion.

He and his group were still cooperative-minded and intended to pursue their plans. They also expected to work through the I. A. A. They also realized that great consideration was due to those who had established a market and encouraged the growing of soybeans. He asked for a few words of encouragement such as were expressed by Mr. Funk on the occasion of the visit to Bloomington. This letter was mailed in care of E. D. Funk and as Armstrong later wrote he had intended to address it to American Milling Co., G. L. F. and Funk Bros. He told Funk that the recommendation to accept the contracts seemed to meet the approval of farmers. They also hoped that the contracting firms were pleased.[36]

Eugene D. Funk, Sr. and his associates thus were instrumental in clarifying a difficult situation. The 1929 contracts were placed in effect. Two signed copies of the contract were to be forwarded to J. W. Shisenand, chairman of the Farm Bureau Committee in Peoria, one copy to be returned to the farmer.[37]

Judgments regarding the success or failure of the contracted price agreements vary. Writing in 1936 L. B. Breedlove in a series of articles said, "Processors Underwriting Failure." [38] Possibly in the long view this statement is correct. But as a temporary remedy for a difficult situation it seems fair to say that G. L. F. was pleased, the farmers were satisfied and the processors were able to keep their mills in operation.

A new wooden elevator with a capacity of 40,000 bushels was constructed by Funk Bros. near the warehouse during the fall of 1928. Early on the morning of March 12, 1929 with the elevator about two-thirds full, fire destroyed the structure. Some beans were destroyed, and many more were water soaked. Arrangements were made with

Allied Mills of Peoria to dry the beans. Some forty to sixty men worked day and night with shovels and portable elevators until the beans were finally loaded into cars and shipped to Peoria where they were dried. All were sold as salvage in Chicago except one car. There was less damage and shrinkage than had been expected. Fortunately the full amount of the insurance was paid.[39] This was indeed a disheartening moment in the development of the soybean business at Funk Bros. Decision to proceed with the construction of a concrete elevator of 140,000 bushel capacity followed almost immediately.

Another important decision was made about this time. E. D. Funk, Sr. advised his officers that it would be to the advantage of the company to purchase from McKenzie Milling Company its mill and elevator at Taylorville, Illinois. Negotiations had been underway for three months in June 1929.[40]

E. D. Funk, Sr. reported that the total acreage of soybeans in Christian County was approximately 11,000 acres. The idea was to install in the new plant three soybean expellers. If additional funds were needed they could be obtained by the sale of $25,000 of preferred stock. I. C. Bradley became the Manager of the Funk Mill at Taylorville. The Daily *Breeze* of Taylorville recorded that Clair Hay, a former County Farm Advisor got in touch with Funk Bros. after their fire at the Bloomington plant. An old friend of the Funks, P. S. Haner, was also active in concluding the negotiations.[41]

A new venture in soybean marketing occurred when the formation of a cooperative became a reality. When the directors of the newly formed Soybean Marketing Association held their first meeting December 7, 1929, John Armstrong invited Eugene D. Funk, Sr., Messrs. Legge, Atwood, McMillen, Heidrich and Eisenschiml to be present.[42] The members of this association operated under a three-year marketing contract, consigning their crop to the Association pool. Funds were secured from the Federal Interstate Credit Bank of St. Louis for financing and marketing. L. B. Breedlove declared that the contracts were made with bonded warehouses operating under Federal license with 200 county elevators and six processing companies. At first, according to Breedlove, the association was hampered by falling prices. An export demand developed in the fall of 1931. Breedlove found that the association had difficulty in trying to operate by a fixed price, "alongside an open market paying prices on day to day developments." After 1933 the association did not conduct a pool for soybeans.[43]

Additional problems arose when Frederich Wand of the Soybean

Division of Archer-Daniels Midland Company's Decatur office inquired regarding the inspection service in the industry. There was no intimation that grades had been established at Decatur prior to their establishment by the U. S. D. A. Wand raised the question of differences in grading by Federal inspectors at different points in Illinois indicating the possibility of higher grading where there were larger receipts. Apparently no definite evidence was presented.[44] W. H. Eastman, president of W. O. Goodrich Company of Milwaukee, a subsidiary of Archer-Daniels Midland, handling its soybean business, stated, on the other hand, that he thought a great deal had been accomplished in developing a uniform basis for Federal grades. This concern employed Federal inspection service at its plants in Toledo, Ohio, Chicago, Illinois, Atchison, Kansas and asked for it at its plant at Fredonia, Kansas. The Bureau of Agricultural Economics had a special committee working on a comprehensive survey of the Grain Standards Act. The report was not available at that time. In the event that the Grain Standards Act should be held to apply to soybeans or amended to apply to their inspection it would become compulsory for those moving into interstate commerce when sold by grade. The inspection service for soybeans under the Market Inspection item in the Appropriation Act was entirely permissible.[45]

The United States Department of Agriculture announced Standards for Soy Beans September, 1925, recommending their use. Revision was made the following September. Grades and classes were described July 9, 1935 effective September of that year. The structure of the grades correspond roughly to that of grades for grain.[46]

A meeting was to be held by Messrs. Fahrnkopf, Armstrong, Smith of the I. A. A. with Funk in the latter's office April 3, 1930.[47] In late April Armstrong wrote that they had visited Mr. Shellabarger at Decatur, Mr. Eastman in Chicago and Mr. Atwood of Allied Mills. On these occasions they explained the purpose of the Soybean Marketing Association to secure direct and orderly marketing without inciting ill will. Dr. Burlison of the University of Illinois attended the meeting in Chicago and said that he felt a movement had been started there to work together for the best interests of the industry as a whole.

The National Soybean Oil Manufacturers Association held its organizational meeting May 21, 1930. The organizational declaration stated that the undersigned were clearly aware of their responsibility in fostering and in encouraging the progress and development of an infant industry in the United States. The declaration continued:

We frankly recognize that there have been and still are certain trade practices in the industry which are unbusinesslike and harmful to producers and consumers alike. Some of the objectives of the Association were to promote mutual confidence, a high standard of business ethics, elimination of trade abuses, the promotion of sound economic business customs and practices.[48]

The organizational meeting was held at the City Club in Chicago, Illinois. Otto Eisenschiml was elected Chairman. Whitney Eastman as chairman of the committee on organization presented the Declaration, Code of Ethics and Constitution and By-Laws. Reports from the committee on Trading rules and the Technical committee were adopted. Eisenschiml became president, Shellabarger first vice president, R. G. Dahlbert second vice president, W. H. Eastman, secretary and I. C. Bradley, treasurer. For the year of 1930–31 Eastman was president, Bradley continued as treasurer and a member of the board of directors.[49] Later Bradley became secretary and president in 1936. E. D. Funk also became a member of the board of directors.

Armstrong indicated that the Marketing Association would welcome such a group. Armstrong also discussed with Fahrnkopf the basis for negotiation with Funk Bros. This involved securing financial help from the Farm Board. A portion of the money should come from the Intermediate Credit Bank which was reportedly careful on the question of approved storage facilities. Armstrong also visited Otto Eisenschiml to secure from him a positive statement that 15 percent of soybean oil could be used in farm painting to good advantage.[50]

Funk Bros. then negotiated an elevator agreement with the Soybean Marketing Association, September 18, 1930. They were to receive all of the soybeans delivered to the company by members of the association from 1930 crop to June 1, 1931. They would establish the grade of member's soybeans on basis of U. S. D. A. standards and whenever possible would place them in separate bins for shipment in carload lots. Records were kept in quadruplicate; one copy to the elevator, one to the grower and the other two copies to the Soybean Marketing Association. The growers were to be paid by the company at prices named by the association for various grades. Prices were to be based on U. S. No. 2 Soybeans and unless otherwise specifically provided to pay a premium of 1 cent per bushel for U. S. No. 1 or better, 2 cents discount per bushel on No. 3 and 4 cents discount for No. 4 beans. They were to ship the beans in carload lots on order of the Association attaching a sight draft to the bill of lading for 80 percent of the advance paid to the growers plus handling charges, the balance to be remitted to the association on basis of grade established at Association's terminal storage, point of delivery or public inspection point. The handling charge was to be mutually agreed upon by the local council of the Farm Bureau. If it seemed advisable for the company to store soybeans in its elevators for a limited period the problems would be taken up with the company and by mutual agreement decided that storage should not exceed 1/30 of one cent per bushel per day. It was fixed at 0 cents but could never be more than 5 cents.

The Marketing Association agreed to pay promptly drafts drawn by the Funk Bros. Seed Co. on carload shipments. The company was also to be furnished a list of members in that community under contract with the association. They also agreed to make final disposition of less than carload lots in hands of the company within thirty days after notice.[51]

Another agreement relating to processing was negotiated by the association on the same day, September 18, 1930, also with Funk Bros. Seed Co. The company was interested in securing a supply of soybeans for processing purposes while the Marketing Association was described as statewide cooperative, warehouse facilities in Bloomington and in Taylorville, under state license and regulations with adequate facilities to warehouse and condition beans. These were designated to Funks on order of the association.[52]

There was also a formal agreement between the General Storage Company and the Soybean Marketing Association. Negotiable warehouse receipts were to be delivered to the association. The association was to provide all labor and material necessary for proper operation of the warehouse service. This agreement was subject to and part of the agreement with Funk Bros. dated September 26, 1930.[53] A second agreement was made between General Storage and Funk Bros.[54]

The question of where the 1930 crop of Illinois beans was going was partially answered by W. H. Eastman when he replied to a statement in the *Champaign News Gazette* charging that his company had a monopoly. Eastman stated that they had purchased over half of the 1930 crop in Illinois with a large amount secured at $1.30 per bushel to dealer, f. o. b. county shipping station for No. 2 beans. Eastman contended that his company was the savior of the soybean industry in 1930 because of soybean purchases compared to what the crop would otherwise have brought without his company in the field. He also added that they would take all they had purchased and that they withdrew from the market in November because they had secured enough at the above price for their needs for 12 months. Therefore, they did not take advantage of the "demoralized market then prevailing." [55]

E. D. dealt directly with the Marketing Association for beans from his own farm as receipts dated October 31 and November 12, 1930 prove. For 4612½ bushels he received $1.05 per bushel and the same price in November for 445⅙ bushels. [56]

Difficulties increased by April 30, 1931. Funk informed Earl Smith of I. A. A. that in the original agreement with the Marketing Association in September 18, 1930 paragraph 4 of this original contract proved that Funk Bros. had the option of taking delivery from time to time of additional amounts at a price that both parties might agree upon. The agreement on November 24 of purchase and delivery was made between the Soybean Marketing Association and the Egyptian Service Company and approved by Funk Bros. Seed Co. for thirty carloads of soybean meal (20 ton maximum weight per car) at prices ranging from $41.50 January 1 to $44.00 per ton. One car of meal was to be taken each week with option on two or more per week up to and including June 1 delivered Flora, Illinois. A price differential was included. There was a memorandum of agreement December 31, 1930 whereby the Marketing Association agreed to sell an additional 40,000 bushels of beans at $1.17. There were difficulties in disposing of the meal which dropped to $26 per ton. Funk faced a problem indeed. He could not afford to take more beans from the association, partly because his competitors who were not in sympathy with cooperatives, were consigning soybean meal in carload lots in Illinois territory where Funk had been operating. Dealers had orders to sell this meal for $1.00 less per ton, regardless of price, than the Funk prices. Funk also pointed out that the association had sold 300,000 bushels of beans recently for 80 to 82 cents per bushel so that the meal from that priced bean entered into competition with the prospective sale of meal produced by Funk Bros. Funk said he was not complaining, only pointing out the problems!

Despite this apparent underselling Funk declared that his records showed that Funk Bros. had carried out their contract. He believed that the requirements of the unexpired agreement with the Marketing Association and the Egyptian Company had not been met by them. Had this been accomplished more beans could have been taken, thus reducing the amount remaining. The Egyptian Service Company had ordered and was delivered 6 cars or 120 tons of meal on the 30 carload contract. [57] Funk said that he had agreed to the

Memorandum Agreement of December 31, 1930 over Bradley's protest. Bradley thought since all of the first 40,000 bushels had not been processed additional lots should have been taken in 5,000 bushel lots based on the price of meal and oil at the time of acceptance.

Funk reminded Smith that he had entered into this cooperative movement because he had "preached cooperation for over thirty years. We are as anxious as anyone can be to see equality brought about for the benefit of agriculture." Funk had made a trip to Washington during May before the September 18, 1930 agreement, discussed the question with Mr. Legge and "received their O. K. to the effect that they were in sympathy with just such a movement as was finally arranged with I. A. A., the Soybean Marketing Association and Funk Bros. Seed Co. as processors of soybeans on a profit sharing basis." This trip also resulted in favoring the financing of the Cooperative Movement in the soybean program.

He added an interesting comment:

We want to see this movement succeed but in doing so we cannot afford to lose a lot of money for our company. The writer told you at Springfield he was willing to turn his soybean mill over to you and process the beans you now have in storage in our elevators at a processing charge of twenty cents per bushel if in that way we could be of assistance. You said you would be unable to accept such a proposition for you had no outlay or setup to dispose of the meal and oil.

Even with these difficulties Funk advised that they try to work out some sort of cooperative proposition that would be fair to everyone. He was interested in a plan that would permit the processing and sale of beans and oil which they held on hand and the beans which the Soybean Marketing Association had stored in "our elevators." [58]

Another agreement was entered into by Funk Bros. with the Soybean Marketing Association May 8, 1931 as a result of the above situation for 5,000 bushels of beans at Bloomington, price to be agreed upon at time of offer. Another agreement of the same date involved 30,000 bushels with 25,000 bushels to be delivered at Bloomington at price of 79 cents per bushel, f. o. b., with 10,000 bushels not later than May 15, 1931; 10,000 not later than June 15, 1931; 10,000 not later than July 13, 1931. This agreement included a statement releasing them from all obligations regarding the Egyptian Service Company. [59]

Six months later Funk undertook a purchasing agreement with D. W. McMillen of Allied Mills, October 6, 1931. Allied Mills had entered an agreement with the Soybean Marketing Association for

500,000 bushels of 1931 soybean crop, marked Exhibit A. Funk Bros. were to process these beans. Allied Mills were to pay 30 cents per bushel for processing the beans but Funks would pay freight and handling costs. As these beans were processed, Funks would pay 30 cents per bushel plus 6 percent interest per annum from date of arrangement with payments made weekly. Meal and oil produced from these beans were to be kept separated from others. Accounts of proceeds from processed products were to be rendered under the same conditions as set up with the Marketing Association.

The contract for processing was in the form of a letter dated October 23, 1931 signed by D. W. McMillen, president of Allied Mills and cosigned for Funk Bros. by H. H. Miller and I. C. Bradley, Allied Mills, Inc., agreed to purchase soybeans to be placed in store at Bloomington and Taylorville and other points to remain the property of Allied Mills. This agreement was the basis for incorporation of Soya Products. Funk Bros. were authorized to process their beans at Bloomington and Taylorville into oil and meal and receive from Soya Products the actual cost for processing not to exceed $5.00 per ton of beans processed. The oil and meal were to be sold by Allied Mills and shipped by Funk Bros. at their direction. The proceeds from the sale were the property of Soya Products. Profits were to be shared on a fifty-fifty basis. Allied Mills reserved right of supervision of process and access to records.[60]

The board of directors for Soya Products, the company formed to handle this transaction, was composed of Eugene D. Funk, Jr., and from Allied Mills Henry Egly, president of Soya Products, Roy Craig, Vice president, Harold Buist, secretary, and Jack Quinlan. Mr. Quinlan recalled that he never worked with an organization more sincere than Funk Bros. Seed Co., in its efforts to establish and maintain good relations within the industry. Mr. Funk, Sr. would often remark, "But he is a grand old fellow and an old customer" of someone he knew. This unselfish attitude in merchandising was marked in the program of E. D. Funk, Sr. That desire for the last ten cents was not always uppermost in his thinking.[61]

The formation of Soya Products enabled Funk Bros. and Allied Mills to cooperate in buying soybeans as well as processing and selling oil meal and soybean oil. The friendly relations between the two companies was thus continued. The agreement proved to be mutually advantageous and gave to Eugene D. Funk, Jr. an opportunity to increase his knowledge of expanding soybean operations.

Along with the production of soybean oil meal for feed, Funk Bros.

also produced soybean flour in small quantities for I. F. Laucks, Inc. in Seattle, Washington. This activity resulted from contacts made by I. C. Bradley, who previously experimented with soybean flour in Chicago Heights. Laucks used the flour to produce a waterproof glue. Funk Bros. shipped flour to the Seattle office for approximately two years before 1929. Freight rates proved to be excessive. As a result I. F. Laucks decided to establish a plant in Illinois.[62] They entered into an agreement with Funk Bros. to establish a headquarters for producing soybean glue in Bloomington, Illinois. These operations were located on the south half of the second floor of the main warehouse at the seed company plant.[63]

Funk Bros. continued for a few years to make the flour from their soybean meal and to deliver it to Laucks for finished processing into their patent glue. Laucks later installed their own machinery to process the meal into flour. The volume of meal taken by Laucks was at times about one-third of the production of Funk Bros. This operation in Bloomington, Illinois was one of the first in the midwest to process domestic soybeans in flour for glue.[64]

The processing of beans to produce meal and flour retaining adhesive qualities required less heat than for commercial soybean oil meal. Laucks operated in Bloomington until 1934 when they built their own plant on the Atlantic coast in Norfolk, Virginia.

During the years of the depression, business problems were not easily solved. At a special meeting of the board of directors of Funk Bros., September 1, 1932 they decided to sell the Taylorville plant to Allied Mills.[65]

After four years of operation in connection with Allied Mills under the Soya Products Corporation, Funk Bros. took stock of their situation. H. H. Miller explained their problems clearly when he advised J. B. DeHaven of Allied Mills of their ideas. With young men learning the business and ready to assume more responsible positions, it seemed wise to take over more direction of their own soybean business. Funk Bros. was at this time not a large concern. Older leadership needed to be supported by trained and responsible young executives to test the measure of their ability. Miller stated that under the first agreement Funks enjoyed a good revenue from meal manufactured for Laucks with the processing rate of $5.00 per ton. Miller was also convinced that a company of the size of Funks could not make money at a lower price if a proportionate share of executive salaries and overhead were charged up to the operation. He also noted that the only advanced installation in five years was one additional expeller. He emphasized the continuous friendly relations that had existed between the two companies but felt certain that J. B. DeHaven and H. G. Atwood as older men would understand and appreciate the desire of younger leadership to test its own strength.[66] Soya Products was terminated and Funk Bros. again operated on their own capital.

Dr. W. L. Burlison of the University of Illinois was a long-time advocate of the soybean and soybean products. Throughout the years he devoted time and effort to the soybean program. His interest was turned to promotion of utilization of soybean oil in paints. An aggressive program was launched when Dean Mumford, director of Illinois Experiment Station asked for the study of the bean's utilization. In 1930 this program was launched by the Experiment Station in Illinois.[67] By 1935, Dr. Burlison noted that the early promise of the soybean in the 1920's was more than fulfilled. The true pre-eminence of the bean came with the development of industrial uses for agricultural products. He stated: "It is with this new outlook for agriculture that the soybean has advanced beyond a substitute crop and has become The 'Wonder' Bean." [68]

At the time Funks terminated the agreement with Allied Mills, in 1935, Harold Abbott joined Funk Bros. Seed Co. as a part time employee maintaining a business in Chicago. Abbott's early career started as an office boy with Albert Dickinson Company in 1898. His abilities were soon discovered. By 1900 he was gathering samples for the Exposition in Paris and assumed responsibilities for the company at the Exposition in Buffalo in 1902. He was first associated with the field seed division at Albert Dickinson. Some time before 1903 he became one of the few men interested in formula feeds, and soon devoted all of his time to this work. After thirty-six years with the Dickinson Company he had risen to membership on the board of directors and a vice presidency when he left the company.

Gene Funk, Jr. who had worked closely with the Allied Mills people in Soya Products became ill in 1936 for several months. Abbott came to help in the soybean operations and later to take full charge. He remained in this position until 1956 when he became consultant and advisor. Those who worked with him recognized the remarkable wealth of information and experience he contributed to the growth of the operations at Funk Bros. He acted as a balance wheel in the organization, as a guide and advisor to the younger men.

At one time soybean and seed corn offices were located in the warehouse. Abbott and Gene, Jr. ran the soybean operations. Abbott remained in charge of soybean operations after Gene Jr. became president of the company in 1944. Under his guidance the department continued to prosper.[69]

Previous to 1928 prices for soybeans were largely determined by demand and supply for soybean seed. Increases in industrial uses and rapid expansion of acreages created a different price structure for commercial beans. Relationship with other competitive products and the fact that both soybean meal and soybean oil move into different fields make the crop different from other corn belt crops. Supplies of cottonseed and linseed oil meals were competitors. About 1930 soybean oil meal began to take the place of linseed oil meal in manufacturing mixed feeds. According to Breedlove, during the last few months of 1934 prices of chief protein meals began to fall and records of imports crowded back the sales of domestic soybean oil meal. These imports came in over the "negligible duty" of $6.00 per ton.[70] During 1933–34 the chief competition in oil was between soybean oil and linseed oil. During the drought of 1934 the demand for seed again contributed to the price for soybeans.[71]

A meeting of considerable interest to the National Soybean Association and to agriculture in general was held in Detroit and Dearborn, Michigan in 1936. The Farm Chemurgic Council attracted 1,000 persons as against 400 the year before. One entire session was devoted to soybeans. The story and problems of the processors were set forth in a series of papers. Among the speakers whose addresses attracted attention were Mr. W. J. O'Brien of the Glidden Company, Mr. E. D. Funk, Sr. of Bloomington and President I. C. Bradley of the Soybean Association.[72]

The reason was easily understood. As Ed Dies commented, the sensation of agriculture in 1936 was the soybean as far as the industrial and chemical worlds were concerned. In 1935, the crop was 39,000,000 bushels, double that of 1934. Henry Ford helped to call attention to the product at the World's Fair in 1933 and 1934. The soybean was a growing factor in the food business and in the field of plastics.[73] The soy was called the Midwest's Miracle Bean.

When Funk, Sr. spoke before the Chemurgic Council at Dearborn, Michigan May 14, 1936 he referred to the early history of the soybean. The farmers who grew the bean in the Carolinas prior to the World War I used them for animal consumption and for seed. These beans were of a late maturing variety. When selected beans of the varieties brought from the Orient tested well in the soils of the Mid West the soybean became popular as a field crop. From some of the imported varieties, plant breeders developed new strains better than the original. We also referred to the early processing and to the guaranteed price.

He emphasized the fact that the soybean as a nitrogenous plant helped to maintain the element in the soil because it utilized free nitrogen from the air. He added the important point that in growing soybeans the farmer as well as the scientist and industrialist must remember that the plant is the heaviest feeder on phosphate of all the grain producing crops. He recalled that many years ago Professor Hopkins of the University of Illinois called attention to the shortage of phosphate in most of the corn producing area of the United States: "A twenty page letter from him in my files written some thirty odd years ago warned me of the fact that if we continued to produce corn and wheat and other grains on our Illinois farms without in some way replenishing our soil with the mineral elements that we are annually taking from the soil with our crops, sooner or later we would wake up to the fact that Dean Mumford of the U. of I. spoke a few days before in the National Chamber of Commerce of the Morrow plots, the oldest soil experiment area in the U. S. These plots showed a difference in production ranging from $17.00 to $115.00 per acre due entirely to depletion and maintenance of soil fertility."

Funk pointed out to his audience that soy beans provided a profitable rotating crop whereas oats were not so profitable. This fact aroused farmer interest who when he sold corn always asked the price. In the case of beans he asked to what market they were going and for what they would be used. The farmer was interested in the Administration's soil Conservation Program. Funk stated that thousands of soybeans would be planted in the spring for a legume crop to be plowed under in the fall for a soil building crop thereby adding humus and nitrogen to the soil. The farmer could also help to reduce the corn surplus; could grow a crop convertible to cash in the fall prior to corn in harvest; exchange his beans for soybean oil meal to feed livestock during the winter months and could help him self by using soybean oil when painting his buildings. He said that soybean oil meal contained an average of 41 to 45 percent protein. He also explained that the packers disliked hogs fed on beans containing all of the oil because the meat was soft and oily. When oil was largely removed from the processed beans with heat, the meal then fed to hogs with corn and minerals was excellent feed. He noted there would be 11 percent less soybeans planted in 1936 than in 1935.

He also presented a good summary of the international competition, pointing to the new lands coming into cultivation in northern Manchuria before Japan took over and to the fact that larger acreages were apparent each year. The soybean rose from a minor place in China's export trade in 1900. In 1928 it constituted 18 percent of the value of China's foreign trade only slightly surpassed by her silk exports. Funk quoted K. E. Beeson, Secretary of the American Soybean Association, who said that there was imported into the United States, 14,129,800 pounds of soybean oil during the first 11 months of 1934. This was the largest importation since 1929. This amount of oil represented the product from about 1,500,000 bushels. Soybean oil meal imported in 1935 exceeded 50,000 tons representing about 2,000,-000 bushels of beans. He added that imports of oil from all oil vegetable seeds in 1935 totaled 2,250,000 lbs. A duty of 3½ cents per pound on imported soybean oil and $6.00 per ton on soybean meal existed but there was no duty on soybean flour. A duty of 2 cents per pound existed on imported beans but comparatively few beans were imported. He said that in 1924 there were only two mills processing beans but in 1936 there were about forty five.

With typical honesty and ability to look the problem squarely in the face he added:

Here is an industry and a farm commodity that during the past ten or twelve years has grown from practically nothing to a very substantial place as an economic factor in the United States. However, the question we are facing is a vital one to Agriculture and to Industry. More processors and less beans means higher prices for beans provided there is an outlet for both meal and oil against importations. If importations increase it seems to me somebody is going to be left sitting on a limb.

Disclaiming the title of pessimist he mentioned that a banker in his home town had recently described him as a "conservative enthusiast." He believed that the soybean had an unlimited field from the point of view of the farmer, the research scientist and the industrialist; but "caution, thought and continued research" must be given to this industry.

L. B. Breedlove noted that the domestic price for soybeans was 60 cents a bushel in the fall of 1935 when an export market developed for 1,560,000 bushels. The price rose and by July 1936 ran to $1.23 per bushel. Officials of the Chicago Board of Trade recommended the establishment of a futures market.[74]

E. D. Funk, Jr. became chairman of the Edible Soybean Committee of the National Soybean Processors Association from 1939–

1947. Representatives of Funk Bros. participated actively in this organization. During these same years Gene Jr., was also a member of the Soybean Grades and Contracts Committee 1939–40; secretary of the association and a member of the executive committee 1940–48. H. A. Abbott was a member of the board of directors 1944–49; a member of the regional committee 1949–54; and chairman in 1944–54 of Illinois, Indiana, Kentucky, Wisconsin and north western Missouri regional committee. Abbott was also treasurer and member of the executive committee 1951–57 and a member of the oil trading rules committee 1950–52.[75] Elias W. Rolley was a member of the fire insurance committee of the association 1946–55.

Funk Bros. were interested in the development of the edible soybean as a means of providing another profitable crop for the farmers. Dr. Earl Sieveking carried on experiments from a western sample resulting in thirty-three type plants. Progeny of these plants was planted separately. The best was the edible variety known as Funk's Delicious produced in 1932 and offered for sale in 1934. Funk's Delicious were vacuum packed in Bloomington but eventually were priced out of the market.[76]

The chief problem in the edible soybean program was to find varieties which were easy to remove from the pods, in the green stage, and which would not shatter out when ripe.[77] This difficulty occurred in almost all of the edible varieties. George Strayer advised of an increased demand for edible soybean varieties in 1943. Victory gardens during the war contributed some of this demand. Food utilizers became more interested in dry edible beans because of their protein content.[78] Commercial canners of green edible soybeans increased their acreage in 1943 approximately four times that of the previous year. Professor W. L. Burlison of the University of Illinois advised that testing and experimental cooking of these varieties were increasing.[79] O. B. Combs of the University of Wisconsin was of the opinion in 1944 that more emphasis should be placed on freezing as a method of preserving green vegetable soybeans.[80] No significant changes were noted in 1945. It was pointed out that "edible" usually meant the green vegetable varieties. Actually certain of the commercial beans were also used in the edible field. Some of the latter were unsatisfactory when canned.[81]

W. L. Burlison pointed to progress in vegetable soybeans in 1946. For many years interest centered around the Giant Green, Banseii and Hokkaido varieties.[82] After the war years interest in the edible soybean decreased, but manufacturers of soybean food products began to realize that the edible varieties had something that ordinary grain varieties did not offer.[83] Few edible beans were grown west of the Mississippi river. Testing and experimentation continued in 1947.[84]

The Regional Soybean Laboratory at Urbana, in charge of Reid Milner, was often contacted for information by representatives of Funk Bros. The work of the laboratory centered on testing the oil content of the beans. The attention of the agronomists had previously been directed to the soybean plant and its yield. Experiments in oil content were carried on in cooperation with the University of Illinois.[85]

During the Second World War, E. D. Funk, Jr. acted as a member of the Soybean Processors Industry Advisory Committee. He was chairman of the task committee regulating tank car movement to insure sufficient use of the supply, and a member of the committee in charge of soybean seed problems for the 1945 crop. The keen demand for soybean oil made this an important chairmanship. A report in January 1943 indicated that the usage of tank cars had been efficient.[86]

In 1943, a brief description of soybean operations of Funk Bros. stated that the department was primarily a milling or processing operation. Soybeans were obtained from growers located primarily within a radius of forty miles from Bloomington, Illinois. The oil produced was sold on the commercial market principally for use in the manufacture of edible foods. For several years almost 100 percent of this product was sold for edible vegetable compound and margarine manufacture in central, southern and eastern areas. The cake which was ground into meal was forwarded in carload shipments to wholesale feed manufacturers and to wholesale jobbers. About 80 percent was distributed by rail from the Pacific to the Atlantic north of the Ohio River. The remaining 20 percent moved to the retail trade direct from the mill.

Several factors affected profitable operations: (1) A sufficient supply of beans to permit continuous operation of the mill, (2) With a regular market for both oil and meal, prices for beans become a controlling factor in operations.[87]

As has been stated, the original production of Funk Bros. in 1924 began with a capacity from 300 to 350 bushels per day using the original two expellers. A third No. 1 type was added in 1927 and two more in 1929, making a total of five No. 1 type with total capacity of approximately 800 bushels. About 1932 two R. B. Type Anderson expellers were added with greater capacity than the No. 1 type, making a total daily capacity of 1,300 bushels. In 1936 one used Hi-Speed R. B. 400 bushel capacity expeller was added, and later in the same year one new Super Duo 600 bushel machine with about 2,000 bushels per day. In 1937 another Super Duo was added and another No. 1 type removed and sold.

During a quarter of a century from 1930 to 1956, soybean acreage jumped from 3,473,000 yielding 13,929,000 bushels to an increase by 1940 up to 78,045,000 bushels. The crop year 1956 indicated planting of 21,000,000 acres with production of 457,000,000 bushels. This important cash farm income was second only to corn in many areas.[88]

Funk Bros. Seed Co. were pioneers in processing of soybeans. They provided a continuous market after 1924. They increased operating volume through the years especially during the period of World War II. Since importation of vegetable oil prior to the war came from the South Pacific Islands there was need for increased American acreages of soybeans during the war. Harold Abbott commented, "Under Governmental control of our economy prices have stabilized, production encouraged and priorities for plant expansion provided. Funk Bros. Seed Co. were permitted to participate to the extent of their physical properties and financial ability."[89] They were classified as medium sized operators and allowed a gross margin of profit of approximately 35 to 36 cents per bushel. Super Duo operations were increased so that daily capacity in 1944 was 4,300-4,400 bushels.[90]

During March 1947 and December 1948 grain storage capacity was enlarged, a new grain drier was installed and a hydraulic truck dump was added. Competitors, however, were turning to solvent extraction so that the board of directors authorized the construction of a solvent type French extractor with equipment and mill directly west of the seed plant.[91]

A new solvent processing plant for soybeans was installed by Funk Bros. in 1951. It began operation January 1952. Soybeans are purchased through marketing channels and shipped to the plant in Bloomington, Illinois by rail or truck from country elevators. Storage in concrete tanks provides a supply easily transferred to the processing unit by a belt conveyor. At the end of the conveyor a surge bin or storage tank of 6,000 bushels is provided so that the conveyor does not run continuously. The solvent extraction plant can thus be fed from this bin.

The principle of the solvent system for extracting oil is to dissolve the soybean oil from flaked soybeans by the solvent, Hexane. The mixture of oil and solvent (miscella) is separated by evaporation and distillation. The extracted flakes are converted into soybean meal by cooking and grinding. The process is continuous and the general practice is to operate the plant during 24 hours per day seven days per week. Expensive equipment requires a higher investment in this solvent process than in the expeller process. Skilled and technically trained personnel is needed to direct and perform the operations.

Proper preparation of the flakes to desired thickness and uniformity is necessary to secure effective rate of oil extraction. After weighing the beans through an automatic dump scale they are put through corrugated rolls, breaking into pieces approximately one sixteenth the size of the original bean. Large smooth rolls then produce thin flakes from these cracked beans where thickness is controlled at 0.008-0.010 inch.

The extractor is of the horizontal type and consists of a series of sieve-baskets on an endless chain each holding about 400 pounds of flakes. These baskets are filled automatically. As the baskets move through the unit the flakes are repeatedly washed with solvent and miscella. This cycle takes about 40 minutes while the oil content of the flakes is reduced from the original 20 percent to 0.5 percent. Great care must be exercised to prohibit sparks or ignition in the area of the plant because the solvent is highly inflammable and volatile.

The oil rich miscella is then subjected to a process where the solvent is separated from the oil. The solvent can be condensed, recovered and used again in the same process. The solvent loss amounts to about 0.5 or 1 percent with each cycle. The oil is cooled and pumped to storage for loading. Extracted flakes are removed to the desolventized toaster where they are "toasted" before being ground into meal. Cooking further prepares the flakes for better feeding purposes. Meal is loaded in bulk or in sacks and usually is shipped by rail. According to D. D. Walker, in charge of Funk Bros. solvent plant, "The selling basis for solvent extracted meal is 12 percent moisture and 44 percent protein." [92]

Delmar Walker of the younger group came to the company after training as a chemical engineer at the University of Tennessee. He saw active duty as a Navy officer in an L.S.T. from Guam to Japan. He held a position as a chemical engineer with the Argo Plant of Corn Products 1946–50. During this time he also found time to acquire a master's degree from the University of Chicago in business administration. After a year at Owensboro in Kentucky, he accepted a position with Funk Bros. in charge of the solvent soybean plant when it opened.

The greatest users of soybean meal include Ralston-Purina, Allied Mills, Arcady Farms, Hales and Hunter and others. Proctor & Gamble, Lever Bros., Glidden, Swift & Co. and Anderson-Clayton and others refine crude or unrefined oil as that produced by Funk Bros. into vegetable oil, shortening, margarine and paint products.

The solvent plant operated at 200 tons per day rated capacity in 1952. The output in 1956 with improvements in efficiency was increased to 330 tons (11,000 bushels) per day. A dependable source of steam is supplied by a new Babcock and Wilcox grate type boiler installed in 1955. A crew of five men works on each shift including the loading of oil and meal. Others are engaged in laboratory and maintenance work during the day.

These plants, in order to operate economically, must produce sufficient volume to take care of the costs of highly trained operators, larger investment and overhead. The solvent process removes more oil from beans than the expeller process. Soybean oil usually brings better prices than the meal.[93]

Approximately 80 percent of Funk's soybean processing production is in the form of soybean oil meal. It is marketed to a limited extent directly to the farmers. The largest percentage finds its outlet through wholesale channels in commercially mixed feed for formulation of many animal and poultry feeds. The crude soybean oil is marketed through vegetable oil refineries for the edible and industrial purposes. Intermediate feed and oil brokers are generally sought for these markets.[94]

The decision by Funk Bros. to install the soybean mill in 1924 gave greater diversification to the seed business. It is an interesting fact in agricultural history that the sudden rise of the soybean to prominence as a cash crop in the 1920's and 1930's paralleled the spectacular advancement in hybrid corn. Eugene D. Funk was a recognized leader in the expanding development of both crops essential to the well being of many Americans. Again Gene Funk led in an effort to better conditions for the farmers in the Corn Belt.

CHAPTER XXVII

Revolution in the Corn Fields

EUGENE D. FUNK saw during the last decade of his life, 1934–44, the rapid acceptance of hybrid corn. There were many men who contributed to the long process of the improvement of corn. Few, however, devoted their lives to advancing commercial and research programs.

Controversy over the comparable contributions of the geneticists to the development of hybrid corn will doubtless continue. For all practical purposes both G. H. Shull and E. M. East exerted influence.[1] As has been related the former produced hybrids developed from inbreds in 1907, presented them to the public in 1908 and defended his "pure line" methods. He spoke both at the Louisiana Exposition in 1904 and at the American Breeders Association at Omaha at the time of the National Corn Association in 1908. Although there is no direct proof, Funk in attendance at both places probably heard him. East, who moved to Connecticut from the University of Illinois, brought forth his ideas about the same time.[2] The story of East and his connection with H. H. Love has been told (see chapters VIII and XVII).

G. H. Shull's ideas were applied by E. G. Montgomery and T. A. Kiesselbach of the Nebraska Experiment Station during 1910, 11, 12. Kiesselbach is reported to have made his first cross between inbreds in 1912, grown in 1913 as the first corn hybrids from inbreds west of Connecticut. They did not prove to be successful in field performance because the eastern germ plasm was not adapted to western climate and conditions.

H. K. Hayes a student of E. M. East produced studies with East dealing with "quantitative inheritance in ear length and other characteristics leading to acceptance of extension of Mendelism"[3] East continued to emphasize varietal crosses. In January 1915, Hayes accepted an appointment in the University of Minnesota Experiment Station as a plant breeder. Here he gave to James Holbert sound advice which he put into practice on the Funk Farms (see Chapter XVII). It was a long route from Charles Darwin to W. J. Beal to P. G. Holden at the University of Illinois and from East to Hayes to

378

Holbert and Funk. Shull as a correspondent of Gene Funk gave him sound advice in 1914 when he told Funk that it would be disastrous for Funk to recommend growing crops from hybrid seed before becoming convinced that this was the answer. Shull also observed that the Funk establishment was on a sound foundation of high esteem among corn growers and "you could afford at least to carry out some fairly extensive experiments to test the value of hybridizing methods." It is clear that the geneticists recognized the need for commercial and field testing of their principles [4] (see Chapter XVI). Richey of the U. S. D. A. also carried on a limited corn breeding project in 1916.[5] When East took an appointment at Harvard, his student Donald F. Jones took over at Connecticut. His work in contributing the double cross has been compared by one writer to that of James Watt in the history of the steam engine.[6] There remained problems in disease resistance that Funk and Holbert were trying to solve in the adaptation of principles of hybridizing to field performance.

It is apparent from the study of work with corn carried on by the Funks that the increased vigor and high yields of the "corn families" were secured through closely bred lines. These were like the varietal crosses advocated by the botanists and agronomists as already explained. These line bred families were so nearly pure that "they exhibited many characters which breeders have subsequently learned emerge only after three to four years of direct in-breeding." [7] This was no small accomplishment for the early years, when the commercial significance of crossing inbreds had not yet been realized.

Corn planted by farmers before the inbred hybrids became so popular was designated as "open pollinated." This term was derived from the uncontrolled reproductive process in the open field. From the date of its organization Funk Bros. Seed Co. was one of the leading producers of open pollinated corn in its area. The most popular of the some twelve open pollinated varieties produced were Funk's Yellow Dent Strain 176A, Funk's 329–100 Day Yellow Dent, Funk's Ninety Day Yellow Dent, Silvermine, Leaming and Krug.

Transition from open-pollinated to hybrid corn in the fields of the central Corn Belt with subsequent expansion to Canada and into the south below the equator as well as to other foreign countries, is a story of the utmost significance in the annals of agriculture. Funk Bros. Seed Co. has contributed in a substantial manner to this development. Few laymen other than farmers comprehend the complicated process that produces those magnificant fields of golden tassel grain.

A description of hybrid corn can be found in the Year Book of 1936 published by the United States Department of Agriculture as "A corn hybrid is a first generation hybrid between two strains of corn. Its value for seed is in the production of a crop of commercial corn. This corn will grow, but cannot be used for seed without loss in yield in the succeeding generations." It must be produced new each generation.[8] This statement is the key to the extraordinary problem of the development of the commercial process. Another description of the term can be found in the Illinois *Bulletin* 330:

> Hybrid Seed Corn as the term is now commonly used, signifies seed resulting from cross fertilization, involving inbred line of corn (and) their combinations; the inbred lines having been self-fertilized until they are reasonably pure.

A double cross hybrid known as "Pure Line Double Cross 250" was sold commercially by Funk Bros. beginning in 1922. This item was found in the company's 1926 Catalogue where after two years notice it was introduced to commemorate the twenty-first anniversary of the company.[9] During the twenties there followed Funk Hybrids 517 and 365. After 1920 there was considerable increase in inbreeding projects. At first a period of eleven to sixteen years was consumed before commercial seed was produced from a given set of hybrids. An appreciable amount of hybrid seed corn was not available to growers until 1933.

Inbreeding or "selfing" occurs when the corn is fertilized with its own pollen. The same plant produces corn inheriting characteristics of the single parent thus "purifying" by "outbreeding" minor or weaker characteristics. Seven or eight years of inbreeding were at first required to establish sufficiently well the desired characteristics. Now the transfer may be made in less time. The best known method of controlled pollination is a combination of "tassel bagging and shoot bagging." Before the silks emerge, a small glassine bag is slipped over the ear shoot to exclude outside pollen. Hand pollination is undertaken when the silks are ready. The tassels are then covered when ready to shed pollen. When the bag covering the tassel has collected pollen it is placed over the covered ear shoot; the smaller glassine bag is removed and the pollen dusted on the silks. The ear shoot is then covered with a larger bag to protect it from contamination of other pollen. Thousands of inbreds are produced in order to find one suitable for use in commercial production of hybrid seed. The purpose of this inbreeding process is to develop strains that may be combined with other unrelated strains to produce corn of definite and good characteristics such as yield, standability and quality.

The next step of combining two or more related strains by means of controlled cross fertilization requires the same care as the inbreeding process. The pollen of one inbred is crossed upon the silks of a second inbred. The result is a single cross. This cross the next year is combined with other experimental single crosses or with single crosses of known performance. The combining of two single crosses results in what is known as a "double cross." An experimental double cross is the laboratory description of seed which if it proves to be a good hybrid is sold commercially. This seed must be planted and tested under a wide range of conditions. An experimental hybrid usually does not represent more than one in a thousand and often not more than one in many thousands. The steps necessary to provide hybrid corn for sale involves constant production of inbred lines and parent single crosses.

The final step in the production of most commercial hybrid seed corn is the process of developing double crosses. Usually two rows of a single cross pollinator are planted adjacent to six rows of single cross seed parent. Thus 75 percent of the land planted actually produces hybrid seed corn sold commercially to the farmer. The pollinator plants are harvested only for commercial use or livestock feed.

The business of producing hybrid seed corn for planting purposes from the first steps in research and breeding to the sale of the double cross is subjected to many financial and climatic risks. If the single cross is a success it is "duplicated commercially by planting the two inbreds in adjacent rows, detasseling the female or ear parent so that its ears are pollinated only by the male or pollinator parent." This single cross or foundation seed as it is called is used in the production of commercial seed corn. There are then two important processes; the production of sufficient amount of foundation seed to secure the best single crosses and the subsequent production of enough hybrid seed sold to farmers for planting. The success of the commercial enterprise is based upon the technical skill and "know-how" of its research personnel.

The operation best known to the general public in the entire procedure is that of planting, detasseling and harvesting the seed fields. These fields are sufficiently isolated from other corn fields to protect them from foreign pollen. Detasseling becomes important because tassels must be removed from the seed parents before they shed pollen. One person can keep the tassels removed from about four acres of corn during the relatively short period of three weeks. Crews of ten to fifteen persons work under supervision. If labor supplies for this program are short, hardships can follow with financial loss to the company. General costs increase because of these factors. Caution must always be exercised not to harvest corn from the pollinator plants because the hybrid seed corn sold is produced only on the detasseled plants. Harvest should be completed before killing frosts arrive, or fungus and mold develop. Harvest should occur when the water line has reached the tip of the kernel i. e. when the corn has matured. The drying of the corn is also an important part of the commercial process. The corn may have a moisture content from 20 to 35 percent as it comes from the field depending upon the strain, time of harvest and weather conditions. Moisture must be reduced to about 12 percent to make it safe for storage. Heated air is forced through ear corn in especially constructed drying bins. The second sorting of the corn occurs after drying because certain characteristics not present in wet corn may become visible. Shelling and grading follow. The first grading or scalping removes the extra large kernels on the top screen and the small kernels from the bottom screen. Chaff and pieces of cob are also eliminated. The shelled corn is graded mechanically by a screening operation from 6 to 10 sizes by width, thickness and length of kernel. It is then subjected to seed treatment in order to control seedling blight and to insure against soil borne organisms. The treated corn is then placed in one bushel bags and stored until shipping time. Samples for germination tests are taken from time to time during the harvest, processing and after the seed is finally graded. The generally accepted requirement is a 95 percent test or better.

Increased acreages of foundation seed including inbreds and single crosses over the years by Funk Bros. Seed Co. are certain indications of their favorable results in breeding and testing activities. Only twelve acres were planted in 1933 for increasing or multiplying developed and tested inbreds. Six years later 92 acres were planted for this purpose. The number of acres given over to inbred-increase in 1943 was 216 while in this same year 1,007 acres were devoted to single crossing. This one percent amounted to 143,000 acres requiring less than 20,000 bushels of seed or about 800 acres from all sources. Sieveking recalls that Funks had about 125 seed acres in 1931. With the knowledge that expansion of the hybrid seed corn program would demand additional labor and investment capital all parts of the activity were continued as far as possible. It should be kept in mind that the depression was in full swing at this time. Moreover unfavorable weather conditions hindered expansion. Not only was additional capital a problem but skilled personnel was difficult to obtain.

Mr. Sieveking stated the situation realistically when he said:

Details of operations during the troubled transition years are hazy, as viewed in retrospect, are often glamorized and clothed in an imaginative splendor that did not actually exist. It was impossible to see ten years ahead. Dreams of the future were extremely bright, but actualities of the day were harsh as to the wherewithall with which to work and progress.[10]

Technical skill alone could not bring this valuable product to the American farmer. Available capital together with the recognized integrity of the people who offered this new product for sale were essential to its introduction. Eugene Funk found himself in the position of continuing to pay the indebtedness on his farm resulting from high inheritance taxes at the time of his father's death as well as responsibilities incurred when banks in the area were closed. Retention of his own land was the first ingredient for success.

From the *Catalogue* of the company in 1920 this message from the president, Eugene D. Funk, appeared under the caption "Agriculture, The Nation's Balance Wheel":

But we are led to think not so much of our selfish selves as the times through which we are now passing. Never in the history of our country have our agricultural interests been confronted with so many momentous and perplexing conditions. Agriculture representing as it does one-third of the population of the United States of America, is in a position to be the balance wheel in the conflict between capital and labor. This being the fact, let us so conduct our business relations to the end that both labor and capital will some day realize the fact that neither can exist without the other and that their big brother (Agriculture) will insist on the same, conservative co-operation in the family circle. We have no use for profiteers; we have no patience for strikes or lockouts. Agriculture has blazed the trails for democracy in this country from the time of the Pilgrim father, and Agriculture may be depended upon to meet the issue, whatever that issue is and whenever that time comes.[11]

This same catalogue showed that the company was continuing to apply the ear to row breeding and multiplying plots. Many of these occupied 40 to 60 acre fields so located that the better strains of corn that had been developed at great expense would not be contaminated by pollen from corn in adjacent fields. Crosses between and within families and strains were made by hand pollination and the progeny multiplied in isolated plots. Ears used in breeding plots were advertised as coming from disease free plants in the field but also passed the disease test on the germinator.

In addition to wide acceptance in the United States, Funks Yellow Dent could be seen during the early twenties in the Philippines, the Nile Valley and the Danube Valley. This corn drew its original strength from the rich soil of central Illinois. Funks Ninety Day was a popular variety in the Argentine.[12]

The cooperative work by the United States Department of Agriculture, the University of Illinois, Purdue and other Experiment Stations, at the Federal Experimental Station located on Funk Farms hastened the Hybrid Corn Era. James Holbert who was a senior agronomist with the U. S. D. A. was in charge of this work. From his experience, leadership and scientific skill came extensive and important accomplishments. The twenties were productive years in research leading to improvement of hybrids.

A *Farmers' Bulletin* 1176 of the U. S. D. A. issued September, 1920 and reprinted November was entitled "Control of the Root, Stalk and Ear Rot Disease of Corn" by James Holbert and George N. Hoffer. An interesting footnote appears on the first page of this bulletin:

> The investigation on which this bulletin is based was conducted in co-operation with the Department of Botany, Indiana Agricultural Experiment Station and Funk Brothers Seed Company of Bloomington, Ill. The destructiveness of the diseases and the necessity of preventing their spread through seed corn was brought to the attention of the Department by Mr. Eugene D. Funk, who had initiated the investigation in Illinois upon his own terms.[13]

This bulletin was the culmination of the work so intensively pursued by Eugene Funk and James Holbert with the cooperation of the U. S. D. A. on the Funk Farms since 1918. It described corn as the most important field crop in the United States with value greater than the combined values of wheat, oats, barley, rye, rice, grain sorghums and buckwheat. Beef and pork industries were also dependent upon its success. Statements in this bulletin applied chiefly to Dent varieties grown in the Corn Belt. Root rot of corn was reported fifteen years previously from southern Ohio, later from Iowa, Nebraska, Illinois, Missouri and Minnesota. It was found in all the corn growing states 1918–1919, with most extensive destruction in the Corn Belt. Investigations showed that certain fungi, particularly Giberella accervales and Giberella scabinetti (cause of wheat scab) with certain bacteria were present in the field. These organisms as well as certain molds also occurred in kernels and seedlings on the germinators. The bulletin described symptoms and control methods.

While the scientists were writing and convincing the men in the laboratories and colleges, Eugene D. Funk was also carrying his continuing part of the burden. He could talk easily to the farmers. "Corn Disease Investigations" was delivered before the 26th Annual Meeting of the Illinois Farmers Institute in Danville, Illinois, April 23, 1921. Again he referred to 1892, when he first began his investigations for the improvement of better corn and farm seeds. He warned in 1921 against 20 percent loss and possibly 50 percent loss in five years unless the diseases in corn were checked. He recalled that "It was in 1913 that our attention was first brought to the realization that our corn breeding work was being seriously handicapped by some unknown disease, but our records show us clearly that we had more or less of the trouble as far back as 1900." He also traced the history of the Illinois Corn in 1909 and his reference to the germinator tests. He again referred to James Holbert's appearance as a summer student in 1913 when he was put to studying the root system which led to the investigation of mold on the germinator. He retold the story of how they had worked three years before they said anything. Then came the startling comparisons of 1907 and 1916 tests with smooth corn. As Funk repeated:

This gave us conclusive evidence that there was some connection between type of corn and the prevalence of the root disease, as well as a correlation between type and yield.

Then came the contact with the U. S. D. A. Here he referred to the Holbert-Hoffer bulletin mentioned above and asked for continued investigation.[14]

Questions arose in 1922 over the problem of distributing the funds for the investigation and control of corn diseases. Indiana had received at first 60 percent of the total and Illinois 30 percent with the other 10 percent scattered among other states. Reports were to be sent in through Purdue University. Comments revealed that "the 30 percent that Illinois received" was being spent largely at Funk Farms and in addition to the appropriation by the department, "it has been estimated that Mr. Funk has contributed about $50,000 a year to the work."[15] Howard Leonard, president of the I. A. A. expressed himself in support of Mr. Funk who thought that no one state should have 60 percent or 30 percent. He preferred an average allowing all states to benefit. Leonard's letter to Secretary Henry C.

Wallace was forwarded to W. A. Taylor, Chief of the Bureau of Plant Industry from C. R. Ball, cerealist in charge.[16] The latter's report referred to the experimental work being done in Woodford County, Illinois and to the work of Mr. Mosher, County Advisor. The second part of the report dealt with corn root stalk and ear rot investigations:

> The prevalence of the corn-rot diseases was first brought to the attention of the Department four years ago by Mr. Eugene D. Funk of Illinois. A prompt appropriation by Congress made it possible to begin work in the summer of 1918. At this time the Illinois Agricultural Experiment Station had no pathological investigations under way and had no pathological research at a station where both equipped laboratories and men were to be found. The Indiana Agricultural Experiment Station at Lafayette was chosen because like Illinois it is fully central to the Corn Belt, was well equipped for this type of research, was easily accessible from Bloomington, Illinois where it was proposed to carry such investigations as could be effectively conducted there, and because Purdue University, the seat of the Experiment Station, was the alma mater of Mr. James R. Holbert then in charge of Mr. Funk's corn breeding program and since then in charge of the cooperative program in Illinois.[17]

Explanations of the fact that the Indiana program was larger included references to its inclusion of field, greenhouse and laboratory studies. The first allotment of funds was $25,000.00 for the fiscal year of 1919 effective July 1, 1918. This appropriation was continued during the next fiscal year. For 1921 and 1922 it was reduced to $20,000 but was supplemented somewhat from general funds. Amounts for Indiana remained stationery but those for Illinois increased. The Illinois Experimental Station became able to participate and some of the equipment for a small laboratory at Bloomington was provided by the Funks.[18]

While Funk and Leonard were in Washington, D. C., attending the Agricultural Conference in 1922, January 30th, they also were available for conferences. Funk was shown the material cited above and reportedly was satisfied with the statements. Leonard's first letter was written to Secretary Wallace before Funk returned home.

Scientific writing continued. James Holbert was fast making a name for himself in the scientific World. He contributed "Control of Corn Rots by Seed Selection" 1920 in *Illinois Circular No. 243;* "Early Vigor of Maize Plants and Yield of Grain as Influenced By The Corn Rot, Stalk and Ear Rot Diseases," *Journal Agricultural Research,* 1923. He co-authored in 1925 "Corn Rot, Stalk and Ear Rot Diseases and Their Control Thru Seed Selection and Breeding," *Illi-*

nois Bulletin 255; "Wheat Scab and Corn Root Rot Caused by Gibberella-Saubinette in Relation to Crop Successions" 1924 *Journal Agricultural Research;* in the same year "The Black Bundle Disease of Corn" and in 1925 "Factors Increasing Lodging in Corn" *Illinois Bulletin* 266.

A. C. Johnson, senior pathologist in cereal disease investigations of the U. S. D. A. by 1925, wrote Funk:

Now that the big bulletin (Ill. Bulletin No. 255) is out we are glad to straighten up and look around and see where we are as we push ahead. Certainly all concerned appreciate very fully the important part that you and your associates have had in the fine progress that has been made. I wish to pass on to you a very sincere appreciation of this. . . . It is a pleasure indeed to know that we have had and are having such splendid cooperation in the work. Surely this is what makes for real progress. Jimmy and others have done their part but I do not think it would have been possible to secure the mass of convincing data without your cooperation from the beginning. . . . Of course, we all realize that many problems still remain to be investigated and we are glad to have your continued cooperation in the work.[19]

Late in 1924 *The Seed World* quoted a letter in part regarding Eugene Funk written by Dr. W. L. Burlison:

He has the ability to recognize fundamental problems, to appreciate the value of their solution and possesses the patience to wait and work for their fundamental solution. He has the ability to evaluate correctly the character of individuals with whom he comes in contact. He has the vision to see beyond immediate difficulties and possesses a strength of character to act wisely and give sound advice, even when it is to his financial disadvantage. Unselfishness constantly characterized his thoughts and actions. His stability of character is outstanding. His devotion to his family and country is a challenge to the best that is in us. He is a true friend, one who does not desert when trouble comes. He has ever been a champion of truth and justice. Truly he is one of God's noblemen—a man among men.[20]

The story of corn progressed. H. A. Wallace informed E. D. on February 17, 1925 of the account of the fifth Iowa Corn Yield Contest taken from *Wallace's Farmer* of the 15th. Holbert's inbreds as developed from Funks Yellow Dent crossed with Iodent inbreds had produced exceptional results. Wallace added, "I was much interested to note on page seven of your 1925 seed catalogue that you are expecting in 1926 to sell something new in the way of seed corn. This will be a very interesting departure." Wallace then called attention to possibilities of advertising in this paper because they had given more attention to reader interest in the possibilities of crossing inbred strains than any other farm paper.[21] In answer to a request from the Henry Field Seed Corn Company in Iowa asking for "some of our strains of inbred corn which we have had under test and which represent years of careful study along with many hundreds of thousands of field trials," E. D. replied in the negative. He wrote:

It is our aim and hope to be able to place the results of this work in the hands of our customers this next year. We are preparing this seed now for this spring's planting but if there is anything to this work of crossing on line breeding (and we have fully demonstrated to our satisfaction that there is) we can hardly be expected to pass these 'pure line strains' along even to our best friends and the writer considers Henry Fields one of them.[22]

Funk then observed that the only patent that a plant breeder can have is to retain the original strains within his own plantation and distribute the results of the hybrids of crosses to the public. He went on to say that he had distributed during the past twenty-five years different strains of Funks Yellow Dent to thousands who set themselves up as so-called corn breeders almost immediately. In competition with his own trade they then proceeded to sell "Funk's Seed Corn" at two or three dollars less than he could produce it with his overhead and research expense. He added:

After this year we feel that we can possibly protect ourselves and perhaps get back at least some of the hundred thousand dollars or more that we have spent in our research and investigational work.[23]

Funk Bros. Seed Co. carried on experiments in "Pure line" breeding of corn to be presented to the public in 1926. *The Seed Trade News* noted that this work had been carried on for the last eight years in an experimental way. Thousands of plants had been selfed and crossed. In order to find one strain with merit it was sometimes necessary to make selections from 50 to 80 thousand individual plants that had been self fertilized. This long time operation required technical skill of a high order with sufficient supply of labor and financial support to carry on the work. Several of these strains had tested yields from 125 to 147½ bushels per acre on one- to three-acre fields without any fertilizer. Corn growers visited these seed breeding plots October 6, 1925.[24]

Kind comments were forthcoming from old friends. Among them P. G. Holden complimented the line of work being done by the company. Funk said he could not accept all of the glory but must refer to the cooperation of many people including Holden. He told his old friend:

Since 1915 we have been practically three years ahead of our schedule which you and others helped to plan many years ago. During the last three years we have been checking up and testing in our trial grounds and multiplying plots with the view to next years offering for the first time to the public some real honest to goodness seed corn, such as we have been dreaming and talking about all these many years.

H. H. Miller, manager of Funk Bros., returned from an extensive trip through Europe in the fall of 1924. He found in the South Pavilion at the British Empire Exhibition at Wembley, England, a very attractive display of corn. This yellow Dent variety looked so familiar to him that he searched out the representative to learn the origin of the seed. He was surprised to hear that the seed was obtained from Funks in Bloomington, Illinois. The exhibit was strictly Funks Utility Type Corn.[25]

About this time, 1926, the speech previously delivered at Danville, "Corn Disease Investigations," was to be revised and reprinted. James Holbert commented:

Probably there is no other person living so well qualified to present the early history of corn improvement as Mr. Funk nor is there any one as well qualified to give the broad background from a national standpoint as is Mr. Funk.[26]

P. G. Holden, the first manager of the company, wrote an article for the catalogue in 1927, twenty-six years after the original idea of a seed company first crystallized. Holden called attention to Funk's desire to do something of service not only for his own generation but also for those to follow. This, according to Holden's views, he accomplished by performing a service that no one farmer could offer but one which the combined efforts of the Funk Bros. could attain. The breeding of disease-free and high germinating corn was sorely needed throughout the Corn Belt. Holden added:

It was a stupendous task to which Eugene Funk devoted his life, but because it was of such vital importance to the country, it was a task worthy of the man . . . few men have ever given so much of their time and their energy and thought and personal resources to better agricultural conditions than has Eugene Funk.[27]

Holden beheld in 1926 what he had hardly dared hope that he might ever see—acre after acre of disease free corn and no visible barren stalks.[28]

Efforts were made to cement friendly relations between the A. S. T. S. and the Experiment Stations. Funk, as chairman of the Committee on Friendly Relations as well as chairman of the Cooperative Committee on Agricultural interests for the Farm Seed Association of North America cooperated with his good friend, W. L. Burlison, president of the National Agronomists Association. Forty or fifty attended a two day session in Bloomington to see the corn breeding plots on the Funk Farms and then to Urbana. The *Seed World* wrote that Mr. Funk had initiated a program capable of producing better understanding if also carried out in other states. An already serious agricultural situation was complicated by a renewed westward march of the corn borer. Funk informed his friend Samuel Guard of the *Breeders Gazette* of his inability to forget his irritation of 1917 when he with others attempted to obtain some drastic action by Massachusetts and federal authorities. The pest at the time of its origin in the country was confined to a relatively small territory. Funk remarked that effective action might have been secured with less than a half million dollars. The only accomplishment was the preparation of a report by a few men. Governor Lowden of Illinois sent the State Entomologist, Mr. Flint, and the State Secretary of Agriculture, Mr. Adkins, to Massachusetts. An agreement to send help to Massachusetts was refused. As Funk looked back in 1927 he realized that the pest had multiplied and spread over a territory approximately 400 miles by 50 to 100 miles wide, extending from the Atlantic Coast to somewhere in Indiana and southern Ohio. Fifty-five additional counties had become infested in Ohio and Indiana since the previous year. The pest might be exterminated if it only traveled on the ground, but the miller could fly 15-20 miles in a favorable wind. The worm could live under water for at least 40 days. It hibernated not only in corn stalks and cobs but on the inside of various weeds and in some instances was found in the bark of trees.

An effort was under way to try to keep it out of the Corn Belt as long as possible. Funk stated that the Government was making some tests "but in my opinion they have not gone into the matter in a wholesale way along all the different lines of contact as I think they should." Ten million dollars of the appropriation by Congress went to clean up old corn fields and to pay the farmers who participated for their labor. Only a small sum of the money was used in investigations. He was especially interested in the fact that the corn borer had a liking for some and a distaste for other varieties of corn. A certain South American corn was death to the young borer which took to Minnesota No. 13 like a bee to honey. Funk suggested planting this later variety around a 40 acre field thus creating a trap. He was informed that there was no money to obtain a 40 acre field for experimentation. Entomologists were of the opinion that it was necessary to learn to live with the borer. As a result the corn breeder was faced with the responsibility of discovering varieties in the Corn Belt that could hold the borer to a minimum degree of infestation. Importing, breeding and liberating enemy wasps and beetles to destroy eggs of the borer was also practiced. Funk continued to believe that the failure to organize in 1917 in addition to the current indifference of the average farmer toward meeting the problem created present difficulties. He pled for action and for a workable agricultural policy. He did not send this information to Sam Guard for publication but to present his views.[29]

A week later he read with pleasure of the luncheon of leaders from the Farmers Union, the Grange and the Farm Bureau in Washington relative to a common policy before Congress. He added, "In my humble opinion this is the only way relief can be brought about."

The *Daily Drovers Journal* called attention in July 1926 to the fact that experimental work in hybrid corn was being carried on in Nebraska, Iowa, Illinois, Minnesota, Tennessee, Louisiana, Indiana, Connecticut and other states. At the Nebraska Experiment Station, Dr. Kiesselbach in a four year test had secured an average of 12 bushels more in yield from a cross than from the original variety. In Iowa the banner trophy in corn yield was given to a corn representing one of these crosses entered by Cassady and Wallace. At Bloomington, Illinois as an average for six years, two first generation crosses yielded 109.7 (corrected on the clipping in pencil to 118) bushels per acre as compared to open pollinated nearly disease free corn. The double crosses known as Burr Leaming were described as outstanding in yield.[30]

The chief problem confronting the scientist by 1926 was to acquaint the farmer with the news. James Holbert consented to give a series of interviews to Curtis S. Bill appearing in the *Daily Bulletin* in Bloomington, Illinois. Here the readers came to understand something of the work and the philosophy as it was expressed by the rising young scientist hard at work in the fields and laboratory. As the acknowledged authority in the United States on corn diseases he headed up the cooperating group of scientists working under his supervision. As a scientist and a humanist his dominant interest after corn was the welfare of his fellow men. Holbert was all the more impressed with the similarity between the problems that had to be solved for corn and those that arose to confront human beings. He felt that seeing and understanding these parallels enabled him to make these scientific explanations clear to both agronomists and to farmers. He also found constant use in Sunday School talks and other kinds of lectures for illustrations from the conduct of corn under varying conditions. Thus the best qualified scientist in the United States regarding corn disease began to talk about these scientific improvements to his neighbors. The F-1 strains on the U. S. experiment plots on the E. D. Funk farms were described as producing the best corn in the world.

"Jim" Holbert believed that corn men had to crawl in this business of corn improvement before they could walk. Now with ten years of controlling two good strains of corn crossed to produce the F-1 strain, they could now walk. Along the way during that decade they had learned that some strains would produce a good crop only in a good season when planted on a large scale. This meant there was something wrong with the root systems so the long process had to be retraced, constantly looking for corn that would stand up under all conditions.[31] Holbert was greatly impressed with the cooperative effort put forth by such men as Dr. C. R. Ball then cerealist in charge of the United States Office of Cereal Investigations and of Dr. W. L. Burlison, head of the Agronomy Department in the University of Illinois. Opportunities to perfect results came with testing in twenty localities in Illinois with F-1 corn. He said:

> Sometimes, I feel that so many men are contributing that a fellow has no right to put his name to a statement concerning the work of all these men. . . . There is no one man developed corn that stands rigorous tests. There are no self-made men in the world, except in a very relative sense. The only real progress is where a group has cooperated.

He emphasized the fact that in the development of the F-1 strain, students of genetics, agronomy, chemistry, geology, physiology, pathology and many other branches of science had contributed. Many of these men had submerged themselves in the picture in order that the great idea could be worked out.[32]

One of the most interesting inventions was Holbert's "pulling-machine" to test the strength of corn. This was a derrick moved down the corn row. Holbert found a close correlation between the amount of resistance and the strength of a stalk in wind storms.[33] He predicted that this method of breeding corn might produce strains of corn more resistant to injury from the corn borer.[34] He also pointed out that persons could pull up certain stalks with ease, but when they tried to pull up one of another line it was too difficult. The pulling machine test revealed that only a 100 pound pull would uproot the average hill of one strain, whereas a 600 pound pull was required to uproot the hill of another strain.[35] This knowledge resulted in hybrids with better standability from these better strains.

Significant experiments continued under the direction of James Holbert. He and his assistants at the U. S. D. A. Station on Funk Farms acquired data that enabled them to lift the curtain of ignorance so long covering the secrets of the improvement of corn. Complete answers have not yet been discovered. These beginnings, however, are indeed milestones in the history of the development of hybrid corn.

Early in the 1920's Dr. C. S. Reddy was working at the Federal Field Station at Funk Farms helping to investigate Stewart's wilt disease of sweet corn. He told the story himself January 7, 1955 as follows:

We had re-isolated the pathogen which causes this disease and were using a hypodermic needle to cross inoculate the pure cultures of the organism from sweet, dent and flint corn into sweet corn plants, exactly where and when we wanted to determine whether they were the same in identity.

He referred to fifteen or twenty dent corn inbreds developed by Jim Holbert given artificial inoculations for some seedling blight diseases. Some resisted. The new organism was introduced into these dent corn inbreds. Several hundred dent inbred plants were eventually isolated. This was probably the first time such a technique was used under field conditions on dent corn. Some of Holberts inbreds shriveled up and died. Others kept growing. Dr. Reddy continued:

Jim and I reasoned that if we already had one inbred that was known to be almost immune to one important corn stalk disease certainly we could find others. We went further in our reasoning. One of the inbreds that was positively ruined by this disease was very resistant to ear rots, and these two inbreds combined to make a very attractive, useful size ear. So we began to speculate on the possibilities of finding segregates out of this cross that combined a high degree of resistance to both a stalk disease and a destructive ear rot disease.[36]

This effort helped to accelerate the discovery of protection against many other corn diseases.

James Holbert planted in 1929 a number of corn hybrids in the center of an open-pollinated hundred acre field, upon advice from W. P. Flint, entomologist at the University of Illinois. These two men had high hopes that the inbreds would be safe from the second brood of chinch bugs. The bugs found some inbreds, however, before they attacked the open pollinated corn. More significant was the fact that there were some inbreds untouched. The experiment was repeated during the following year. Holbert and his assistants then began to breed bug-resistant lines into their experimental hybrids. Big yields of sound corn on standing stalks resulted. It was later discovered that several resistant hybrids were necessary because no one resistant hybrid could cover all corn growing areas where chinch bugs were numerous. Richard Best, president of Columbiana Seed Company, an associate of Funk Bros. Seed Co., finds the resulting hybrids especially valuable in southern Illinois and in Missouri where chinch bugs once held away in the corn fields.[37]

Two important subjects of investigation in addition to the studies in control of root, stalk and ear rot diseases carried on in the 1920's by Dr. James Holbert during his association with the United States Department of Agriculture's station located on the Funk Farms were cold resistance and seed treatment.

Studies in cold resistance were undertaken in 1928–31. They revealed that corn grown on soil rich in plant food was more resistant to cold. Intelligent soil-improvement programs would help to reduce this hazard.[38] During a symposium on the general subject of temperature and life, James B. Dickson of the University of Wisconsin and Dr. James Holbert at a meeting of the Society of Naturalists in Nashville, Tennessee, December 30, 1927 read a paper entitled "Relation of Temperature to the Development of Disease in Plants." [39] At a meeting of the Society of Agronomists in 1925 they had previously presented their conclusions regarding the influence of temperature upon metabolism and disease resistance in selfed lines of corn.[40]

This problem of cold resistance was investigated in an interesting experiment carried on at Research Acres when movable frost-making chambers were set over corn plants. Each refrigerator chamber with electric power units, coils and controls weighed more than two tons, had the capacity for removing the same amount of heat as 1,600 pounds of melting ice in 24 hours. Equipment was provided for moving and operating the apparatus to various locations in the field. Dr. W. L. Burlison, head of the Agronomy Department in the University of Illinois, worked closely with James Holbert on this experiment. Professor Burlison generally telephoned his observations from inside the chamber to Holbert who recorded the data and handled the temperature control panel at the field station on the Funk Farms. About midnight temperatures were dropped to the usual levels for early spring and fall nights. Dr. Burlison observed the immediate effect of cold on different corn plants. Some twisted and shook. When the leaves became transparent, the corn would not recover. Other corn which retained its green color but did not resume growth when the temperature rose was marked for future experimentation. Dr. Burlison remarked that in these studies corn was found that could be "knocked out" at temperatures of from 40 to 45 degrees. A few plants could survive below freezing temperature for a few hours and then resume growth in a normal way under normal temperatures. According to Dr. Burlison, it was James R. Holbert who used these findings to develop hybrids with cold resistant germ plasm eventually producing commercial hybrids for wide distribution in the Corn Belt. These hybrids also retained balance in other qualities producing high yields.[41] These findings were published in a U. S. D. A. circular in 1933.[42] Other combinations and some commercial varieties withstood temperatures below 32 degrees for six hours and a few hybrids survived temperatures at 28 degrees. These experiments were reported by W. L. Burlison and J. R. Holbert in *Phytopathology* during 1929 and 1931. They noted that "Progeny studies in the field of yellow dent corn plants" from mature seed unexposed and exposed ten hours to the three successive temperatures of 32, 23 and 14 degrees F. in these field refrigeration chambers during the fall of 1929 showed injury. They saw marked differences between different inbred and crossbred strains. Application of phosphate to soils prior to planting increased cold resistance of young plants.[43]

A great chapter in hybrid corn was in the making as a result of these cold resistance studies. As the two authors later stated in U. S. D. A. Circular 285, "The economic advantage of resistance to injury from exposure to untimely chilling and freezing temperatures prior to maturity of the corn is very great." [44]

Members of the Agricultural Committee of the Chicago Association of Commerce visited the Funk Farms to observe their experimental work. They were particularly interested in the electrically operated freezing chamber to produce low temperatures for testing first resistance of inbreds and hybrids. Clifford Gregory of *The Prairie Farmer*, Oswald of the *Seed World* and L. M. Smith of the *Grain World* arranged for a delegation September 18th from Chicago. Funk asked Henry Ramsey to advise members of the Chicago Board of Trade to accompany the group. The president of the Chicago & Alton Railroad overheard the conversation regarding plans and offered to bring them to Bloomington himself in a private car.[45]

Similar experiments were performed later on young seedling plants in the spring to determine reaction to cold and resistance to wet weather occurring in early planted corn. This information proved valuable in future production of fast early starting hybrids.

About 1930 Dr. James Holbert and corn breeders working with him sought certain inbred strains of corn to resist earworms. The next step was to combine earworm-resistant inbreds with others. New hybrids for different corn growing areas were thus developed. G-90 became one of the hybrids that few earworms bothered. The earworm can be a menace all the way from the Sugar Belt to the northern Corn Belt as well as in the western and eastern Corn Belts. Therefore research and seed foundation teams for Funk Bros. Seed Co. constantly seek improved hybrids with earworm resistance.[46]

Proper treatment for corn seed also interested James Holbert. He discovered early that a solution of mercuric chloride for this purpose reduced vigor and did not aid in the increase of yield or quality in corn. When organic mercury compounds were introduced from Germany after World War I for seed treatment, Dr. Holbert proceeded with caution. The first of these, Upsulum, revived his faith in organic mercury compounds. Dust treatments of this compound soon replaced the older procedure of soaking in water solution. At this point the Du Ponts became interested in the problem. Dr. Engleman, known for his work along these lines in Germany, was brought to this country with an assignment from Du Pont to find a better product. This activity led to the eventual introduction of Semesan, Jr. It is believed that the first field trials after these compounds were introduced following World War I were undertaken on the Funk Farms. Dr. C. S. Reddy and Dr. J. R. Holbert were deeply interested in these activities. Before satisfactory seed treatments were available such diseases as Diplodia and Giberella caused great loss for the young seedlings in the spring. Pithium was the most difficult of the soil borne diseases to combat. Effective seed treatment aids in protecting the bred-in benefits of hybrid corn.[47]

The results of these experiments helped to influence the Du Ponts to proceed with the development of seed corn treatments. They became one of the first leaders in the production of seed treatments through their Chemical Division. Again Research Acres was a proving ground. Relationship with the Du Ponts continued over the years.

Direct challenges to improve corn often came to Dr. Holbert from various sections of the United States. One of these came from Frank Scully of the Scully estate north of Springfield. His request crystallized the demands of many farmers in the corn growing areas south of Indianapolis, Peoria, Des Moines or Omaha. All efforts had failed to produce a hybrid to excel open pollinates in that territory. The required "dream hybrid" should be later in maturity, resist chinch bugs, endure drouth and grow a better stalk than had been formerly known in these sections. James Holbert regarded these requests as assignments. He considered this a real job that had to be done. He mapped a bold new approach to the problem. Up to that time it had been an accepted policy that corn for given areas must be developed from local or native strains. Dr. Jim instructed his staff to assemble inbreds from widely separated areas. This was indeed a new method. One of these inbreds with high yield and late maturity was developed from an open pollinated variety from Pennsylvania. A Kansas inbred contributed high drouth and heat resistance. Another came from a late Funk Yellow Dent variety. A fourth was derived from an Indian corn with good ear and fine stalk qualities. Out of these blends came first the single crosses and then the final double cross. Thus an "experimental" hybrid was born.

The extensive Funks G nationwide research program enabled experimental Funk hybrids to survive many tests in one season in the Funk proving grounds year after year across the nation. Funks G-94 was one result, a popular hybrid from the valleys of Colorado to the Maryland shore. This same approach has been the pattern for the development of many outstanding G Hybrids.[48]

Comparable stories can be told for the North Central states where hybrids from four famous open pollinated strains including one from Funk's Yellow Dent, one from Reid's Yellow Dent and two others from widely used Iowa open pollinates produced a result containing the good qualities preserved by more than a century of corn selection.[49]

It has been said that corn growing in many of the northern areas and in high altitude regions might be compared to a hundred yard dash. Professor Ed Walters, corn extension agronomist at Pennsylvania State College, challenged the Funks to produce a hybrid as rapid starting and fast drying as early Butler strains from which the inbreds were derived. These inbreds went into hybrid combination with other Funk pure lines. Some of these originated in the Dakotas and in Minnesota. Corn history was in the making in the proving plots of Funks national research program.

Demands for improved hybrids in different parts of the country continued. H. H. Miller in conversation with an experiment station worker in the south heard the following: "If you want to breed a hybrid for the South, with better shuck coverage and acceptable weevil resistance, here's something to start on. Tell Jim Holbert to get busy." The speaker pushed an ear of corn across the desk. It put weevil resistance into G-70 hybrid combinations. The product was G-714.

Similar progress was reported for the Southwest where Texas and Oklahoma lacked good hybrid corn. Dry weather and insects were the enemies in these parts of the country. Funk's network of research concentrated on solving this problem. New inbreds were isolated from native southern and southwestern open pollinated strains. Thousands of different experimental hybrids were developed in combinations with other pure lines. Funk's G-711 came out of pure lines from Texas Sure Cropper, Furgeson's Yellow Dent and the famous Kansas Sunflower. This hybrid was also useful in Missouri, Arkansas, Tennessee, Kentucky and southeastern Virginia.[50]

During the decade of the forties the nationwide G-Hybrid proving plots took some of the gamble out of corn growing. Across and up and down the country, thousands of these plots were designed to cover the entire range of growing conditions. The farmer no longer had to experiment with the variations in weather, soil, insect and disease conditions for himself. Funk Bros. undertook this responsibility in securing proof of performance and adaptation of the company's products. Research became the key to better hybrids.

Many people believe that hot weather is hard on man and dog but good for corn. Everett Mitchell has remarked that the corn might object to this statement if it could be heard. Excessively high temperature, like too low temperature, has adverse effect on the corn plant. James Holbert began his heat resistant studies in 1934, a very hot summer. He stated:

In this particular location we did have adequate soil moisture. As the temperature passed 90 in our first test plots, I began to see dead flecks of white in the leaves of some corn plants. Then, in a few days the whole leaf might turn yellowish or even die. Some other plants would do fine until the thermometer would hit 95. At 98 a great number of the early hybrids would break down. You could see big changes in them within the space of a single hour.[51]

Some strains die in the heat; others sit and wait, then possibly grow again; others continue growth through the heat. It became apparent that higher heat tolerance could be bred into good hybrids along with resistance to cold. Proper balance was the essence of success in the breeding of good hybrids.[52]

During the drouth year of 1936 cornfields received little rain from May to August. The thermometer rose to 114 degrees. At this time 100 bushel corn yields on field or farm basis was unusual, but James Holbert and Al Lang of the University of Illinois Soils Department undertook an assignment on the G. J. Mecherle farm operated by Walter Meers near Bloomington, Illinois. A thirteen acre field was chosen for the test. Improved drainage and additional fertilizer were recommended. For two weeks from July 3, the heat in Bloomington ranged between 102 and 114 without rain. But the Walter Meers field of hybrids was always green. The heat subsided a little but drouth and relatively high temperatures continued to mid-August when the rains came. These hybrids came through with their drouth resistance qualities showing. One hybrid yielded 121 bushels. The official yield for the field was 101.3 bushels.[53] One hundred bushel yields on a field or farm basis were almost unheard of at this time. The G. J. Mecherle story of thick planting on balanced high fertility on well drained soil with high temperatures without rain signalled a new day in corn growing.[54]

James Holbert was once embarrassed by a comment from his banker friend, Grover Helm of Bloomington. Helm had compared an early, slow starting hybrid to the advance made by open pollinated corn. Holbert knew he had a real assignment. He produced and bred into his hybrids qualities of early, rapid starting and continued growth, described as sustained rapid growth.[55]

Paul Stewart of Waterloo, Nebraska, an agronomist for Funk's G hybrids recalled Ed. Magill who about 1918 tried out a mechanical picker which he had seen at the Nebraska State Fair. It worked best when three mules and three big Percherons were fresh early in the day. It was hybrid corn that made mechanical corn picking a practical undertaking. Dr. T. A. Kiesselbach of the University of Nebraska has been reported as saying: "Holbert's old A. by L. was the first hybrid corn that really brought home to us the great possibilities of hybrid corn. It yielded well and it stood up so much better than our open pollinated corn that it was just in a class by itself." From that time the possibility of a successful mechanical picker was assured.[56]

Eugene D. Funk, as has been noted, became interested in the mechanical corn picker before the First World War. E. L. Oheim, a vice president for Deere & Company declared that they worked hard to produce mechanical corn pickers in the 1920's but not until hybrid corn did they come into widespread use in 1930. He said: "In Iowa and Illinois where hybrids were first available, only about one acre in ten was harvested with pickers in 1930. Five years later, machines were used to pick about one acre out of seven. But by 1945 seven acres out of ten were picked mechanically." As wartime shortages lessened they came into greater demand. Good standability in corn, meaning good stalks and roots, contributed to getting the corn up off the ground. Time is saved; picking takes only ten days or two weeks. Investment in horses was no longer a necessity for the corn producer.[57]

The hybrid corn industry at Funk Bros. in Bloomington reclaimed Dr. Holbert in 1937 after his experience in charge of the federal corn experiment plots located on the Funk Farms. The *Pantagraph* noted that "his connection with the United States department started when Mr. Funk succeeded in interesting the department in a study of corn diseases and methods of avoiding their damage. He provided the land for the study and space in the seed house here for headquarters and 'loaned' Dr. Holbert to the department to conduct the studies." [58] Dr. Holbert became vice president of Funk Bros. in charge of the corn breeding program.

With the gradual acceptance by farmers of this new hybrid corn, a new and larger drying and processing plant was established on the E. D. Funk Farm in 1935–36. The following year the company leased the Sutton and Ainsworth buildings in Mason City, Illinois, purchasing the latter in 1936. During the same year property of the Bloomington Canning Company on Division Street in Normal, Illinois was acquired. Additional office space was provided when the new office building was constructed in 1937–38. During 1938–40 new properties were acquired in Iowa and in 1941 a complete corn drying and processing plant was established at Belle Plaine, Iowa.[59]

The development and the increase in the demand for hybrid corn paralleled the years of the *Surplus*. There was consequently consistent effort to discover new uses for absorbing the excess production. Eugene D. Funk, Sr. and James Gray attended meetings held in Detroit, Michigan in 1935 composed of farm, science and industrial representatives (see chapter XXVI).

Winter Research Acres in southern Florida are planted before Thanksgiving. Inbred lines from hybrids are ready for detasseling the following January. The seed is harvested and dried in April, then sent to the home office for distribution to field laboratories in the

Corn Belt. Time is thus gained in producing and testing new germ plasm.[60]

The counties of Essex and Kent across from Detroit in eastern Ontario are excellent farming areas. A shorter growing season to the east and northeast near Ottawa demanded early maturing hybrids. Over the years Funks G Hybrids have met the needs of Canadian farmers helping to carry the Corn Belt north among the lakes and pine tree county.[61]

Hybrid corn also invaded the South. By March 7, 1954 it was estimated that 50 percent of the corn acreage in the South would be planted with hybrid corn. Twenty-five percent more of the farmers showed an interest in the product. Acreage controls for cotton released more acres for corn. Realization that corn and forage crops could go along together was an advantage. As a result new hybrids were constantly being developed for the South. The livestock industry was also possible of increase in this section of the country with increased use of hybrid corn.[62]

Great achievements in production of Funks G Hybrids in the south take one back to the interest shown by Eugene D. Funk, Sr. when he took his National Corn Show to Columbia, South Carolina and to Dallas, Texas.

A farm near Canton, Mississippi owned by Funk's former general manager, H. H. Miller, who envisioned expansion in the South, was also a nucleus of activity in the early years.[63]

A significant result in the world of corn production occurred in October 1955 when Lamar Ratliff, in his mid-teens, living in Prentiss County, Mississippi, became the first in recorded history to harvest more than 300 bushels of corn per acre. The official yield was 304.38 bushels of Funks G Hybrid G-711. Wheeler McMillen's prediction became a reality. Gene Funk's recognition of the opportunities for improvement of corn in the South as early as the first decade of the twentieth century and Holbert's scientific "know-how" contributed to this epoch-making event. This kind of news in domestic and foreign accounts brought acclaim to American farm youth and American agricultural skill.[64]

When James Holbert was working with the U. S. D. A. he carried on his experiments in part at the Funk Farms. Some activities were carried on in the State of Illinois and outside the Corn Belt. Holbert stated: "Prior to my time in the Corn Belt, there were no corn breeders in the sense that we think of them now. I relied, of course, on the works of Dr. E. M. East and Dr. G. H. Shull." He also stated

that the hybrids developed by East in Connecticut were not successful in the Corn Belt: "They did not yield as much as the good old varieties because they did not have bred into them the disease and insect
resistance required to make good, and that is why it was necessary
to start over again." When asked if he started with the principles of
these men, Holbert replied: "I started with their principles but not
their germ plasm." He also believed that others worked on hybrid
corn, "But as far as I know, in the first ten or fifteen years, I was the
principal one working on disease resistance," when he was an employee of the U. S. D. A. and studying on Funk Farms. In regard to
aid from others Holbert stated:

I do not know that I solicited the aid and assistance of others in doing
the breeding work. I did solicit their aid in advertising the results of the
breeding work but not their assistance in the breeding work. There is quite
an important distinction there.

He also stated that there were a number of inbreds developed as
the result of his work with the U. S. D. A. that were distributed to
all of the land grant colleges requesting them and also to commercial
breeders. In 1930 there was a policy of free exchange between the
different land grant colleges and the commercial companies. It was
impossible to keep these results secret since he was a federal employee.[65]

By the time Holbert returned to Funk Bros. there were three companies, De Kalb, Pioneer and Lester Pfister besides Northrup King
with research staffs of their own.[66] When Holbert returned to Funk
Bros. in 1937 there was a free exchange of material, but in 1957 there
was not.

It became increasingly significant to understand that when Holbert
left the U. S. D. A. anybody who had the same inbreds and seeds
that he had could have used them as a starting point. But they would
not necessarily be the same two years from that time because they are
not stable entities.

Holbert also pointed out that there is a world of difference between "exchange of experiences" among scientists and "exchange of
seeds." This meant that "germ plasm" is not exchanged but that relating experiences in production of the product might be told.

Holbert also has explained that some of the experiment stations in
more recent years have decided not to try to develop new inbreds in
corn because the hybrid seed corn research program was being so
well handled by private companies.[67]

Holbert pointed out that in his work with the U. S. D. A. he had called in all the different strains of hybrids. He, St. John of De Kalb and later Baker of Pioneer found differences in yields for those that looked alike. He added:

What I know now is that these inbreds are living biological entities which do change according to the way they are taken care of and handled, and the fact that they do go by some name on paper does not mean anything in regard to their performance.[68]

He also pointed out that the continuing research problem was essential because market demands shifted continuously; germ plasm shifts and the competitive situation changes. Actually in 1956 Funk Bros. did not produce any of the same hybrids as in 1942 or 1938. Insect population and disease conditions also affected the need for new hybrids.[69]

When asked if Funk Bros. used the hybrid lines developed at the time of U. S. D. A. work, Holbert in 1956 answered: "We do not. We would not be in business if we had not developed some better ones." When asked if Funk Bros. used any hybrids made available by agricultural stations or land grant colleges, he answered: "We do not. We do make use of all the inbreds released and test them out to determine if they will make a contribution. For several years we have not been able to use the releases until we have crossed them over and reworked them." [70]

Funk Bros. Seed Co. is regarded as one of the four largest companies in hybrid seed corn operations. Others are DeKalb, Pioneer and Pfister Associate Growers. These companies all operate in different patterns of organization from Funk Bros.[71]

The research department maintained by Funk Bros. was established in 1956 to include over twelve college graduates trained in research and foundation seed production relating specifically to hybrid corn. Some of the salesmen and other personnel are also chiefly trained in research and devote part time to the work. These number about twenty. If those who plant, harvest and record observations are included, the total would be more than one hundred.[72]

Shifting agricultural production has been a factor in the hybrid seed corn business of Funk Bros. Only 143,000 acres were estimated as planted with hybrid seed corn in 1933 of 110 million acres of corn in the United States. Twenty-five years later, 89.2 percent of corn planted on 81,799,000 acres was hybrid corn. Reduced acreages brought increases in other crops. Some acreages have been converted to roads, airfields, home and industrial sites. In these twenty-three years there was an increase of nearly a billion bushels of corn.[73]

CHAPTER XXVIII

Consistently Good, Year After Year

A CIRCULAR IN 1936 announced that hybrid corn at Funk Bros. had definitely passed the trial or experimental stage. Hybrids were available for corn producers in almost all locations in the Corn Belt. A summary of yields for Funk's Hybrids contrasted with those of open pollinated varieties in 1933 and 1934 showed increase to favor the hybrids of 8.3 bushels per acre in 1933 and 12.5 bushels per acre in 1934. Funk's Hybrids yielded in 1934, a drouth year, only 12 bushels average less than in 1933 while the open pollinated varieties [1] yielded 16 bushels less. Funk's Hybrids gave a better account of themselves in this unfavorable season than the open pollinated varieties.

R. J. Laible wrote in *The Furrow*, 1936, published by Deere and Company of Moline, Illinois, that "out of the worst drouth in the history of America's Corn Belt comes one welcome discovery which may, in the years to come, repay farmers many times over the losses they suffered in 1936." Slowly it was learned that hybrid corn produced a satisfactory crop during a drouth where ordinary open pollinated corn failed. It appeared certain that hybrids would outyield ordinary corn.

Dr. James Holbert of Funk Bros. reported that he was emphasizing not only yield but also ability to stand up well, quality of grain, drouth resistance, cold resistance and resistance to grasshopper attacks. Results of 1935 were summarized in a *Bulletin* issued by the Illinois Farmers Institute, Springfield.[2] Mr. Laible also warned against accepting all hybrids. Some were poor and were offered by unscrupulous sellers. In such cases farmers were better off with a good variety of open pollinated corn.[3] Expansion in the business of a seed company would thereby be slow. Additional acreages of foundation seed would be an expensive item. Commercial production of hybrid seed corn demanded capital, risk and vision.

Adoption of an Associate Grower system solved the problem of retaining the foundation seed as the property of Funk Bros. Seed Co.[4] Early agreements were only verbal with a definite Memorandum of

Agreement formulated in 1937. During the first few years everyone in this new enterprise cautiously felt his way. Farmers were traditionally proud of their own corn. Before the farmer would buy hybrid seed corn he must be informed of its advantages. Salesmen spoke of this new "good corn" but the higher prices of the hybrids contrasted to those of the open pollinated became a deterrent to sales. Open-pollinated corn sold from $3.50 to $5.50 per bushel, and seed could be stored for the next planting. Hybrid seed corn was priced as high as $15.00 per bushel, and must be purchased every year.[5]

A glance at the list of Associate Growers reveals their location during 1930–40 as chiefly in Illinois where the Funks were already well known. Whenever the Funks stepped into a new area they always started in a relatively small local region with a good growing season. This selected area could in turn serve surrounding areas as demand grew. Almost immediately they concentrated on securing the best adapted germ plasm for the specific area, in order to cross it with available good germ plasm.[6]

When Claire V. Golden graduated from Iowa State College, he was in his own words "something of a young crusader," who thought it might be possible to change the world. Through the influence of the farm adviser in Rock Island county, Palmer Edgerton, he took what seed corn he had and sent it down to James Holbert in 1919 at the U. S. D. A. station on the Funk Farms. He received one peck out of 25 bushels. This peck was known as Utility Type corn or Disease Free corn. Golden, who lived at Cordova, Illinois came to know the professors at the University of Illinois who were interested in experimentation and became acquainted with Eugene Funk and Earl Sieveking. As he recalls the story, Mr. Funk and James Holbert came to his farm about 1928 looking for someone to produce seed corn. When E. D. Sr. looked at the countryside he wondered where anyone could produce corn in this part of the country.[7] Time proved that the combination of the enthusiasm of a Claire Golden, the scientific knowledge of James Holbert and the experience and integrity of Eugene Funk could produce desired results. Claire Golden produced seven acres of hybrid corn in 1930 according to Funk Bros. records and later in 1933 became the first of many successful Associate Producers in the Funk System.

E. D. Sr. wrote to his friend, J. L. McKeighan of Yates City, Illinois during April 1934 that the demand for hybrid corn was increasing and that its future seemed assured. He informed J. L. McKeighan that Funk Bros. had spent several years testing the adapta-

bility of different hybrids in various sections of the state. Funk had
reached the place where he was considering the advisability of placing with some friends a few of these strains of hybrids at strategic
points on a cooperative basis. He asked for a conference with J. L.
to determine whether or not he would be interested in working with
the Funk organization. Eugene Funk saw that:

> There will be a period during the next few years when some so called
> corn breeder(?) will attempt to take advantage and put out Hybrid corn
> regardless of its adaptability.[8]

J. L. McKeighan answered in the affirmative. E. D. Sr. then explained some of his ideas, referring to the fact that for the past year
corn had been produced in cooperation with Claire Golden. Funk
supplied the foundation stocks for planting the field. For compensa-
tion Funk received a percentage of the gross sales from hybrid corn
produced from this field.[9]

McKeighan's early Golden Dent was known for many years dating
back over a half century to a yellow corn brought about 1850 from
Ohio to Fulton County, Illinois. It was grown there for years by
farmers including James McKeighan, who moved to Knox County,
Illinois in 1855. This improved corn became widely known as Mc-
Keighan's Yellow Dent from his Willow Run Farm. Inbreeding was
thought to decrease yields. As early as 1905 McKeighan had grown,
bred and sold a pure bred seed corn.[10] He also followed the ear to
row system. McKeighan's booklet for 1925 pointed out that Reid's
Yellow Dent was his choice as McKeighan's ideal of a type of corn
closely resembling what was then called Utility Type. McKeighan
advertised his improved strain of Reid's Yellow Dent as this Utility
Type Corn with considerable recognition 1921–24.[11]

McKeighan obtained from Funk three bushels of 176A in the ear
in 1918. It stood up better than the average corn. Finally he discarded
everything for this.

Both Claire Golden and J. L. McKeighan remembered Eugene D.
Funk, Sr. for his ability to judge men. They held him in high esteem
and were proud to be associated with the calibre of men chosen as
the Funk Associate Growers, who were men of proven integrity.
They were long friends of Eugene D. Funk, Sr. They knew him and
he knew them. Many of them were competitors in the open pollinated days who respected the business ability and the name of
Funk in the seed business.

John T. Smith and Sons of Tolono, Illinois became an Associate in

1934. John T. Smith first sold seed corn in 1898 as a large farm operator and early soybean seed enthusiast. Smith was a contemporary of Eugene D. Funk, Sr. He became interested in hybrid corn through contact with the University of Illinois and by observing Funk Bros. demonstrations. The territory included Champaign and Douglas Counties and the south half of Piatt.

Richard Best who managed the farm for Edward G. Boyle at Columbiana near Eldred in Greene County, Illinois during the early twenties became one of the early Associates in 1936. Boyle, a well known Chicago attorney developed river bottom land along the Illinois. He has been described as one who did a pioneer's work in 15 years instead of 100. The river valley at Columbiana is wide, located about thirty miles north of the mouth of the Illinois river. Boyle was a purchaser of Funk's corn as early as 1910. He was a good friend of Eugene Funk, Sr. and helped him reorganize the company. The two men were opposite in temperament but both accomplished a great deal. Boyle thought of Funk as the Dean of Seedsmen, a man who had given his skill back to agriculture along with some good money. Richard Best had a seed business and as manager for Mr. Boyle came to know the Funks. They sold 176A, Funks 329 and other varieties in the early days. Boyle's railroad from Eldred to Boyle near Columbiana put the place on the map. Best experimented with the inbreeding and crossing of corn in 1930.[12] During the 22 years of association with the Funk System he has expanded the area served by the Columbiana Company until it is one of the largest of the associates. His knowledge of the hybrid seed corn business has enabled him to contribute constructively at all levels in the operations.[13]

O. J. Sommer of Pekin, Illinois planted his first breeding plot in 1910. For some 15 years while working with various lines of corn he visited Funk Bros. at Bloomington. Consultation with James Holbert and Dr. C. M. Woodworth of the University of Illinois convinced Sommer that certain detectable characteristics of an ear of corn could be associated with better performance in the field. He was one of a group formulating the Utility Corn Score Card. This card enumerated numerically characteristics and was first tried out at Galesburg in January 1921. This Galesburg Utility Show marked the discard of the old rough show corn type of ear, and of the old type show card. Sommer's corn received first and second place at this show. The next annual state show at Urbana in 1922 was judged on this basis of germinating ten kernels for ten day test. By this method their true resistance to disease could be evaluated. Sommer's corn again was awarded first place, sweepstakes and Grand Champion for the state.[14]

O. J. became the first president of the Illinois Crop Improvement Association in 1923.[15] Twelve years later E. D. Funk, R. J. Laible, Sieveking and J. R. Holbert visited the Sommer Bros. Company. Their object was to interest Sommer in becoming a cooperative hybrid corn grower. It was agreed to participate on 40 acres in 1936. In order to meet the agreement it was necessary for Sommer to give up all his breeding work carried on since 1909.[16] Sommer's Yellow Dent was by this time recognized by the College of Agriculture in the University of Illinois as a distinct variety.[17] During the following year, 1935, the Fred McCulloch Seed Farms at Belle Plaine, Iowa joined the Funk organization. McCulloch, a personal friend of E. D. Sr., established an outstanding open pollinated variety widely used in Iowa. His loyalty and knowledge of Funk leadership during the early years was not forgotten by the Funk family. The J. C. Robinson Seed Company of Waterloo, Nebraska, with some 1500 acres located in the Elkhorn Valley, became associated in 1935. E. T. Robinson was a past president of the A. S. T. A. in addition to serving the Nebraska area for Funks, and the Robinson Seed Company was well known for their vine seed business, with branches in Colorado and California. The following year, 1936, Claude W. Thorp and Sons of Clinton, Illinois, well known in De Witt County, joined with Funks. As early as 1920 Claude had produced open pollinated seed corn. They serviced De Witt County, the southern half of Logan and the northern half of Macon and Piatt.

Expansion continued in Illinois during 1937. Located in central Illinois with a sales area in part of Marshall, Putnam, Peoria, Stark and Fulton counties, Harold and George Shissler brought their seed company into the Funk Associate program. They had produced open pollinated varieties for years and had ear tested corn for disease resistant strains prior to hybrid corn production. In later years they also cooperated with the field seed department at Funk Bros. The Swansons near Galesburg, Illinois as early as 1929 and 1930 conducted strip tests in conjunction with Dr. Holbert and their county agents in relation to seed treatment and hybrid corn. The Swansons, who belonged to a family of Knox County pioneers, also joined the Funk System in 1937. Near St. Francisville, Arthur and Clarence Akin were outstanding farmers in southeastern Illinois. They produced Funks 176A in 1935. They operated about 4,500 acres in Lawrence County, serving as Funk Associates in 1937, Richland,

Wabash, Edwards and parts of Crawford. S. B. Moore, of Humboldt, Illinois, a well known farmer in Coles County, also joined the Funk Associates during the same year.

Other Illinois companies joining the Funk Associate group in 1937 included Condon Bros. of Rockford. Leonard Condon also a past president of the A. S. T. A. brought an old established seed firm into the organization. Corn Belt Hatcheries of Kankakee, Joliet and Watseka operated by the Roth family of Gibson City, Illinois, also joined in the same year. Waldo Roth, husband of Ruth Funk, was in charge of the Kankakee branch. Another old friend of E. D. Funk, Frank Garwood and Sons of Stonington, Illinois, with some 500 acres in Christian County, became associated during the same year.

In neighboring Indiana, Ray Cannell of Knightstown, who was a tenant of Prof. Hackleman of the Agricultural Experiment Station, University of Illinois, became an Associate in 1937. Funk's Hybrids were developed in the eastern part of the United States along with Blakeford Farms, Inc. of Queenstown, Maryland, owned by George Moffett of Corn Products Refining Co. Funk's Hybrid Corn showed superiority over local corn in that area during 1935. It was first used in Maryland in 1930. George Moffett contacted E. D. Funk, Sr. and James Holbert in 1936. James Moffett, his son, believed that Corn Products should devote more of its time to developing its raw material, corn. Trial plantings on the Blakeford farm occurred in 1937 when an agreement was arranged. Test plots were then set up in Maryland, Pennsylvania, Virginia, Delaware and North Carolina.[18]

It was also in 1937 that the company decided to reorganize the personnel. At this time, James Holbert returned from his long affiliation since 1918 with the U. S. D. A. During this time his headquarters remained in Bloomington, Illinois. After this valuable experience his return to Funk Bros. was significant. The board of directors was increased from three to five, with J. R. Holbert and LaFayette Funk as the two new members. At this time, H. H. Miller resigned as vice president but continued as general manager. Holbert became vice president and corn breeder; E. D. Funk, Jr. was named office manager; R. J. Laible became agricultural adviser; LaFayette Funk was manager of the company department of farm crops; E. G. Sieveking manager of the department of soils; Theodore Funk was farm manager; Harold Goodwin was field seeds manager and Paul Funk, field seeds salesman. A new processing plant was placed in operation on the Funk Farms in December 1936.[19]

The Associate Growers system had increased to sixteen by 1938.

These growers might well have been competitors because many had well established clientele. Contracts with Funks required them to produce hybrid corn exclusively from foundation seed stock supplied by the Funks. They were required to advertise Funks G Hybrid Seed Corn, devoting one side of the seed corn bag to the Funk name. The growers at this time paid Funk Bros. Seed Co. a required percentage of gross sales.[20] The corn sales organization in 1938 was divided into two groups. There were many dealers located in the State of Illinois who had done business with the Funks over a long period of time. A second group was described at that time as "Community Agents." There were 48 in Indiana, 66 in Iowa, 106 in Illinois and 8 in other states or a total of 228. Funk Hybrids were showing well in performance tests in Iowa, Illinois and Indiana. R. J. Laible pointed out that the first real sales effort for Funks G occurred in 1937.[21]

It is apparent that Funks G Hybrid organization grew rapidly in the five years from 1935 to 1940. Although the center of operations was in Illinois, Associates were located in Nebraska, Iowa, Indiana, Pennsylvania, Missouri and Maryland.[22]

The Peppard Seed Company of Kansas City, Missouri, long established in the West became an Associate in 1939. As one of the larger wholesale handlers of blue grass and alfalfa seed they were able to service Kansas, Western Missouri, Oklahoma and Texas with Funks G Hybrid. Their long association with Funk Bros. in field seed operations resulted in mutual confidence before the hybrid corn era. Because of their extensive corn growing areas, expansion was rapid with ever present problems of finding adapted resistant Hybrids to combat the hot winds, drought and insect damage in the Southwest.[23] A. H. Hoffman & Company, established in 1899 at Landisville, Pennsylvania, also joined with the Funk organization in 1939. When E. D. Funk, Sr. visited this section he was amazed by the amounts of corn produced by the many religious sects in that area. This company serviced the northeastern part of the United States for Funks.

During the next decade of the 1940's James Grant & Son at Cottam, Ontario, Canada were established as Associates in 1943. They helped to push the Corn Belt north and eastward. They had worked with open pollinated seed as early as 1915 and with hand selection of ear types for many years. In 1931 they received the highest reward at the Provincial Seed Show. They service all of Canada with grain corn growing areas chiefly in the provinces around Ontario and Quebec where the climate is tempered by the Great Lakes and the St. Lawrence River. They find adapted hybrids significant in extending the Corn Belt northward. Peterson-Biddick of Wadena, Minnesota found the same situation true in that state where they also contributed to the great expansion of the Corn Belt. They became an associate in 1943.

During the same year the Louisiana Seed Company was incorporated as an Associate in one of the important corn growing areas of the south near Alexandria, Louisiana. Funks recognized the great significance of corn in the economy in the South. The expansion of the Corn Belt north and south was made possible by scientific research producing adapted hybrids for given areas.

The Wisconsin Seed Company, a group of certified seed producers located at Spring Green and operating a retail seed business, joined the Funk program in 1949. They now serve all the corn growing areas in that state. Other Associates operating during the 1940's were R. E. Lambert & Sons of Darlington, Alabama; H. H. Miller Farms of Madison Station, Mississippi; and McNair Yield Tested Company of Laurinburg, North Carolina.[24]

There were 26 processing centers by 1947 with 40 seed production areas and dozens of warehouses scattered across the nation from the Atlantic Coast to the Rocky Mountains to the Great Lakes. The Funks G Hybrids were advertised in 1947 as fast starting, resistant to insects, disease, heat and drought with superior standability, easy husking, high quality for feeding or market and high yields.[25]

Agricultural Laboratories, located in Columbus, Ohio joined the Associate Group during 1951. They were designated as Ag-Lab Products, Inc. in 1954, serving the state of Ohio. During the decade of the fifties adjustments were made whereby some associates expanded territory to include new plants. This was especially true of Columbiana Seed Co.[26] and Louisiana Seed Company.

A glance at the roster of Associates in the appendix reveals the fact that many continue under their original founders. These companies are all well established and strategically located within their areas. Their founders and present managers were either well known to E. D. Funk, Sr., to James Holbert or to the Funk Bros. now in charge of the company.

Eugene D. Funk, Sr. presided April 20, 1938 over what he called "the first annual meeting of our cooperators." Although there had been a meeting the previous year, scarcely anyone had formulated definite ideas of procedure at that time. He continued:

It is this very organization which we have tried to perfect which has brought realization to a dream some of us have had for several years. Just how to perfect it depends entirely upon the personnel. I am expecting it to become one great big family. We started out to select and choose each of you to build our own family. It got around some way that we are taking on cooperators and we have had a 'heck' of a time making excuses for not taking on any more than we needed.

The original concept behind the growth of the Associate system was well described by Mr. Funk when he stressed the following points before this group (1) it is up to us to work together, (2) to feel that we are one family, (3) to feel that we have a common interest, (4) that we can trust each other absolutely, (5) and above all to work together to produce the best seed corn that can be produced. He closed with these words of warning: "If we cannot do these things we have no business trying to undertake this work."

There are other indications of the basic philosophy in the Funk leadership and guidance of the seed company:

You men understand corn breeding and production and merchandising and just what we are aiming to do. We will make mistakes of course. We are human just like everybody else. But we are going to be honest and correct these mistakes when brought to our attention and found out. I don't want to preach in any sense of the word except that as time goes on we must learn from each other—to take advice and to give advice. Don't hesitate at any time to bring your troubles to us, and we will bring ours to you. By such united efforts I feel confident that our program is absolutely sound. We have a future before us that is unlimited in scope; the size of our business will depend entirely upon our ability to put it over.

The Associates met at Funk Farms, August 5, 1939 on the site of the old Government Plots. Eugene D., as he looked up at the Osage orange hedge at Research Acres, told the story of when his Father LaFayette set out the trees. Fourteen inch holes were already dug, and the youngster, (E. D., Sr.) trying to help, fell headfirst into one of the holes. LaFayette said, "Yes, the 'brat,' always wanting to do something. I'll give him something to do all right when he gets old enough." E. D., Sr. remarked that he had "been a loafer ever since." [27]

When Eugene, Sr., returned from Florida in April 1940 he attended the meeting of the Associates, declaring that he was mighty glad to get back home. He described some of the corn "down there" as knee high with some plants ready to tassel within ten days or two weeks.[28] Problems of price always confronted the producers. E. D. had his own ideas on this subject and did not hesitate to express himself:

We have led this corn business for 50 years. Funk Brothers have always had the highest price on seed corn. When we are selling corn at $5.00 a bushel, our competitors were selling at $3.00 or $4.50 a bushel. We are

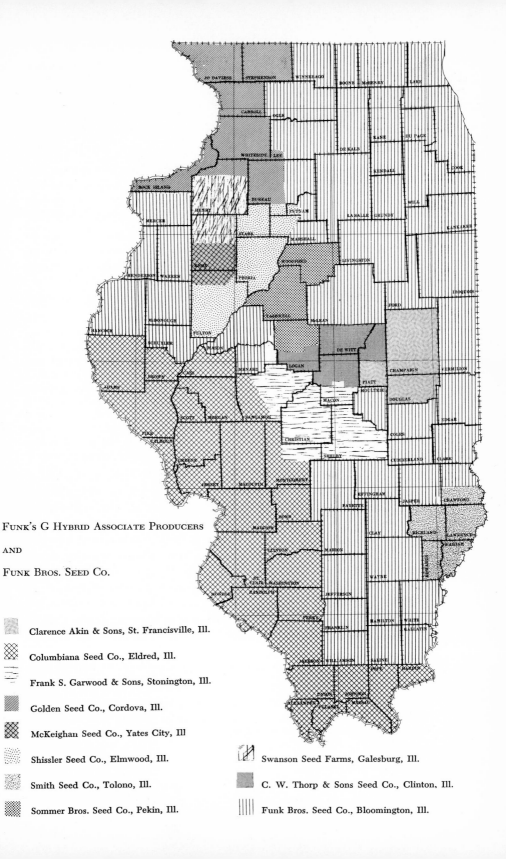

FUNK'S G HYBRID ASSOCIATE PRODUCERS

AND

FUNK BROS. SEED CO.

Clarence Akin & Sons, St. Francisville, Ill.

Columbiana Seed Co., Eldred, Ill.

Frank S. Garwood & Sons, Stonington, Ill.

Golden Seed Co., Cordova, Ill.

McKeighan Seed Co., Yates City, Ill

Shissler Seed Co., Elmwood, Ill.

Smith Seed Co., Tolono, Ill.

Sommer Bros. Seed Co., Pekin, Ill.

Swanson Seed Farms, Galesburg, Ill.

C. W. Thorp & Sons Seed Co., Clinton, Ill.

Funk Bros. Seed Co., Bloomington, Ill.

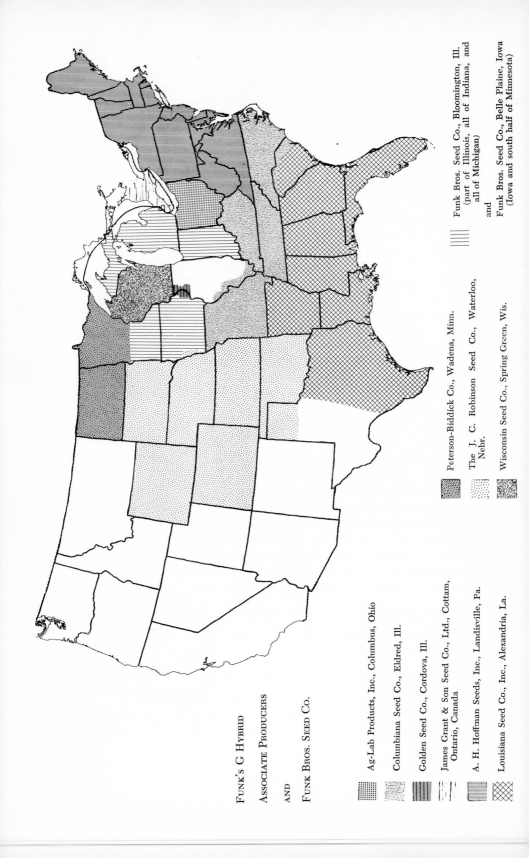

FUNK'S G HYBRID

ASSOCIATE PRODUCERS

AND

FUNK BROS. SEED CO.

Ag-Lab Products, Inc., Columbus, Ohio

Columbiana Seed Co., Eldred, Ill.

Golden Seed Co., Cordova, Ill.

James Grant & Son Seed Co., Ltd., Cottam, Ontario, Canada

A. H. Hoffman Seeds, Inc., Landisville, Pa.

Louisiana Seed Co., Inc., Alexandria, La.

Peterson–Biddick Co., Wadena, Minn.

The J. C. Robinson Seed Co., Waterloo, Nebr.

Wisconsin Seed Co., Spring Green, Wis.

Funk Bros. Seed Co., Bloomington, Ill. (part of Illinois, all of Indiana, and all of Michigan)

and

Funk Bros. Seed Co., Belle Plaine, Iowa (Iowa and south half of Minnesota) still in the business, and we have bought out two of our competitors at their request. If we don't stay in the lead, we have no business being there at all. . . . We are told and I agree, that we have to sell all our corn except the last ten per cent or we don't make any money. I am willing to take that licking and let the ten per cent . . . They'll say there must be something the matter or else they wouldn't have to lower the price. If we can't drill into our salesmen that our corn is better than our competitors, then it is our fault. We must convince our salesmen. We know we have a better product than our competitors and we know it's worth the price we are asking.[29]

Eugene D., Sr. recognized the pressing world problems confronting the United States in 1940. He had learned of the undercover work in the country during his winter months in Florida. He believed that conditions would be the same as in the First World War and that "people will be called upon for greater and greater sacrifices for the sake of the preservation of our ideals." [30]

Funk remained in the South during the April meeting of 1941 where he continued to test new inbreds in an effort to discover those adaptable in Florida. With this winter program, a year or more could be gained in the testing program. Eugene, Jr. referred to the bugs and the hard rains as obstacles in Florida and then paid tribute to his father's untiring efforts:

Through it all he is sticking to the task, with his characteristic determination to overcome all obstacles . . . I think that is one of his greatest traits and I think that is one of the fine things about this whole organization. You have the ability to stick with the problems and see them through.[31]

E. D. Funk, Sr. had formulated his own review of the situation for the December meeting of Associates in 1941 after five years of Associate Producer activity. He observed that if a company existed for five years, chances for continued survival were good. World War II provided a serious responsibility and challenge with politics fading into the background: "We are all soldiers and ready to do our part." He contrasted these days with those of World War I saying:

The open pollinated days are gone and now the farmers are depending on hybrid corn growers accordingly, and these farmers are depending on we fellows who are producing this hybrid corn. It is a serious matter. We have something to furnish and we must furnish it. It may possibly be more serious before we get through with the real settling of this war because if the farmer cannot get the grain to produce the food—why anybody can answer that question. Food will win the war and then when the last war was over we had to furnish food for other nations for several years.

Funk supported the idea that food is a whole arsenal of weapons in the struggle for human freedom; the driving force behind production and the performance of workers and armed forces. The national interest and humanitarian ideas challenged the performance of the task in a way that would write history.[32]

Another idea was close to the heart of Eugene D. Funk, Sr. in 1941. He expressed it clearly and forcefully as follows:

> Now there is one thing more I want to say. My observation as the years have gone by is this—I have noticed that companies have started out and many of them have grown rapidly like we have and many of them have gotten the idea that they want to be the largest and biggest and have striven for that. Then there comes a time when a little reaction takes place and it is much easier to go down here than to go up . . . Let's always strive to give the best that we can in quality and service for we can never attain perfection but remember . . . We can get too big.[33]

During the December meeting in 1941, James Holbert called for a written summary from the Associates on the outstanding accomplishments during the past five years and the important objectives to strive for in the future. These comments were distributed at the meeting. The report included photographs of some 25 new inbred strains developed by Dr. Holbert during these five years. Some of these formed the basis for outstanding new "G" Hybrids.[34]

The spirit of the Associates was expressed in 1941 by Claire Golden when he said, "Unlike some companies, the Funk Bros. Growers feel that they have a very real and important part to play as a member of the organization." Golden was pleased with the first five years. He advised pledging resources to National Defense, continuing with the same pattern with a few changes for the next five years. He advocated a meeting only for the executives of the Associates, who would pay their own expenses.[35] Clarence Akin offered some suggestions for resistance factors in corn for his particular area.[36] Virgil Givens and Vaughn Dunbar pointed to the fact that Funks "G" Hybrids won the 10-acre yield test for five consecutive years. "Rusty" Laible knew his "G's" well enough to add the description of their weaknesses and strengths in the territory he managed from the Bloomington office. Through the eyes of Lewis Falck of the Belle Plaine, Iowa staff, one could easily understand the analysis of use of certain hybrids as related to certain areas. I. W. Hepperly of J. C. Robinson Seed Company was of the opinion that much had been learned. Under "Production" he listed growing conditions, acreages demanded, detasseling, adjustment of parent stocks relative to pollination dates, harvest, grading and storage; Under "Sales" he listed block system, advertising; Under "Research," better seed and better hybrids.[37] R. D. Herrington, also of J. C. Robinson, commented on the formation of the Associate Group as the outstanding accomplishment. He said: "The name 'Funk' has for generation after generation meant quality in the seed industry and has been looked up to. We should all strive to maintain this reputation." [38]

The Memorandum of Understanding and Franchise Agreement between Funk Bros. Seed Co. and the Associate Producer provides that the latter will produce Funks G Hybrid Seed Corn exclusively from foundation seed supplied by the Company. The Associate agrees to advertise only Funk's G Hybrids as part of the nationwide franchise agreement. Acreage for production from the foundation seed for each year as well as hybrid combinations to be grown are mutually agreed upon by the Company and the Associate. Foundation seed continues to be the property of the company at all times. Inspection of production fields of Associates and of the growers for the Associates to determine proper isolation, detasseling, harvesting and final grading are supervised by the Company, whose judgment is final in terms of what constitutes proper handling. The judgment of the company is also final regarding the disposition of the crop. The company further agrees to maintain a competent corn breeding staff to produce a comprehensive research program for mutual benefit.

(a) The isolation of new inbred selections with superior performance values in hybrid combinations.

(b) The determination of areas in which specific Funk's G Hybrids will be of most value to the customer thru adequate performance tests.

(c) The maintenance of adequate and pure seed stocks of nursery or desirable inbreds and single crosses.[39]

One of the agencies of the Associate Producer and of the Company is known as Funk's G Hybrid Sales, Promotion and Advertising Committee. This committee supervises a fund used for the following purposes: to buy national magazine advertising; to finance radio programming; to produce motion pictures; for production cost of sales pieces; for display of material to strengthen overall Funks G Hybrid sales promotion and advertising program not readily obtainable by any individual associate. This interesting arrangement provides that the fund and the authority for its expenditure shall be vested in a committee known as the Information Committee appointed during June of each year, composed of two members representing the Company and not less than seven members representing and selected from the various Associates with no more than one member from each Associate.[40]

This overall program does not relieve the Associate from responsibility for his own specific advertising. Associates agree to conform to territorial division lines (see map). They will produce or offer for sale only such hybrid seed corn as is produced from Funks Hybrid Seed Corn as long as agreement is in effect. Associate agrees to compensate the Company for foundation seed, research and for other services rendered by a descending scale of charges on total volume of gross sales.

Corn grown for seed purposes is produced under a "Growers Contract" between the individual farmer and the Company providing that the Company will furnish the pollinator and seed parent for planting. The farmer agrees to prepare ground and to plant the seed under instructions furnished by the Company. He is under obligation to provide highly productive ground. Both parties to the agreement have the intention of producing good yield of high quality seed corn. The corn grown is at all times the property of the Company. Detasseling of the ear parent rows is controlled by the Company either under contract or by hired personnel. At the time of the harvest a crew to sort the seed corn operates in the field. Discarded ears unsuitable for seed go to the farmer as feed or for commercial purposes. Associate Producers operate under a similar program with their growers.

The procedures followed to implement Funks nationwide research and sales program include the major steps of (1) Research, (2) Advertising, (3) Delivery and (4) Sales.[41] The research program designed under the Five Stars had as its goal the production of hybrid corn possessing wide tolerance under varying conditions. Of especial interest to any commercial organization is the attitude of the farmer toward the product. Weather conditions may also affect the entire program. The farmer's needs in buying hybrid seed corn determine the kind and amount purchased. Is he especially interested in livestock? Is he a straight grain farmer or a dairy farmer? Cattle farmers may or may not demand silage corn. Hog men may demand early corn to "hog off." Resistance to early cold, wet soil may be a necessary ingredient in the Hybrid. Research programs for commercial seed producers include many aspects of these problems. The emphasis on the Five Stars also included research for higher oil content.[42]

The research program in hybrid corn is geared to the needs and requests of Funk Associates throughout the world. It includes opportunities to exchange ideas and information leading to the expansion of the entire program. Demands of Associate Producers will be somewhat controlled by his sales for the past year and by goals for the present. Production of sufficient foundation seed for the needs of these Producers becomes the great challenge in the Hybrid Corn Division. Expansion of the winter program located in Florida enabled Funks and other hybrid corn producers to develop new germ plasm for foundation seed that has proven desirable. Use of the southern proving ground indicated that year-around production of foundation seed on a 5 to 10 acre plot was highly advantageous. One of the greatest hazards, frost, continues to interfere with southern production.[43]

An extensive advertising program included the media of farm magazines such as *Successful Farming, Farm Journal, Prairie Farmer, Progressive Farmer,* radio and television. The well-known voice of Everett Mitchell has brought the introductory sentence, "It's a beautiful day in Bloomington," for many years into farm homes throughout the United States. Since 1938, the advertising agency of E. H. Brown in Chicago has handled the Funk account. Joe Bumgarner and L. H. Harvey were first in charge, followed by Richard Crabb, who was long effectively associated with James R. Holbert. At the present writing the agricultural department of the Brown agency is under the supervision of James Roe and George Johnson, who carry on the Funk's G Hybrid sales promotion program. R. J. Laible coordinates the development for Funk Bros. and Associates.

Road signs and dealer signs utilizing the Funk's "G" emblem and mats for local newspaper advertisements are also employed. Two motion pictures produced by Funk's organization have won wide attention and praise, *Research Acres* and *The Great Story of Corn.* They have been shown before farm dealers, school groups, agricultural classes, G. I. educational groups, Rotary, Kiwanis and Exchange clubs. These pictures have both historical and educational value. They have become permanent acquisitions of many university libraries. Funk Bros. have been highly complimented for these productions. Funk Bros. continue to support educational programs among them, the awarding of the Holbert Medal to a student each year at Illinois State Normal University who shows competence in the study of the corn plant.

During the spring, delivery of the hybrid corn seed is largely undertaken by truck because less handling is required and more direct routes to consumers can be followed. This is especially true to smaller distribution points. In addition to the main storage supplies at the home plant, warehouses are located strategically for purposes of supply and delivery. Storage and processing plants are in Bloomington-Normal, Mason City, Illinois and Rockville, Indiana, Belle Plaine and Traer, Iowa, facilitating prompt and efficient distribution through the central Corn Belt. Other distribution points will be found where Associate Producers are located.[44]

A new sales program usually begins in early summer of every year with a price announcement, usually in August, for the following season. Educational meetings for dealers are often held at Research Center in Bloomington. Here spokesmen for the Funk Bros. activities inform dealers and farm agents what the company has to sell for the next year. New hybrids are discussed and presented in demonstration plots to farmers and dealers. After the dealer sees Research Acres he believes and sells with greater assurance. The educational program centers around activity at Research Center and Research Acres in Bloomington, Illinois, and similar activities are carried forward in Iowa. Supervisors are informed here and they in turn carry information to dealers in their localities. A highly developed dealer training plan for the use of store and aisle displays, banner displays, with corn data notebooks and guides together with selling approaches are also a part of this program. Approximately 80 percent of the hybrid corn for spring planting is sold by January 1st. This includes bookings to dealers, agents and farmer customers.

On December 5, 1946 the Hybrid Corn Section of the American Seed Trade Association held its first meeting in Chicago. James R. Holbert of Funk Bros., who initiated the idea, was the first chairman of this group and W. L. Burlison of the University of Illinois was the program chairman of the educational meeting. Mutual problems were under consideration by members of the hybrid seed industry together with research workers from agricultural experiment stations and from the United States Department of Agriculture. Representatives of top management and industrial research staffs from organizations which were large users of corn, including wet processors, feed manufacturers and cereal mills, were included in the discussion groups. The purpose was to give opportunity for the discussion and exchange of ideas and to study new approaches. The papers were limited to one problem, *Corn Quality*. It was evident that solutions for individual problems could only be secured through the cooperation of others.[45] It was hoped that the papers and discussions would challenge both industrial and institutional research then under way.

The Hybrid Seed Corn Division of the American Seed Trade Association heard some interesting statements relative to the general development of the seed business in June 1947. James R. Holbert acted as chairman of this group. He introduced Everett Mitchell who in turn introduced a number of persons. W. A. Roberts, ex-vice president of Allis-Chalmers made a plea for understanding the problems of world trade. He believed if they would learn to trade with the rest of the world and secure a sound and stable agricultural prosperity there would be no need for subsidies. J. D. Sayre of the United States Department of Agriculture spoke on "Satisfactory Storage Conditions for Maintaining High Seed Values in Carry Over Seed Corn." George H. Dungan of the Agronomy Department of the University of Illinois talked about "Yield Results from Seed Corn More than One Year Old." Mr. Dungan reported that information based on trials at the University of Illinois indicated that year-old seed corn may be as good or even better than new crop seed. The tests were conducted first on open pollinated corn and later on various lots of hybrid seed corn.

At the same June meetings Arthur Page of Radio Station WLS broadcast a discussion panel including Fred Lehmann of Pioneer Hi-Bred Corn Co., Thomas Roberts of De Kalb, H. D. Hughes of Iowa State College and W. L. Burlison of the University of Illinois.

Dr. Burlison gave an excellent summary of how hybrid corn had changed farming practices:

1. Because of high yields less land needed to plant in corn thus permitting use of rotations including non-cultivated crops and legumes, making for better maintenance of soil fertility, and erosion control.
2. Because of good standing ability hybrid corn has speeded up use of mechanical equipment for harvesting. This has made farming more mechanized.
3. Because hybrid corn is able to make efficient use of available soil fertility, farmers are investing in and applying more commercial fertilizer than formerly.
4. Farmers now depend on hybrid seed corn companies for their seed corn.
5. Greater net income and therefore an increase in living standards.
6. Hybrid corn has permitted a heavier rate of planting than open pollinated corn, and this is a factor in increased yields.

7. Hybrid corn ripens uniformly permitting earlier harvest and fall plowing in many cases.

He then quoted Dean Rusk of the Department of Agriculture, University of Illinois, who in commenting on hybrid corn pointed out that average yields in Illinois before the introduction of adapted hybrid varieties exceeded forty bushels an acre only seven times in a period from 1866–1935. Whereas in the decade 1937–47 the average yield exceeded this amount every year. He added that with contributions to the wartime economy and the feeding of war-torn nations, "It is no exaggeration that the plant breeders of this country deserve to be classed among the molders of destiny."

Thomas Roberts of De Kalb stressed the responsibility of the industry to furnish and distribute to farm customers the best seed corn that could be produced. The Corn Belt had been pushed North, South, East and West by the discovery of earlier hybrids and those able to stand the rigors of southern and western climates. Soil fertility and proper cultural practices must be included in programs.

H. D. Hughes emphasized the greater dependability of the corn crop because of inbred strengths. Upon the dependability of the crop rests the whole livestock industry production program. Meat and milk and eggs depend upon the corn crop. Higher production meant lower costs to consumers. These results also represented advances in better care of seed, seed treatment and adapted varieties for given areas.

Fred Lehman of Pioneer looked to future problems which in many instances were continuations of older ones. The seed for newly developed hybrids adaptable to areas using open pollinates and the development of special oil and protein corns he believed would claim attention.[46]

The sixty-fifth annual convention of the American Seed Trade Association was held at French Lick, Indiana, June 23–26, 1948. James R. Holbert in his presidential address, "Planning For the Future," observed that in a period of rapid change when orderly living is difficult, one of the constant truths is:

Anything for permanent worth in life requires tremendous investment of human and material resources, together with coordination of these investments. First to inaugurate and establish it, and second, to maintain and preserve it.

He believed that the American Seed Trade industry and the Association existed "because enough persons were willing to invest sufficient human and material resources, to provide this important artery of strength for our agriculture and our nation." Realistically he added that no less important was the cost of maintaining the industry. The industry was called upon to invest again more human and material resources to keep the country strong. Problems of international co-operation involved many complications. Here he hoped for a gain on the part of the industry in stature and standability "by remembering that the goals of peace and human progress" are high goals also to be attained with a great investment of these same material and human resources. He asked that they apply the Christian approach for America, for living and for business.[47]

James Holbert wrote in 1948 that since the early days of the twentieth century hybrid corn had passed through the pilot plant stage. He declared that it had evolved into an industry affecting American agriculture "more than any single thing since the steel plow came to make possible the farming of the boundless prairies." This contribution to the American way of living like many other great events crept unnoticed into the economy. Few persons realized what had happened."[48]

Holbert also noted that hybrid corn to the hundreds of thousands of American farmers who used it meant corn that stood up until the crop could be harvested: "If it doesn't, it is not a good hybrid by their standards of judgment and will not likely be used again." He also believed that hybrid corn helped to stabilize land values, and corn farming became less of a gamble. Crop rotations and better soil management practice also were made possible. Stabilization of livestock production increased because of added drouth, heat and insect resistance in hybrid corn. Confidence of farmers that their efforts would bring rewards in the face of adverse conditions came from the consistent performance of hybrid corn.[49]

At the third Hybrid Corn Division meeting held in December 1948, Earl Sieveking of Funk Bros. presented a paper on "Fertilizer and Tilth." [50] Here he called attention to the constantly declining organic matter in soil and stated that a fertility revolution was essential. Then he pointed out that as organic matter decreased, tilth and fertility decline and crop production shows ever deepening valleys in seasons of unfavorable weather. The 1947 and 1948 corn crops illustrated the point. A number of factors, including excess spring moisture in 1947, contributed to a very poor soil condition. Corn rooted shallow.[51]

"Progress in Corn Production" was the theme of the 1949 divisional meetings. Donald F. Jones commented that after 35 years experience with inbred corn, the outcome that surprised him the most was the failure to secure inbreds that are not more productive than in 1949. He added: "At the present time our best inbreds are less than half as productive as the original varieties from which they have been derived and most of them are only one-third or one-fourth as good in size, general vigor and yield of grain. . . . Inbreds having appreciably better yielding capacity and ability to withstand unfavorable growing conditions than ones we now have would be of inestimable value. How to produce such inbreds is a problem for future research." He noted that in the early development of hybrid corn much was said about the uniformity and constancy of inbred strains. It was now realized that there was no such thing as absolute fixity of type. He also explained cyto plasmic—sterile plant production.[52]

At this meeting Wheeler McMillen, editor in chief of *Farm Journal,* Philadelphia, Pennsylvania gave the main address entitled "Rainbows in the Cornfields." He declared that at one foot of the rainbow in the cornfield a yield of 300 bushels an acre awaits the man who gets there first. At the rainbow's other foot there awaits, for those who acquire the requisite knowledge to reach that point, vast new markets to consume more profitable yields of corn." [53] The prediction of 300 bushels to the acre became a reality with Funk's G in 1955 (see above, Lamar Ratliff).

Succeeding meetings of the Hybrid Corn Division were equally significant in emphasizing the problems facing the industry and the new advancements in improving the product. The general theme of the meetings held in 1950 was *Improved Techniques in Hybrid Seed Corn Production,* presented in three parts: (1) Detasseling and Chemical Control of Pollen; (2) Breeding for Disease Resistance in Corn; (3) European Corn Borer in 1950.[54] Major areas of discussion in 1951 were directed toward the following: (1) Elimination of Detasseling by Genetic Means; (2) Efficient Methods of Developing and Improving Inbred Lines; (3) Reduced Costs Through Higher Yields of Corn.[55] John McGovern spoke on "The Importance of Research to the Nation's Food Supply and American Agriculture."

The report in 1953 centered on the use of male-sterile stocks in the production of corn hybrids under: (1) Improved Techniques in Corn Breeding; (2) Development in Storage and Production; (3) Future Potentials for Corn Production.[56] During this meeting James R. Holbert acted as moderator for a panel discussion under Part II on "Control of Insects in Storage of Hybrid Corn." [57] Donald F.

Jones presented a "Progress Report on Male Sterility" under Part 1 of the 1953 meeting entitled "Breeding Research." Part II dealt with "Research in Utilization and Production." Lewis Falck of Funk Bros. discussed "Planter Problems in this Section." Part III dealt with "Factors Affecting Stands." [58]

Continuing emphasis on many of the subjects troubling the industry in the twenties can be recognized in many of the papers of the 1954 sessions. Problems receiving constant attention were Heat and Drought damage; Breeding for Drought and Heat Tolerance; Breeding for Resistance to Stalk Rot; Resistance to the European Corn Borer and to the Ear Worm, as well as Breeding for Pollen Restorers. The speech of Michael Chinigo of International News Service dealt with "Agriculture in the World's Future." [59]

Papers of interest were presented in the 1955 meetings were Evaluating Hybrids in the South; Wide Row Planting; Ridge Planting; Picker Performance; New Developments in Insect Control; in Chemical Weed Control; Field Trials of Irrigation for Corn, and Modern Irrigation Equipment. A challenging and interesting address was presented by Henry A. Wallace under the title, "Public and Private Contributions to Hybrid Corn." He believed that the contributions of state and federal corn breeders were of necessity different from those of private corn breeders. [60]

These programs crystallized and analyzed the problems of the industry and brought to the attention of participants the direction for the future. Funk Bros. Seed Co. has stayed abreast of the times. It contributed leadership both in the original idea of organization and in the continuation of this highly important branch of the American Seed Trade Association. Their extensive research program enabled them to apply the lessons of the times. Evidence of this fact is the constant work carried on at the well-known Funk Research Center and Research Acres.

Recognizing the highly competitive status of the hybrid seed corn business, Funks like other companies placed considerable emphasis upon dealer meetings in the spring or summer, as well as at the mid-winter conference in January, to enable the representatives of the Funk organization to attain coordination otherwise lost. One of the most significant mid-winter conferences was held in Bloomington, Illinois, February 1, 1950. At this meeting James Holbert in his capacity of general manager for the parent unit in the Funks G Hybrid organization pointed the way forward for the Golden Decade. In his dual role of director of research and manager, he pointed to five achievements in the 1940–50 period, as the basis for expanded operations in the Golden Decade 1950–60:

1. The Funk organization was sufficiently effective that it earned the right to supply about ten per cent of the hybrid seed corn used by American and Canadian farmers.

2. Funk Bros. were able to continue Funk's G Hybrid research work on aggressive basis right through the critical manpower shortages imposed by the war years. Hybrid corn research being what it was, the value of this achievement was only now beginning to come to light. Holbert said, "We are now (1950) in the strongest position ever—with new, different and valuable germ plasm as a basis for new, different and better Funks G Hybrids than ever before."

3. During the decade the Funk organization earned independence from the publicly supported hybrid corn breeding programs. . . . Funks G Hybrid development would go forward without the slightest interruption even if tomorrow all publicly supported corn breeding programs ceased to exist. Holbert added, "However, we shall continue to follow closely all Research work of publicly supported institutions."

4. "I regard as the most important development of the last decade the rising consciousness throughout our organization of the need to employ in our sales program the same basic procedures that have proved so successful in the development of our Funks G Hybrids."

5. During the decade 1940–50 a highly trained personnel was developed in the hybrid organization enabling an expanded program for the Golden Decade to proceed more efficiently.

James Holbert added that progress during the decade 1940–50 allowed Funk Bros. to emerge as one of the leaders in the highly competitive hybrid corn industry. During this same decade more than 2,000 producers of hybrid corn competed for the market. Many observers recognized the effectiveness of Funk's research program. An effort to increase the efficiency of the sales program in the Golden Decade was the natural sequence. This comparatively new industry of hybrid corn was rapidly maturing, to the extent that the rules in competition for the market would probably crystallize during the all important decade 1950–60. As Holbert saw the picture, there were two important steps to be taken by Funk's in order to secure a larger percentage of the nationwide market and thereby remain a leader in the industry. First they must shape goals for growth and second they must attain their objectives as outlined year by year.[61]

James Holbert, who did as much if not more than any corn scientist to make possible the widespread use of hybrid corn, was the man responsible until 1957 for the direction of Funk's nationwide research. This undertaking was described as the "largest corn improvement program ever directed by one individual." Every year Holbert and his research staff traveled a quarter of a million miles, equal to ten trips around the earth, to keep in touch with their observers.[62] The Funk nationwide research organization became a well balanced group built over a period of fifty years. It was first led by Eugene D. Funk, Sr., and subsequently directed by producers across the United States and eventually in foreign countries.

Inside Research Center, erected on West Washington Street in Bloomington, there is located the best equipment and finest facilities for keeping records. There is a storing space for kernels of corn, holding the germ plasm necessary to produce new hybrids in the future. Cold chambers, chemical laboratory, and germinator serve the research, seed production, distribution and service men who work for Funk Bros. Seed Co. The germinator checks the growing power of every lot of corn grown and sold by the Funk organization. This new building was dedicated August 2, 1955.[63] James Holbert stated at this time that the work in the improvement of corn had just begun. He anticipated corn better adapted to new ways of farming; corn with greater capacity to resist hot weather hazards and more potent insect pests as well as more virulent diseases. He also foresaw hybrids capable of higher yields of quality corn to reward greater investments in soil improvements.

The story of the development of commercial hybrid corn cannot be written without Research Acres on the Funk Farms clearly in mind. During the 1890's Eugene D. Funk, Sr. fenced off an isolated five acre field in the large virgin prairie pasture, about 80 rods to the northeast of what is now the entrance-way to Research Acres. He devoted this piece of land to breeding corn during the early years of his experimental work. Here the ear to row method produced those corn families that in turn contributed some germ plasm for the original commercial open pollinations such as Funk's 329 and Funk's 176A. The latter proved to be a most valuable source for many inbreds.[64] About a quarter of a mile to the north and west of these acres were located

the corn breeding plots in which were developed by inbreeding (starting in 1916) and subsequent selection for disease and drouth resistance, the oldest inbreds, outside of those in Connecticut, that gained wide attention and use in the commercial hybrid corn program.[65]

As quotation from the motion picture, *Research Acres,* produced by Funk Bros. Seed Co. tells the story:

Rich in history are these acres; from their soil and the vision of the men who work it have come great milestones in corn improvement. . . . Yes, rich in history are these acres—but visitors come here and scientists work here, not for the past but for the future. The task of the corn breeder is to keep on endlessly improving the germ plasm of corn, for that continuous improvement holds the promise not only of better corn, but of a better life for the men who raise it, and for every member of the farm family in whose field there grows America's most ancient, widespread valuable crop.

Here the dream of Eugene D. Funk was born. Largely through his foresight and courage this cradle of research and experimentation was preserved and recognized by others as a mecca for corn scientists and geneticists from many states and foreign countries. According to Eugene D. Funk, Jr., his father did a remarkable job of improving corn in the open pollinated days. And from these strains or families came germ plasm that produced some of the best early inbreds developed by the first hybrid corn breeders.

The study of the corn plant, undertaken by Eugene D. Funk, Sr. in 1892, developed by 1958 into a commercial program of considerable proportions. Research Acres continued as the center of this activity on the Funk Farms in the middle of the twentieth century. Here educators, governmental representatives and practical farmers continue to find in these seventy-two acres the proof that scientific experiments are applicable in field production to improve corn and other farm crops.

A trip through Research Acres in July or in August with the American Flag floating high in the breeze above the sturdy wooden entrance-way to this historical center gives one a truly inspiring scene of "America the Beautiful." The deep green of the tall straight stalks of long leafed corn against the blue of the Illinois sky behind the protecting border of Osage orange trees planted in the mid-nineteenth century is a sight not soon to be forgotten. Here science illustrates its lessons well with the help of Mother Nature as the pages of books come alive.

The chief purpose of the Research Program devoted to the corn plant is to discover new and valuable germ plasm for new hybrid combinations. The visitor first receives a practical and valuable lesson in history showing the development of the corn plant by viewing the hard flint corn once used by the Indians to make corn meal. There is also a soft flour corn that produces a sticky type of meal for such products as tortillas. Sweet corn and popcorn also grown by the Indians may also be seen here.[66] Dent varieties were "apparently produced by mixing long-grained, soft dent strains from Mexico with flints from the northeastern part of the United States and then selecting until a fair degree of uniformity could be maintained." [67]

Significant accomplishments at Research Acres through the years have included three principal and continuous operations: (1) Production of new Funks G Hybrids of superior performance; (2) Demonstration of research achievements; (3) Testing different methods for growing corn; [68] (4) Trial and demonstration plots for other field crops.

The first of these activities centered upon efforts directed toward finding germ plasm to produce hybrids possessing resistance to disease, insects and drouth which also have the ability to grow rapidly and stand well. These are the qualities contributing to top yields and excellent quality for the farmer. Approximately fifteen acres are devoted each year to this corn work. The remainder of approximately sixty acres is devoted to field crops. Thus Research Acres became the hub of the Funk Bros. research program. Similar work is carried on in Louisiana, southern Illinois and in Iowa.[69] Two other steps in the general research procedure are: (1) growing new hybrids in evaluation plots; and (2) producing limited quantities to be planted on a field scale by dealers and customers. These are the procedures ensuring consistent efforts to secure superiority in adapted areas.[70]

The second of the activities in the continuous operations at Research Acres in the corn section is found in the demonstration plots. Here thousands every year are attracted by the examples of the five basic types of corn; flint, flour, sweet, pop and dent mentioned above.[71] Beyond these interesting examples there is a live picture of how a hybrid is produced. Inbred A may have a good stiff stalk; Inbred B, a good root system; Inbred C is resistant to disease and insects, while Inbred D yields well. Combinations of these Inbreds will produce single crosses, AxB and CxD. Then there will follow an example of how single cross AxB will be planted in six rows as the parent plant, to be detasselled with two rows of single cross CxD as the pollinator plant in the production fields.[72]

A trip through the demonstration plot during the typical year 1956 portrayed corn from other lands. A Mexican variety from the Jala Valley was especially interesting because of its unusual height, often reaching 22 to 24 feet. Although this open pollinated variety will not ripen in the growing season of central Illinois it has some excellent qualities such as resistance to the southwestern corn borer. Research personnel are hopeful of producing germ plasm which will add this resistance to hybrids produced for growth in Kansas, Oklahoma and Texas. A variety from Brazil and an Argentine flint as well as an Italian open pollinate are also under study for possible contributions to better hybrids.

The visitor may be asked for a test of his own strength. Well anchored and poorly anchored plants provide good tests. There are some inbreds requiring 150 and 200 pounds to pull them out of the ground; others are easily removed. Those with the greatest resistance are bred into hybrid combinations.

Along the line of demonstration appears the contrast between corn with average and high sugar content. Average content is about 6 percent; high may be between 14 and 16 percent. High sugar content is desirable in ensilage corn.[73] Other contrasts to be found in these demonstration plots are open husked and tight husked hybrids. The former are especially well liked in northern Corn Belt areas, whereas the tight husks which help to protect the grain against the weevil are adapted for the south. There are also contrasts between single crosses that are resistant to leaf blight and those which are susceptible to it. Visitors are always interested in oddities in the corn. These examples include Midget Corn, Dwarf Corn, Pop Corn, Brachtic and Purple Corn.

The center block immediately to the right as one enters Research Acres is devoted to the growing of modern Funks G Hybrids planted on different planting dates, as May 9th, 19th and June 8th. Those who come may see exactly how the many hybrids actually look. They are placarded so that those adaptable for certain areas may be seen under actual growing conditions. The prospective seller, buyer, scientist and farmer as well as the ordinary citizens who seek to know the how, why and result in commercial hybrid corn, can see for themselves what science has contributed to the cornfield in recent years.

One of the most interesting developments in recent years is the male "cyto sterile process." It was thought at first that this method would save considerable in the cost of detasseling the cornfields. The work in the Research Department in producing and keeping the corn cyto sterile proved to be more expensive than detasseling the corn. However, the hybrid produced by cyto sterile corn when compared with a hybrid produced with a fertile tassel yielded more bushels per acre. This result naturally interested customers.[74]

The third activity at Research Acres is devoted to corn growing methods. For many years corn has been grown in forty to forty-two inch rows. Recent studies have been made at Research Acres com-

RESEARCH ACRES WITH MEMORIAL PLAQUES

paring yields and other performance features derived from various growing methods. These differences are of significance to farmers. These new methods include "wide row planting" of corn sixty to eighty inches apart to allow corn as a nurse crop for the establishment of seed legumes and grasses. Plant pollinations per acre, however, are the same as in forty inch rows. "Mulch or till" planting is possible with a machine which stirs the soil but does not turn it. Crop residue is kept on top to act as a cushion for rainfall. The procedure is simplified for planting the corn crop to a single operation. "Rough or wheel track planting" delays spring plowing until corn planting time. Immediately after plowing, the corn is planted in the wheel track of the tractor which pulls the planter. This idea has been accepted more frequently in the northern Corn Belt than elsewhere. "Back furrow planting" of two rows of corn on the back furrow was tried at Research Acres. Row spacings of forty-eighty—forty-eighty resulted. This method is now under additional study.[75]

Additional experiments and demonstrations are presented in alfalfa, soybeans, oats and wheat varieties.

To the right of the entrance to these Acres one may see appropriately mounted on a huge granite boulder from the Funk Farms a bronze plaque placed by the Corn Foundation of Michigan State University on August 2, 1955. The plaque admirably describes both the purposes and the contributions of the Funk family:

This tract of Prairie has been permanently set aside by the Funk Family for Agricultural Research. Here privately and publicly supported Corn Improvement work has been done continuously for more than fifty years which in terms of duration and contribution to Corn Farming is unique on this continent. Work done here has contributed notably to Bringing the Benefits of Hybrid Corn to Farmers in the United States, Canada and Europe.

This memorial at Research Acres was the second erected by the Corn Foundation. The dedication ceremonies were part of the midsummer meeting of Funk Hybrid Corn Organization held in Bloomington, Illinois 1955. Eugene D. Funk, Jr. in accepting this plaque for the Funk family said:

We pay honor to the past and yet have still greater things to do for the future. We must not fail to go forward and continue to build on the foundation of the past for the agricultural people of the United States and foreign countries.[76]

Three years later the Funk G Hybrid Organization added two commemorative plaques during their mid-summer meeting. One in honor of Eugene and Mrs. Eugene D. Funk, Sr., commemorated leadership in Agriculture, rural living and corn improvement. As Dr. Dungan remarked of Eugene Funk, "He traveled unblazed trails and plowed unmarked furrows. . . . As a young man I had the feeling that Mr. Funk could see through great spaces." Of Mrs. Funk he said, "She has a mother's love and an artist's heart, a prophet's insight, and an apostle's patience." Of James Holbert: "Dr. Jim was more than a scientist. He was a person of rare human qualities. . . . So on this day we leave these stones and plaques in grateful memory of these great benefactors of mankind." [77]

Thus the dream of Eugene D. Funk, Sr. materialized. His confidence in men, in land and in the dream despite hardships and failures finally succeeded even beyond his own hopes. There continue in the Funk family those who treasure the Heritage, who accept and acknowledge the responsibility inherent in their obligation to do something for mankind and who remember that they themselves are only tenants on the land.

CHAPTER XXIX

Tomorrow's Hybrids Today

INSPIRATION AND EXAMPLE for the crystallizing ideas of Eugene D. Funk, Sr. in 1890 came from his visit to western Europe, especially the Vilmorin Estate, in France. From these ideas came the significant contributions of the Funk lands in mid-western United States. Wide distribution of the Funk open pollinates through the world in Europe, Africa, Hawaii and Australia, occurred during the earlier years of the Funk corn program. With the advent of hybrid corn the hub of Research activity for the Funk system at Research Acres near Shirley, south of Bloomington, Illinois, almost in the center of the great Mississippi Valley, once again became a distributing point for seed corn throughout the world.

One of the earlier Funk Associate Growers, George Moffett, whose friendship with Eugene D. Funk, Sr. resulted from his acquaintanceship with H. G. Atwood of American Milling Co. during the twenties, remembered well the performance of the Funk corn. He became one of the Associates at Blakeford Farms in Maryland, because of his great interest in corn and all of its products. During the time that James Holbert was manager of Funk Bros. he also came to know the Moffetts through introduction by Mr. Funk. Holbert and Gene Funk, Jr. on occasions attended meetings with Gene Sr. and George Moffett when mutual problems were discussed. George Moffett was one of the guiding leaders in the development of Corn Products Company.[1]

During the decade of the nineteen thirties, possibilities for the growth of a program in foreign countries were considered on several occasions by these men. Some of these conferences were held in Bloomington, Illinois, some in the New York office of Corn Products Company and some at Blakeford Farms in Maryland. They discussed the possibilities of development in the Argentine and Italy. After the Second World War the conversations were resumed. Upon the death of Mr. George Moffett in December 1951, Jim Moffett resumed responsibilities at Blakeford Farms. These operations were eventually discontinued.[2] However, Jim Moffett continued to keep in close

431

touch with Funk Bros. because of Corn Products Company's expanding activities. Open pollinated corn, however, did not produce a sufficient supply of corn. By 1950, when Europe was cut off from the agricultural areas of the Ukraine by the Iron Curtain, it was necessary for Italy to import corn.[3]

As early as 1947 in the post-war years, the Funks were well informed regarding favorable and unfavorable conditions for hybrid corn in western and southern Europe as well as in northern Africa. Earl Sieveking traveled in these countries and submitted a penetrating and descriptive report to the executives of Funk Bros. His observations proved to be accurate and dependable.[4] The ground work was laid for further possible developments.

Discussions with the Moffetts occurred again in the fall of 1949. Dr. James Holbert reported after consultation in New York in February of 1949 a proposed program whereby Funk Bros. would furnish foundation seed for limited production, also testing material and one man in Italy during the year. Corn Products would in turn pay the costs involved. These arrangements were made through James Moffett, president of Corn Products International, and through Robert Blattner in charge of foreign operations for Corn Products in Europe. Considerable time was spent by Funk Bros. for selection of the supervisor for their part in this project. A McLean County boy, Wayne Runge, was the final choice. His qualifications for the position included a good farm background, well-grounded knowledge of corn research, practical experience in development of hybrids and an ability to understand and communicate with people.

A revolution was beginning in the coarse red soils of the fields along the Appian Way. American boys who landed on the Anzio beachheads remember the small town of Littoria. As the *St. Louis Post Dispatch* pointed out in 1929, "bigger changes than a switch in names are happening here." Two energetic American men, Ralph German, a 39-year-old redhead from Fairview, Kansas, and his boss, Harry McClelland of San Francisco, a vice president of the Bank of America, were confident that they could save Italy from poverty with hybrid corn. McClelland at the time was at the head of the agricultural section of the Economic Co-operation Administration mission in Rome. These men believed that hybrid corn in Italy and in other parts of Europe would be a spectacular contribution. Mindful of the fact that hybrid corn had revolutionized farming and cattle raising in the middlewestern part of the United States, they expected a similar development in Europe. They were aware that the corn was needed not only for cattle and poultry but also for human food. Polenta, a mush made from corn meal is used throughout Italy, especially in the northern sections.[5]

With several varieties of hybrids including G-114, German and McClelland undertook to show farmers of the Agro Pontino that peasants could increase yields from 25 to 40 percent. The Italian economy was more dependent on agriculture than in some other western European nations. But after the war, the country as a whole was in need of assistance. Nearly 60 billion lira from E. C. A. counterpart funds, money deposited, according to the *St. Louis Dispatch,* by the Italian government in the Bank of Italy equivalent to direct American aid, were earmarked for agricultural improvements. The sum came to nearly $100,000,000. German estimated that the seed for the first tests in 1944, 1945 and the two succeeding years cost less than $300. Fifty tons of hybrid corn were bought in 1948, while in 1949 Italy imported 2,000 tons for $400,000.[6]

Clearly 1949 was the year for consideration of any expansion of the hybrid seed corn business into Italy. The choice of Wayne Runge as the Funk-Corn Products representative, placed a McLean County, Illinois, boy in the front lines of hybrid corn advancing into Europe.

Earl Sieveking noted in 1947 that rainfall, irrigation and distribution dictated agricultural practices in Italy. Rainfall ceased about the first of April and started again about the first of November. This same situation was reflected across southern Europe. There is a long season without frost. Irrigated areas were limited but farmed intensively. A dry summer would limit production mostly to fall seeded crops. Farming practices were often comparable to truck farming in the United States. Population pressures also created definite problems in this country with an area double that of Illinois.[7] Sieveking's instructions to Runge were wise and indicative of his deep understanding of the problems involved. He urged Runge to spend time studying the farms, the soils and the people. The Funk program would try to meet existing conditions as to crop rotation, fertilizer practices, planting methods and rates as well as cultivation and harvesting.[8]

Wayne Runge's appointment carried with it a real challenge. Those who have traveled in Italy or who have remained on the continent understand what adjustments were necessary for the young man from central Illinois. He discovered that certain agricultural customs must be carefully considered in making reports. He learned that Italians weigh their corn to estimate yield only after it has been shelled.[9] Many Italian farmers were enthusiastic about American hybrids in general. Some, however, became discouraged because they had previously received varieties not adapted to their needs. Runge observed after arriving in Italy what many farmers also learned—that many of the hybrids were distributed on a kind of "hit and miss" system "with no trials or tests of any kind." As a consequence it became necessary to build farmer confidence in order to win back those who received unadapted hybrids.[10] The Funk-Italian company proceeded with the usual testing program to determine best adapted hybrids for Italy.

The test year for Funk Bros. in Italy proved successful enough to result in a formal agreement between Corn Products and Funk Bros. to establish Compagnia Ibridi Mais with the main office located in Milan, Italy.[11] Activities centered in the province of Cremona near the Po Valley, with the plant located at Soresina.

The first year for Funk was largely experimental. Funk Bros. under the guidance of the renowned corn breeder, James Holbert, and with the able assistance of soils expert Earl Sieveking, supported by the financial judgement of Eugene D. Funk, Jr. and Elias W. Rolley, were unwilling to move too quickly until they were certain that their hybrids would bring real value to the Italian farmer. The same caution and care was always exercised by the Funk management when it moved into new sections. Again adequate study of the performance by Funk's G's would bring desired results in given geographical areas. Italian farmers responded quickly when they saw the increased yields without increased acreages. The Italian Government also was interested in reducing imports.[12] Where open pollinates had averaged production of about 80 bushels, by 1957 one hundred bushels per acre was common and there were numerous instances of 150 bushels per acre of Funks G Hybrid. Italian farmers learned well to apply fertilizers and to irrigate their land.

Runge found that labor was plentiful and comparably cheap. Italian Government requires male labor to be used on farms, varying from area to area and ranging from one man for each seven or eight acres to 70 man hours per hectare or almost 30 man hours per acre, according to Dr. Earl Sieveking.

The operations of Compagnia Ibridi Mais increased appreciably after the production of 1,200 bushels of seed corn in 1949. Increased attention was given to sales policies. The amount produced in 1955–56 was over 100,000 bushels of Funks G Hybrid corn. Processes are similar to those employed in the United States, except for more dependence on hand labor. One chief difference in processing is the fact that corn was shelled and dried in place of drying corn in the ear as in the United States. Farming is done on smaller acreages, with fields consisting of 5, 10 or 15 acres.[13]

Any examination of the political complexion of Italy after the Second World War would reveal its significance. Perhaps it is not too much to suggest that the plant breeder and the commercial seed company combined to enable many farmers in Europe and especially in Italy to gain that sense of economic security so vital in the fight against the Utopian arguments of Communism. Hybrid corn proved that "standability" could also contribute in winning "cold wars."

The success of the Italian company encouraged Corn Products and Funk Bros. to establish a second European center of activity in Spain. The new plant was located at Borjas Blancas 1954–55 in an irrigated section of the province of Lerida. The corporation here is composed of Spanish interests as well as the American companies. Technical direction comes from the Italian company. Corn producing areas in Spain include Lerida, Zaragoza, Terragona and Huesca, Bilbao, in the area near the Bay of Biscay and Badajoy along the Portuguese border close to the Guadalquivir River in the province of Sevilla. Seed production increased from 2,000 bushels in 1954–55 to 12,000 in 1955–56. American competition is a little stronger here than in Italy.[14] The title of the Spanish Company is Maices Hibridos Y Semillas, (Mahissa).

The nationally and internationally recognized plant breeder, James Holbert, as general manager for Funks in charge of research in corn from 1937 to 57, observed during his European trip in 1954 that Funks had a real assignment in Italy. In Cremona, the heart of the Po Valley, land had been farmed for centuries. Adequate water for irrigation in this valley is provided from Alpine snows. Yields of 150 bushels of corn to the acre with Funk's G were described as commonplace by Holbert in 1954. One variety, G-77A, turned out an all time official high for Italy of 208 bushels plus per acre. Holbert said, "Pretty good, I thought, but not Professor Merli." Merli was connected with the Agricultural Extension Service in Cremona. He needed a hybrid that would do everything that G-77A did, but accomplish this result a week to ten days earlier. If this could be accomplished, Italian farmers could do a better job in getting corn off the land, to secure a better preparation of the seed bed for wheat.

With considerable pride James Holbert told Gene Funk, Jr. that Funk Bros. had a hybrid for that difficult assignment. Then came the question, "When can we have it?" Fortunately Dr. Holbert could answer, "Again we are in position to give our customers to-morrow's hybrids to-day. In Italy as in America, progressive agricultural leaders are not satisfied with to-day's best for to-morrow." As Wayne Runge said, "They want it yesterday."

Dr. Holbert also reported Jim Moffett as saying, "You may not realize it, but Compagnia Ibridi Mais is the largest hybrid corn company in the world outside the United States." Dr. Jim was enthusiastic and optimistic when he said, "In Europe as in America progress creates problems . . . with the fine organization that Mr. Blattner and Wayne have developed, I am confident that we can continue to give farmers here (Italy) tomorrow's hybrids to-day. Balanced Five Star performance pays off in Europe just as it does in America." [15]

Robert Blattner as the able director of European operations for Corn Products was instrumental in organizing the company. Dr. Holbert recognized that research work in Italy could also contribute to progress in America.

He was impressed by the reclaimed lands near the mouth of the Tiber River on the Mediterranean and in the areas below sea level north of Venice and Trieste. Another large area was located at the mouth of the Po River on the Adriatic Sea. He also believed that Spain was destined for great improvement in the future.[16]

A representative of Compagnia Ibridi Mais who spent several months during 1955 at the Bloomington office and Research Acres could say in 1956 that the results of the sales campaign in Italy were gratifying above the 100,000 bushel line. He was confident of future gains because of the excellent calibre of the research team, the improving sales service and the help of the Funk organization, as well as the leadership of Robert Blattner.[17] By means of a Christmas card with three golden ears of corn as a reminder of Funks G, Compagnia Ibridi Mais called immediate attention to the worldwide operations of the company organized so many years before through the foresight and constant determination of Eugene D. Funk, Sr.

Corn production in Mexico had interested the executives of Funk Bros. Seed Co. from the time of the Corn Association meetings in Omaha, when Senor Dominguez participated so effectively. Many years later Dr. Holbert made his first trip to Mexico where he with other leading corn experts in the United States contributed information and advice to the Corn Commission in that country.[18] Although Dr. Holbert's trips to Mexico were personal, his observations were naturally of great interest to the company. Representatives from the

Department of Agriculture in Mexico visited Funk Bros. Seed Co. in Bloomington to observe their hybrid corn program.

Funk Bros. were asked to help prepare the prospectus and blueprints for a corn plant to be built in Mexico.[19] Both LaFayette Funk and Howard Reeder visited the new plant to help supervise the installation of the machinery. Funk Bros. assisted in the purchase of nine carloads of this machinery for the construction of one of the largest hybrid seed corn plants in Mexico. This was another example of the contribution of time and "know how" by Funk Bros. Seed Co. in the interests of hemispheric good will.

Dr. Holbert's opinions were respected and his abilities as a plant breeder were held in high esteem wherever he traveled. His constant search for sources of germ plasm from any available spot on the globe, enabling him to produce better corn for man's constant needs, drove him forward with the enthusiasm of the dedicated scholar-scientist. Two years before his death he wrote, "I am literally made prayerful by the great things I have discovered in the last six months. I know great new discoveries are sure to come in the next six months." [20]

Representatives of Corn Products and of Funk Bros. Seed Co. decided upon a joint operation in Argentina during 1956. At first, as in Italy, the activities were only experimental. The plant of Corn Products is located at Baradero, and the main corn growing areas are near Buenos Aires, Cordoba and Santa Fe. Eugene D. Funk, Jr. observed after his trip to South America in 1954 that there were marvelous possibilities with plenty of problems in this country. The problems included the attitudes of the successive personnel officially conducting the government, the rainfall and that ever present "Mañana" spirit combined with not-so-modern farm equipment.[21] Wayne Runge, who had proved himself capable in the development of the operations in Italy and in Spain, was assigned, in cooperation with Frank Hall, director of Latin American operations for Corn Products, the responsibility for setting up experimental activities in Argentina.

When Runge arrived he realized that changes in the government program could be advantageous. Ever present poorly repaired farm machinery was always a hindrance. Poor facilities for transportation from agricultural sections also hampered the progress.[22] Recent efforts to transplant labor to the cities to strengthen labor unions, together with low prices for farm products, lessened desires of farmers to invest more capital in better seeds and in new implements. If hybrid corn could bring equality and increased yields, then the farmer could prosper. Again the educational program would take time. Funk Bros. delayed their expansion until they were certain that their hybrids were adapted to the area, again following the sound and cautious advice of Jim Holbert. Funks G hoped to contribute substantially to the welfare of Argentine farmers through their usual test demonstration plots and their adapted hybrids.

Arrangements were under way for planting, testing and observing Funk G Hybrids in Brazil during 1958 in order to better understand their agricultural practices and problems. This operation will also be in cooperation with Corn Products Company in Sao Paulo, Brazil. Representatives from Brazil first visited Funk Bros. in Bloomington, Illinois as early as 1934. Representatives from Funk Bros. visited Brazilian officials in 1954 and 1958 to observe governmental work. Close cooperation with their program was planned.[23]

The Funks G trademark is now registered in Italy, Holland, Belgium, Switzerland, Turkey, Egypt, France, Yugoslavia, West Germany, Portugal, Spain, Argentina, Uruguay and Brazil.[24]

Through the years, germ plasm from different countries has been available by exchange through various media. Funk Bros. have participated in this activity over a long period of years. Germ plasm from Italy, Mexico, Brazil, Venezuela and from many other countries on the face of the globe has become available for research and experimentation. Valuable and adapted inbreds for any corn growing section can only be produced after years of experimentation in crossing and development.[25] As Wayne Runge said, "The balanced Five-Star performance of Funks G knows no language barriers."

CHAPTER XXX

Funk Bros. Seed Company · 1944–1958

AGRICULTURAL LEADERSHIP lost one of its ablest representatives with the death of Eugene D. Funk, Sr. in 1944. As he sought throughout his lifetime to crystallize the ideas and purposes of those who had preceded him in his own family, he also left a continuing influence on those who followed him. From 1867 his life covered some of the most important decades in the development of the United States. After an active and interesting leadership within his own company, he became chairman of the board of directors during the last two years. Eugene Jr. became president of the company. He and his three brothers, with Dr. James Holbert continuing as general manager and vice president, formed the board of directors.

Gene Jr. possessed a likeable personality, with practical business ability and a kind of patience enabling him to ride waves of tribulation with an amazing tenacity. Some saw in him a combination of characteristics reminiscent of his great grandfather, Isaac, of his grandfather, LaFayette, and of his father, Eugene Sr. His brothers shared with him the responsibilities for major decisions but left day to day administrative guidance of the company to Gene Jr. LaFayette assumed more and more responsibility for the building program as the expansion of the nationwide research developed. Paul was responsible for the care of Mrs. Eugene Sr., and for the Florida and Homestead properties. Theodore continued to operate the farm with especial attention to livestock and crops. His responsibilities in livestock organizations and National Advisory groups created heavy demands upon his time.

During his lifetime Eugene D. Funk Sr., witnessed the gradual division and subdivision of his grandfather's original holding of land. As each succeeding generation received its share the individual farms became smaller. Not all of the descendants chose to live on the land. Some was sold and some was lost to the banks through mortgages and obligations assumed when the depression of the 1930's found some of the third generation continuing as stockholders in the banks. Eugene Duncan Funk Sr., and his brother DeLoss shared the estate

439

of their father LaFayette. With eight children Eugene recognized that division of his own land would produce small holdings. After considerable thought and planning he decided in 1941 to establish the Funk Farms Trust. His original idea of preserving the Funk lands through the cooperation of his own generation now found another application when he applied it for the benefit of his children. This Trust was established for his eight children and for their childrens' children with a life expectancy of seventy to eighty years depending upon the life span of the members listed as beneficiaries. The home of Eugene D. Funk with about 300 acres of land was left to his widow for life.

After the death of Eugene D. Funk, Sr., in 1944, the Funk Homestead Trust was established in 1946 to carry out the original thoughts of E. D. Funk. It included the homestead, Timber in the Grove and the Florida property. Both the Funk Farms Trust and the Homestead Trust are directed by four members of the family. Funk Farms Trust operates the farm land as a unit with a live stock program feeding 2000 to 3000 head of cattle and 1000 to 1500 sheep a year.

It is not unusual to see hundreds of black Angus or Herefords driven along the road in front of the E. D. Funk home toward the feeding areas. This program is efficiently operated by Theodore Funk who with his son Ted, his brother Paul or others of the Funk family may come riding along on one of the most interesting "short drives" in the cattle business.

The four sons of Eugene D. Funk seek to carry out his wishes by perpetuating his ideas and by adapting them to current needs and problems. They recognize his hope to provide a pattern of cooperation within his own family comparable to that he had initiated in 1901 among his cousins. The original land holding of Isaac has gradually been relinquished by descendants of the eight branches of the family until approximately one half remains. This situation has been almost inevitable as time and different interests have called the constantly increasing number of descendants to other activities. The family of Eugene D. Funk has held the land belonging to him from the estate of LaFayette and operates it according to the arrangements already explained.

Dr. James Holbert brought distinction and recognition to the company through his abilities as a scientist and his acknowledged contributions to the improvement of hybrid corn. As vice president, general manager and research director for the corn division, he combined the responsibilities of three positions in one. His research work won recognition through the established Funk organization and widely known name in the seed business. Thousands of dollars were at his disposal for research and experimentation. His success in turn contributed effectively to the growth and expansion of the hybrid corn division. Interdependence resulting from deep ties of mutual respect created a challenging combination of leadership within the company. Mrs. Eugene D. Funk, Sr. provided in the years after her husband's death a continuing inspiration for her four sons and for James Holbert, who held her in the highest esteem.

The four daughters of Eugene Sr., Gladys, Elizabeth, Ruth and Mary, also continue their interest in the company. They can be found in attendance at annual meetings or at other group activities held near Research Acres. Through banking, real estate, industrial and other agricultural pursuits their husbands have widened the range of family activities and contacts. The entire family supports actively their chosen church affiliations and community organizations.

Policies of Eugene, Sr. are continuously reflected. His sons are constantly aware of the necessity for adapting them to current needs, but the general philosophy is traceable as the company expands. The sudden death of James Holbert in 1957 at the height of his scientific career was a loss to the company, community and to the scientific world. Fortunately adjustments within the company could be made with little noticeable difficulty because of a continuing policy advocated by Eugene Funk, Sr., to have two men capable of filling every major position. Dr. Earl Sieveking became general manager of the hybrid corn division, R. J. Laible took over the responsibilities of vice president and director, and Leon Steele, son-in-law of Holbert, became director of hybrid corn research. Eugene Funk, Jr. combined with the presidency more supervision of overall operations. Delmar Walker was appointed assistant to the president and Calvin Rehtmeyer became assistant secretary to the board of directors.

Administrative personnel continued to include the same people who were for the most part with the company during the lifetime of E. D. Sr. Harold Goodwin remained in charge of the field seed division, Mac Convis supervised the soybean division, Elias Rolley continued as comptroller, until October 1958, when Paul Krueger was appointed to the position. Vaughn Dunbar was in charge of credit and collections. The traffic department was under the direction of Ernie Radley. Howard Reeder supervised plant operations. budget and insurance were under the supervision of A. A. Baker, while Howard Springer continued in charge of accounting. Wesley

Wilcox was responsible for the personnel department. The foundation seed operation was under the direction of Wright Hardin. Lewis Falck directed the Iowa Division and Ray Shoemaker was in charge at Rockville, Indiana. These experienced, loyal people have enabled Funk Bros. to continue their outstanding leadership.

Another policy followed by Eugene D. Funk, Sr. was to bring into the business those of succeeding generations if they showed interest in the company. This situation is apparent in the case of Calvin Rehtmeyer, youngest son of the oldest child, Gladys, of Eugene Funk, Sr. He was born in Normal, Illinois and later moved with his family to Pittsburgh, Pennsylvania. He spent many summers with his grandparents and learned how the company operated in the fields. His training at the University of Michigan as a chemical engineer was interrupted by two years with the Army Air Corps including 22 missions over Western Europe. Upon completion of his engineering course after the war, he worked for a year with E. I. DuPont de Nemours at Richmond, Virginia. When the new solvent soybean plant was placed in operation in Bloomington, he returned as chemist in the soybean division. Since that time he has also acquired office training where he has obtained a better overall understanding of financing and other operations. He recalled his grandfather, Eugene Sr., as a leader in basic or fundamental research who was often ahead of his contemporaries. He believed that he was a man of vision, determination and tenacity, with a definite desire to improve the lot of the human race through the betterment of agriculture.

Three other grandchildren also work for the company. Two sons of LaFayette, eldest son of Eugene Sr.—Richard and LaFayette III—have been employed after graduation from college. LaFayette or "Bud" Funk worked in the field laboratories during the summers of 1939, 1940 and 1941. After serving in the army he completed a B. S. degree in business management at the University of Colorado; worked as a salesman for Swift and Company in Denver, and returned to the Farms in 1953, where he worked with Theodore Funk at Funk Farms Trust. Since 1956 he has been manager of the Mason City plant of Funk Bros. Seed Co. His brother, Richard, began work with the company in 1948 in the foundation seed department, then worked with the production department and in the field seeds division, where he was employed in the office. He has also had experience with chemicals used for seed treatment and weed and insect destruction. Currently he is acquiring operational knowledge of the newly installed I. B. M. equipment.

Eugene Funk III or "Dunk," as he is called to distinguish him from his father and grandfather, has worked summers for the company in the hybrid corn nursery and in the warehouse following the same general preparation as his father. This type of training and participation on the part of the younger men has contributed to the respect of the employees for their continuing direction of the business.

As his grandfather and his father contributed both leadership and time to agricultural organizations and to community projects, so has Eugene Funk, Jr. participated in a long list of activities over a period of twenty-five years. During the thirties and forties he gave considerable time as director and president of the Bloomington Association of Commerce, director of the Soybean Processors Association and as president of the Illinois Seed Dealers Association. He also became a director and vice president of the Illinois State Chamber of Commerce, including chairmanship of the Agricultural Committee, president of Bloomington Rotary Club, director of the University of Illinois Foundation, a member of the Illinois State Normal University Foundation and Advisory Committee during the decade of the fifties. He added to these duties a directorship of the Chemurgic Council, director of the New Orleans and Great Northern, a subsidiary of the Gulf, Mobile and Ohio Railroad, director of the University of Illinois Alumni Association. He has also found time to be a director of the Funk's Grove Grain Company, director of the Bloomington Federal Savings and Loan Bank, director of the McLean County Historical Society, trustee of Second Presbyterian Church of Bloomington and director of the Western Avenue Community Center. Currently he is a director of the McLean County United Fund. Membership in Rotary and activities as a 32nd degree Mason also consume time. His contacts are many and varied as many trips to Chicago, St. Louis and Washington, D. C., Kansas City and South America testify. Often he has preferred to pass along the recognition in agricultural groups to personnel in the company. Yet his indirect guidance and his counsel are sought on many agricultural and governmental problems.

Participation of this type keeps channels of communication open enabling leadership to give generously of time and information as well as to keep alert to the lines of activity in the business world. Employees speak with pride of the recognition given their president. Management has approved participation in both agricultural and community organizations on the part of its personnel.

The idea of the family company stressed by Eugene Funk, Sr. has also been maintained wherever possible as the company has grown. Company parties include employee families. An acceptable employee benefit program including pension and retirement provisions is in operation. The same cooperative spirit is present in labor management relations. A union has existed since 1944 when a local of the then named American Federation of Grain Processors was organized at the plant among the employees of the field seeds and soybean divisions. Few year-round laborers except in the processing of soybeans were formerly employed because of the dependence on seasonal employees for almost all operations. With the advent of hybrid corn, more workers including research personnel were required. The first effective contract was negotiated with the presently named American Federation of Grain Millers International (A.F.L. & C.I.O.) with headquarters in Des Moines, Iowa. A new contract was written on a yearly basis until 1956, when a two year contract was negotiated. There have been some differences of opinion, but only three times in fourteen years has more than one meeting for contract discussions been necessary.

Employees for the most part have been consistently aware of steady employment based on a 48 hour week with base pay on a 40 hour week with time and one-half for all overtime. Employees recognize that the welfare of the company requires longer hours during different seasons of the year. Wet weather, early freezes and other climatic risks are beyond the control of management or any individual. Management agrees that a properly run Union contributes to any organization. Labor leadership at Funks respects management and recognizes the good standing of the company in the Seed business. Management in turn is proud of the fact that labor leadership from the local union is represented at their divisional meetings. Labor points to the fact that the local Union has brought fewer grievances before its divisional council than any other within that group. Mutual confidence seems to be the basis for this respect together with realization that they need each other to operate a successful economic enterprize. Awareness of this interdependence provides a more enlightened climate for continuing negotiations.

Management also recognizes the benefit of counsel with long time employees as plans for continued expansion crystallize. These people often emphasize the objectives and basic philosophies of Eugene Funk, Sr. Some 60 employees other than the family own stock. They believe that quality products, attention to integrity and a continued emphasis on these human qualities so often present in a family enter-

Staff and Directors, 1959

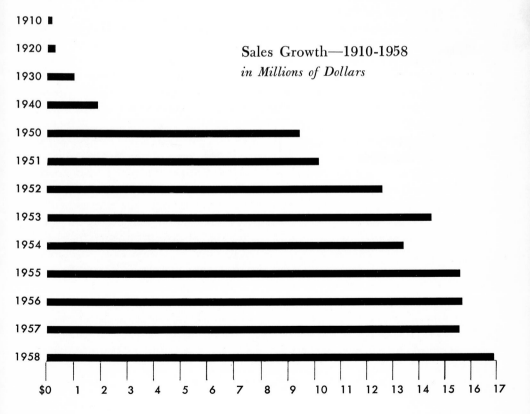

Sales Growth—1910-1958
in Millions of Dollars

1910
1920
1930
1940
1950
1951
1952
1953
1954
1955
1956
1957
1958

$0 1 2 3 4 5 6 7 8 9 10 11 12 13 14 15 16 17

prise produced the desired results. Common stock is closely held by the family. Preferred stocks are sold to the public. Indicative of a new policy of coordination introduced by Eugene Jr. in 1957 is the staff meeting preceding each regular meeting of the board of directors. Interdepartmental understanding has been increased by presentation of reports and by discussion of company problems. The Iowa Division is represented at these meetings. The results of these discussions are clear in the minds of the directors whose meetings follow.

Agricultural policy as a whole has long been of interest to the Funk family in the company, who also speak as farmers who have held the land originally left to their grandfather from the estate of Isaac. In this respect the family of Eugene D. Funk, Sr. and his brother, DeLoss, differ from some of the other Funk descendants. It is not an unusual sight to see all of the sons of Eugene Sr. if hands are needed working in the fields as they did when they were growing up on the farm. They can look at agricultural policies from the point of view of the seed business, the grain elevator and the farmer. They know that all operations are vital to them; there would be no advantage in overbalancing any interest.

There would be little opportunity to escape the ever present problem of the Surplus or as people in the seed business describe it "the increases." Recognition that adequate supply of food is one of the world's greatest needs is consistently part of the humanitarian ideal in increased production. The ultimate well being of the human race is a goal long sought by those who have hoped to raise the world standard of living. Management at Funk Bros. is fully aware that revolution and power concepts are often influenced by great groups of people who do not produce enough food. The concept of plenty is in its way a factor in the strength of democracy throughout the world.

For those who think only in terms of one years production, consumption and accumulation it often appears that increased emphases on sales programs, stirring sales talk stressing competitive records and efforts to hold the fair share of the market are exclusive. As management at Funks sees the sales effort, it is part of the larger picture. Often their answers to the surplus are these: What would you do if *one* adverse season occurred? What if disaster or sudden atomic war overtook this land? Is a six months or twelve months supply of grain an oversupply when civilian populations are targets in modern warfare and food supplies are munitions? These questions are difficult to answer despite the economic problems inherent in over-production for a given year.

Funk Bros. hope that controls will disappear with some reasonable return to supply and demand as important factors in determining prices. Even if readjustments would hurt temporarily they believe that the country would be better off as a result. On the other hand they believe that adjustments must be gradual and that as long as other groups like labor and factory type industries receive governmental subsidy of one kind or another agricultural incomes should not be the only ones sacrificed. In other words removal of supports without the crucifixion of agriculture is a desired goal.

But the Funks are practical men. They see in their research programs the efficiency of the corn plant to produce more bushels per acre on less land. They understand that less expense in production with newer farming methods for tilling the soil and with chemical treatment will also add to the efficiency of farm operations. Hybrid corn programs must of necessity be geared in the future to these patterns. They have seen the expansion of the corn belt in the United States and they recognize potential expansion in foreign countries. They are aware of possible growth of the field seed division in established localities where the Bloomington company operates. Continued evaluation of newer systems for distribution of all field seeds as in the case of alfalfa are underway. Emphasis will be continually placed on the extension of soybeans operations to capacity in order to keep a reasonable balance between the divisions within the company to insure continuity.

Thus the small organization incorporated in 1901 by Eugene D. Funk, Sr. and his cousins has succeeded beyond the hopes of its founders. This success was in no small part due to the fact that Eugene Sr. maintained abiding faith in his original ideas. The company in 1958 in all of its operations including Funks Hybrid Corn Associates' sales approximated $25,000,000.00. The accomplishment has been possible in highly competitive areas because of combinations of factors including the Funks themselves and their competent staff of experienced and highly trained personnel. Changes in crops, production areas and merchandising methods constantly occur. An understanding of national and world wide business and political conditions becomes increasingly necessary. Development of an adequate philosophical approach to current economic and operational problems imposes inescapable and complex responsibilities upon leadership in the mid-twentieth century.

Epilogue

THE WESTWARD MARCH of agrarian democracy under republican forms brought the frontiersman face to face with the problems of survival. Often fortified with the knowledge of seeds, he sought to adapt them to the lands he cleared and cultivated. Improvements in many plants dated almost from the discovery of America. As early as 1621 the Indian Massasoit was requested to exchange corn for seed with early settlers to obtain those best suited to their soil. From the Atlantic to the Pacific and the Lakes to the Gulf, the problem of adapting seeds to soil and climate provided continuing challenges to Seedsmen and Scientists.

Long unheralded for a major part in assuring the continuation of the American system, the Seedsman has contributed with vigilance, knowledge, skill, foresight and wisdom to the very lifeblood of Democracy, its food supply. Bountiful harvests are the result. The city dweller is deep in his debt. Without his accumulation of information and experience the land of plenty could become a mere will o' the wisp, discovered but never realized.

Eugene Duncan Funk walked across the fields of his forebears among men of vision who dared to dream a little. He possessed the courage to put ideas into action. His erect carriage and farseeing eyes glimpsed the to-morrow from the past as he lived effectively in the present. His continuing influence is reflected as other members of his family seek the humanitarian goal of a better life in a better world. He rests beneath a granite boulder from the Farms near many members of his family in Funk's Grove. As a tireless spokesman for the Betterment of Agriculture in his determination that the Funk lands become useful to the world, he himself became one of the Good Tenants On The Land. He possessed in abundance those qualities found in many men of his generation who helped the United States to become a great nation.

Appendix I

GEORGE W. FUNK lived at the old homestead until the death of his parents. As the oldest child of Isaac, born May 14, 1827, his early education was obtained in the school at Funk's Grove until he was about ten years old. Afterwards he attended only during the winters. He worked on the farms until he reached the age of twenty-one. The summer months were spent happily herding the cattle, plowing corn and wielding the cradle and scythe. For many years George was responsible for buying, selling and shipping stock for his father. From the age of eighteen to twenty-five he drove stock to market in Chicago. About the year 1854 he began to ship to New York by rail. By 1887 he held 4,400 acres of land in McLean County with 1600 of the total located in Funk's Grove Township. He owned Old Indian Town in West Township.[1]

Miss Susan Pumpelly became Mrs. George Funk in January, 1868. She was a native of Ohio who moved first to Kentucky and then to Illinois. After a short illness she died December 15, 1868 leaving an infant son, Isaac G. George's country home was located north of McLean, Illinois in the southwest corner of the original Funk land. Some years later in 1876 George married Miss Rosealtha Fitzwilliams of Bloomington, Illinois. They established a home in the city located at 401 E. Washington Street.[2]

George Funk became a member of the lower house of the Illinois Legislature in 1870. He attended the sessions faithfully during his term of office. He was also interested in banking in Atlanta, Lincoln, Springfield as well as in Bloomington.[3] During his lifetime he was close friend and counselor to his younger brothers. His experience in managing his father's business and his ability in dealing with farm problems was especially valuable. At his death, aged 84, he left an estate valued well over a million dollars.

Three children of the second marriage were Madeline (Mrs. William McCullough), William F. (died in infancy) and Julius. Isaac G. married Bessie Florence, a niece of the wife of LaFayette.

JACOB FUNK was born April 7, 1830. He also herded cattle on his father's farm during the summer months. At the age of 12 he was chosen to visit his Uncle Absalom in Chicago. There he herded sheep on land subsequently occupied by the old Pacific Hotel. He tired of the city after about ten months, returning to his father's farm. At the age of 14 he returned

[1]Chapman and Brothers, (eds.), *Portrait* and *Biographical Album of McLean County,* (Chicago: Chapman Bros. 1887), p. 1124.
[2]Gladys Funk, *Remembering* I, p. 19.
[3]Interview with Mrs. Madeline Funk McCullough, June, 1955.

to the city. After an illness while on a trip to Indiana he remained at Funk's Grove. His marriage to Miss Mary Waltman occurred November 18, 1858. Their home was located north of McLean, Illinois, a little to the north and east of his brother George. Jacob owned 2,600 acres of land in 1887.

At one time Jacob occupied a residence in Bloomington located on lower Front Street and Gridley, south of George's residence and one block from the home of A. B. on East Grove Street. The two older brothers were close neighbors in town and country.[4] During his later years Jacob remodeled the old residence of Judge Weldon at 407 East Grove.[5] His brick country home was described as "one of the most elegant in the Prairie State." [6] Mrs. Jacob Funk was a clever needlewoman whose quilts and aprons were exquisitely made. She loved to entertain with fresh linens for every meal.[7]

Jacob was a well-known banker in central Illinois. He continued for 36 years as President of the State National Bank of Bloomington. He became a Trustee on January 6, 1888, of the Citizens Gas Company when judgments against the company prompted transfer. This action appeared to improve a situation which four years later enabled a twenty-year lease of the Gridley works to carry heavy rentals.[8] Jacob and his son Deane were widely known as breeders of fine Angus livestock. Their cattle were often prizewinners at the Chicago International Livestock Shows.

Two sons lived nearby. The older, Charles A., was located a little to the east. Deane lived about two city blocks distant from the brick home in a low rambling frame home located on the site of the original house of Jacob. To the north of the beautifully landscaped grounds a large acreage of peonies was enjoyed by the many friends of Mrs. Deane Funk, who sold them commercially. Her love of beauty and her talent as a concert pianist endeared her to the family and the community. Clara, only daughter of Jacob, remained at home until her marriage to Howard Humphreys. They resided at the Oaks on East Grove.[9]

DUNCAN M. FUNK retained his part of the original holdings of his father located in the north central sections. He was born June 1, 1832. He also was educated at Funk's Grove and herded cattle for his father in his younger days. His marriage to Miss Elizabeth Richardson from Indiana occurred April 16, 1857. For seven years he was engaged in the dry goods business with Mr. William Temple of Bloomington.

He established a residence in a brick home located on the corner of Chestnut and East Streets in Bloomington, where the Mennonite Nurses' Home now stands. The deaths of Isaac and Cassandra Funk occurred in January, 1865 at the home of Duncan. After disposing of the interests in

[4]Interview with Mrs. Madeline Funk McCullough, January, 1954 and Arthur Funk, December 11, 1952.
[5]Interview with Mrs. Madeline Funk McCullough, June, 1955 and with Donald and Jacob Funk, Jr., June, 1955.
[6]Chapman Brothers, (eds.), *op. cit.*, pp. 281-282.
[7]Gladys Funk, *op. cit.*, p. 12.
[8]*Weekly Pantagraph*, Jan. 6, 1888.
[9]The Oaks was the original home of Asahel Gridley, a contemporary of Isaac Funk.

the dry goods business Duncan turned his attention to the raising of stock in 1873.[10]

During this same year he became president of the First National Bank in Bloomington. Later when the First and Third National Banks were consolidated, he was again chosen as president. During the years 1877–87 he was a trustee of the Sailors' and Soldiers' Home at Normal, Illinois. From 1874–87 he served as a supervisor from Bloomington Township. The rosters of membership in the House of Representatives for the State of Illinois carried the name of Duncan M. Funk during the 40th, 41st and 42nd sessions (1897, 1899 and 1901). During the Louisiana Purchase Exposition held at St. Louis in 1904, Duncan Funk was a member of the Illinois Commission. He also became a stockholder in the First National Bank of Shelbyville and director of the Bloomington Gas Company, as well as a director in the Walton Plow Works.[11]

Land held by Duncan M. in 1887 included 2,400 acres in Funk's Grove and Dale Townships, where he was primarily interested in breeding stock. A daughter, Isabelle or "Belle," became Mrs. H. M. Rollins, who lived for some years in St. Paul and in Chicago. She later became a resident of Bloomington. A son, Isaac L. or "Linc," remained at home for a number of years. His early married life was spent in Bloomington.

Duncan held a bank presidency for 39 years until his death in 1911. The long term bank presidencies held by Jacob and Duncan are probably records with few parallels in the history of banking in the State of Illinois.[12]

A continuing interest in agriculture prompted Duncan, while in the state legislature, to promote a measure providing that the appropriation made for the teaching of agriculture in the University of Illinois, should, in fact, be used for that purpose rather than diverted to other uses as in past years. His influence contributed to the prominence accorded to agriculture in the curriculum at the University.

LAFAYETTE FUNK (information regarding LaFayette Funk appears more in detail in the context of the story about his son, EUGENE) was born January 20, 1834. He also worked on his father's farms. He was the first of the sons of Isaac to graduate from college. He attended Ohio Wesleyan University at Delaware, Ohio, where he graduated from the Scientific Department. During his college years he was a charter member of Sigma Chi Fraternity. He increased the land received from his father's estate to about 2,200 acres. His land holdings were located in the northeastern corner of the original estate.

He was the one son of Isaac who lived consistently on the original land, never establishing a home in Bloomington. His life in the country, however, did not deter him from participating in local and state wide civic and agricultural responsibilities. He became a member of the state House of Representatives in 1884 and later was elected as a State Senator. He became supervisor from Funk's Grove Township for a number of terms. He

[10]Interview with Mrs. Madeline Funk McCullough, January, 1954.
[11]Chapman Brothers, (eds.), *op. cit.*, p. 1163.
[12]*Daily Pantagraph*, December 18, 1911.

was a member of the State Board of Agriculture of Illinois for many years, a member of the State Highway Commission, Director of the Union Stock Yards in Chicago. He also was director in the State National and First National Banks of Bloomington. By virtue of his presidency of the State Board of Agriculture, he acted as president of the Illinois Commission for the Chicago World's Fair in 1893. Under his portrait at the Saddle and Sirloin Club there is a statement giving him partial credit for the founding of the Illinois State Fair. Through his efforts as a member of the State Board of Agriculture, more scientific courses were offered at the University.

LaFayette married Miss Elizabeth Paullin of South Charleston, Ohio, January 12, 1864. Three children, Eugene D., De Loss and Edgar Paullin (who died in infancy), completed the family circle.

FRANCIS M. FUNK, born 1836, also owned a 2,200 acre farm. He served as a member of the Board of Education in Bloomington for over twenty years. He was an active supporter of Methodism. During his youth he also drove stock to Chicago along with his brothers. At the age of twenty-one years he entered Wesleyan College in Bloomington for three years. His home, occupied in 1875, in the city was located at 317 Chestnut Street. He married Miss Mary E. Houser on April 16, 1857. Two years later he entered temporarily into the drugstore business with Mr. Ira Lachey. As a large stockholder in the First National Bank he, like his brothers, kept closely in touch with the financial affairs of the community. Interest in two ranches located in Kansas, one comprising of 5,000 acres, kept him well occupied. He also, at one time, owned a 1,200 acre stock farm in Russell County. During his membership on the Bloomington Board of Education he held the Presidency of the Board at different times. He also served as a supervisor for Funk's Grove Township and a central committeeman for the Republican Party. His interest in politics was not so pronounced as that of some of his brothers. His early death in 1899 explains the shorter account of his activities.

The surviving children were Grace Funk, who became Mrs. Dwight F. Bracken, and J. Dwight Funk.

BENJAMIN F. FUNK, born 1838, remained at home until the beginning of the Civil War when he enlisted as a Union soldier in Company G. of the 68th Illinois Vol. Infantry. He served only six months near Alexandria, Virginia. B. F. remained in Bloomington. His residence was built at the cost of $12,00. His marriage to Miss Sarah Hamilton occurred August 21, 1865.[13] The site of the home was in what was then known as Major's Addition. The builder of this home possessed sturdy ideas. The construction of this sixteen-room house, which at this time stood in open country, was of brick which was covered with weatherboarding and thus well insulated. Five white marble fireplaces were installed. Full length mirrors, all deeply recessed, were also included. The only son of the family, Frank H. Funk, was born here [14] and later made it his home.

[13]Chapman Brothers, (eds), *op. cit.*, p. 195.

[14]*Daily Pantagraph*, February 23, 1941. This home was located where the present site of the Gailey Clinic is found on North Main Street.

The political career of Ben Funk included, in addition to being a supervisor from Normal in 1870–71, five successive terms as Mayor of Bloomington 1871–75 and one term in the United States House of Representatives from the 13th Illinois District during the 53rd Congress 1884–85. He remained only one term in Congress. His interest in education was shown when he accepted the presidency of the Board of Trustees of Wesleyan University in 1877. Later he became a director of the Bloomington Loan and Building Association and a stockholder in the Walton Plow Works.[15] A new accident company organized September 1886 in Bloomington elected Ben Funk as President.[16]

As an alternate delegate to the Republican National Convention 1876, he was interested in the success of Presidential candidate Rutherford B. Hayes. He became a trustee of the Blind Asylum at Jacksonville in 1885 appointed by Governor Oglesby. Although his farms were operated by tenants in 1887, B. F. retained supervision. Usually he maintained about 500 head of cattle and 25 horses of Clydesdale and Norman stock. One of his nieces describes him as an urbane individual.[17] His granddaughter remembers him as kindly and generous with an excellent business ability.[18]

ABSALOM or A. B. FUNK, called "Abb," born 1841, also herded cattle on the broad prairies. Starting early in the morning with his lunch, he would return in the evening with the cattle. Often they roamed for five or ten miles while grazing. Absalom made the trip only once overland to Chicago. Railroads soon appeared to make these long drives unnecessary. A. B. remained on the farms until 1868 when he moved to Bloomington. His marriage to Miss Sophronia Vendervender of Bloomington occurred in 1870. Absalom received two years of education at Wesleyan in Bloomington. He also participated in the Civil War.

Later he added 330 acres of ranch land in Montana to the 2,280 acres he received from his father's estate. In addition to the cattle interests he owned 40 horses, mostly Clydesdale and Norman, which he sold when they were 4 years old.

A. B. became a stockholder and director in the First National Bank as well as a stockholder in the Gas Company.[19] His residence was located on East Grove Street, a center and gathering place for the family and for social and literary interests in Bloomington. Like its owners, it was a quiet, calm place.[20]

When Mr. and Mrs. A. B. Funk returned from their honeymoon trip to Europe in 1870 they lived, for a few years, with her stepfather, Mr. Masach Pike, at the corner of Chestnut and Clinton Streets in Bloomington.

After 1876 when Mr. and Mrs. A. B. Funk moved into their home at 307 East Grove Street, aunts, uncles, cousins and friends gathered in this hospitable home. "Aunt Fronie" was always cordial when the babies were

[15]Chapman Bro., (eds), *op. cit.*, p. 195.
[16]*Weekley Pantagraph*, September 10, 1886.
[17]Interview with Mrs. Madeline Funk McCullough, January, 1954.
[18]Interview with Mrs. Florence Funk DeVries, December 1954.
[19]Chapman Bros. (eds.) *op. cit.*, p. 1041.
[20]Interview with Mrs. Madeline Funk McCullough, January 1954.

left with her while mothers from the country went shopping. Life with Mrs. A. B. was always one of many interests and enthusiasms.

The house at 307 East Grove Street held many memories of life in Bloomington in the late nineteenth and early twentieth centuries. The walls of the living room were covered with "lincustra," described as having a dull gold background with a design of soft blue and gold. The dining room was panelled with honey locust wood with a built-in sideboard of the same construction. A parquetry floor with a design around the border of walnut completed the room. A side panelling three feet high was of mixed black and white walnut (or butternut) wood. The walls were frescoed with branching blackberries, wild grapevines and other plants native to Funk's Grove. Round painted panels showed quail, woodcock and prairie chicken. During the illness of the decorator, Mrs. A. B. painted a scene of elves drawing a cart full of food which elicited many compliments.

The varied interests of this charming lady enabled her to initiate art courses, French and German classes, philosophy and music groups whenever any talented teacher came to the community.[21]

The younger generation later frequented the place. Bill Evans, Owen Reeves and Frank Aldrich might request, as they often did, that a dance floor be created. Soon the furniture was moved back and the big canvass was tacked down over the living room carpet. Young ladies appeared with their dancing slippers in their slipper bags. "Germans" or cotillions were popular in these days. Once a perpetual house party during the Governor Fifer's term took place here. Florence Fifer, (now Mrs. Bohrer), Felecita Oglesby (later Countess Cenci), Ethel Quigg (who became Mrs. John Porter, a relative of Leonard Swett), and Estelle Smith (Mrs. Walter Baird). The group moved on to the Governor's mansion. Mr. and Mrs. A. B. went along. Gertrude Lewis, wife of the Governor, and Fronie VanDevender had been lifelong friends.

A Pink Domino party, requiring long pink dominoes to be worn over evening clothes, and pink masques brought over two hundred guests. This was, indeed, a sight to behold. The table later was laden with shrimp salad, slices of ham, pink strawberry ice cream and cake with pink icing. As Hazel Funk later wrote, "the coffee, alas, was black!"

Mrs. A. B. could spark the community to participation in a floral parade or a charity ball. She gave generously of her time to the Withers' Public Library, the Bloomington Art Association and the Amateur Musical Club. As a member of the board of directors of the Library for twenty-one years and president in 1898, she rendered estimable service. The Bloomington Club at one time leased the top floor of the Library Building. Through Mr. Thomas Kerrick, brother of L. C. Kerrick, the men were influenced to build their own club building close by. The Amateur Musical Club organized with four charter members in 1894. Mrs. A. B., although not a charter member, became president of the organization for nearly eleven years. During this time "Star Concerts" were initiated.

---

[21]Hazel Funk Holmes, *Memories of My Mother, Sophronia J. Funk* (Mrs. A. B.) *at 307 East Grove Street*, typed copy, pp. 1-27. Another painting by Mrs. A. B. Funk "Shoeing the Old Gray Mare" may be seen at Funk Bros. Seed Co.

ISAAC FUNK, II, was born May 13, 1844, the youngest son of Isaac and Cassandra Funk. When he was only eight years of age he began to herd stock in numbers from one to 2,000 head. He also attended school in the winter months. At the age of twenty he enlisted in 146th Illinois Infantry, serving for one year until March 20, 1865. At the time of his father's death he made special application to President Lincoln through Judge David Davis, Sr., for a discharge which was granted.[22] When Judge Davis presented the request, President Lincoln recalled that he had once helped this boy set a calf loose when he stopped at the Funk farm. By the President's action, Isaac, II, then returned to the farm for three years. In 1866 he attended Wesleyan in Bloomington for one year. He married Miss Frances Correll of Sangamon County, October 28, 1869. They made their home at the old Homestead until 1881 which they called Ersthome.[23] There were three children, Arthur, Lawrence and Helen F.[24]

A fine residence was purchased in the fall of 1881 in Bloomington at East Chestnut and Prairie Streets on the southwest corner of Franklin Park.[25] The family spent considerable time in the country during the summer where Isaac continued to own 2,260 acres. Mrs. Isaac Funk was active in social circles in the city where she was one of the promoters of the Letetia Green Stevenson Chapter of the D. A. R. She acted as regent 1896–97. She was a charter member of the History Club and active in the First Methodist Church.[26]

One of the saddest events in the history of the family was the occasion of the sudden death of Isaac, II, when he was killed by a train at the Funk's Grove crossing in 1909.[27]

SARAH FUNK and L. H. KERRICK Leonidas H. Kerrick became closely identified with the Funk family as a result of his marriage October 28, 1868 to Sarah Funk or "Sally or Sallee" Funk as she was called by her brothers. Mr. Kerrick was a dependable legal advisor and a warm friend of the brothers. He was born in Franklin County, Indiana, October 19, 1846, the son of Reverend Nimrod Kerrick, a pioneer Methodist preacher. Kerrick was reared on a farm and tutored in a log cabin as well as in the schools of Woodford County. He attended Wesleyan College in Bloomington in 1863, graduating in 1866. Two years later he married Sarah Funk. One daughter, Idelle, became the wife of Thord Ewing of Decatur in later years.

Before his marriage Mr. Kerrick became principal of the model school at the college. He joined the Powell expedition to Colorado.

[22]Interview with Arthur Funk, December 11, 1952. This story was reportedly told at the Lincoln Centennial in 1909.

[23]*Daily Pantagraph*, May 2, 1910.

[24]Chapman Bros. (eds.), *op. cit.*, pp. 1113 and 1114.

[25]Interview with Arthur Funk, December, 1952 and Mrs. Madeline Funk McCullough, January, 1954.

[26]*Daily Pantagraph*, May 2, 1910.

[27]*Daily Bulletin*, December 2, 1919.

Appendix II

MRS. EUGENE D. FUNK, SR., nee Mary V. Anderson, was also descended from pioneers. Her grandparents, Mary Fay [1] and Charles Wesley Bryant,[2] with two children, Alta and Lee, made the difficult trip from New York to Oregon in 1853. They left Dudley Bryant's house in North Java, located near Buffalo, New York in March. Amos Fay and Joseph Bryant escorted them to Buffalo. Their wagon was put on the boat at Buffalo, proceeding across Lake Erie thence by rail to Michigan City and by boat to Chicago. The next stop by train was Peoria, where they shipped the freight ahead to Kansas City. They took a boat on the Illinois River to St. Louis. The next destination was Westport (Kansas City) where they camped for three weeks. Here they joined a group of Methodists who had journeyed from New York by way of Cincinnati. Among these people were Obidiah (Dyer) Hines, his wife Eliza and their daughter Celinda, (later Mrs. A. R. Shipley). Others in the party were Gustavus Hines, his wife Libby and her sister Julia Bryant, a distant cousin of Charles W. Bryant; as well as Jason Lee's daughter Luciana Maria Lee; Harvey Hines and his wife Elizabeth (Libby) and her sister Martha Graves. Mr. and Mrs. Judson, their daughter Alma and later their son "LaBonte," born on the plains, also accompanied the group.[3]

The wagon train prepared to leave Kansas City about May 18, 1853. The Bryant family assembled their wagons, bought five yoke of oxen and a cow known as "Old Red" to add to their dog "Towser," who came with them from New York. The Hines party waited for the Bryants to arrive and prepare for the departure. Gustavus Hines was made Captain of the group because he had made the trip before. There were three preachers in the party. Prayer meetings were held every Thursday. Services occurred on Sundays, with night and morning worship every day.

This assemblage was described as a "Missionary Train" of five wagons.

[1]Mary Fay was descended from Dr. John Fay who married Susanna Morse; their fifth child, David Fay, married Sarah Larkin; their ninth child, Edward Fay married _____?; their third child, Isrel Fay married Mary Torrey; their sixth child, James Fay married Chloe Torrey; their first child, Silas Fay, married Rhoda Allen; their third child was Mary Fay.

[2]Charles W. Bryant was descended from Dudley Bryant and Betsy Vesper. Dudley Bryant was the grandson of Ebeneezer Bryant who married Mehitabel _____? their son Daniel married Bertha Newton. Their son Dudley who married Betsy Vesper (descended from Thomas and Hannah Vesper of London, England) were the parents of Charles W. Bryant.

[3]The drivers were Robert Nelson, a Swede, for the Judsons. Martin and Miner guarded the cattle and rode the horses. They drove for the Bryants.

A distance of twenty miles a day was described as a long journey. Indians were only friendly and curious. They often teased little Alta Bryant, aged three, as she rode in the front seat of the Bryant wagon holding a cattle whip for protection.[4]

A record of the meeting of the Bryants with the Hines and Judson families was recorded by Celinda Hines in her Diary.

The Diary of Celinda Hines, later Mrs. A. R. Shipley, gives an account of the trip to Oregon, undertaken by her family and by the Bryants and the Judsons.[5] This party finally united at Westport. The Hines family proceeded from New York by a route different from that taken by the Bryants. From Buffalo they had gone to Dunkirk where they had occasional views of the lake. They reached Cincinnati via Erie, Pennsylvania and Columbus, Ohio. The trip by boat to St. Louis consumed about five days. After spending some time at Independence, the family moved along to Westport. There Celinda recorded that a Mr. Bryant from New York on his way to Oregon, called, "He wishes to go with us."[6] The Bryants camped nearby on the evening of April 30, 1853.[7]

This account is substantiated by notes kept by Mrs. E. D. Funk, Sr. and Mrs. Bertha Anderson Holmes of reports told them by their mother, who was Alta Bryant.

Mr. Judson, a Presbyterian minister, also decided to join the party. The men made preparations to cross the Kansas River at the Delaware ferry. The roads became hilly, rough and muddy, thus alarming the women. At the river they encamped with the men guarding the cattle all through the night. The ferrying of the teams and cattle across the river to Little St. Louis in Nebraska consumed almost all day. Friendly Indians came to their camp. One intelligent Delaware Chief advised the group to take the "divide route instead of the government road by Ft. Leavenworth, as it is nearer and they say a better road."[8]

At the crossing of the Grasshopper the wagons had to be unloaded and let down the bank with ropes because of the steep embankments and the deep river. It took all day to cross at this place. At one ravine they were obliged to stop while a bridge was constructed.[9] They crossed the Vermillion River on May 17th and on the next day the Little Vermillion:

Very cold. Country uneven. Crossed the Little Vermillion. See dead cattle every day along the road. Saw two men who were 50 miles behind their Co., gave them some sea-bread. Overtook another Co. of Californians with a drove. Camped near a ravine. Traveled 24 miles.[10]

A wagon tipped over going down the bank of the river near the middle

[4]Mary Anderson Funk, "Story told by My Mother."
[5]_____"Diary of Celinda Hines," *Transactions of Forty Sixth Annual Reunion of Oregon Pioneer Association,* June 20, 1918, (Portland, Oregon: CHausse-Proudhomme Co., Printers 1921), pp. 70-71.
[6]*Ibid.,* p. 86.
[7]Alta Bryant Anderson, "Trip to Oregon" (typed Copy), told to Mrs. Holmes and Mrs. Funk.
[8]Celinda Hines, *op. cit.,* p. 88.
[9]*Ibid.,* p. 89.
[10]*Ibid.,* p. 90.

fork of the Blue. Because of the high water they decided to go north about seven miles. On May 21st Celinda noted that a "Wagon run on Mrs. Bryant's foot." It was necessary to await their turn among about 100 wagons in order to cross the Blue. Across this river they found themselves in Pawnee country. By the 27th of May they crossed the Big Sandy and the Little Sandy where they camped.[11]

Fort Kearney was passed on June 3rd. People were forbidden to camp within three miles of the Fort so the next morning the men proceeded to the Fort to obtain shoes for the horses and mules. The description of the Fort is an interesting one:

> Government has a blacksmith shop for the accommodation of emigrants but at present there is no smith. Aunt E. M. J. and I went with Pa in the carriage . . . The barracks are made of mud. There is a store where they sell about the same as in Kansas. There are sixty soldiers there. They have no fortifications and it was probably built more for the accommodation of emigrants and to awe the Indians than for a defense. The sergeant invited me to his house and we were pleasantly entertained. The Captain informed Pa that there had passed here 85,000 head of cattle and 8,000 men who were crossing the plains this year, also that most of the emigration was going to Oregon. Our route lies up the river to South Fork on the south side.[12]

Five days later they forded the South Fork. The river was about a mile and a quarter wide in low water. At the time the water was high but shallow. All of the oxen were placed on the wagons, ten being attached to one of the wagons. The wagon road followed close to the river but soon led upon the bluffs. They identified Ash Hollow, Castle Bluff, Courthouse Rock and on the night of June 16th came to Chimney Rock which could be seen for a distance of 15 miles.[13] It was a pillar of rock standing 250 feet high. At noon on the 17th they came to Scott's Bluff, then proceeded six miles up the river. A herd of 50 buffaloes was chased by Indians and at camp some of the Sioux came to obtain food. At Laramie Fort on June 21st they found 150 wagons ahead of them.[14] Celinda's uncles exchanged the mules for a heavy wagon, three yokes of oxen and two cows, giving $200.00 to boot.[15]

A description of Fort Laramie followed:

> It is on the north side of Laramie River and is overlooked on the north by a hill where stands the burying ground. I visited the fort and was much surprised at seeing no fortifications. There are at present 64 soldiers.[16]

Here the group received mail.

Pushing along to the Black Hills, they had viewed Laramie Peak for a week. They were advised by a trader to take a cut-off thereby shunning the Black Hills and twenty miles where there was no good water. They

[11]*Ibid.*, p. 91.
[12]*Ibid.*, p. 93 June 4th.
[13]*Ibid.*, pp. 95-96.
[14]*Ibid.*, p. 98.
[15]Ibid.
[16]*Ibid.*

passed Horse Creek and a place where the Platte cuts through the mountains. The record showed that on June 26th:

After dinner we went through the Gorge. The scenery surpasses for grandeur, sublimity and peculiarity anything we have yet seen on the road. The river passes through what seems to be a natural fissure in the earth. I should think 400 feet in height. We went to the top of the bluff. How grand, how magnificent. Several miles of the road with teams and camps. The river with its various windings, with its valleys and bluffs on either side. Laramie Peak in the distance with its snow capped crest was before us in all the grandeur of which a landscape can be possessed. We returned to camp and found we had an addition to our company in a little boy named Labonte Judson.[17]

Successively they passed Mud Creek and crossed the North Platte on a bridge, paying six dollars a wagon and one shilling a head for loose stock. On July 2nd they passed "Rocky Pass" and the Alkali Swamps, Wire Creek, Greasewood Creek; and on July 3rd camped near Independence Rock. The fourth of July they got up an Independence dinner with all the company eating together. They approached Independence Rock on the next day. Six miles from here Devel's Gate marks the place where the Sweetwater River passes straight through the mountain. Their road lay up the Sweetwater. The Sweetwater mountains paralleled the river on the north and near to the stream, appearing on the south far off as one continuous granite chain. The party crossed the river three times on July 6th and on the following day Mr. Bryant came near upsetting his wagon. Before noon on July 9th the group came in full sight of the Rocky Mountains and camped for the last time on the Sweetwater July 11th:

Captain Grant and Co., from Ft. Vancouver called and made us a visit. Captain took tea with us. He had been to Ft. Hall to dispose of some government property, also to Salt Lake. He brought us a few potatoes.[18]

The night of August 18th was spent near Barrel Springs and three days later the Boise River came into sight.[19] Here Indians came to exchange food in the form of fish for clothing. The Indians (The Diggers) could not understand English. A sad event took place when Obidiah Hines undertook to aid the animals in one of the crossings of the river on August 26th. Expert Indian divers were unable to recover his body but the bereaved party pressed forward.

The record of the crossing of various rivers, streams and creeks became the chief means of identifying the route followed by the travelers. The Malheur River was crossed on August 29th and in the following days they crossed the Burnt River nine times. Pushing along to the Powder River Valley they beheld the Blue River.[20] With the Columbia River as their objective they passed through the Grande Ronde valley, the Umatilla Valley, John Days River, De Shoots River and by September 17th were in

[17]*Ibid.*, p. 99.
[18]*Ibid.*, p. 111.
[19]*Ibid.*, p. 113.
[20]*Ibid.*, p. 117.

sight of Mt. Ranier.[21] Joseph Hines came to meet them near the Columbia River.

Eventually they arrived at the Dalles and the Cascades, taking the only steamboat that plied between the two. Few boats except those of the Hudson Bay Company ran over the Cascades. This company lost about one in ten boats.[22] Messrs. Bryant and Judson left the group with their families on September 26th.[23] The long journey of seven months was nearing its end.

The Bryants had been in Oregon only three weeks when their boy, Lee, died. The family persevered with Mr. Bryant working at Salem and at Oregon City.[24] Later Alta Bryant married Asbury Anderson, son of Levi Anderson, on August 3, 1870.[25]

Two years after their long trip over land to Oregon C. W. Bryant wrote from Succer Creek, Oregon Territory to his brother on January 22, 1855. He thanked his eastern relatives for boxes sent:

They arrived at San Francisco the 10th of December and at Astoria the 1st of Jan. They were then sent up by steamer to Portland where they lay a week before I found it out as the steamer that had mails from California was supposed to be lost . . . . the things were in good order except the dried fruit was mouldy.[26]

A box of tools delighted this carpenter as well as the coat and hat which was included. Mr. Bryant continued:

There are plenty of deer here yet, we saw seven at one time playing and feeding in front of the house not 20 rods off last week.

Partridge were also nearby. Wild geese were plentiful since they came to feed on the wheat. Partridge sold at 25 to 50 cents a piece but ducks were so plentiful that they brought only 20 to 25 cents a piece. Swans were in best demand at $1.50 to $2.00 a piece. He also noted the division of their county "and we are annexed to Clackamas County, Oregon City is the County seat." Portland became the county seat, Multnomah County. He advised his eastern relatives to address mail to him at Oswego, Clackamas County, since their town was not yet named, "but where we live is called Succer Creek." It was a mile from the north line of the Bryants to Succer Lake, a body of water ¼ mile wide and about 3 miles long. There was a good mill privilege at the outlet, Oswego, where the head of the tide water was located. He advised his brother to take up the study of engineering if he intended coming to Oregon.[27]

[21]*Ibid.*, p. 117-121.
[22]*Ibid.*, p. 122.
[23]*Ibid.*, p. 125.
[24]From Notes kept by Mrs. E. D. Funk, Sr., of accounts related by her mother.
[25]Levi Anderson was a member of the constitutional convention in Oregon Aug. 1857 see J. B. Horner, *Oregon*, (Portland: J. K. Gill Co., 1921), p. 158.
[26]Copy of Letter, C. W. Bryant to brother, January 22, 1855, original in possession Mrs. Bertha Anderson Holmes and Mrs. E. D. Funk, Sr.
[27]*Ibid.*

Appendix III

COATES P. BULL

Born 1872 at Edina Mills, Minnesota; He lived on a farm until 1897; He graduated from The University of Minnesota, 1892; Again entered the University in 1897, specialized in Plant Breeding and general farm crops; Accepted Assistant Professorship of Crops, Agronomy, University of Illinois 1901–1902; Returned to University of Minnesota as Assistant Agriculturist 1902; advanced to Full Professorship; Was associated with Prof. W. M. Hays; Prepared and installed Plant Breeding Exhibit World's Fair, St. Louis, Missouri, 1904; Same year helped organize Minnesota Crop Improvement Association; 1907–21 helped organize and acted as Director of National Corn Association; Author of many bulletins from Minnesota Experiment Station; Contributed to development and developed many varieties of Farm Crops.

R. A. MOORE

Born 1861, Kewanee County, Wisconsin; Interested in rural growth; became assistant to Dean Henry of Agricultural College, Wisconsin in 1895 where he took charge of Short Course in Agriculture; in 1901 he organized the Short Course group and The Wisconsin Experiment Association which organization helped to introduce and distribute better grains throughout the state and nation; Prof. Moore valued the agricultural exhibit and field demonstrations; He believed that advancement came from "seeing what others were doing."

CHARLES W. PUGSLEY

Born Woodbine, Iowa, 1878; 4 years instructor Woodbine, Iowa Normal School; B. S. 1906 University of Nebraska; 1908 became Assistant Professor in Animal Husbandry; Head of Agronomy and Farm Management 1911; Was one of pioneers in Middle West in studying economic and marketing phases of Agriculture; Became Director of Agricultural Extension; Editor *Nebraska Farmer* 1918; Assistant Secretary Agriculture under Henry C. Wallace 1921–23; President South Dakota State College 1940.

LEONARD B. CLORE

Born 1866, White River Township, Indiana: Business education and farm experience; Showed corn as a young man at Johnson County Fair; organized Johnson County White Dent Corn; Won prize as First International Corn Grower at Paris, France Exposition in 1900; Grand National Sweepstakes for 10 ears of corn at N. C. F. 1907 and in Omaha 1908; He was called "Corn King of the World" 1909; Offered position as Advisor in Agriculture to Russian Czar in 1909—refused. President Indiana Corn Growers Association 1911; General Manager of New England Corn Exposition; Supt. Indiana Agriculture Exhibit, St. Louis World's Fair, 1904; President Indiana State Board of Agriculture; Served two terms Indiana State Legislature, Clore Bill 1911 credited; Dept. Agriculture Extension at Purdue; Associated 17 years with Federal Land Bank of Louisville, Kentucky.

WILLIAM SHULL

Born Marengo, Illinois 1850; Educated University of Illinois; Entered investment business; established firm of Stull Brothers at Lincoln, Nebraska 1886; Removed to Omaha 1897 where he continued as a leading financier of the city; His well informed analyses of farming conditions throughout the Middle West made him a valuable member of the Board of Directors; he also recognized the need for increased education for the farmer.

E. G. MONTGOMERY

Born May 10, 1878 at Milan, Missouri; lived near Lincoln, Nebraska; In 1899 entered Nebraska Agricultural School and graduated from the University, 1906; Received Masters Degree 1909; He worked from 1900 on the Agricultural College Farm; In charge of Field Experiments 1904–1912; In Charge of Experimental Agronomy from 1906; Field work emphasized Plant Breeding chiefly in Corn and Wheat; He began, according to his own statement, "first work with inbreeding corn in the Corn Belt in 1908." From 1906–1912 published a dozen bulletins based on experimental work. In 1906 became Secretary Nebraska Corn Growers Association and a Vice President of National Corn Association; He became Professor of Agronomy, January 1912 at Cornell; Joined the U. S. Department of Agriculture, March 1920 and the U. S. Department of Commerce August 1921; He retired in 1948. In 1957 he was living at the age of 79 in Chevy Chase, Maryland.

Appendix IV

A GROUP INCLUDING James M. Davison, A. A. Dunbar, George Marsee, Arthur Barling, Dean Beal, Earl Sieveking and Charles Flinspach remained 30–35 years.

Arthur Barling has been a familiar figure in the Field Seeds operations in the warehouse. He recalled well the helpful manner and the direction of H. H. Miller. Complete records of all shipping were required by H. A. Abbott whose businesslike methods and diplomacy impressed Barling. He also recognized the importance of feeling that top management is not removed from the group. He recalls playing basketball in the old Gym. of the Second Presbyterian Church with Ted and Paul Funk. Barling can recall when Gene, Jr. was warehouse foreman, accustomed to rough and hard days of handling 150 pound bags of beans.

A number of employees have a record of 25–30 years, Harold Goodwin, Howard Holt, R. H. Savidge and Ira Beal.

An example of a family working for a family can be found in the Beal group. Dean Beal began work with the company in 1926 and Howard Beal, his brother, in 1929, before the expansion in the soybean and hybrid corn divisions occurred. They learned every phase of the mechanical operations as the plant grew. Their experience qualified them for responsible maintenance positions where their constructive and loyal leadership is apparent among their co-workers. Ira Beal, a third brother began working in the Warehouse at the age of fifteen. Seven members including the father, William Beal, have been employed by Funks. Their attachment to the family and to the company is understandable. From working closely with H. H. Miller through hand pollinating and detasseling for Holbert, Ira Beal was eventually promoted to plant superintendent for Hybrid Seed at Normal, Illinois. This plant was acquired in 1938 for the grading, processing and distribution of the home company's operations. It has continued to handle the bulk of this activity with plants at Mason City and Rockville, Indiana carrying their shares of the activity.

Again a new person was introduced to office operations in 1931 when Ralph Savidge obtained a permanent assignment. He recalled that the office door of E. D. Funk, Sr. was always open and that the President of the company often helped after hours with any incomplete task. Savidge also drove the sound truck in the early days and worked with both Sieveking and Holbert. Eventually his interests were channelled into the Soybean operations where he became a dependable assistant to H. A. Abbott, and later to Mac Convis as his Assistant in Sales and Purchasing in this same Department.

The policy of promotion was also applied in the Grain Elevators and

Warehouse organizations. Howard Holt came to the company in 1931. For ten years he was operator of the Grain Elevator. Later he was Superintendent of Soybean Processing 1942–52 during these years of the Expeller Process (see below). When the Solvent Plant was installed he became Supervisor of Maintenance for the Grain Elevators and Warehouse. Having observed the successful growth of the business through the decades of the twentieth century he consistently advocated the continuation of the family policy. He contends that if it brought present advancement there is no reason to believe that it may not be the key to continued success with expansion.

Those who claim association with the Company for twenty to twenty-five years include Boyd Frye (deceased), Bernard Dahlquist, Glenn Jensen, Walter Gang, John S. Davison, Vernon Curtis, Lester D. Mehlberg, Lyle Wilcox, F. P. Lewis, Sr., Harold Abbott, R. J. Laible, Lewis Falck, Howard Reeder and Ross Vinson.

Employees who worked with James Holbert in the program for the U. S. D. A. from 1925 to 1937 were Boyd Frye and Wright Hardin. Frye was stenographer and secretary assisting in the summer with pollinating, inbreeding and detasseling in the Corn Plots. They returned to the company with Holbert. Frye was at first employed when he came to the company as a sales accountant keeping a constant inventory of sales records.

Wright Hardin worked with James Holbert as chief assistant in field operations with the U. S. D. A. 1927–1937. He came to Funk Bros. in 1937 when Holbert returned to the company. Hardin supervised production of Foundation Seed and was closely associated with the research development of the early Funks G Hybrid. He became manager in 1940 of the Foundation Seed Department for all of Funk Bros. Foundation operations including amounts needed for Associate Growers and foreign countries. He also supervised research work in Southwestern Illinois, Kentucky, Tennessee and Eastern Missouri. The close association of Hardin with Holbert has given him a deep insight into the production of the bred-in qualities of Funks G Hybrids.

During 1934 a young high school student Bernard Dahlquist worked in the summer learning how to sew bags and also at the nursery plots on the Moberly farm. He became a full-time employee in 1938. H. H. Miller hoped to keep him in the office but the young man preferred the outdoor work. Nevertheless he learned the methods of the General Manager and continued to advance as an able assistant to Harold Goodwin. From these two capable men he learned to evaluate the worth of seed and to know what his farmer friends were thinking. This combination contributed to his recognition as a valuable employee in the organization.

Another employee, Ross Vinson, hired in February 1936 has gained experience in more than one department of the plant. His first work was with the Soybean Department followed by some responsibility in the Commercial Department. When Foundation Seed and Research were combined in the earlier days he joined that staff under the supervision of Wright Hardin. After 1941 when these two groups were separated Vinson remained with James Holbert in Research. In this work he learned practically every phase of the activity and eventually was placed in charge of the

Laboratory facilities for testing high oil content in inbreds. The significance of this type of testing was early recognized by E. D. Sr., when the company was first working with open pollinated varieties. The processes of the present are different but some of the problems are the same.

Alvin Mohr came to the company's Research Department in 1941 as supervisor of nursery and research plots located in Bloomington, Southern Illinois and northern Iowa. He also supervised the harvesting and processing of the commercial seed crop. He was designated as Assistant Manager of Research to 1946 when he was placed in charge of the production of Commercial Funks G Hybrids for the Bloomington area. Later his work included responsibility for coordinating production from Mason City and Rockville, Indiana with the Bloomington office. Mohr's ability to express his overall knowledge of agricultural problems to the farmer friends of Funk Bros. is a distinct asset. His experience and success in soil management have contributed to increasing high quality in Funks Hybrids. With experience in Research Department with corn, his knowledge of the production of G. Hybrids is well integrated with the responsibilities of his present position.

Another able assistant, Robert Spry, came to the company from the Midwest Agronomist Division of Armour & Co. where he gained valuable experience from the study of soil improvement. He graduated from Iowa State College and the University of Illinois. Recognizing that Hybrid Corn would remain an integral part of the agricultural pattern he saw in Funk Bros. Seed Co. a strong organization. Spry believed that there are few comparable companies of the size and competence. After 1945 he worked closely with Earl Sieveking learning the organization operation of the Associate Growers. With the advancement of Sieveking to the management of the Hybrid Corn Division in 1957 Spry took charge of the Associate Grower program. Like his contemporaries he has proved himself dependable and qualified to assume varied responsibility. His knowledge of soils and fertilizers is an asset in the hybrid corn department.

Ward Alderman and James Barnes were added in the Field Seed Department. Alderman was first employed in 1935 in the warehouse, learning to bag and clean the seed. He acted as salesman throughout the territory, becoming an administrative assistant in the field seed department. Typical of his ability to master a situation is the fact that he joined the service in World War 2 as a private and emerged as a Major. These qualifications have enabled him to assume continuing responsibilities in his work. His knowledge of seed values and his trading ability in both buying and selling have contributed effectively to the program at Funk Bros. Like Miller and Goodwin he possesses that indefinable "know how" in the Field Seed business.

Joseph E. Barnes was called from the staff of the University of Illinois to Springfield, Illinois, following the revision of the Illinois Seed Law, in charge of the Seed Germination Laboratory. He acted as chief analyst until 1942. He introduced new techniques for seed testing and designed new germinator equipment. Barnes developed the "Daylite" germinator standard today; produced "walkin" room type germinators and devised an improved type *trier* which actually reached the center of the bags of seed.

H. H. Miller brought Barnes to Funk Bros. in 1942 where he supervises the Seed Laboratory as Seed Technologist. Barnes' knowledge of weeds of all kinds is depended upon and recognized throughout the area serviced by Funk Bros.

A group of twenty has a record of employment for fifteen to twenty years. This group came to the company only a year or so before the death of Eugene D. Funk, Sr. They did not experience the formative years during his active leadership. Yet they know and appreciate his contribution. Many of this group were added to the roster at the time of the expansion in the Hybrid Corn Division under the company presidency of Eugene Funk, Jr. and the general management of James R. Holbert. Some were salesmen, some secretaries and some research personnel. Of the last classification, Leon Steele, A. R. Mohr and Robert Spry have attained administrative positions.

Howard Springer joined the accounting department of Funk Bros. in 1943 after accounting experience with the First National Bank and W. P. A. in Peoria, Illinois and with grain companies in the Armington and Bloomington area. He was placed in charge of the accounting department of Funks in 1946 where he has proved capable in the supervision of personnel in the accounting department and in keeping financial records of the seed business.

An assistant to E. W. Rolley was added in 1945 when A. A. Baker was employed. After some years of experience in the teaching field he spent more than a year in the military services as an instructor and Supervisor. His work with Funks since 1957 has been as manager of the Insurance and Budget Department where his work has been both dependable and valuable.

FUNK BROS. SEED CO. EMPLOYEES OF FIVE YEAR STANDING OR MORE

As of July 1, 1958

MAIN PLANT

25–30 Years or More

	Yr. Mo.
Arthur Barling	30– 9
Bernard Dean Beal	31–10
Howard Beal	28– 9
Ira Beal	29– 9
J. M. Davison	32– 4
Andrus A. Dunbar	31– 5
Vaughn Dunbar	36– 1
E. D. Funk, Jr.	37– 4
La Fayette Funk	39– 6
Paul Funk	32– 5
Harold Goodwin	28– 1
Howard Holt	26– 9
Ernest Radley	36– 4
Ralph Savidge	26– 6
Margaret Schertz	36–10
Earl Sieveking	30
Frank L. Thomas	25– 3

20–25 Years

Harold A. Abbott	22–10
Merle Cook	21–10
Vernon Curtis	20–10
Bernard L. Dahlquist	23– 4
John S. Davison	23–10
Walter Gang	23– 9
J. Wright Hardin	21– 3
Glenn Jensen	22– 8
Russell J. Laible	21– 3
Franklin P. Lewis, Sr.	21– 5
George E. Marsee	21–10
Albert Irl Melton	20– 8
Howard E. Reeder	21–10
Ross Vinson	22– 4
Lyle Wilcox	20– 5

15–20 Years

Ward Alderman	19– 9
Jesse James Armes	16– 8
LaVerta Arnold	16– 6
Elsie Ashworth	16
Roscoe Ross Ashworth	19– 4
Joseph E. Barnes	16
Eben Canfield	18– 2
Russell Casey	17– 1
Roy Chambers	15–10

	Yr. Mo.
Mac Convis	15– 1
Theodore Funk	15
Ivan Hefner	15– 9
H. Edward Kelley	17– 9
Arthur Kiper	18
Edwin R. Lederer	16– 3
Manuel Mc Goldrick	17– 6
W. J. Mathis	16–10
Paul K. Melton	19– 9
Alvin R. Mohr	17– 3
Larrence Moretz	15– 8
Clarence Mosimann	17–11
Elias W. Rolley	15– 9
Raymond A. Schultz	15– 9
L. W. Sears	15–11
Harold R. Smith	16–10
Oliver Leon Steele	17–10
James P. Ward, Sr.	18– 3
James R. L. Ward	18– 9
J. Wesley Wilcox	15

10–15 Years

A. A. Baker	12– 7
Alma Barnes	11–10
Rena Beal	10– 9
Henry Byford	12– 9
Junior Adron Carwile	11– 6
Russell Dorsey	10– 9
J. Walter Elgin	10– 9
Eugene C. Ford	14– 5
Gilbert Ford	14– 9
Richard C. Funk	10
Bessie Gottschalk	12– 8
Dempsey G. Griffin	10– 5
Luther Darrell Hardin	14– 9
Albert Hermeling	13– 9
Robert K. Irvin	14– 8
Robert O. Johnson	10– 2
Franklin P. Lewis, Jr.	12
Forrest E. Long	14–10
William M. Malcom	12–11
James Marvin	12– 6
Lester O. Mehlberg	12
Rufus L. Miner	12– 2
Harold Nelson	14– 2
Ralph L. Primm	12– 4
Delmar E. Runge	11– 6
William T. Schreiber	12– 4

	Yr. Mo.
Howard B. Springer	14–11
Robert H. Spry	14–10
Chester Uszienski	11– 3
George W. Ward	11– 8
Deceased Oct. 20, 1958	
Fanny Weaver	13– 2
Alva A. West	13– 9
Wesley C. Wilcox	12

5–10 Years

Merle Baird	6– 6
Gilbert Dean Baker	9– 5
Joseph Birckelbaw	7– 9
Noel Blair	4– 9
Clarence Butcher	9– 8
Russell C. Carwile	6– 9
Helen Cook	8– 7
Leonard A. Embry	4– 9
Robert A. Fitzgerald	7– 4
Earl S. Garner	6– 9
Victor C. Hamlow	6– 8
George W. Hawkins	7– 9
Glenn Hextell	7– 1
Robert Hisle	6–11
Gerald Hornke	4–11
Hugh B. Horsley	6– 6
Lorin K. Jump	8– 1
Charles R. Kelch	5– 5
Donald G. Lee	6
Every Logsdon	6– 9
Hubert Lyle Mason	7– 3
Elmer J. Mehlberg	7– 1
Robert L. Moretz	6– 8
C. Ursel Parmele	7– 3
Trop Phillips	8– 9
Walter J. Raney	5– 9
Calvin A. Rehtmeyer	6–10
Vera F. Schreiber	6– 9
William Schurr, Jr.	8– 5
Earl Shankel	8–11
Arlyss E. Shiley	6– 6
Harvey A. Singletary	9– 9
John W. Smith	7– 9
Marguerite E. Storm	7–10
Ernest W. Studebaker	6– 5
Conus C. Taylor	8– 3
Russell L. Trunnell	4– 9
Elizabeth L. Vaughn	6– 5
Delmar D. Walker	7– 4
Rudolph Weigelmann	4– 8
Robert E. Wellenreiter	8– 4
Robert W. Wright	5– 1
Fred Zink	7– 9

	Yr. Mo.
Robert C. Zink	7– 8
Wendall Shield Zink	6– 8

BELLE PLAINE, IOWA

20 Years or More

Lewis L. Falck	20– 1
Cecil F. Franklin	20

15–20 Years

Norris W. Anderson	16–10
John C. Baker	17– 4
Joan Burrows	15–10
Alice Clemmer	18– 3
Walter H. DuToit	15– 2
George D. Ealy	15– 9
John C. Ellis	15–11
Clifford H. Fisher	16– 9
Russell J. Hecht	16
Charles R. McMillin	18– 3
William A. Milburn	19– 9
James C. Pech	18– 9
Charles H. Rabe	17– 4
Richard L. Rabe	17– 4
Alvin O. Schnarr	16–11
Richard Squiers	16
Dewey M. Swagert	17– 1
Edward D. Uchytil	17– 4
James H. Uchytil	17– 9
William N. Vandivier	16

10–15 Years

Alfred Athey	13–10
Effie Cleckner	13–10
Joseph C. Drahos	13–10
Arthur C. Dvorak	11– 1
Fred F. Dvorak	10– 3
Milo R. Formanek	10– 1
Monzetta B. Franklin	11– 4
Barton L. Haupert	10– 7
Arthur L. Janss	14–11
Charles W. Kalina	13– 9
Karl P. Longnecker	14
Willis H. Magdefrau	14– 1
Edward H. Rogers	11
Beverlee Sherwood	13
Grant M. Silver	14
Norman D. Yanda	10– 1

5–10 Years

Robert John Anderson	7–11
Raymond A. Bell	6
Helen A. Carlson	7– 1

	Yr. Mo.
Maurice Edw. Cornelis	5– 1
Victor Cyriel Cornelis	6– 2
Ruth L. Drahos	5– 9
Hugo A. Drews	6– 9
Mildred Dusil	8– 5
Neil Bruce Ealy	7– 8
John P. Hanzelka	6–10
Edward E. Hoekstra, Jr.	7–11
William F. Houska	7– 4
Joseph A. Kolash, Jr.	6–10
Fred E. Kopecky	5– 9
William J. Krezek	6– 8
John J. Lebeda	6–11
Merritt D. Lewis	7– 9
Dean Logan	7– 3
Don McGillivray	7–11
Edward L. Martin	6– 2
William Oscar Meade	6– 1
Gerald B. Reutzel	6
Robert C. Schlotfelt	7–10
James D. Seda	6– 6
Roland L. Seda	5–11
Virgil J. Slater	5–11
James R. Smith	6–10

	Yr. Mo.
Lawrence E. Smith	7– 2
Harold F. Thede	8– 3
Leslie R. Tippie	6– 2
Bernard P. Uchytil	9– 9
Ralph J. Upah	7– 9
Eleanor Mae Wehman	6– 1

MASON CITY, ILLINOIS

20 Years or More

Charles E. Flinspach	34– 5

15–20 Years

Curtis D. Carter	19–10
Vertus Dewey Elmore	15–10
Roy A. Huffman	19–11
Glenn M. Reeder	17–11

5–10 Years

Harry E. Hoit	5–11
Forrest E. Howard	6– 5

ROCKVILLE, INDIANA

Ray B. Shoemaker	15–11

Appendix V

FUNK'S G HYBRID ASSOCIATE PRODUCERS

Name of company	Date Founded	Founders	Date became associate	Present management
GOLDEN SEED CO. Cordova, Illinois	1925	Claire V. Golden	1930	Claire V. Golden John A. Golden
McKEIGHAN SEED CO. Yates City, Ill.	1906	R. J. McKeighan J. L. McKeighan	1934	J. L. McKeighan James R. McKeighan Robert L. McKeighan
JOHN T. SMITH & SONS Tolono, Ill.	1934	John T. Smith, Sr.	1934	
SMITH SEED CO. Tolono, Ill.	1950	Robert W. Smith		Robert W. Smith
J. C. ROBINSON SEED CO. Waterloo, Nebraska Incorporated	1884 1904	J. C. Robinson	1935	Edward T. Robinson Agnes Robinson Robert D. Herrington
COLUMBIANA SEED CO. Eldred, Illinois	1921	Edward Boyles Richard Best	1936	Richard Best Olga Best Robert Best
SOMMER BROS. SEED CO. Pekin, Illinois	1909	Arthur U. Sommer Oscar J. Sommer	1936	Oscar J. Sommer, Chm. Bd. Arthur U. Sommer, V. Chm. Bd. Theodore L. Sommer, Pres. Arthur P. Sommer, V. Pres. Estella M. Groen, Sec. Treas.
CLAUDE W. THORP & CARL E. THORP PARTNERSHIP Clinton, Ill.	1929	Claude W. Thorp Carl E. Thorp	1936	
CLAUDE W. THORP & SONS Clinton, Ill.	1946	Claude W. Thorp Carl E. Thorp Ernest Thorp		Carl E. Thorp Ernest N. Thorp
CLAUDE W. THORP & SONS CO. Clinton, Ill.	1949 Inc.	Carl E. Thorp Ernest N. Thorp		
FRANK S. GARWOOD & SONS Stonington, Ill.	1937	Frank S. Garwood F. Donald Garwood Harold L. Garwood	1937	Frank S. Garwood F. Donald Garwood Harold L. Garwood

470

Name of company	Date Founded	Founders	Date became associate	Present management
SWANSON SEED FARMS Galesburg, Illinois	1937	Earle N. Swanson Milton Swanson (Bro) Max Swanson (Son) Raymond Swanson (Son)	1937	Earle N. Swanson Milton Swanson Max Swanson Raymond Swanson
CLARENCE AKIN & SONS St. Francisville, Illinois	1936	Arthur Akin Clarence Akin	1937	Clarence Akin
SHISSLER SEED CO. Elmwood, Ill.	1935	Harold Shissler	1937	
SHISSLER SEED CO. Elmwood, Ill.	1937	Harold Shissler George Shissler Partnership		Harold Shissler George Shissler
A. H. HOFFMAN SEEDS, INC. Landisville, Pennsylvania	1899	A. H. Hoffman	1939	E. M. Godshalk Wm. F. Hoffman Lester L. Hug
LOUISIANA SEED CO. INC. Alexandria, Louisiana	1934	E. S. Voelker	1941	J. F. Percy
JAMES GRANT & SON Cottam, Ontario, Canada	1939	James T. Grant Evan R. Grant (Son)	1942	
JAMES GRANT & SON SEED CO. LTD. Cottam, Ontario, Canada Incorporated	1949	James T. Grant Evan R. Grant		James T. Grant Evan R. Grant
PETERSON BIDDICK CO. Wadena, Minnesota	1910	J. F. Peterson Dan Biddick	1944	Harold Peterson, Mgr.
GROUP OF CERTIFIED SEED PRODUCERS	1938			Karl F. Mueller Gen. Mgr.
WISCONSIN SEED COMPANY Spring Green, Wisconsin (Organized)	1946	Claude Jackson Franklin D. Austin Harry W. Kindschi Elmer D. Kindschi K. F. Mueller	1949	
AGRICULTURAL LABORATORIES, INC. Columbus, Ohio	1933	Hugh Nesbit M. M. Elmers	1951	
AG-LAB. PRODUCTS, INC. Columbus, Ohio	1954		1954	Roy Brendholtz & Associates (Owners) James M. Beardsley, Mgr.

Italy	1949
Spain	1954
Argentina	1957

Notes

(Correspondence is located in Eugene D. Funk, Sr., Papers or in Eugene D. Funk, Jr., Papers unless otherwise cited.)

CHAPTER I

1. Helen M. Cavanagh, *Funk of Funk's Grove*, Farmer, Legislator and Cattle King of the Old Northwest, 1797–1865, (Bloomington, Ill.: Pantagraph Printing Co., 1952), Chapters I through VI.
2. *Ibid.*, Chapter VIII. Some accounts give the date of Isaac's death as Jan. 30, 1865; the tombstone records Jan. 29, 1865.
3. One outside claim was settled by litigation and was proved illegal.
4. *Interview* with Dana Rollins.
5. Helen M. Cavanagh, *Funks Grove Timber*, Pamphlet, (Bloomington: Funk Bros. Seed Co., 1957), p. 3; Orme Evans supplied the information regarding the architecture.
6. Gladys Funk Rehtmeyer, *Remembering I*, Feb. 1955, pp. 10 and 16. See Appendix I for summaries of the activities of the second generation and their families.
7. *Interview* with Arthur Funk, May 18, 1954.
8. Gladys Funk Rehtmeyer, *op. cit.*, p. 1.
9. Eugene D. Funk, *Speech to Shirley Lodge* #582, Nov. 30, 1943. LaFayette was a charter member of this Lodge. Members of the Shirley Lodge from the Funk Family include De Loss, LaFayette II, Eugene, Jr., Paul, Theodore, LaFayette III, Richard and Calvin Rehtmeyer.
10. See Appendix I.
11. *Interview* with The Reverend Sydney A. Guthrie, June 17, 1955. He recalled working for his grandfather, who managed The Ark, and hearing the conversations of The Old Timers. See *Daily Pantagraph*, Feb. 5, 1950.
12. *Interview* with Mrs. Madeline Funk McCullough, daughter of George Funk, June, 1955.
13. *Daily Pantagraph*, Sept. 8, 1919.
14. Gladys Funk Rehtmeyer, *op. cit.*, p. 3.
15. *Ibid.*, p. 7
16. LaFayette Funk, *Diary*, Jan. 1–31, 1867.
17. *Ibid.*, Feb. and March 1867; also Gladys Funk, *Remembering II*, p. 2.
18. LaFayette Funk, *Diary*, April, 1867.
19. Cal. G. Tyler to E. D. Funk, Jr., Sept. 26, 1953.
20. *Interview* with Eugene D. Funk, Jr., Dec. 7, 1957.
21. Hazel Funk Holmes, *Memories of my Mother*, Sophronia J. Funk.

CHAPTER II

1. Helen M. Cavanagh, *Funk of Funks Grove*, chapter 3.
2. *Daily Pantagraph*, Aug. 17, 1868.
3. *Ibid.*, Aug. 20, 1868.
4. *Ibid.*, Aug. 24, 1868.

5. Third Annual Report, Union Stock Yards, 1869, as reported by Ernest Staples Osgood, *The Day of the Cattleman,* (Chicago: University of Chicago Phoenix Books, 1929), p. 44.
6. *Daily Pantagraph,* March 27, 1874: others were W. R. Duncan, Wm. Smith, Nelson Jones and W. O. Davis.
7. *Ibid.,* Apr. 24, 1874.
8. *Weekly Pantagraph,* May 8, 1874, May 5, 1876 and Apr. 13, 1877.
9. *Ibid.,* July 13, 1877.
10. *Weekly Pantagraph,* Jan. 2, 1880.
11. Helen Cavanagh, *Funk of Funks Grove,* chapter 6.
12. *Weekly Pantagraph,* Oct. 11, 1890. The increase in valuation for the county was estimated to be 66 and ⅔%.
13. *Ibid.,* May 27, 1881. Interview with Arthur Funk. Stated they first were at Ogallala. Funk Family Yosemite Valley visit 1874 listing those in the picture from left to right:

Back Row	Middle Row	Front Row
Duncan Funk	Mrs. Duncan Funk	Linc Funk
Jacob Funk	Mrs. Jacob Funk	Deane Funk
Belle Funk	Mrs. LaFayette Funk	Charlie Funk
George Funk	Cousin Clara Funk	Eugene Funk

14. LaFayette Funk, *Diary,* 1883.
15. *Ibid.*
16. Eugene D. Funk, *Account of Hunting Trip,* Aged Seventeen, 1884.
17. Interview with Arthur Funk, December 11, 1952.
18. Osgood, *op. cit.,* pp. 75-96. The peak of prices occurred on the Chicago market in the summer of 1882 when top prices reached a level higher than since 1870. From that time the decline especially in higher grades was steady, p. 105.
19–29. Eugene D. Funk, *Diary,* July 21–25 through August 7, 1885.
30. *Weekly Pantagraph,* June 15, 1888.
31. *Ibid.,* Oct. 21, 1888.
32. *Ibid.,* Sept. 24, 1886.
33. *Daily Pantagraph,* Oct. 31, 1886.
34. *Ibid.*
35. *Weekly Pantagraph,* Nov. 4, 1887.
36. LaFayette Funk, *Diary,* Jan. 3, 1889.
37. *Ibid.,* Jan. 4 and 5, 1889.
38. *Ibid.,* Jan. and Feb., 1889.
39. *Ibid.,* Feb. and March, 1889.
40. *Ibid.,* March 26, June 23, 30, Sept. 8, 1889; also July and August 1889. Construction of a new hay barn occupied attention in July 1889. State Fair business necessitated trips to Peoria and Chicago. The Funk-Stubblefield reunion was usually held late in August. Old Settlers Reunion was held in Atlanta, *Ibid.,* September 3, 1889; Fairs at Clinton, Springfield and Monticello were attended. Gene returned to school in the fall. *Ibid.,* Sept. 13, 1889. LaFayette was responsible for incoming stock exhibits at the State Fair at Peoria. He was always concerned about attendance. He returned home tired and worn out after all the responsibility. In a few days he was off again to attend to the business of the Fat Stock Show in Chicago and and in another day he departed to the St. Louis Fair with his family, *Ibid.,* Sept. 28, Oct. 5, 8–11, 1889.
41. *Ibid.,* Oct. 13, 1889.

42. *Ibid.*, Oct. 23, 24 and Nov. 8, 16, 1889; for reference to the Stubblefields, *Weekly Pantagraph*, May 1, 8, 1874; to the Dillons of Normal, see *Daily Pantagraph*, Feb. 12, 1870; *Weekly Pantagraph*, Jan. 8, July 12, 1872, June 6, 1873, May 2, 1873.
43. Clipping (unidentified) Funk Papers.
44. LaFayette Funk, *Diary*, Nov. 22, 24, 28, Dec. 5, 17, 26, 1889.

CHAPTER III

1. Helen Cavanagh, *Funk of Funks Grove*, Chapter VII.
2. Ernest L. Bogart and Charles M. Thompson, *The Industrial State*, 1870–1893 Centennial History, Vol. IV, (Springfield: Illinois Centennial Commission, 1920), p. 217.
3. *Daily Pantagraph*, April 18, 24, 1868. A state convention was held in Decatur, April 14.
4. *Ibid.*, Sept. 8, 1868.
5. *Ibid.*, Sept. 12, 1868.
6. *Ibid.*,

	Grant	Seymour	Palmer	Eden
Funks Grove	91	55	91	55
McLean County	5895	3858	5894	3872

7. *Ibid.*, June 9, 1870.
8. *Journal*, House of Representatives, 27th General Assembly State of Illinois, (Springfield: Illinois Journal Printing Office, 1871), pp. 10-12.
9. *Ibid.*, pp. 633-635.
10. *Ibid.*, pp. 359 and 367.
11. A. E. Paine, *The Granger Movement in Illinois*, University Studies, (Urbana: University of Illinois Press, 1944), pp. 20-21, see also *Prairie Farmer*, Feb. 18, 1871. The purpose of this so called Farmers Ring was to check the powers of the railroads and to make more bearable some of the economic burdens of the farmers. Sixty-five members of the State Legislature were reported to have met in the rooms of the State Agricultural Society "for the purpose of organizing farmers and mechanics clubs to look after the interest of the producing class, to subject all bills and measures to thorough and free discussion and by unanimity of action to secure legislation as will relieve the necessities of the mechanical and agricultural interests of the state," *Ibid.*, pp. 20 and 21 also *Prairie Farmer*, February 18, 1871. *The Daily Illinois State Register* also noticed the formation of this Legislative Farmers Club in the State Agricultural Rooms February 7, 1871. The meeting was called to order by N. Williams of Whiteside County. Organization was effected with G. G. Armstrong of La Salle as President; L. D. Whiting of Bureau County as Vice President, and Secretary, W. C. Flagg of Madison County, Ass't Sec'ty. J. H. Stuart of Adams County. *Daily Illinois State Register*, February 9, 1871. The committee reporting the above officers was also listed. References to this Legislative Farmers Club are few. Sometimes it is referred to as a Farmers Ring. This was the day of "rings." Such acceptable agricultural publications as the *Prairie Farmer* recognized the existence of the group. According to this paper agricultural leadership was not so well organized as might be inferred but it was strong enough to be felt. It asserted that the *Chicago Times* in editorial column suggested that the Farmers ring was running things their own way and in opposition to the lawyers. The reporter of the *Prairie Farmer* found this not strictly in accordance with the facts but "we are glad to say that there is a grain of truth at the bottom of it." Accordingly this publication believed that farmers only believed that

there were certain enactments needed by the population that "does three-fourths of all the labor, pays three-fourths of all the taxes." It noted that several members of the group were lawyers and that the farmers did not vote blindly but discussed the legislation. They did vote solidly in the matter of salaries for judges of the Supreme Court. With "railroad rings," "warehouse rings" and "State House Rings" depending not on membership in the legislature but on lobbies for influence who could blame the farmers. *Prairie Farmer,* March 18, 1871.

12. A. E. Paine, *op. cit.,* also *Weekly Pantagraph,* December 13, 1872, noted Judge Tipton's decision and that of Judge Wood of the Kankakee district who had ruled that the corresponding act regulating passenger charges was constitutional. The *Pantagraph* said, "We do believe that this grand war between the railroads and the people can only terminate at last in the peoples' victory"; also Bogart and Thompson, *op. cit.,* p. 93.

13. Paine, *op. cit.,* p. 22.

14. *Weekly Pantagraph,* December 20, 1871.

15. Paine, *op. cit.,* p. 22 and *Weekly Pantagraph,* February 28, 1871; see Murray R. Benedict, *Farm Policies of the United States, 1790–1950,* (New York: Twentieth Century Fund, 1953) p. 100.

16. Paine, *op. cit.,* pp. 6 and 10. Numbers included:

1869–2	1872–69	1875–50
1870–1	1873–761	1876–27
1871–5	1874–704	

17. *Ibid.,* p. 11, see Benedict, *op. cit.,* p. 97 footnote, for an estimate of the comparative influence of the Grange.

18. Paine, *op. cit.,* pp. 6 and 10.

19. *Ibid.,* p. 13.

20. *Ibid.,* p. 31.

21. *Weekly Pantagraph.,* Jan. 31, 1873.

22. *Journal of the House of Representatives,* 27th General Assembly vol. 2, (Springfield Illinois: Journal Office, 1872), p. 137.

23. *Weekly Pantagraph,* April 19, 1872.

24. *Ibid.,* May 3, 1872.

25. *Ibid.*

26. *Ibid.,* November 15, 1872.

27. *Weekly Pantagraph,* January 17, 1873.

28. *Ibid.,* February 28, 1873.

29. *Ibid.,* March 7, 1873.

30. *Ibid.,* March 28, 1873.

31. *Ibid.,* March 21, 1873. Other officers were J. F. Boulware as Vice President and James Quinn as Treasurer.

32. *Ibid.,* June 27, 1873.

33. *Ibid.,* November 7, 1873. The Peoples Ticket was successful in Chicago; the Anti monopoly party was strong in Livingston and Ford counties, Piatt and Woodford but divided in DeWitt and Tazewell.

34. *Weekly Pantagraph,* October 17, 1873. The decision in the lower court sustained the state's right to regulate. The Supreme Court of Illinois upheld the lower court in 1873. The United States Supreme Court sustained the decision in 1876. The case had far reaching influence throughout the United States.

35. *Weekly Pantagraph,* March 24, 1876.

36. *Ibid.,* March 30, 1876.

37. *Journal of the House of Representatives,* 33rd General Assembly, (Springfield; H. W. Rokker, State Printer and Binder, 1883).

38. *Transactions of the McLean County Historical Society,* Vol. II (Bloomington: Pantagraph Printing Co., 1903), p. 634.

39. *Transactions, Department of Agriculture,* Illinois, 1911, Vol. 49 (no pub given) pp. VII-XVI. LaFayette Funk was continuously a member from 1883 to 1911 with the exception of 1894–96 and 1898–1903–22 years.

40. Bogart and Thompson, *op. cit.,* p. 80 suggests that the Liberals failed to advance specific inducements to the farmers. The farmers saw no advantage in turning out the republicans who had secured whatever there was of advancement in railroad regulation.

CHAPTER IV

1–14. LaFayette Funk, *Diary,* Jan. 16–Aug. 30, 1891.

15. *Weekly Pantagraph,* Aug. 21, 1891.

16–23. LaFayette Funk, *Diary,* Sept. 1–21–Dec. 30, 1891.

24. *Ibid.,* Summary 1891.

25. *Ibid.,* 1892.

26. Henry B. Fuller, "The Growth of Education, Art and Letters" in E. L. Bogart and J. M. Mathews, *The Modern Commonwealth.* Vol. V. Centennial History, (Springfield: Centennial Commission, 1920), p. 30.

27. LaFayette Funk, *Diary,* Jan.–May 1893.

28. *Ibid.,* May 1893, also June 6, 1893.

29. *Chicago Daily Tribune,* May 2, 1893.

30. _____*The Illinois Building and Exhibits Therein* at the World's Columbian Exposition, (Chicago: John Morris Company, 1893) volume prepared by Board of Commissioners to serve partly as a guide to the exhibits in the Illinois State Building and partly as a souvenir.

31. *Chicago Daily Tribune,* May 18, 1893.

32. *Ibid.,* May 19, 1893.

33. *Ibid.*

34. LaFayette Funk, *Diary,* May 18, 1893.

35. *Ibid.,* June 1, 1893.

36. *Ibid.,* June 8 and 9, 1893.

37. *Ibid.,* Nov. and Dec. 1893.

38. *Ibid.,* Jan. 1894.

39. *Ibid.,* Feb. 1894. John Pancake was ill at the time. His funeral occurred May 8, 1894.

40. *Ibid.,* April 5, 1894. LaFayette Funk seldom expressed any emotion in the pages of his Diaries. Statement of factual situations appeared to be sufficient. His pleasure or displeasure seldom reached the written page.

41. *Ibid.,* April 24 and May 3, 1894.

42. *Ibid.,* Jan. 18, 1894.

43. *Ibid.,* May 23–28, 1894.

44. *Ibid.,* June 1–15, 1894.

45. *Congressional Record,* 53rd Congress, First Session, House of Representatives vol. XXV (Washington: Government Printing Office, 1893) p. 199, 554.

46. *Ibid.,* First Session, Vol. XXV, Part II (Washington: Government Printing Office, 1893) p. 2259.

47. *Ibid.,* Second Session, Vol. XXVI, Part I (Washington: Government Printing Office, 1894) p. 147.

48. *Ibid.,* First Session, Vol. XXV, Part II (Washington: Government Printing Office, 1893) pp. 1368, 1802.

49. *Ibid.*, Second Session, Vol. XXVI, Part I p. 261 and Vol. XXVI, Part VII pp. 6919, 6920.
50. *Ibid.*, Part I, p. 320. The famous Newby alias Dan Benron case.
51. *Ibid.*, 53rd Congress, Second Session, House of Representatives Vol. XXVI, Part I (Washington: Government Printing Office, 1894) pp. 905–909.
52. *Ibid.*, Vol. XXVI, Part I pp. 908, 1069, 1111.
53. *Ibid.*, 53rd Congress, Second Session, House of Representatives Vol. XXVII, Part I, (Washington: Government Printing Office, 1894) p. 149.
54. *Ibid.*, Vol. XXVII, Part II, (Washington: Government Printing Office, 1895) p. 1197.

Chapter V

1–4. LaFayette Funk, *Diary*, July 7–Nov. 1894.
5–6. *Ibid.*, April 19, 20, 1896.
7. *Ibid.*, Nov. 8–13, 1896.
8. Eugene D. Funk, *Diary*, Nov. 8, 1896.
9. LaFayette Funk, *Diary*, Nov. 12, 1896; also Benedict, *op. cit.*, p. 139. The Farmers National Congress achieved some significance by crystalizing ideas but was loosely organized with little or no local organization from 1880–1920. During part of this time a legislative representative was maintained in Washington.
10–22. LaFayette Funk, *Diary*, Feb. 16, 1897–Dec. 16, 1898.
23. Eugene D. Funk, *Diary*, Dec. 24, 1898.
24. LaFayette Funk, *Diary*, Dec. 31, 1898.
25. Eugene D. Funk, *Diary*, Jan. 19, 25, 1898.
26. De Loss Funk, *Historical Items*, March 14, 1956.
27. LaFayette Funk, *Diary*, Jan. 3, Feb. 16, March 28, April 14, June 1–12–16, 1899.
28. *Ibid.*, June 21, 22, 1899.
29. *Ibid.*, Sept. 21, 1899; also Eugene D. Funk, *Diary*, Sept. 21, 1899.
30. LaFayette Funk, *Diary*, Oct. 9, 1899.
31. *Ibid.*, Oct. 20, Nov. 1 and Dec. 8, 1899.
32. *Ibid.*, Jan. 12, 1900; also Eugene Funk, *Diary*, Jan. 12, 1900.
33. *Ibid.*, Jan. 18, 20, 25, 27, 1900; Oct. and Sept. and Nov. 1901.
34. *Ibid.*, Mar. 22, 23; Apr. 18, 20, 21, 1900.
35. Eugene D. Funk, *Diary*, Mar. and April; also at Jakes, April 22, 1900.
36. LaFayette Funk, *Diary*, May 9–14, 1900; Eugene D. Funk, *Diary*, May 10, 1900.
37–42. LaFayette Funk, *Diary*, May 29–June 19, 1900.
43. *Ibid.*, June 20, also Eugene D. Funk, *Diary*, June 14 and July 7, 1900.
44. *Ibid.*, July 6 and 7, 1900.
45. L. H. Kerrick, *The Farm and the Town*, Jan. 13, 1899.
46. *Ibid.*
47. *Ibid.*
48. *Breeders Gazette*, Dec. 20, 1899.
49. *Ibid.*, Jan. 10, 1899.
50. *Ibid.*, Nov. 10, 1897.
51. *Chicago Daily Drovers Journal*, March 21, 1900.
52. *Prairie Farmer*, Sept 22, 1900.
53. *Chicago Daily Drovers Journal*, Sept. 22, 1900.
54. *Ibid.*, Nov. 24, 1900.
55. *Chicago Daily Drovers Journal*, March 20, 1900; in April LaFayette's cattle

sold 16 head, 1657 lbs. at $5.75; Eugene Sr., sold in September a load of cattle selling at $5.80, *Ibid.*, Sept. 3, 1900.

56. Eugene D. Funk, *Diary*, Jan. 22, 1900; the estate of F. M. Funk left bank stock which was sold with George taking 20 shares; I. G., 10 shares; D. M., 10 shares; Wm. H. Brown, 10 shares; Eugene Funk, 10 shares; and Elizabeth P. Funk, 10 shares. Will Bracken and A. B. Funk were executors of the estate. LaFayette paid $6,210.85 for 64 and ⅘ acres of land and for 3,589 bushels of corn in addition to 16 shares of stock for $3,200. He drew notes on the First National Bank and on the State National Bank for the sum of $5,500 at this time.

57. LaFayette Funk *Diary*, Mar. 11–18, 1900; also Eugene D. Funk *Diary*, Mar. 10, 1900; LaFayette Funk, *Diary*, Oct. 18–22, 1900; *Chicago Daily Drovers Journal*, Oct. 22, 1900; LaFayette Funk, *Diary*, Mar. 10–17, 1901.

58. Eugene D. Funk, *Diary*, Nov. 15, 1900.

59. *Prairie Farmer*, Nov. 10, 1900.

60. *Breeders Gazette*, Nov. 21, 1900; see picture p. 739 and the cover for Gateway to Stockyards. There are those who say that one figure is Isaac Funk.

61. *Prairie Farmer*, May 26, 1900.

62. *Chicago Daily Drovers Journal*, Mar. 14, 1900.

63. LaFayette Funk *Diary*, Dec. 3 and 6, 1900; also Eugene D. Funk, *Diary*.

64. *Prairie Farmer*, Nov. 17, 1900.

65. *Chicago Daily Drovers Journal*, Dec. 4, 1900.

66. LaFayette Funk, *Diary*, Dec. 3 and 6, 1900; also Eugene D. Funk *Diary*, Dec. 3–6, 1900.

67. *Prairie Farmer*, Dec. 15, 1900; also *Breeders Gazette*, Dec. 19, 1900; see picture p. 964.

68. *Prairie Farmer*, Dec. 22, 1900.

69. *Breeders Gazette*, Nov. 21, 1900.

70. Eugene D. Funk, *Diary*, Jan. 5, 1896; also LaFayette Funk, *Diary*, Jan. 4, 1896; burial occurred at Funks Grove Cemetery, April 13, 1896.

71. *Journal of House of Representatives*, 40th General Assembly, Illinois (Springfield; Phillips Bros. 1897) pp. 17, 104, 131, 132, 134, 135.

72. *Ibid.*, 41st Assembly, Illinois (Springfield; Phillips Bros. 1899) pp. 77, 78, 79, 83.

CHAPTER VI

1. An older group of grandchildren of Isaac Funk included in 1890: Belle, aged 32, daughter of D. M.; Charles, 31, son of Jacob; Clara, 29, daughter of Jacob; Grace, 25, daughter of F. M.; Deane, 23, son of Jacob; Eugene, 23, son of LaFayette; I. G., 22, son of George; Frank, 21, son of Benjamin and Arthur, 19, son of Isaac II. A younger group of grandchildren included Madeline, 12, daughter of George; J. Dwight, 12, son of F. M.; Lyle, 16, son of A. B.; Lawrence, 12, son of Isaac II; De Loss, 8, son of LaFayette; Julius, 7, son of George; Helen, 6, daughter of Isaac II; Idelle, 6, daughter of Kerricks; Hazel, 4, daughter of A. B.

2–9. Eugene D. Funk, Sr., *Diary* at Wymans Institute, Jan. Mar. 15, 1884.

10. Other occupants were C. D. Bliss, New York City; J. L. Emerson, Titusville, Pa., P. Fuller, New Haven, Conn., H. B. Mc Cormick, Harrisburg, Pa., E. E. Gwynne, New York City; D. C. Haldeman, Harrisburgh, Pa., R. Merrill, Milwaukee, Wis., H. N. Morris, Chicago, Ill., G. A. Orvis, Manchester, Vt., J. Parsons, New York City; J. A. Phillips, Pittsburgh, Pa.

11. Other members: E. B. Bishop, Newton Center, G. B. Hollister, Rutherford, N. J., W. J. Ogden, Chicago; W. W. Parker, Mifflintown, Pa., A. J. Stone,

Andover, E. C. Hollister, Rutherford, N. Y., C. Morgan, Aurora, N. Y., A. H. Preston, Omaha, Neb., J. H. Field, Richmond, Va., R. Merrill, Milwaukee, Wis., S. E. Farwell, St. Paul, Minn., W. G. Preston, Omaha, Neb., F. K. Hollister, Rutherford, N. J., J. T. Carr, Dubuque, Iowa.

12. Russell H. Chittenden, *History of the Sheffleld Scientific School of Yale University,* 1846–1922, (2 vols.; New Haven: Yale University Press, 1928), I, Chapter one.
13. *Ibid.,* p. 42.
14. *Ibid.,* p. 55.
15. *Ibid.,* p. 89.
16. *Ibid.,* p. 270.
17. Eugene D. Funk, *Scrap Book,* Telegram from Walter Camp and clipping from *Boston Globe,* December 2, 1888.
18. *Ibid.*
19. *Daily Pantagraph,* August 31, 1889.
20. Eugene D. Funk, *Diary,* July 16–18, 1890.
21. *Ibid.,* July 19, 1890 reference is to Bloomington, Illinois.
22. *Ibid.,* July 20, 1890 also letter E. D. to family, undated.
23–30. *Ibid.,* July 26–Aug. 1, 1890.
31. *Ibid.,* Aug. 1, 1890. He also noted that the absentee landlords in many cases were Irish.
32. *Ibid.,* Aug. 5, 1890.
33. *Ibid.,* Aug. 6, 1890.
34. *Ibid.,* Aug. 8, 1890. Gene's estimates included wages for hired man and cost of farm implements.
35. *Ibid.,* Aug. 9, 1890.
36. *Ibid.,* Aug. 11, 1890. The inscription here impressed Funk:
> Good Friend for Jesus sake forbear
> To dig the dust enclosed here,
> Blest be ye man that spares this stone
> And curst be he that moves my bones.
37. *Ibid.,* Aug. 13, 1890.
38. *Ibid.,* Aug. 14, 1890.
39. *Ibid.,* Aug. 14, 1890.
40. *Ibid.,* Aug. 16, 1890. Robert Lincoln was the son of President Lincoln, friend of Isaac Funk. The boys were disappointed not to see him.
41. *Ibid.,* Aug. 17, 1890.
42. *Ibid.,* Aug. 18, 1890.
43. *Ibid.,* Aug. 27, 1890.
44. *Ibid.,* Aug. 28, 1890.
45. *Ibid.,* Aug. 29, 1890. The waiter said "that there were a number of Funks scattered all over Germany—several of whom he knows are titled people."
46–67. *Ibid.,* Aug. 30–Sept. 28, 1890.
68. E. D. Funk to family Sept. 29, 1890.
69. Eugene Funk, *Diary,* Sept. 29–Oct. 4, 1890.

CHAPTER VII

1. The following marriages occurred 1882–1901:
   Clara Funk to Howard Humphreys, Sept. 11, 1888.
   Belle Funk to Herbert Rollins, Oct. 19, 1882.
   Eugene D. Funk to Mary Anderson, July 19, 1894.
   Deane N. Funk to Fern Shores, Oct. 3, 1894.
   Isaac G. Funk to Bessie Florence, Oct. 31, 1894

Frank H. Funk to Florence Risser, Dec. 11, 1895.
Grace Funk to Will Bracken, June 19, 1895.
I. Lincoln Funk to Mrs. Watrus, June 5, 1895.
Lyle W. Funk to Irene Armstrong, Oct. 12, 1898.
Charles Funk to A. Stokes, Nov. 21, 1901.
J. Dwight Funk to Grace Wilcox, June 5, 1901.
Arthur Funk to Louise Metz, Jan. 9, 1901.

2. See Appendix II.
3. *Interview* with Mrs. Eugene D. Funk, Sr., July, 1952.
4. *Ibid.*, Gene made a trip to Oregon in 1892 with the Bloomington Hunting Club including Frank, Deane and Linc Funk as well as J. C. Stevenson, J. B. Stevenson and C. T. Stevenson. J. B. Stevenson was a brother of Adlai Stevenson, J. C. and C. T. were nephews. They spent some time in the Okanagon country, (see clipping, *Evening Telegram*, Oct. 4, 1892).
5. *Interview* with Mrs. Eugene D. Funk, Sr., July 1952.
6. Eugene D. Funk, *Diary*, Feb. 1896.
7. *Ibid.*, July 4–30, 1896.
8. *Ibid.*, Oct. 6, 1896. In Nov. LaFayette shipped two carloads of cattle; some were bought the previous March by Eugene at 3 and ¾ with weight about 950; They were fed all summer and sold at $5.00 with weight in Chicago 1045.
9. *Ibid.*, March 26, 1898.
10. *Ibid.*, March 27, 1898.
11. Eugene D. Funk, Jr., *List of trees at Eugene D. Funk Sr. Home*, 1957.
12. Eugene D. Funk, *Diary*, May 2, 1898.
13–17. *Ibid.*, May 5–June 2, 1898 to Jan. 1, 1899.
18. *Ibid.*, Jan. 12, 17, 31, 1899; Aug. 30, 1899; Oct. and Dec. 2, 1899.
19. *Report of Illinois Farmers Institute 1895* (Springfield: E. F. Hartsman State Printer, 1896), pp. 288-289.
20–27. E. D. Funk, *Diary*, Jan. 31, 1899–June 26, 1899.
28. LaFayette Funk, *Diary*, May 21, 1899.
29–35. E. D. Funk, *Diary*, July 1899–Dec. 24, 1899.
36. LaFayette Funk, *Diary*, Dec. 25, 1899.
37. Eugene D. Funk, *Diary*, Feb. 1900.
38. *Ibid.*, Feb. 28, 1900.
39. *Prairie Farmer*, March 17, 1900.
40. *Ibid.*, March 21, 1900.
41. *Ibid.*
42. *Ibid.*
43. *Breeders Gazette*, Jan. 10, 1900.
44. *Orange Judd Farmer*, Nov. 3, 1900; says germinating power of 95%, Feb. 9, 1901.
45. *Chicago Daily Drovers Journal*, Oct. 15, 1901.
46. *Orange Judd Farmer*, Oct. 20, 1900; *Prairie Farmer*, Oct. 20, 1900.
47. *Ibid.*, Oct. 19, 27, 1901, The Fourth Annual Peoria Corn Exposition is dated Oct. 6–8, 1902.
48. Eugene D. Funk, *Diary*, May 6, 1900.
49. *Ibid.*, June 14 and July 7, 1900.
50. *Ibid.*, Feb. 7–14 and April 23–28 and May 25, 1900 and June 26, 1900.
51. *Ibid.*, Aug. 25, 1900.
52. *Ibid.*, June 26, 1900; LaFayette also recorded in October a day spent on John Noble's farm digging for Indian bones and relics; "a very considerable number of people gathered for the work" but nothing very auspicious was discovered; LaFayette Funk, *Diary*, Oct. 17, 1900.

53–56. Lafayette Funk, *Diary,* Aug. 18, 1900–Sept. 16, 1900.

57. Eugene D. Funk, *Diary,* Sept. 14, 18, 1900.

58. LaFayette Funk, *Diary,* Oct. 10, 1900 and Eugene D. Funk, *Diary,* Oct. 10, 1900.

59. *Ibid.,* Nov. 24, 1900. A paper of the same title was delivered before McLean County Farmers Institute. See *Annual Report of Illinois Farmers Institute,* (Springfield, Phillips Bros., 1902), pp. 488–490.

60. *Prairie Farmer,* Nov. 24, 1901.

61–69. Eugene D. Funk, *Diary,* Jan. 15–17, May 20, 1901.

70. *Breeders Gazette,* May 29, 1901.

71. Eugene D. Funk, *Diary,* May 22, 1901; LaFayette Funk, *Diary,* May 22, 1901.

72. Eugene D. Funk, *Diary,* July 13 and 21, 1901.

73. LaFayette Funk, *Diary,* Aug. 14, 1901.

74. *Ibid.,* Aug. 18, 1901.

75. *Ibid.,* Nov. 13, 30, 1901 and LaFayette Funk, *Diary,* Nov. 13, 1901.

76. Eugene D. Funk, *Diary,* Dec. 10, 1901.

77. LaFayette Funk, *Diary,* Oct. 10, 1901.

78. Eugene D. Funk, *Diary,* Dec. 29, 1901.

79. *Ibid.,* Dec. 30, 1901.

Chapter VIII

1. Hugo DeVries, *Plant Breeding,* (Chicago: The Open Court Publishing Company, 1919 (Copyright 1907), p. 104.

2. *Ibid.*

3. *Ibid.,* p. 105.

4. *Ibid.,* p. 52.

5. *Ibid.,* p. 62.

6. *Ibid.,* p. 101; also *Bulletin* 92, Agricultural Experiment Station of Minnesota.

7. De Vries, *op. cit.,* p. 102.

8. M. L. Bowman and B. H. Crossley, *Corn,* (Des Moines: The Kenyon Printing and Mfg. Company), p. 426.

9. *Ibid.,* p. 429.

10. United States Department of Agriculture, *Year Book of Agriculture,* 1936, 74th Congress, 2d Session House Document No. 338 (Washington: U. S. Gov't Printing Office, 1936), pp. 465-467.

11. *Ibid.,* p. 469.

12. *Ibid;* Also The Experiment Station at the University of Illinois reported corn experiments from 1892. In the April *Bulletin* of this year the effect of removing tassels was included; in May 1892 G. W. McCluer, assistant Horticulturist in an article on "Corn Crossing" recognized that outside of Experiment Stations little work had been done and recorded in the breeding of new varieties of corn, wheat and oats. McCluer concluded that corn could not be improved by self fertilization. Work for the basis of his report had begun in 1889 when Thos Hunt, assistant agriculturist at Illinois crossed dent corns, "During this first year 16 ears were produced by crossing varieties of dent corn, no crosses being made between varities of different colors." Cloth bags were used in the experiments. See G. W. McCluer, "Corn Crossing," May 1892, No. 21, *Bulletins of Agricultural Experiment Station, University of Illinois,* Vol. 2, 1891–94, (Urbana: 1894), pp. 82-101; also G. E. Morrow and F. D. Gardner, "Field Experiments With Corn, 1892," *Bulletin* No. 25, *Ibid.,* see Experiment 89.

Field Experiments with corn were continued at the University in 1893 as related in Experiment 89. Cross fertilized ears produced larger yield and larger stalks. Corn from self-fertilized ears was more uniform in character than from the cross fertilized. It was thought that after some years of selection, after crossing, corn fairly uniform could be produced. G. E. Morrow and F. D. Gardner "Field Experiments with Corn, 1893," March 1894, Bulletin No. 31, *Ibid.*

Cross fertilization was continued in 1894: "The ten most promising crosses selected from 1892 and grown in 1893 were again grown in 1894 on plats of considerable size. Farmers were advised they could produce cross bred seed in considerable quantities by crossing varieties." F. O. Gardner, "Field Experiments with Corn," March 1895, *Bulletin,* No. 37, *Ibid.*

For experiments by C. G. Hopkins regarding the protein and oil content of the corn kernel see Bulletins 55 and 128, University of Illinois Agricultural Experiment Station.

13. Parlin & Orendorff, *How to Grow Pedigree Corn,* (Buffalo, N. Y. Gies and Co. Printers, 1894). This pamphlet was found in Eugene D. Funk's collection. This company explained what was meant by the "pedigree system." It noted that about one half of ordinary corn was inbred and one half was not. Parlin and Orendorff who were manufacturers of Canton Plows, Planters, Listers, Cultivators and other implements, described how to bring the quality of corn above the present standard in a small publication entitled *How to Grow Pedigree Corn* copyrighted 1894 as follows:

"Suppose we get some from Neighbor b, same color as ours and as near like ours as possible—suppose it is Champion White Pearl, and you have Silver Beauty. Plant three or four rows of Silver Beauty and then one of Pearl and continue in this way through a small field. Mark each row with the name of the corn planted therein. When the tassels first come out (before the blossom falls) cut every tassel of the Pearl. When the corn gets ripe, pick this separate. What kind of corn is it? It is not Champion White Pearl because the pollen came from Silver Beauty as there were no tassels left on the Pearl to give Pollen. It is Silver Beauty Corn? No, because it is bred on Champion White Pearl stalks. We have an exact cross between Silver Beauty (male) and Champion White Pearl (female) just as complete as you could breed your female swine to a neighbors. The cross is perfect, but what shall we call it? Remember this is a *new kind*—it has new blood, not the big ears of an old degenerated field. Let us call the new kind thus formed A No. 1. Next year we plant four rows of A No. 1 to one row of Hickory King, just as we did the previous kinds. Cut the tassels off the Hickory King and what kind of corn have we? A No. 1 as male and Hickory King as female, and A No. 1 formed by Silver Beauty as male and Champion White Pearl as female. Let us call the last kind A No. 2.

We have a small form of pedigree (M is for male   F for female)

$$
\text{A No. 2} \begin{cases} \text{M A No. 1} \begin{cases} \text{M Silver Beauty} \\ \text{F Champion White Pearl} \end{cases} \\ \\ \text{F Hickory King} \end{cases}
$$

You can see how soon a lengthy complete pedigree could be carried out. If corn is bred this way and proper care is used not to breed related seed, it will not 'run out' but rather run to higher perfection. You can cross two colors this way and every grain will be a perfect cross."

14. E. D. Funk to O. M. Allyn, March 24, 1914, also copy of a card issued by Mr. Murdock of his seed corn. A notation by E. D. Funk on this card states "from which we have been breeding Funks Ninety Day since 1893." Murdock's description of his corn follows:

> A medium sized, extra early and exceedingly handsome yellow Dent variety with deep, oily grain and a small red cob; it is always sound, not easily damaged, very heavy and the best in quality. The seed is sure to grow, producing strong vigorous plants, which outstrip the most thrifty weeds in growth. The stalk is medium in height, strong and stocky and not easily broken down. Its time of maturity is 85-100 days and is certain to yield more in value than any other sort. It is a standard and well defined variety—"an old favorite" with both man and beast. It has been carefully grown for many years in a climate and soil best suited to its development and with special reference to improving and permanently fixing its character and is now the best of its type.
>
> It is especially recommended for the first (for early feed etc.) and the last planting in the Southern and Middle States, and for all purposes in the more northern. Seed properly prepared, ready for the planter, per bushel $3.00 sacks free. Per sack of two bushels $5.00.

15. Perry G. Holden, *Interview*, January 11–13, 1955.
16. Perry G. Holden, *Corn Breeding at the University of Illinois, 1895–1900* (Charlevoix, Michigan, October 25, 1948), Holden declared that experimental work in corn breeding at Illinois was begun when he and Eugene Davenport came to the university in 1895 and was continued under his personal supervision until the spring of 1900. Both men had studied under Dr. W. J. Beal at Michigan Agricultural College, Lansing, Michigan. The idea of "controlled parentage" had dominated Beal's experiments. Holden once heard him state as a lecturer in Traverse City, "What would you think of a man who would select a good cow for breeding and pay no attention to the kind of sire he used? That's what you do with your corn."

The following questions remained unanswered for Holden when he left College in 1893. If crossing increases yield, as shown by Dr. Beal's experiments, does selfing decrease yield? To what extent is corn naturally crossed and to what extent selved in the field? Would it be possible to get the full benefits of crossing within one variety and without detasseling, so as to avoid practical difficulties inherent in Beal's method which involved two varieties and detasseling.

After a visit to the University of Illinois about his new position Holden requested his good friend Davenport to supervise an assistant, Frazier, in the production of inbred seed until he returned. Holden recalled: "During the following months I corresponded frequently about plans for setting up the crops work and also sent Frazier instructions on how to self pollinate corn with the use of bags and how to take care of the details." In the fall when he arrived he was able to harvest second generation seed. Two other professors at Illinois were familiar with Beal's ideas, namely Morrow and Gardner who had already checked on Beal's work. See f.n. 2 above. Holden's summary of his Experiments showed that the corn was normally largely cross pollinated in the field. Then he asked what was there about Beal's variety crossing that gave better yields than the natural crossing within a variety? Are these variations within a variety of such a nature that crossing certain plants would give seed which would produce larger yields than the original seed or than seed produced by crossing other pairs of plants. In order to look into this problem he undertook to select a large number of ears. A row was then planted from each and the ear remnants saved. Ears and tassels were bagged and crosses were made between plants from different pairs of rows. The next season individual rows were planted with seed from the different crosses and with seed from the ear remnants, the rows were harvested; yield and other information was recorded.

17. *Breeders Gazette,* November 14, 1900. Despite the fact that Richard Crabb in the *Hybrid Corn Makers* refers on page 28 to time worn records at the University of Illinois, Professor Burlison, retired head of the Department of Agronomy, informed the author that no such records were available in the fall of 1954. Professor Burlison was of the opinion that the Holden story must be accepted. R. Crabb must be given credit for getting nearer to the actual story of early experimentation at Illinois before Holden's story became known, than any other writer. His book is a pioneering work.

See also Donald F. Jones and Herbert L. Everett, "Hybrid Seed Corn" *Bulletin* 532, Connecticut Agricultural Experiment Station, May 1949. The authors trace the early development of Hybrid Corn in an understandable and logical manner. They concluded that the early inbreeding was considered highly injurious and that there is no indication that these early investigations would have resulted in Hybrid Corn as known today.

It should also be noted that C. P. Hartley of the Bureau of Plant Industry did some inbreeding about 1900. Later A. D. Shamel produced inbred lines. Shamel reported in 1905 the yields of two lines which he had selfed for three generations and of the first generation cross between them. This was "the first reported yield of a cross involving inbred lines." See *Agricultural* Year Book of 1936, p. 469. Hartley recognized that increased yields could be obtained from crosses between inbred lines but he thought there were better ways to improve corn.

18. Those who assisted Professor Holden were A. D. Shamel, Claude Chapman and Jim Boyd.

19. Interview with Perry G. Holden at Michigan State University, Lansing, Michigan, June 24, 1953 with Eugene Funk, Jr., Paul Funk and author.

20. Eugene D. Funk, *Diary,* June 23, 1901.

21. Interview with Perry G. Holden, June 24, 1953.

22. E. D. Funk to P. G. Holden, July 20, 1942, Perry G. Holden *Papers.*

23. Eugene D. Funk, *Diary,* November 1901; also record of *Minutes of Funk Brothers* Seed Company. Lists of stockholders differ slightly.

24. *Orange Judd Farmer,* Nov. 15, 1902.

25. *Record of Minutes Funk Bros. Seed Co.* 1901. E. D. Funk Papers, *Diary, Nov.* 1901 shows following:

40 shares in my name (E.D.)	LP 10	WK & FB 15
AB . . . . . 15 shares	AC 10	
LF . . . . . 15 shares	Isaac 10	210
BF 15	JD 15	
Deane . . 30	ED 15	P G Holden. 15
FH 15	IK 15	I G 15
LW 15	LHK 15	Julius 10

26. E. D. Funk to P. G. Holden, Oct. 12, 1901.

27. E. D. Funk to A. D. Shamel, Oct. 12, 1901.

28. *Farmers Voice and National Rural,* January 25, 1902.

29. *Weekly Pantagraph,* January 2, 1902.
30. "Handwritten Copy of Description of Early Work" found in E. D. Funk *Papers.* This copy was included in a section of papers signed by Frank Funk. Examination of Frank Funk's handwriting show similarity; see also *The Orange Judd Farmer,* Nov. 15, 1902 and original copy of E. D. Funk, *Commercial Corn Breeding,* 1904.
31. *Ibid.*
32. *Orange Judd Farmer,* Nov. 1, 1902.
33. *Ibid.*
34. *Ibid.*
35. *Ibid.*
36. C. G. Hopkins to E. D. Funk, May 9, 1902, E. D. Funk *Papers,* Hopkins noted that cooperative work was underway with other corn breeders in the state of Illinois.
37. Clipping in E. D. Funk Papers, no date; see also *Weekly Pantagraph,* March 28, 1902.
38. *Ibid.*
39. *Ibid.*
40. *Ibid.*
41. *Orange Judd Farmer,* Nov. 15, 1902.
42. *Country Gentleman,* Dec. 18, 1902, article by W. P. Lloyd.
43. *Farmers Voice and National Rural,* Jan. 25, 1902.
44. E. D. Funk, *Speech delivered by E. D. Funk before Landowners, Tenants and Overseers* at Dwight Funk Seed House, April 25, 1902; LaFayette Funk, *Diary,* April 25, 1902; "The Seed Company had a meeting at Dwight's Seed House to discuss the methods of growing the different kinds of cereals contemplated growing this year and the manner of cultivating the same."
45. LaFayette Funk, *Diary,* Feb. 24, 1902.
46. *Ibid.,* March 30, 1902.
47. *Ibid.,* May 26, 1902
48. Interview with P. G. Holden, June 24, 1953.
49. Interview with Joe Henderson by Eugene D. Funk. P. G. Holden in an Interview in July 1953 attached considerable significance to this incident.
50. *Orange Judd Farmer,* Nov. 13, 1902.
51. *Iowa Homestead,* Nov. 1902.
52. *Ibid.*
53. *Ibid.*
54. *Ibid.;* also *Weekly Pantagraph,* Nov. 28, 1902.
55. *Ibid.;* Nov. 21, 1902.
56. *Ibid.;* also LaFayette Funk, *Diary,* Nov. 19, 1902; *Country Gentleman,* Dec. 4, 1902.
57. P. G. Holden to E. D. Funk, Nov. 25, 1902.
58. *Ibid.*
59. P. G. Holden to E. D. Funk, Oct. 22, 1902.
60. *Country Gentleman,* Dec. 18, 1902.
61. C. F. Curtiss to E. D. Funk, Aug. 16, 1902. Professor Curtiss informed Funk that they "were endeavoring to secure Professor Holden to take charge of the Agronomy work. He tells me that the matter of his leaving has been laid before your company with a full understanding of the situation. We dislike to take him away from you but we are in need of such men as Prof. Holden in this institution and if he comes to us it must be with your concent[sic] and approval."
62. Interview with Lyle Johnstone and Eugene D. Funk, Jr., Nov. 23, 1952.

63. Lyle Johnstone to Eugene D. Funk, Jr., Jan. 22, 1955.
64. *Ibid.;* also interview with Robert Griffin by Eugene D. Funk, Jr., and the author, April 31, 1954.
65. *Records.* Funk Bros. Seed Co.; also *Agronomists Report,* J. D. Funk, April 4, 1903.
66. *Ibid.,* May 2, 1903.
67. *Ibid.,* June 6, 1903.
68. *Ibid.,* July, 1903.
69. *Ibid.,* November 14, 1903.
70. *Ibid.*
71. *Ibid.*
72. *Ibid.,* May and June, 1904.
73. *Ibid.,* February 5, 1904.
74. A summary of points as emphasized in this chapter which represented the best thinking in central Illinois on the problem included:
    1. *Approved Methods Observed in Breeding*
       Two grades of Seed Corn—highly bred seed and stock seed. By the highly bred seed is meant "seed that is the very highest representative of the improved types." Stock seed is one generation removed from highly-bred seed.
    2. *Influence of the Soil.*
    3. *Soil Preparation.*
    4. Description of Breeding Field-Plots arranged in Rows each of 100 hills. Description of the principle underlying plan of selection and planting.
    5. *Barren Stalks would be cut out or detasseled.*
    6. *Corn is Cross-Pollinated.*
       "By detasseling two rows and leaving two rows with tassels, enough pollen will be provided for the complete fertilization of the fields. "The Illinois Experiment Station found that by inbreeding that is, placing the pollen of the stalk upon the silks of the ear, on the same stalk, the size of the ear and stalk would be eventually decreased. In other words it appears as though inbreeding corn tends to develop weakness and a general deterioration of the vitality of the plants. "The crossing of varieties, however, is now known to lead to variation in any one variety to select from, and by introducing foreign characteristics it becomes very difficult to fix any of them. Further as corn naturally crosses within the variety it would seem that there is little danger from the evil effects of inbreeding, in the judicious selection of seed from one variety or strain."
    7. *Seed Corn Storehouses.*
    8. *Selection of Seed Corn in Field.*
    9. *Shipping Seed Corn.*

CHAPTER IX

1. Eugene D. Funk Papers, Program of Meeting.
   Eugene Funk had checked papers on his program. He was particularly interested in the following: Professor Hugh DeVries, "Investigation into the Heredity of Sporting Varieties"; Professor W. M. Hays, Distributing Valuable New Varieties and Breeds"; Professor H. J. Webber, "Plant Breeding in the U. S. Department of Agriculture"; Dr. C. B. Davenport, "Inheritance of the Effects of Training." Others who appeared on the program include Professor Cyril Hopkins "Experiments in Corn Breeding"; C. F. Curtiss "Experiments in Animal Breeding"; Professor E. Dav-

enport, "Teaching Thermatology." Mr. J. D. Funk of Bloomington also was listed with a paper on "Commercial Corn Breeding." Also E. D. Funk Papers typed and signed, "Presidential address"; James Wilson, 9th Annual Meeting of American Breeders' Association. At the ninth Annual Meeting of the American Breeders' Association the Honorable James Wilson, Secretary of Agriculture and President of the Association reviewed the history and work of this organization. Willet M. Hays, upon returning from the first Hybridizers or Genetics Congress in London in 1899 brought to Wilson's attention the need for an American Breeders' Association. Wilson recommended the formation of a committee. This was done in 1901 with Hays as chairman. Other members were: L. N. Bailey of Cornell, T. F. Hunt of Cornell, C. F. Curtiss of Iowa and H. J. Webber of the U. S. D. A. Some delay was occasioned by the international meeting of hybridizers under the auspices of the N. Y. Horticultural Society. The first meeting was held at St. Louis, December 1903. The next annual meeting convened at Champaign, Illinois early in 1905. Public proceedings of these two meetings comprised the first Annual Report. Successive Annual meetings were held in Lincoln, Nebraska; Columbus, Ohio; Washington, D. C.; Columbia, Missouri; Omaha, Nebraska; Columbus, Ohio and Washington, D. C.

2. Fred Rankin to E. D. Funk, Jan. 20, 1904.
3. E. D. Funk to F. Rankin (copy) Jan. 16, 1904.
4. F. Rankin to E. D. Funk, Jan. 20, 1904.
5. E. D. Funk to H. J. Webber, Jan. 1904 (handwritten).
6. E. D. Funk to Webber, Jan. 12, 1904 (typed); also J. J. Webber to E. D. Funk, Jan. 7, 1904. Webber said that if farmers growing an ordinary strain would purchase a small quantity of highly bred Boone County White or Reid's Yellow Dent and plant it in alternative rows, possibly detasseling the female parent the next year's product grown from the seed of the detasseled stalks would probably show desirable results as an effect of the crossing. This would increase yield for farmers.
7. Funk Bros. Seed Co., *Corn Register*, 1902–05.
8. *Proceedings of the Twenty Second Annual Seed Trade Association.*
9. *Catalogue*, 1903. The following were included in the catalogue: *His Excellency*, bred from Reid's Yellow Dent for more oil and protein; *Boone County Special*, from Boone County White Corn; *Gold Standard Leaming*, from J. S. Leaming Corn, oldest distinct variety, originated 1826; *Silver King*, from Silver Mine pure white corn on white cob; *Golden Eagle*, early feed for stock; *Improved Mastodon*, famous ensilage yellow corn; Riley's Favorite, yellow corn for the north. *The Improved Calico*, "This is the only hybrid corn" that was recommended. "Its characteristics are of such quality that it ranks second to none in some of the most important uses of corn and is the *only cross* to our knowledge meriting continuation. We are now breeding Improved Calico for increase in yield and these characteristics which mark a high bred corn."
10. Funk Bros. Seed Co., Early Ledger, supports this idea.
11. Eugene D. Funk, *Introduction to Commercial Corn Breeding*. Original typed copy delivered at St. Louis, 1904. E. D. Funk *Papers*.
12. *Ibid.*, printed copy, p. 4. At this point in his discussion Funk brought in an example of a high yielding and Grand Champion Mother Ear into the second and third generations. In the spring of 1901 a certain ear, No. 12 A, yielded at a rate of 64 bushels per acre, considered a large yield because of the dry year. Only two ears were good or better than the Mother Ear. These two ears were numbers 24 and 120 of this variety. They were

planted in individual rows not side by side, but with other pedigreed ears of high merit in two separate fields. Both were Grand Champions of their breeding block with 91 and 90 bushel yield respectively. The following year from ear No. 24 there were 5 ears, with yields of 123, 93, 118, 117, 137 bushels per acre. Of the 5 ears from 120, three were located in one breeding block and 2 in another. All were Champions of their blocks.

13. *Ibid.*, pp. 6 and 9.
14. *Ibid.*, p. 7.
15. *Ibid.*, p. 8.
16. *Ibid.*, p. 10.
17. *Ibid.*, it should be noted that some of this address was reported verbatim in a speech by E. D. Funk given during 1912 entitled *Some Results of Ten Years of Corn Breeding* before the Illinois Corn Growers Association at Urbana, Illinois when he repeated his point as he had also done three years previously in 1909 with regard to smooth corn. See forward, chapter XVII.
18. J. Dwight Funk to Dr. R. O. Graham (no date) but attached to correspondence dated Dec. 7, 1905 and written in pencil obviously in answer to an inquiry from E. D. Funk dated December 6, 1905.
19. Interview with Professor H. H. Love, April 18, 1957; also Richard Crabb, *op. cit.*, p. 24.
20. This information may have been presented before the 1905 Breeder's Association Meeting held at Urbana.
21. *Prairie Farmer*, May 10, 1906.
22. LaFayette Funk, *Diary*, July 17, 1906 stated that a famous German Botanist visited the farms. A letter to J. D. Funk, who was at the Battle Creek Sanitarium, Aug. 13, 1906 indicated that De Vries would visit the farms then. Lyle Funk was given credit for inviting him. Funk Bros. Seed Co. to J. D. Funk, Aug. 13, 1906.
23. Hugo De Vries, *Plant Breeding*, Preface.
24. *Ibid.*, Some question has been raised about one of the pictures, Fig. 41, p. 139 in this publication which was copyrighted in 1907. P. G. Holden was of the opinion that this picture was taken at the University of Illinois. The figure of the man in this picture on close examination is thought to resemble C. G. Hopkins. Correspondence between Hopkins and E. D. Funk, Sr., dated Sept. 22, 1902 indicates that he sent some pictures unidentified in the letter to Funk. It should also be noted that the *Catalogue* of Funk Bros. Seed Company for 1906 carried a picture with similar background including the signs marked *Selfed* and *Not Selfed* without any figure which is believed by Funk descendants to be one certainly taken on the Funk Farms. In the *Catalogue* of the Company for 1912 there appears a larger picture showing an isolated breeding block with background of timber labelled on the Funk Farms. The timber plot has been used for breeding corn on the Funk Farms since the establishment of the company. It was still in use in 1958. The Funk descendants advance no definite claim to the picture in DeVries book and only offer existing records to show adequately how their early work was carried on.
25. Richard Crabb, *op. cit.*, chapters 2, 3 and 4.
26. *Ibid.*
27. *Chicago Drovers Journal*, Oct. 18, 1907.
28. *Ibid.*
29. Robert Griffin to E. D. Funk, Jr., June 3, 1954.
30. Funk Bros. Seed Co., *Catalogue*, 1907.

31. *Ibid.*, p. 13.
32. *Ibid.*, 1908, p. 4.
33. *Ibid.*, 1909, p. 4.
34. *Ibid.*
35. Lyle W. Funk, *Advertising Reports,* July 9, 1904.
36. *Record of Minutes of Board of Directors,* Funk Bros. Seed Co., June 14, 1902, p. 42.
37. *Ibid.*, August 23, 1902, p. 45.
38. *Ibid.*, February 7, 1903, p. 53.
39. *Ibid.*, November 14, 1903, p. 50.
40. *Ibid.*, December 14, 1903.
41. *Ibid.*, July 9, 1904.
42. *Ibid.*, October 1, 1904.
43. *Ibid.*, February 18, 1905.
44. *Ibid.*, Stockholders Meeting, July 15, 1905, p. 70.
45. *Ibid.*, Directors Meeting, May 5, 1906.
46. *Ibid.*, Stockholders Meeting, July 6, 1906 and Directors Meeting, Sept. 1, 1906, p. 82 and Nov. 4, 1906.
47. *Ibid.*, Stockholders Meeting, Aug. 23, 1907.
48. Eugene D. Funk, *Diary,* April 4, 1908.
49. *Ibid.*, Oct. 6, 1908.
50. LaFayette Funk, *Diary,* Sept. 5, 1908.
51. Eugene D. Funk, *Diary,* June 6, 1908.
52. *Ibid.*, Nov. 14, 1908.
53. *Ibid.*, April 3, 1909; June 2, 1910.
54. *Ibid.*, Dec. 24, 1909.
55. LaFayette Funk, *Diary,* June 9, Nov. 5, 1910.
56. Eugene D. Funk, *Diary,* Jan. 21, 1910.
57. *Ibid.*, Nov. 15, 1919; March 22, 1911; March 25, 1911; April 20, 1911.
58. *Record of Minutes Stockholders Meeting,* Funk Bros. Seed Co., Nov. 4, 1908.
59. *Ibid.*, Special Meeting Stockholders, Nov. 14, 1908.
60. *Ibid.*
61. Eugene D. Funk, *Diary,* Nov. 1, 1911 and Nov. 15, 1911—480 acres made about 25,000 bu., a little more than 52 bu., to the acre. Two fields were badly eaten by grasshoppers. These made only 30-40 bu., one field of 81 and one of 78 bu.
62. *Ibid.*, Nov. 4, 1911.
63. *Ibid.*, July 6, 1912.
64. *Ibid.*, Sept. 26, 1912.
65. *Ibid.*, July 17, 1912.
66. *Farmers Voice,* Aug. 1, 1912.
67. Eugene D. Funk, *Diary,* August 10, 1912, also LaFayette Funk, *Diary,* Aug. 11, 1912.
68. Eugene D. Funk, *Diary,* Sept. 8, 1912.
69. LaFayette Funk, *Diary,* July 30, 1912.
70. *Farmers Voice,* Aug. 15, 1912.
71. LaFayette Funk, *Diary,* May 7, 1912, and Eugene D. Funk, *Diary,* May 9, 1912.
72. *Farmers Voice,* Aug. 1, 1912.

CHAPTER X

1. Eugene D. Funk, *Report of Trip to Minneapolis and Madison,* 1902.
2. *Ibid.*

3. A. D. Shamel to E. D. Funk, October 30, 1902.
4. J. W. T. Duvel to F. H. Funk, Dec. 12, 1903.
5. J. W. T. Duvel to F. H. Funk, Dec. 14, 1903.
6. E. Brown to E. D. Funk, Aug. 18, 1904. Experiments continued with corn, see Renewed Agreement, U. S. D. A. with E. D. Funk, May 31, 1905. An agreement relating to the growth of red clover was renewed May 31, 1905, Jesse B. Norton to E. D. Funk, February 17, 1906; also Charles J. Brand to E. D. Funk, March 9, 1906. The cooperative program in oats continued in 1906, J. M. Westgate to E. D. Funk, March 9, 1907.
7. E. D. Funk to Professor C. G. Hopkins, June 4, 1901, Letter Book, E. D. Funk, *Papers.* Some years later Gene Funk related his first experience in growing alfalfa. He referred both to Kansas and to Nebraska as sources for the soil he imported. He reportedly told the story relating it to either state, Illinois Farmers Institute, *Bulletin,* No. 18, March 1912, pp. 63-65.
8. C. G. Hopkins to E. D. Funk, June 8, 1901.
9. *Ibid.*
10. E. D. Funk, *Diary,* July 26, 1901.
11. *Breeders Gazette,* Dec. 31, 1902.
12. *Illinois Farmers Institute Bulletin,* No. 18, March 12, p. 64.
13. C. G. Hopkins to E. D. Funk, May 10, 1903.
14. Undated account written on back of an envelope filed with 1903 materials, *Ibid.* Interview with Wm. Necessary who helped with this alfalfa planting, June 16, 1954.
15. LaFayette Funk, *Diary,* Jan. 19–13, 1902; also Feb. 17, 1902, also accounts 1903, 1904, 1905, 1906.
16. *Ibid.,* Feb. 1–10, 1902; see March 4, 1902; Directors were C. D. Martin, Pres., J. T. Hoblit, H. M. Fellows, Brown, Brewster, Littlewood and Funk, Charles Martin, Sect'y.
17. *Ibid.,* March 15, 18, 21, 1902.
18. *Ibid.,* April 3, 6–9, 1902; also May, 5–8, 1902 and June 2, 1902, July 5, 1902, and June 2, 1902, July 5, 1902, Aug. 23–25, 1902, Oct. 16 and Dec. 19–21, 1902. Another trip to Chanute occurred when LaFayette attended a bankers reception and danced for a while. LaFayette decided the oil fields were difficult to visit.
19. *Ibid.,* April 10, 1902.
20. *Ibid.,* April 19–24, 1902.
21. *Ibid.,* April 11, 1902 and May 12, 1902.
22. *Ibid.,* May 28, 1902 and Sept. 5, 1902; see *Diaries* through 1906. In 1906 A. G. Leonard was elected director to take Mr. Doud's place, Jan. 17, 1906.
23. *Ibid.,* June 7, 1902. This first meeting included E. D. Funk, De Loss Funk, W. H. Young, Joseph Fulkerson, Lyle Funk, P. G. Holden, F. H. Rankin, Frank Funk, B. F. Harris, D. S. Dalbey, A. D. Shamel, C. B. Dorsey, Leigh Maxey, Roy B. Simpson. Officers included Eugene Funk, President, J. W. Fulkerson, Vice President and A. W. Jamison, Sect'y-Treas.
24. *Breeders' Gazette,* July 2, 1902.
25. *Ibid.*
26. E. D. Funk, *Address at Colonel Fulkerson's Home,* June 8, 1902, also LaFayette Funk, *Diary,* August 13–15, 1902.
27. *Chicago Drovers Journal,* Nov. 14, 1901; *Prairie Farmer,* Sept. 14, 1901 where Kerrick referred to the "Market Topping Beef Cattle."
28. *Ibid.*
29. *Orange Judd Farmer,* Feb. 15, 1902. Vice Presidents included A. W. Jamison, J. D. Funk, R. L. Wilson, George A. Hunt, C. L. Orich, R. Winterberg; Secretary, John Clisby of Arcola and Treasurer H. A. Winter

of Winona. The Corn and Stockmen's Convention also met. Progressive young farmers were also present. Officers of the convention included President, Frank Funk; Vice President, J. Fulkerson; Secretary, Will H. Young.

30. *Breeders Gazette,* Oct. 8, 1902. LaFayette was a Board member until 1911.
31. La Fayette Funk, *Diary,* July 30, 1902, Nov. 25, 1902.
32. *Ibid.,* July 21, August 19, 1902.
33. *Ibid.,* Sept. 17, 21, 1902.
34. *Ibid.,* Dec. 1, 2, 3, 1902.
35. *Ibid.,* Dec. 27, 1902.
36. L. Kerrick, *Address before Board of Agriculture, State of Ohio,* enclosed in a letter Brown to Kerrick, L. H. Kerrick Papers.
37. Herbert Mumford to E. D. Funk, Nov. 6, 1901.
38. Herbert Mumford to E. D. Funk, Dec. 12, 1901.
39. University of Illinois Experiment Station, *Bulletin* 73.
40. Herbert Mumford to E. D. Funk, Feb. 6, 1902; April 2, 1902, May 26, 1902.
41. H. Mumford to Funk, June 24, 1902; July 17, 1902.
42. H. Mumford to Funk, Aug. 6, 1902.
43. H. Mumford to Funk, Aug. 11, 1902.
44. H. Mumford to Funk, Nov. 6, 1901; See *Pantagraph,* July 18, 22, 1902. See *Live Stock World,* Dec. 2, 1904.
45. E. D. Funk to H. Mumford, Aug. 8, 1902.
46. H. Mumford to E. D. Funk, Aug. 6, 1902.
47. E. Funk to Mumford, Aug. 8, 1902.
48. H. Mumford to Funk, Aug. 26, 1902.
49. Interview with C. P. Bull, March 1955.
50. *Prairie Farmer,* Nov. 20, 1902.
51. *Orange Judd Farmer,* Nov. 20, 1902.
52. LaFayette Funk, *Diary,* Jan. 1903, also March 7, 1903.
53. Eugene F. Funk, *Diary,* Feb. 8, 1903.
54. *Ibid.,* Feb. 12, 1903.
55. *Ibid.,* Feb. 17, 1903.
56. *Ibid.,* Feb. 23, 1903.
57. *Ibid.,* May 8, 1903.
58. *Ibid.,* June 6, 1903.
59. *Ibid.,* Aug. 15, 1903 also LaFayette Funk, *Diary,* Sept. 14, 18, 25, 1903; also Nov. 16, 17, 1903.
60. Eugene D. Funk, *Diary* June 25, 1903 also LaFayette Funk, *Diary,* June 25, 1903.
61. *Ibid.,* July 12, 1903; August 24, 1903.
62. Eugene D. Funk, *Diary,* Sept. 1, 1903.
63. LaFayette Funk, *Diary,* Sept. 9, 1903; *Breeders Gazette,* Office to E. D. Funk, Sept. 11, 1903.
64. LaFayette Funk, *Diary,* Sept. 9, 1903.
65. *Ibid.,* Sept. 23–25, 1903.
66. *Ibid.,* Oct. 16, 1903.
67. *Ibid.,* Oct. 29, 1903.
68. *Ibid.,* Oct. 21, 1903.
69. *Ibid.,* Nov. 2, 1903.
70. *Ibid.,* Nov. 13, 1903.
71. *Ibid.,* Nov. 21, 1903.
72. *Breeders Gazette,* Dec. 9, 1903.
73. *Ibid.,* Dec. 9, 1903.

CHAPTER XI

1. *Inter Ocean*, May 1, 1904. This article also reviewed the careers of Isaac Funk and his sons.
2. Robin Jones to Eugene D. Funk, March 12, 1903.
3. Cyril G. Hopkins to E. D. Funk, March 19, 1903. Hopkins was of the opinion that the use of commercial fertilizers would become part of the farming business in Illinois. He hoped that farmers in the state would not adopt the system of using highly manufactured and highly priced fertilizers.
4. C. G. Hopkins to E. D. Funk, Jan. 5, and Jan. 6, 1904. Hopkins referred to Funk as one of the presiding officers at the recent meeting of the American Breeder's Association at St. Louis. See C. G. Hopkins to Wheeler, copy in E. D. Funk Papers.
5. E. D. Funk, to F. Rankin, Jan. 16, 1904.
6. *Ibid.*
7. F. Rankin to E. D. Funk, Jan. 20, 1904.
8. F. Rankin to E. D. Funk, April 4, 1904.
9. *Daily Pantagraph*. Aug. 5, 1904.
10. *Ibid.*
11. *Ibid.*
12. *Ibid.*, July 14, 1905.
13. *Weekly Pantagraph*, Nov. 25, 1904.
14. *Daily* Pantagraph, July 1, 1904.
15. *Ibid.*, Dec. 9, 1904.
16. *Ibid.*, Dec. 9, 1904.
17. *Ibid.*
18. *Breeders Gazette*, Dec. 7, 1904.
19. LaFayette Funk, *Diary*, Jan. and Feb. 1905.
20. *Ibid.*, March 2, 1905.
21. *Ibid.*, March 5, 1905.
22. *Ibid.*, March 9, 1905.
23. *Ibid.*, March 17, 1905, April 13, 1905.
24. *Ibid.*, April 15, 1905.
25. *Ibid.*, May 15–22, 1905, and May 26, 1905.
26. *Ibid.*, June 3, 9, 18, 1905.
27. Clipping July 10, 1905, unidentified.
28. *Daily Pantagraph*, Sept. 15, 1905.
29. LaFayette Funk, *Diary*, Nov. 19, 1905.
30. *Ibid.*, Dec. 4, 1905.
31. *Ibid.*, Dec. 16, 1905; also *Prairie Farmer*, Dec. 28, 1905.
32. LaFayette Funk, *Diary*, Dec. 26, 1905.
33. E. D. Funk to C. G. Hopkins, March 19, 1905.
34. *Farmers Voice and Rural Outlook*, March 1905. L. H. Kerrick was a member of the Board of Directors. A. P. Grout was an officer.
35. *Ibid.*
36. *Daily Pantagraph*, June 3, 1905. Those present included also Frank H. Fulkerson, of Jerseyville; Secretary, A. W. Jameson of Peoria; Eugene Funk, Deane N. Funk, Frank H. Funk, Lyle Funk, Isaac Funk, Lawrence Funk, Julius Funk and of the older generation of the family B. F. Funk and LaFayette Funk and Frank Aldrich and Lyle Johnson (sic) all of Bloomington. Mr. Norton of the U. S. Department of Agriculture who was conducting the Oats experiment on Funk Farms; Will H. Young of Athens; J. R. Clisby of Arcola; Leigh F. Maxcy of Curran; Charles F. Mills of

Springfield. Dean Davenport, Herbert Mumford, Prof. Wilber, J. Fraser, C. G. Hopkins, F. H. Rankin, E. E. Chester, N. Harris of Champaign and Pantagraph Editor, Bill.

37. *Daily Pantagraph,* June 3, 1905.
38. E. D. Funk to F. Rankin, June 7, 1905; Rankin to Funk, June 7, 1905.
39. Lafayette Funk, *Diary,* Aug. 21–28, 1906.
40. *Ibid.,* Oct. 25, 1906 and Oct. 22, 1906.
41. Eugene D. Funk, *Diary,* Sept. 27, 1906.
42. *Ibid.,* Dec. 7, 1906.
43. L. H. Kerrick, *Speech* (partial) at First Baptist Church, Bloomington, Illinois, Oct. 21, 1904, L. H. Kerrick Papers.
44. L. H. Kerrick, *Reciprocity,* Hooper Hall, Farmers Institute, *Ibid.*

Chapter XII

1. L. H. Kerrick, "Some Phases of Beef Production" *Bulletin* No. 1, Indiana Livestock Breeders Association.
2. *Ibid.*
3. Daily *Pantagraph,* March 15, 1907; LaFayette Funk, *Diary,* March 13–16, 1907; Eugene D. Funk, *Diary,* March 13–16, 1907.
4. *Ibid.*
5. *Ibid.,* March 13 and 15, 1907; and LaFayette Funk, *Diary,* June 25, 1907.
6. Eugene D. Funk, *Diary,* June 16, 18, 1911 and Nov. 17, 1911.
7. LaFayette Funk *Diary,* Jan. 1, 1911; Eugene D. Funk, *Diary,* Jan. 1, 1911.
8. *Ibid.,* May 13, 1907 and June 25, 1907.
9. *Ibid.,* Aug. 17, 1907.
10. *Ibid.,* May 17, 1910.
11. *Ibid.,* May 19, 1908.
12. LaFayette Funk, *Diary,* Jan. 12, 15, 16, 27; Feb. 15; Mar. 29, 1908.
13. Eugene D. Funk, *Diary,* Feb. 6, 1908.
14. *Ibid.,* Dec. 1, 1908.
15. LaFayette Funk, *Diary,* Dec. 1, 1908.
16. *Breeders Gazette,* Dec. 9, 1908.
17. *Ibid.,* Nov. 4, 1908.
18. E. D. Funk to A. J. Loveyoy, Sept. 13, 1909.
19. Wm. T. Hutchinson, *Lowden of Illinois,* (2 vols.; Chicago: University of Chicago Press, 1957) I, p. 178.
20. Unidentified clipping.
21. E. D. Funk to A. P. Grout, Feb. 20, 1909.
22. E. D. Funk to Gov. Chas. S. Deneen, Feb. 20, 1909.
23. E. D. Funk to Charles F. Mills, Feb. 27, 1909.
24. E. D. Funk to A. P. Grout, Feb. 27, 1909.
25. F. A. Warner to E. D. Funk, Mar. 1, 1909.
26. E. D. Funk to S. Corsa, Mar. 4, 1909.
27. Fred H. Rankin to E. D. Funk, April 17, 1909.
28. Professor Mumford to E. D. Funk, May 14, 1909.
29. *Ibid.*
30. E. D. Funk to Fred Rankin, Aug. 14, 1909; Rankin agreed.
31. E. D. Funk to F. Rankin, Aug. 28, 1909.
32. E. D. Funk to F. Rankin, May 8, 1909.
33. Fred Rankin to E. D. Funk, Mar. 17, 1909.
34. E. D. Funk to L. E. Ingram, July 5, 1909.
35. E. D. Funk to Mumford, July 26, 1909; also E. D. Funk to Phil Haner, Aug. 28, 1909.

36. E. D. Funk to Phil Haner, July 29, 1909.
37. P. R. Barnes to E. D. Funk, Nov. 4, 1909.
38. E. D. Funk to Phil Haner, Aug. 28, 1909.
39. E. D. Funk to Curt M. Treat, June 7, 1909; also March 11, 1910 and April 13, 1910; Curt Treat to E. D. Funk, May 25, 1910.
40. LaFayette Funk, *Diary,* Feb. 15, 1910.
41. Eugene D. Funk, *Diary,* May 5, 1911.
42. *Ibid.* May 26, 1911.
43. Eugene Davenport to E. D. Funk, Oct. 21, 1910.
44. E. D. Funk to Chicago Examiner, Jan. 2, 1909; copy to Gov. Deneen.
45. S. A. Foley to E. D. Funk, Apr. 21, 1910; Funk to Foley, Apr. 23, 1910, Funk to Allan, June 20, 1910; Funk to Ross, Sept. 23, 1910; Aldrich to Funk, Oct. 14, 1910; Funk to Aldrich, Oct. 24, 1910; Allan to Funk, Oct. 28, 1910; Funk to Allan, Nov. 16, 1910; LaFayette Funk, *Diary,* Aug. 24–29, 1910.
46. Eugene D. Funk, *Diary,* Sept 30, 1910.
47. LaFayette Funk, *Diary,* Dec. 7, 1910.
48. Eugene D. Funk, *Diary,* July 4, 1911; also E. D. Funk to Henry Rumsey, June 27, 1911.
49. LaFayette Funk, *Diary,* Sept. 5–7, 1910.
50. Eugene D. Funk, *Diary,* Oct. 6, 1910.
51. D. N. Niver to E. D. Funk, July 21, 1910; E. D. Funk to Niver, July 25, 1910.
52. Circular.
53. Eugene D. Funk, *Diary,* Sept. 6–11, 1910.
54. E. D. Funk to G. Muntz, Nov. 8, 1910.
55. Eugene D. Funk, *Diary,* Dec. 25, 1910.
56. E. D. Funk to N. Kaumans, Imperial German Special Commissioner for Agriculture to United States, March 15, 1911.
57. N. Kaumans to E. D. Funk, Oct. 29, 1911.
58. A. P. Grout to E. D. Funk, June 20, 1911; also the *Farmers Voice,* July 15, 1911.
59. E. D. Funk to A. T. Peters, Nov. 18, 1911; E. D. Funk to C. A. Lowry, Nov. 24, 1911.
60. Eugene D. Funk, "Look Ahead Farmers," *Farm Magazine,* July, 1911.
61. Eugene D. Funk, *Diary,* Feb. 28, May 22, June 10, July 9, Aug. 3, Oct. 12, Nov. 21, 1911.
62. *Ibid.,* Mar. 12, April 26, 1912.
63. *Ibid.,* Nov. 30, 1912; also LaFayette Funk, *Diary,* Aug. 19, 1912; *Farmers Voice,* Dec. 15 and Oct. 1, 1912.
64. Eugene D. Funk, *Diary,* Aug. 9, 1912 and Feb. 24, 1912.
65. *Farmers Voice,* June 15, 1912.
66. Eugene D. Funk, *Diary,* June 17, 1912.
67. *Ibid.,* April 6, 1912.
68. *Ibid.,* April 10, 1912.
69. *Ibid.,* Sept. 17, 1912.
70. *Weekly Pantagraph,* April 9, 1912.
71. *Ibid.,* April 19, 1912.
72. *Ibid.,* Aug. 2, 1912.
73. *Ibid.,* Aug. 9, 1912.
74. *Ibid.,* Aug. 23, 1912. No records or papers of Frank Funk have been found. Members of his family have no manuscript collection in their possession according to statements made to the author by his daughter, Mrs. Mary Funk DeVries, by his son, Benjamin Funk, Jr. and by Mrs. Frank Funk.

75. Henry Woods (Compiler), *Illinois Blue Book* 1913–14, (Danville, Ill.: . . . Printing Company, 1914), pp. 568–570.
76. Eugene D. Funk, *Diary,* Nov. 5, 1912.
77. Objects of Organization, Illinois Highway Improvement Association, E. D. Funk Papers.
78. W. R. Baldwin to E. D. Funk, July 31, 1912, *Ibid.,* LaFayette Funk, *Diary,* August 3, 1912; Eugene D. Funk, *Diary,* July 24, 1912; LaFayette Funk, *Diary,* Mar. 17, 1913.

CHAPTER XIII

1. Coates P. Bull, *The Significance, Import and Purpose of the National Corn Association,* Handwritten Copy, June 1955.
2. This Board of Directors included: E. D. Funk, Bloomington, Ill., Wm. Stull, Omaha, Neb., C. W. Pugsley, Lincoln, Neb., W. H. Young, Athens, Ill., L. B. Clore, Franklin, Ind., C. P. Bull is the only living member (1958). See Appendix III for short biographical sketches.
3. C. P. Bull, *op. cit.*
4. E. S. Fursman to E. D. Funk, May 21, 1906; also *Prairie Farmer,* May 31, 1906.
5. Eugene D. Funk, *Organization and Progress of the National Corn Association.* (probably written 1912) E. D. Funk Papers; also *The State* Columbia S. C., Jan. 29, 1913.
6. *Prairie Farmer,* May 31, 1906.
7. E. S. Fursman to E. D. Funk, June 22, 1906.
8. Curt S. Treat to E. D. Funk, June 19, 1906, *Ibid.,* also Eugene D. Funk, *Diary,* April 11, 1906.
9. Eugene D. Funk, *Organization and Progress of N. C. A.* p. 2; *Diary,* April 13, 1907.
10. *Ibid.,* April 18, 1907. Funk said that he nominated A. D. Shamel to take the place of Fursman.
11. Daniels Scenic Studio to E. D. Funk, July 15, 1907.
12. *Ibid.,* July 5, 1907; see Premium List, National Corn Exposition, Chicago, Oct. 5–9, 1907 for list of officers of National Corn Exposition; also for members of the Executive Board.
13. *Chicago Daily Tribune,* Oct. 6, 1907 and *Chicago Daily Drovers Journal,* Sept. 10, 1907.
14. *Corn,* Chicago, Oct. 1907. The following took part in the Corn Congress: Prof. Wilett Hays, Ass't. Sect'y. Agriculture; E. H. Rankin, O. D. Center, E. D. Funk, J. D. Funk, C. F. Mills, O. L. Campbell, J. A. King, K. R. Burr, Asa Turner, G. I. Christie, A. T. Wianco, L. B. Clore, J. R. Overstreet, Harvey Gray, R. A. Moore, Rob't Lachmond, C. P. Bull, W. A. Wheeler, O. E. Young, E. G. Montgomery, Arnold Martin, A. M. Ten Eyck, E. G. Shafer, J. M. Gilman, H. C. Crain, A. W. Schloser, A. D. Shamel, N. H. Brewer, T. R. Garton of England, C. W. Fair.
15. *Chicago Daily Farmers and Drovers Journal,* Oct. 8, 1907.
16. Interview with C. P. Bull, March 22, 1955.
17. Eugene D. Funk, *Diary,* Oct. 16, 17, 1907.
18. Interview with C. P. Bull, March 22, 1955; also Sept. 4, 5, 6, 1956. The group included E. D. Funk, W. E. Young, E. G. Montgomery, O. D. Center, J. W. Jones, C. P. Bull, R. A. Moore.
19. Statement by Eugene D. Funk, Sr.
20. *Chicago Tribune,* Sept. 10, Oct. 6, 1907.
21. *Chicago Drovers Journal,* Sept. 10, 1907 and Oct. 5, 1907.

22. *Ibid.*, Oct. 8, 1907.
23. *Ibid.*, Oct. 5, 1907.
24. *Prairie Farmer*, Oct. 17, 1907.
25. *Chicago Evening American.* Oct. 7, 1907. This clipping was found carefully filed in the General Correspondence in the Records of the Bureau of Plant Industry of the Department of Agriculture. Leaming saw that like produced like so he carefully chose his seed corn giving his name to several varieties, all yellow. J. S. Riley of Corntown, Boone County, Indiana was another early scientific grower. He was responsible for "Boone County White." J. L. Reid of Tazewell County, Illinois, moved from Ohio in 1845. He obtained additional seed from Dr. Mills, who lived near the present site of the University of Illinois. This corn proved to be of a different variety from that brought from Ohio. From this crop he carefully selected seed and planted again.
26. *Prairie Farmer*, Nov. 14, 1907; also *Corn*, Oct. 1907.
27. John R. Clisby to E. D. Funk, Nov. 5, 1907.
28. P. G. Holden to E. D. Funk, Dec. 27, 1907.
29. F. H. Rankin to E. D. Funk, Dec. 27, 1907.
30. E. D. Funk to W. M. Hays, Jan. 25, 1908.
31. J. Wilkes Jones to E. D. Funk, Feb. 10, 1908.
32. *Ibid.*
33. J. W. Jones to Secretary Wilson (copy) Feb. 13, 1908.
34. J. W. Jones to W. M. Hays (copy), Feb. 14, 1908.
35. J. W. Jones to A. D. Shamel (copy), Feb. 15, 1908.
36. *Prairie Farmer*, April 1, 1908. C. P. Bull recalled that some feared that the leadership of the International might overshadow those interested in grains. Interview with C. P. Bull, March 22, 1955.
37. J. W. Jones to A. D. Shamel (copy), Feb. 15, 1908. A note at top of letter says *Rewritten*.
38. E. D. Funk to J. W. Jones, Feb. 16, 1908.
39. *Ibid.*
40. Eugene D. Funk, *Speech Before Commercial Club*, Omaha, Neb., March 6, 1908; also E. D. Funk, *Diary*, March 5, 1908.
41. *Ibid.*
42. *Ibid.*
43. *Ibid.*
44. J. W. Jones to F. L. Haller (copy) to Funk, April 11, 1908.
45. E. D. Funk to John Clisby, May 12, 1908.
46. E. D. Funk to Gov. Deneen, May 21, 1908.
47. E. D. Funk to J. W. Jones, June 18, 1908.

CHAPTER XIV

1. E. D. Funk to Chas. F. Mills, July 4, 1908.
2. *Automatic Flagman*, Union Pacific Railroad Folder, no date.
3. E. D. Funk to W. H. Olin, July 28, 1908.
4. E. D. Funk to J. W. Jones, July 24, 1908.
5. E. D. Funk to J. W. Jones, Nov. 20, 1908.
6. H. G. Hawk to E. D. Funk, Nov. 11, 1908. Hawk, who originally came from central Illinois, noted at the end of the letter "Glad to note your growing and well deserved prominence in this very important association."
7. E. D. Funk to DeWitt Wing, Nov. 12, 1908.
8. E. D. Funk to J. W. Jones, Dec. 22, 1908.

9. *Report of the Second Annual National Corn Exposition,* Omaha, Neb., Dec. 9–19, 1908 (Published by the Exposition), p. 1-2.
10. Interview with C. P. Bull, Sept. 4, 1956.
11. Members of the Commission were L. H. Bailey, Henry Wallace, K. L. Butterfield, Gifford Pinchot and Walter Page.
12. *Premium List,* National Corn Exposition, Omaha, Neb., Dec. 9–19, 1908, p. 7.
13. Will A. Campbell, "National Corn Association," *The American Review of Reviews,* Dec. 1908.
14. *Report of the Second National Corn Exposition,* Omaha, Neb., Dec. 9–19, 1908.
15. E. D. Funk to C. O. Rosewater, Jan. 23, 1909.
16. J. W. Jones to E. D. Funk, Jan. 26, 1909; also T. F. Sturgess to Funk, Feb. 20, 1909, Sturgess was editor of *Twentieth Century Farmer;* also Funk to Sturgess, Mar. 13, 1909.
17. E. D. Funk to J. W. Jones, Feb. 5, 1909.
18. E. D. Funk to Sturgess, Feb. 17, 1909; also T. F. Sturgess to Funk, Feb. 20, 1909; also J. W. Jones to E. D. Funk, Jan. 26, 1909.
19. T. F. Sturgess to E. D. Funk, March 2, 1909.
20. T. F. Sturgess to E. D. Funk, March 6, 1909.
21. E. D. Funk to Sturgess, March 13, 1909.
22. The *Prairie Farmer,* March 15, 1909.
23. E. D. Funk to R. A. Moore, April 13, 1909.
24. *Ibid.*
25. E. D. Funk to J. W. Jones, May 3, 1909.
26. E. D. Funk to Chas. A. Rowe, May 3, 1909.
27. *Ibid.*
28. *Ibid.*
29. E. D. Funk to G. W. Stevenson, May 14, 1909.
30. E. D. Funk to E. G. Montgomery, July 5, 1909.
31. Clipping Omaha Bee, June 20, 1909; see also Sturgess to Funk, June 3, 4, 1909; Funk to Sturgess, June 7, 1909; Funk to Stevenson, June 9, 1909; Funk to Holden, June 14, 1909; Holden to Funk, June 15, 1909; Stevenson to Funk, June 20, 1909; Funk to Montgomery, July 5, 1909.
32. E. D. Funk to G. I. Christie, June 25, 1909.
33. W. O. Paisley to E. D. Funk, July 8, 1909.
34. *Ibid.*
35. *Prairie Farmer,* March 15, 1909.
36. E. D. Funk to R. A. Moore, July 12, 1909 and Funk to Christie, July 12, 1909.
37. E. D. Funk to C. P. Bull, July 23, 1909.
38. T. F. Sturgess to E. D. Funk, Aug. 5, 1909.
39. T. F. Sturgess to Paisley, Aug. ?, 1909.
40. C. P. Bull to E. D. Funk, Aug. 9, 1909.
41. Interview with C. P. Bull, March 22, 1955.
42. E. D. Funk to G. Stevenson, Aug. 10, 1909.
43. *Ibid.*
44. E. D. Funk to C. P. Bull, Aug. 14, 1909; Funk to J. J. Hill, Aug. 21, 1909; Funk to L. W. Hill, Aug. 21, 1909; Funk to Max Bass, no date, also J. J. Hill to Funk, Aug. 23, 1909; L. W. Hill to Funk, Aug. 31, 1909; Max Bass to Funk, Sept. 2, 1909.
45. E. D. Funk to R. A. Moore, Aug. 21, 1909.
46. T. F. Sturgess to E. D. Funk, Aug. 17, 1909.
47. E. D. Funk to R. A. Moore, Aug. 21, 1909.
48. E. D. Funk to R. A. Moore, Aug. 28, 1909.

49. E. G. Montgomery to E. D. Funk, Oct. 27, 1909.
50. E. D. Funk to E. G. Montgomery, Oct. 30, 1909.
51. *Ibid.*
52. *World Herald* (Omaha), Nov. 26, 1909.
53. A list of participating Agricultural College and Experiment Station leaders included: Professor H. W. Mumford of Illinois; H. J. Waters, President of Kansas Ag. Coll.; H. Webber, director of the Experiment Station of Cornell, Ithaca, N. Y.; Professor I. M. Jordan of the University of Missouri; E. A. Burnett, Dean of the Nebraska College of Agriculture; Dr. C. F. Curtiss, Dean of Iowa State College at Ames; David Starr Jordan, President Leland Stanford University; Governors of four states, Nebraska, Colorado, North Dakota and Missouri had places on the program.
54. *World Herald* (Omaha), Nov. 26, 1909; *The Omaha Sunday Bee*, Dec. 5, 1909.
55. *World Herald* (Omaha), Dec. 2 and 5, 1909.
56. The program included:

Monday, Dec. 6

      2:00 P. M. Welcome by Gurdon Wattles, Mayor Dahlman. Greetings from James Wilson, Sect'y Agriculture, from Pres. Diaz and E. D. Funk.

      4:00 P. M. Concert—Mexican Band.

      8:00 P. M. Address—Governor Shanforth.

Dec. 7 —Women's Day.

Dec. 8 —National Corn Association Day.

      Henry Wallace, Editor *Wallaces Farmer,* presiding, "program of Organized Agriculture;" Testimony of State Vice Presidents.

      1:30 P. M. C. G. Hopkins.

      3:00 P. M. Joseph Wing.

      4:00 P. M. Concert.

      8:00 P. M. *Travelogue,* "Across the Pacific at Honolulu and Japan."

Dec. 9 —Livestock Day.

      10:30 A. M. Clovers.

      2:00 P. M. G. W. Wattles presiding; Address—J. J. Hill.

      3:00 P. M. H. W. Mumford.

Dec. 10 —Educational Day, Nebraska Boys and Girls Work.

Dec. 11 —Nebraska University Day.

Dec. 12 —Music Lovers Day.

Dec. 13 —Dry Farming Day.

Dec. 14 —Irrigation Day.

Dec. 15 —Good Roads Day.

Dec. 16 —Grain Dealers Day.

Dec. 17 —Wheat Day.

Dec. 18 —10:00 A. M. Program—E. D. Funk.

57. Eugene D. Funk, *Diary,* Dec. 6, 1909.
58. *Ibid.*
59. *Omaha Bee,* Dec. 5, 1909.
60. *World Herald,* Dec. 5, 1909.
61. *Omaha Bee,* Dec. 7, 1909.
62. C. P. Bull, *Interview,* Mar. 22, 1955.
63. *World Herald,* Dec. 10, 1909; *Omaha Bee,* Dec. 12, 1909, carried front page pictures of J. J. Hill and Louis Hill among the exhibits from the Great Northern Territory.

64. *Addresses of J. J. Hill*, (U. of Chicago Libraries) Hill was in demand as a dinner speaker on a variety of subjects 1905–1909.
65. E. D. Funk to Prof. Davenport, Dec. 20, 1908.
66. *Ibid.*
67. *Omaha Bee*, Dec. 19, 1909.
68. Eugene D. Funk, *Diary*, Dec. 10–13, 1909.
69. E. D. Funk to Geo. Stevenson, Jan. 1, 1910.
70. C. P. Bull to E. D. Funk, Jan. 4, 1910.
71. E. D. Funk to C. P. Bull, Jan. 6, 1910.
72. C. P. Bull to E. D. Funk, Jan. 20, 1910.

CHAPTER XV

1. Geo. W. Stevenson to Alfred Atkinson (copy), April 6, 1910. Stevenson said that a representative of Great Northern called on him. He would try to get Hill to come to Columbus. Stevenson said that he would ask Bull to secure Hill's attendance.
2. E. D. Funk to Directors N. C. A., April 7, 1910.
3. Stevenson to B. X. Belden, April 16, 1910; also L. B. Clore to W. H. Young, May 12, 1910; Funk stated in a letter to Stevenson, June 27, 1910 that if he were accused of squandering Omaha money he could say it cost me out of my own pocket a good thousand dollars besides my own time and some of those that are accusing extravagance still owe me a few dollars that they borrowed one evening ". . . Personally, I never handled a dollar of their money for either 1908 or 1909 Exposition. I OKed a bill for 1908." The situation in Omaha worried Funk as he told E. G. Montgomery he (Funk) and Stevenson were being "held for extravigant (sic) expenditure of $70,000 of Omaha's good money and that we pulled away from there when we promised we would remain there forever with the National Corn Exposition." See Funk to E. G. Montgomery, Aug. 2, 1910.
4. *Ibid.*
5. *Ibid.*
6. W. M. Hays to E. D. Funk, June 14, 1910.
7. E. D. Funk to E. C. Montgomery, Aug. 2, 1910.
8. E. D. Funk to C. P. Bull, Oct. 9, 1910.
9. E. D. Funk to G. Stevenson, Sept. 2, 1910.
10. E. D. Funk to G. Stevenson, Oct. 10, 1910.
11. E. D. Funk to G. Stevenson, Dec. 25, 1910.
12. *Prairie Farmer*, Jan. 1, 1911.
13. E. D. Funk Scrapbooks—Clippings from Post, San Francisco, Cal., June 14, 1911; *Star*, Poughkeepsie, N. Y., Jan. 31, 1911; *Advertiser*, Trenton, N. Y. Jan. 13, 1911; *Time*, Brockton, Mass., Jan. 16, 1911. These and following clippings were collected by Burrell Press Clipping Bureau: *Sun*, Lowell, Mass., Jan. 12, 1911; *Gazette*, Houghton, Mich., Jan. 13, 1911.
14. *Ibid.*, *Call*, Piqua, Ohio, Jan. 19, 1911.
15. *Ibid.*, *Breese*, Columbia, Alabama, Jan. 20, 1911.
16. *Ibid.*, *State*, Columbia, S. C., Jan. 20, 1911.
17. *Ibid.*, *Journal*, Freeport, Illinois, Jan. 24, 1911.
18. *Ibid.*, *Republican*, Barnesville, Ohio, Jan. 27, 1911, other programs, Feb. 8th. "The Country and Community"; Feb. 9th "Social Cooperation in the Rural Community"; Feb. 10th. "Cooperation between Producer and Consumer" and Feb. 11th, "State Day Program."
19. *Ibid.*, *Dispatch*, Erie, Penn., Jan. 31, 1911; *Plain Dealer*, Cleveland, Ohio, Jan. 31, 1911; described a 46 Gun Salute by Battery B at the State House.

20. *Ibid., Commercial,* Buffalo, N. Y., Jan. 29, 1911; *Journal,* Kansas City, Mo., Jan. 30, 1911; *Republican,* Springfield, Mass., Jan. 30, 1911; *Gazette Times,* Pittsburgh, Penn., Jan. 30, 1911; *Express,* Portland, Me., Jan. 30, 1911; *Globe,* New York City, Jan. 30, 1911; *News,* Indianapolis, Ind., Jan. 30, 1911.
21. *Ibid.*
22. *Ibid., Farmer,* Augusta, Me., Feb. 9, 1911.
23. *Ibid., Gazette Times,* Pittsburgh, Penn., Feb. 11, 1911; *Sun,* Baltimore, Md. Feb. 11, 1911; *Herald,* Chicago, Ill., Feb. 11, 1911; *Register,* Sandusky, Ohio, Feb. 11, 1911; *Examiner,* Chicago, Ill., Feb. 11, 1911. This was an Associated Press account.
24. *Ibid.*
25. *Ibid.*
26. Geo. H. Stevenson to E. D. Funk, February 24, 1911.
27. Geo. H. Stevenson to E. D. Funk, February 25, 1911.
28. Geo. H. Stevenson to E. D. Funk, April 25, 1911.
29. Geo. H. Stevenson to E. D. Funk, April 26, 1911.
30. *Ibid.*
31. E. D. Funk to Geo. H. Stevenson, May 1, 1911.
32. *Ibid.*
33. Geo. H. Stevenson to E. D. Funk, May 5, 1911.
34. Geo. H. Stevenson to E. D. Funk, May 5, 1911.
35. Geo. H. Stevenson to E. D. Funk, May 8, 1911.
36. E. D. Funk to C. P. Bull, May 20, 1911. The Ohio State Board of Agriculture asking $1,000.00 for broken glass on seats and destruction to lawns and roads.
37. Geo. H. Stevenson to E. D. Funk, May 19, 1911. Stull thought that all Directors should sign the note.
38. C. W. Pugsley to E. D. Funk, July 25, 1911.
39. Fred McCulloch to E. D. Funk, August 10, 1911.
40. E. D. Funk to Pugsley, September 25, 1911.
41. *Ibid.*
42. E. D. Funk, *Diary,* April 4, May 30, July 3, Aug. 10, 20, Oct. 11, 1911, also March 20 and Aug. 13, 1912.
43. C. W. Pugsley to E. D. Funk, Sept. 29, 1911.
44. C. P. Bull to E. D. Funk, Oct. 12, 1911.
45. *Ibid.*
46. E. D. Funk to Geo. H. Stevenson, Nov. 24, 1911. Funk also urged Stevenson to have a definite understanding as to what part of the net proceeds, if there were any that could be expected by the N. C. A. at the end of the Exposition.
47. E. D. Funk to Geo. H. Stevenson, Nov. 24, 1911.
48. *Ibid.*
49. C. P. Bull to E. D. Funk, Nov. 28, 1911.
50. E. D. Funk to R. A. Moore, Jan. 22, 1911.
51. E. D. Funk to C. W. Pugsley, April 2, 1912.
52. E. D. Funk to A. N. Hume, Dec. 30, 1912; also Funk to L. C. Burnett. Nov. 4, 1913, said loss at Columbus was $15,000.
53. E. D. Funk to Thos. L. Cannon, Dec. 16, 1912.
54. *Ibid.*
55. The *State,* Columbia, S. C., Jan. 4, 1913.
56. *Ibid.,* Jan. 4, 1913.
57. *Ibid.,* Jan. 8, 1913.
58. *Ibid.,* Jan. 10, 1913.

59. *Ibid.*, Jan. 20, 1913.
60. *Ibid.*, Jan. 22, 1913.
61. *Ibid.*
62. *Ibid.*, Jan. 25, 1913. The States were: Texas, R. I., Wash., Mo., Mich., Ill., Ga., Wis., S. C., Iowa, Del., Ala., Ind., Md., N. C., N. Y., Ohio, Kan., Va., Miss., Minn., La., Neb., Va., S. D., Ky., Okla.
63. *Ibid.*, Jan. 28, 1913; also Jan. 29, 1913, for E. D. Funk, "How Corn Exposition Came To Be A Reality."
64. *Ibid.*, Jan. 29, 1913. Geo. Stevenson to E. D. Funk, Jr., Oct. 10, 1958, refers to P. E. Gonzales of the State Company and his brother, was was editor of *The State,* as especially helpful.
65. *Ibid.*, Jan. 25, 1913.
66. *Ibid.*, Feb. 5, 1913.
67. *Ibid.*, Feb. 8, 1913.
68. E. D. Funk, *Diary,* Feb. 5, 9, 1913.
69. E. D. Funk to E. G. Montgomery, Aug. 22, 1913.
70. Interview with C. P. Bull, Mar. 22, 1955.
71. *Southwestern Merchant,* Aug. 1, 1913; also *Christian Science Monitor,* Feb. 20, 1914.
72. E. D. Funk to C. P. Bull, Oct. 1, 1913.
73. *Ibid.*
74. E. D. Funk to C. P. Bull, Nov. 26, 1913.
75. E. D. Funk to L. C. Burnett, Nov. 4, 1913.
76. E. D. Funk to C. P. Bull, Dec. 15, 1913.
77. *Ibid.*
78. Funk to C. W. Hobson, Dec. 17, 1913. A letter to C. P. Bull, Dec. 22, 1913, indicates that this letter was not sent.
79. E. D. Funk to F. K. Mc Ginnis, Dec. 26, 1913. Funk referred to Omaha and that some parties had dropped remarks that led him to believe they would have 'liked to start something.'
80. E. D. Funk to C. P. Bull, Dec. 28, 1913.
81. E. D. Funk to C. P. Bull, Dec. 28, 1913.
82. *Ibid.*
83. *Ibid.*
84. E. D. Funk to A. G. Leonard, Dec. 31, 1913.
85. E. D. Funk to C. P. Bull, Dec. 22, 1913. Pugsley, Young, Bull, Montgomery and Stevenson were on the original $5000.00 note. Funk kept up interest payments at State National Bank. See Funk to C. P. Bull, Jan. 3, 1914. The problem of past indebtedness continued to command attention. Funk said "In regard to paying off pro rata some of the indebtedness with the money now on hand, I agree with Mr. Stull that would be the thing to do. I don't see how anyone could object." He observed that in his own case he had borrowed $2,500 from a party two years ago in order to pay half of the $5,000 at the local bank and to keep the banks from crowding them. The individual wanted his money within ten days, and that means "I have been laying awake nights to figure out how I am going to meet this demand. I tried to get him to let the note run until the first of next March but he says he cannot accommodate me any longer. The note was due last June." Funk to C. P. Bull, Jan. 3, 1914. The money was telegraphed to Funk, who said "and at a mighty good time for me. Am short 10,000 bushels of my corn crop this year, besides having lost over $3,000 worth of hogs by cholera and paying for our experience with the Farmers' Voice matters—cost me—I hate to admit it—all of which

just about had me up against a tough proposition. Our banks are not loaning any money outside of straight commercial business."

86. *Dallas Morning News,* Feb. 8, 1914; *Circular* of N. C. A. and Official Program of N. C. A., 1914; also advertising folder.

87. *Official Program, Premium List and Rules, Sixth National Corn Exposition,* Feb. 10–24, 1914, p. 6.

88. *Dallas Morning News,* Feb. 10, 1914.

89. *Ibid.,* Feb. 12, 1914.

90. *Ibid.,* Feb. 12, 1914.

91. *Ibid.,* Feb. 15, 1914.

92. *N. C. A. Circular.*

93. Official Program, *op. cit.,* Col. Exall died before the Exposition opened.

94. *Ibid.,* p. 15.

95. *Ibid.*

96. *Dallas Morning News,* Feb. 16, 1914.

97. *Ibid.,* Feb. 15, 1914.

98. E. D. Funk to Wm. Stull, Mar. 24, 1914.

99. E. D. Funk to Wm. Stull, Mar. 24, 1914, E. D. Funk and Wm. Stull assumed more of the financial responsibility than other directors of the Association. Funk out of curiosity spent a day going over his books for the previous seven years to determine "just what the high honor of being President has cost me—traveling expenses, notes, checks, for the 'Betterment of Agriculture.' The total dated from 1907 to the close of the Sixth Corn Exhibition. He had no intention of submitting all of the personal accounts. These were separated from the notes. He requested Mr. Stull to submit the same kind of a report to C. P. Bull to be held against any possible questions.

100. *Dallas Sunday News,* Mar. 8, 1914, clipping papers, C. P. Bull.

101. E. D. Funk to Eugene Davenport, April 4, 1914.

102. C. P. Bull to E. D. Funk, April 7, 1914.

103. E. D. Funk to C. P. Bull, May 20, 1914. See also C. P. Bull, final accounts. A final meeting was held in June 1914, to settle the problems. Funk, Bull, Stull and Young divided the funds received from Dallas in order to pay as far as possible for money advanced because of the indebtedness of the Association. William Stull received $3,520 out of $5,020 due him; to H. Young and C. W. Pugsley received $590 each due to them; C. P. Bull was to receive $489; E. D. Funk received $1,932.67 out of $4,000 due him. Young and Pugsley agreed to pay Funk $489 each, equally, one-fourth of $1,956.44. This amount was assumed by Bull, Pugsley, Young and Funk. Mr. Bull paid his amount. Funk carried $1649.11. At the end of the Sixth Association, a debt assumed by these abovenamed Directors amounted to $4,616.99 which they absorbed. If the other directors had assumed some of the obligation the amounts would have been reduced. This was not the case.

104. Eugene D. Funk, *Diary,* June 12, 1914 also E. D. Funk to C. P. Bull Oct. 10, 1914.

105. E. G. Montgomery to E. D. Funk, June 3, 1914.

Chapter XVI

1. *Catalogue,* 1908, Funk Bros. Seed Co., p. 5.

2. *Catalogue,* Funk Bros. Seed Co., 1908, p. 5.

3. *Catalogue,* 1912, Funk Bros. Seed Co. An account of the Funk Farms was

written by a visitor with a group studying under Professor Wianko from Purdue.

4. Interview with E. D. Funk, Jr., June 27, 1955; also *Catalogue,* 1912; Funk Bros. Seed Co., p. 13.
5. *Ibid.,* p. 4; see also *Funk Egg Farm,* Lyle Funk Sole Owner, Spring Price list, 1919, and Leghorn Lore, Funk's International Strain.
6. *Ibid.*
7. *Ibid.,* p. 14.
8. *Farmers Voice,* May 15, 1913.
9. *Funk Farm Facts,* copyright 1919, Funk Hog Farm, Bloomington, Ill.
10. *Ibid.,* quotes *Breeders Gazette,* Aug. 9, 1917.
11. C. P. Hartley to E. D. Funk, July 8, 1913.
12. Eugene D. Funk, *Diary,* July 28, 1913.
13. *Ibid.,* July 27, 1913.
14. *Ibid.,* Aug. 30, 1913.
15. LaFayette Funk, *Diary,* Sept. 8, 1913, see also Helen M. Cavanagh, *Funk of Funks Grove,* p. 68, for a listing of the points on the old cattle drive from Bloomington to Chicago.
16. *Pantagraph,* January 13, 1914.
17. E. D. Funk, *Diary,* Jan. 20, 1914 and April 20, 1914.
18. E. D. Funk, *Diary,* Jan. 21, 22, 1913; H. Cavanagh, *op. cit.,* p. 3.
19. *Ibid.,* see also E. D. Funk to H. J. Sconce, Mar. 2, 1913.
20. E. D. Funk, *Diary,* Mar. 4–11, 1913; also Lafayette Funk, *Diary,* Mar. 4–11, 1913.
21. E. D. Funk, *Diary,* Mar. 15, 1913.
22. E. D. Funk, *Diary,* Mar. 24–26, 1913. L. Burns share, $4,643.85; Sconce, $3,482.89; Inman, $3,482.00; Rankin, $171.44; E. D. Funk, $1,741.44; Deane Funk, $870.72; Melluish, $870.72; Unknown, $1,741.44; $18,-575.39.
23. H. J. Sconce to E. D. Funk, Mar. 14, 1913.
24. E. D. Funk to L. Burns, Mar. 26, 1913.
25. J. H. Melluish to Prof. Rankin, no date.
26. Day Letter Western Union, H. J. Sconce to E. D. Funk, April 20, ?
27. Lycurgus Burns to E. D. Funk, June 14, 1913.
28. Meeting Stockholders Peace Valley Company, Sidell, Illinois, Aug. 5, 1913. with L. Burns as President; L. H. Duncan, Sect'y; R. H. Halton, Treas., Directors, E. D. Funk, H. J. Sconce, R. J. Hatton, and Fred Rankin. E. D. Funk, Papers.
29. Minutes of First Meeting of Stockholders, P. V. F. Co., Aug. 30, 1913, *Ibid.*
30. Minutes of Special Meeting, P. V. Farms Co., Nov. 10, 1913, *Ibid.*
31. Clipping, *Florida Chief,* Nov. 13, 1913, *Ibid.*
32. *Pamphlet, Ibid.*
33. Lycurgus Burns to E. D. Funk, May 7, 1915.
34. Letter Heading of Livestock Breeders Association.
35. Jas. R. Monroe to E. D. Funk, July 22, 1916.
36. E. D. Funk to G. S. Williams, July 25, 1916.
37. *Daily Pantagraph,* July 10, 1915.
38. *J. P. Shinn* to E. D. Funk, July 2, 1915.
39. Copy, Henry Wallace, Speech at Dedication of Monument to Isaac Funk, July 11, 1915, *Ibid.*
40. *Ibid.*
41. *Daily Pantagraph,* July 10, 1915; also John W. Cook to E. D. Funk, July 11, 1915.
42. E. D. Funk to J. W. Cook, July 14, 1915.

43. LaFayette Funk, *Diary,* Jan. 19, 1916; also E. D. Funk, *Diary,* Jan. 19–20, 1916.
44. E. D. Funk to B. A. Heide, Nov. 25, 1916.
45. E. D. Funk to W. E. Grimes, Sept. 21, 1916.
46. F. A. Pearson to E. D. Funk, no date, 1916 (probably).
47. E. D. Funk to Frank Wagner, Oct. 14, 1916.
48. J. R. Brown to E. D. Funk, April 4, 1917, and E. D. Funk to J. R. Brown, April 7, 1917.
49. E. D. Funk to H. G. Hastings, April 11, 1917.

CHAPTER XVII

1. Eugene D. Funk, *Some of the Leaks in Our Corn Fields,* Address at Columbia, Mo., Jan. 18, 1922, E. D. Funk Papers.
2. *Ibid.*
3. *Ibid.*
4. See supra Chapter VIII for an analysis of this speech in 1904; also E. D. Funk, *Some Results From Ten Years of Corn Breeding,* delivered at Urbana, Illinois, Jan. 19, 1912.
5. *Ibid.*
6. *Ibid.,* p. 8.
7. E. D. Funk, *Diary,* June 10, 1913.
8. E. D. Funk, *Address at Columbia, Mo.,* p. 5.
9. *Twenty-fifth Anniversary Pamphlet,* Funk Bros. Seed Co.
10. *Ibid.*
11. James R. Holbert, "Thirty Years Experience in Hybrid Corn Breeding," *Modern Agriculture,* Jan. 1939.
12. E. D. Funk, Sr., "Speech before Chicago Agriculture Club," (Union League Club Banquet) April 6, 1936, typed copy.
13. Interview with Professor H. H. Love, April 18, 1957, declared that these were bulked.
14. R. Crabb, *op. cit.,* Chapters III and IV.
15. J. R. Holbert, "Thirty Years Experience with Hybrid Corn," *Funk G Hybrid Corn Bulletin,* Harvest Number, Autumn, 1939, p. 2. The printed copy of the letter appears in this article. Holbert stated in the article that historical materials were given to him by Mr. Funk including this letter. These have never been located.
16. J. R. Holbert to E. D. Funk, Mar. 7, 1914.
17. E. D. Funk to J. R. Holbert, Mar. 26, 1914.
18. Jas. R. Holbert, Ms copy "My Early Experiences with Plant, Ear and Germinator Selections with Open Pollinated Corn," pp. 1-3.
19. *Ibid.,* p. 6.
20. *Ibid.*
21. *Reports* American Breeders Association, Vols. IV, V, 1908 and 1909 (Washington: 1909).
22. Holbert, Ms copy, *op. cit.,* p. 7.
23. E. D. Funk, *Speech at Columbia, Mo.,* 1922, pp. 5-6.
24. *Daily Pantagraph,* Nov. 25, 1916.
25. *Ibid.*
26. Interview with Dave Thompson, Oct. 29, 1954, recalled that E. D. Funk told him that he was advised to keep quiet. He answered that he could wait and they would find that he was right. Thompson believes this to be another mark of strong leadership and patience. Funk Bros. did not par-

ticipate in Corn Shows. Funk knew enough not to take the bit in his
mouth and run away from his gang.

27. *Daily Pantagraph*, Nov. 25, 1916.
28. *Ibid.*
29. *Ibid.*
30. *Ibid.*, see also *The Prairie Farmer*, Jan. 13, 1917; *Orange Judd Farmer*,
    Nov. 10, 1916.
31. *Daily Pantagraph*, Nov. 25, 1916, and Dec. 2, 1916.
32. *The Florists Review*, July 31, 1930. Clipping, E. D. Funk Papers.
33. *Catalogue*, Funk Bros. Seed Co., 1923, p. 5.
34. *Twenty-Fifth Anniversary Booklet*, Funk Bros. Seed Co., 1940, Chapter 4.
35. Holbert, Ms copy, *op. cit.*, p. 11; Merle T. Jenkins, "Corn Improvement,"
    Yearbook 1936. United States Department of Agriculture. See tables.
36. *Daily Pantagraph*, Oct. 13, 1917. Sixty seven farmers of McLean county
    contributed some of the best selected seed for this experiment, see *Orange
    Judd Farmer*, Nov. 10, 1917.
37. When the U. S. D. A. set up its experimental station on the Funk farms
    this work begun by the Funks was the only basis on which to build.
38. *Daily Pantagraph*, Oct. 13, 1917.
39. Clipping Peoria paper (unidentified), Sept. 27, 1917.
40. *Daily Pantagraph*, Oct. 13, 1917.
41. *Orange Judd Farmer*, Nov. 10, 1917.
42. *Twenty-Fifth Anniversary Booklet*, Funk Bros. Seed Co., Chapter 4.
43. *Twenty-Fifth Anniversary Booklet*, Funk Bros. Seed Co., 1940, and J. R.
    Holbert, Ms copy, "My First Specific Assignment with Funk Bros. Seed
    Co." Feb. 7, 1955. The remainder of this chapter is drawn from this ac-
    count.
44. *Ibid.*

Chapter XVIII

1. William Clinton Mullendore, *History of the United States Food Administration, 1917–18* (Stanford University, Cal.: Stanford University Press,
   1941), p. 121.
2. *Ibid.*, p. 123.
3. *Ibid.*
4. *Ibid.*, p. 124.
5. *Ibid.*
6. *Ibid.*
7. *Ibid.*, p. 125.
8. *Ibid.*, p. 127.
9. E. D. Funk to Wm. Stull, July 17, 1917, refers to fact he was in Washington,
   middle of June, 1917.
10. E. D. Funk to H. G. Hastings, June 15, 1917.
11. Henry C, Hawk to E. D. Funk, Aug. 15, 1917, said that the country ought
    to be congratulated on Funk's selection, also W. H. Olin to E. D. Funk,
    Aug. 16, 1917.
12. E. D. Funk, Form Letter, June 25, 1917.
13. *Report of the Fourth Annual Meeting of the Illinois Agricultural Association*,
    Jan. 21–22, 1919, p. 24; also Circular Letter, June 25, 1917.
14. Wm. Stull to E. D. Funk, Aug. 31, 1917.
15. *Report of the Fourth Annual Meeting of Illinois Agricultural Association*,
    Jan. 21, 22, 1919, p. 22.

16. Eugene D. Funk *"Report"* Aug. 28, 1917, Committee on Prices, *Wheat,* Aug. 17–29, 1917, pp. 1-10, Appendix 38, copy in E. D. Papers.
17. *Ibid.*
18. *Report of Fourth Annual Meeting I. A. A.,* as cited, p. 24.
19. H. Cavanagh, *Funk of Funk's Grove,* for an analysis of this speech.
20. E. D. Funk to Herbert Hoover, May 4, 1928 enclosing letter to C. J. Gross, Pres., Piatt County Farm Bureau.
21. Herbert Hoover to E. D. Funk, Jr., Nov. 7, 1955, in answer to questions prepared by the author.
22. E. D. Funk to J. B. Johnson, Aug. 27, 1928.
23. E. D. Funk to C. P. Bull, Sept. 10, 1928.
24. E. D. Funk to R. A. Oakley, Sec'ty Seed Stocks Comm., Dept. Agriculture Jan. 22, 1918.
25. E. D. Funk to Wm. Stull, Jan. 26, 1918.
26. C. V. McGregor to E. D. Funk, Mar. 26, 1918.
27. E. D. Funk to Wm. G. Eckhardt, Mar. 30, 1918.
28. Report on Seed Corn Sub Committee, Advisory Committee, April 2, 1918.
29. E. D. Funk to H. L. Russell, U. S. Food Administration, June 1, 1928.
30. D. F. Houston, Sec'ty Agriculture, Western Union Telegram, Mar. 9, 1918. Funk's acceptance was dated Mar. 11, 1918.
31. Frank M. Surface, *American Pork Production in the World War,* (Chicago: S. W. Shaw Co., 1926), Introduction.
32. *Ibid.,* p. 32.
33. *Ibid.,* p. 33.
34. *Ibid.,* p. 34.
35. *Ibid.,* p. 37.
36. *Ibid.,* pp. 39-41.
37. *Ibid.,* p. 47. Finally they distinguished between small and large packers to prevent packers, except 5 larger ones to earn an annual report of 2.5% total annual sales, net after expenses. Profits not to exceed 4% of average capital for large packers.
38. Wm. Stull to E. D. Funk, Dec. 24, 1917.
39. *Ibid.,* Jan. 2, 1918.
40. Surface, *American Pork Production,* p. 63.
41. *Ibid.,* p. 69.
42. *Ibid.*
43. *Ibid.,* p. 70.
44. Typed copy No. 1217, Sept. 25, 1918, E. D. Funk Papers.
45. Typed copy No. 1269, Oct. 26, 1918, *Ibid.*
46. *Ibid.,* also Surface, American Pork Production, p. 71.
47. E. D. Funk to C. P. Bull, Sept. 10, 1928.
48. *Ibid.*
49. E. D. Funk to Frank Fulkerson, Oct. 19, 1928.
50. *Ibid.*
51. *Ibid.*
52. *Ibid.*
53. *Ibid.*
54. Resolutions Agricultural War Board, Oct. 21, 1918, typed copy, E. D. Funk Papers.
55. Herbert Hoover to S. Insull, typed copy, Oct. 26, 1918, *Ibid.*
56. Lewis Straus to E. D. Funk, Nov. 1, 1918.
57. Elbert Goodwin to E. D. Funk, Aug. 29, 1918; E. T. Meredith, publisher of *Successful Farming* was chairman of the Committee; other members were Thomas Marshall, H. G. Hastings and G. H. Mc Masters.

58. Chamber of Commerce, United States, "Press Bulletin," June 28, 1918, *Ibid.*
59. E. D. Funk to Snyder Powell (Western Union telegram), pencilled copy, Nov. 9, 1918.
60. E. D. Funk to Everett O. Brown, Chairman, Stabilization & Control, Union Stock Yards, Chicago, (Western Union Telegram), Nov. 19, 1918, *Ibid.*
61. *Meetings Board Directors and Stockholders,* Funk Bros. Seed Co., June 29, 1917–Dec. 1, 1917.

CHAPTER XIX

1. Gladys Funk Rehtmeyer, *Remembering* II, p. 3.
2. *Ibid.,* June, 1956.
3. Gladys Funk Rehtmeyer, *Remembering* III, p. 2.
4. Gladys Funk Rehtmeyer, *Remembering* II.
5. Gladys Funk Rehtmeyer, *Remembering* III, p. 14.
6. *Ibid.,* p. 15.
7. Check.
8. Gladys Funk Rehtmeyer, *Remembering* III.
9. Gladys Funk Rehtmeyer, *Remembering* II and III.
10. E. D. Funk, Jr., *Summary,* June 26, 1956.
11. The *Prairie Farmer,* July 18, 1936.
12. Gladys Funk Rehtmeyer, *Remembering* II.
13. The *Prairie Farmer,* July 18, 1936.
14. Interview, E. D. Funk, Jr.
15. Gladys Funk Rehtmeyer, *Remembering* III, Karl Porter and O. P. Tieman were also present.
16. Gladys Funk Rehtmeyer, *Remembering* II, p. 3.
17. Consolidation of County Schools, *Bulletin,* Dec. 1, 1904, University of Illinois, second edition.
18. Gladys Funk Rehtmeyer, *Remembering* III, p. 3.
19. Gladys Funk Rehtmeyer, *Remembering* III, p. 2.
20. *Ibid.*
21. Gladys Funk Rehtmeyer, *Remembering* III.
22. *Ibid.*
23. *Farmers Wife,* March, 1939.
24. *Ibid.*
25. *Prairie Farmer,* July 18, 1936.
26. *Daily Pantagraph,* April 22, 1913.
27. Summary of Farmers Institute Meeting at Galesburg, Ill. 1930, E. D. Funk Papers.
28. Poems often quoted by Mrs. Eugene D. Funk, Sr. included many from John Masefield, Edna St. Vincent Millay, Robert Frost, Robert Browning, Amy Lowell, Joyce Kilmer, Emily Dickinson, John Keats, Lew Sarrett.

CHAPTER XX

1. C. H. Longman to E. D. Funk, Oct. 4, 1919, and W. N. Richard to E. D. Funk.
2. J. G. Brown to E. D. Funk, Feb. 2, 1920.
3. *Ibid.*
4. E. D. Funk to J. P. Lucy, March 21, 1920.
5. The Funks were interested in the Baird Corn Harvester.
6. E. D. Funk to H. Hoover, April 10, 1920; see also Robert Stevenson, to E. D. Funk, April 20, 1920 and E. D. Funk to Robert Stevenson, Jr.

7. William T. Hutchinson, *Lowden of Illinois*, Vol. II, (Chicago: University of Chicago Press, 1956), chapters 18 and 19; also Wesley M. Bagby, "The Smoke Filled Room and the Nomination of Warren G. Harding," *Mississippi Valley Historical Review*, March 1955, pp. 657-74.
8. E. D. Funk, Nov. 10, 1920.
9. Letters were sent to the President in behalf of Funk and to others from (1) M. Sansom, Chairman Board of Stockyards, Ft. Worth, Tex., (2) Albert R. MacKusick through Massachusetts friends of Coolidge and Lodge (3) Wm. Stull of Omaha, Neb.
10. E. D. Funk to J. G. Brown (Monon, Ind.), Jan. 29, 1921.
11. *Ibid.*
12. James H. Shideler, *Farm Crisis*, 1919–23. (Los Angeles: University of California Press, 1957), pp. 141-51.
13. E. D. Funk to J. G. Brown, Jan. 29, 1921.
14. E. D. Funk to Frank Funk, July 27, 1921.
15. E. D. Funk to Henry Wallace, Aug. 11, 1921, and E. D. Funk to Herbert Hoover, Aug. 11, 1921.
16. E. D. Funk to D. O. Thompson, Aug. 12, 1921.
17. Murray Benedict, *Farm Policies of the United States*, 1790–1950, (New York: Twentieth Century Fund, 1953), p. 200.
18. E. D. Funk to H. Hoover, Nov. 28, 1921.
19. H. Hoover to E. D. Funk, Dec. 1, 1921; also Shideler, *op. cit.*, p. 181.
20. Henry Wallace to E. D. Funk, Jan. 15, 1922.
21. E. D. Funk to Al Blackman, Feb. 7, 1922.
22. Shideler, *op. cit.*, p. 203.
23. *Ibid.*
24. Ibid., p. 201-202.
25. *Report of the National Agriculture Conference*, 67th Congress, 2d Session, 1921–22, House Documents Vol. 115, pp. 15-27.
26. M. Benedict, *op. cit.*, p. 200.
27. *Report of the National Agricultural Conference*, *op. cit.*, pp. 31-33.
28. *Ibid.*, pp. 168-70.
29. *Ibid.*
30. Shideler, *op. cit.*, p. 206.
31. E. D. Funk to O. D. Center, Feb. 1, 1922. Gompers was a delegate.
32. Shideler, *op. cit.*, p. 209.
33. *Ibid.*
34. E. D. Funk to O. D. Center, Feb. 1, 1922.
35. E. D. Funk to Al Blackman, Feb. 7, 1922.
36. *Pantagraph*, July 5, 1922.
37. E. D. Funk to Geo. Stevenson, Mar. 28, 1922.
38. J. R. Mitchell to E. D. Funk, Mar. 6, 1922; also Shideler, *op. cit.*, p. 171, for discussion of agricultural criticism of Board policy.
39. Geo. H. Stevenson to E. D. Funk, Mar. 18, 1922; E. D. Funk to Geo. Stevenson, Mar. 28, 1922.
40. E. D. Funk to J. R. Mitchell, May 29, 1922.
41. F. I. Mann to E. D. Funk, July 27, 1922. The reference was to Mrs. Antoinette Funk.
42-47. Fred H. Rankin to Hon. Wm. B. McKinley, June 5, 1922.
   A. W. Mellon to Medill McCormick, undated copy. Mellon said he would give consideration.
   Henry C. Wallace to Dan Rankin, June 5, 1922. Wallace would keep it in mind.
   Ira S. Whitmer to Wm. B. McKinley, June 14, 1922; A. Dolan to M. Mc

Cormick, June 14, 1922; George Ogle and Sons to F. B. McKinley, June 15, 1922; W. Stone to H. K. Hoblit, June 18, 1922.

Sect'y to Pres. Harding to Dave Thompson, June 20, 1922.

Frank Lowden to E. D. Funk, June 21, 1922. Lowden endorsed Funk.

48. H. N. Owen to W. G. Harding, July 6, 1922.

49. E. D. Funk to J. R. Mitchell, November 23, 1922. Cannot be certain that this letter was sent.

50. E. D. Funk to H. Hoover, April 10, 1923, *Ibid.* Funk also wrote letters to some of the men who served with him on the Food Administration in 1918. He did so reluctantly, continuing to believe that the job should seek the man. E. D. Funk to E. S. Bingham, S. Albans, N. Y.; H. W. Jeffers, Plainsboro, N. J.; D. M. Massie, Chillicothe, O.; W. F. Pratt, Batavia, N. Y.; H. C. Stewart, Elk Gardens, Va.; C. J. Tyson, Floradale, Penn., April 12, 1923. Stewart and Tyson gave support.

51. E. D. Funk to J. R. Mitchell, April 12, 1923; see A. G. Leonard to E. D. Funk, April 11, 1923 (telegram).

52. Medill McCormick to President (copy).

53. E. D. Funk to Owen Reeves, April 10, 1923.

54. E. D. Funk to Senator Medill McCormick, April 10, 1923.

55. E. D. Funk to A. G. Leonard, April 10, 1923.

56. E. D. Funk to Henry C. Wallace, April 10, 1923.

57. McKinley to E. D. Funk, April 18, 1923.

58. E. D. Funk to McKinley, April 23, 1923.

59. *Ibid.*

60. E. D. Funk to Fred Rankin, April 24, 1923.

61. E. D. Funk to DeWitt Wing, May 15, 1923.

62. *Ibid.*

63. E. D. Funk to Frank Lowden, Dec. 1, 1923.

64. M. Benedict, *op. cit.*, pp. 195-196.

65. *Ibid.*, pp. 194-195.

66. *Ibid.*, pp. 207-208.

67. E. D. Funk to Frank Funk, April 21, 1924. See W. T. Hutchinson, *op. cit.*, for discussion of Illinois politics in the twenties.

68. H. E. Cunningham to E. D. Funk, Dec. 6, 1923, and E. D. Funk to H. E. Cunningham, Dec. 11, 1923.

69. E. G. Montgomery to E. D. Funk, Dec. 18, 1923.

70. E. D. Funk to E. G. Montgomery, Dec. 26, 1923.

71. *Ibid.*

72. E. D. Funk to Frank H. Funk, April 21, 1924.

73. *Ibid.*

74. E. D. Funk to Herbert Hoover, May 22, 1924.

75. Herbert Hoover to E. D. Funk, May 31, 1924.

76. Wm. T. Hutchinson, *op. cit.*, pp. 543-544, and Benedict, *op. cit.*, f.n. p. 197.

77. Benedict states that Henry Wallace had begun to show an interest in the McNary Haugen idea. Thereafter the administration was unfriendly, Benedict, *op. cit.*, p. 219.

78. Frank O. Lowden to E. D. Funk, Nov. 3, 1924.

79. J. D. Harper to E. D. Funk, Nov. 8, 1924.

80. E. D. Funk to J. D. Harper, Nov. 24, 1924.

81. E. D. Funk to George Stevenson, Nov. 14, 1924; see also W. T. Hutchinson, *op. cit.*, pp. 536-541, for discussion of the refusal of F. Lowden to become a vice-presidential candidate.

82. E. D. Funk to W. R. Crothers, Dec. 30, 1924.

83. *Ibid.*

84. E. D. Funk to Chas. E. Stewart, Dec. 30, 1924.

85. E. D. Funk to Alexander Legge, Jan. 8, 1925.

86. Herbert Hoover to E. D. Funk (telegram) Feb. 3, 1925.

87. H. C. Hawk to E. D. Funk, Feb. 12, 1925, telegram, also letter same date. Hawk called upon Washington friends to help.

88. E. D. Funk to H. C. Hawk, Feb. 12, 1925.

89. *Chicago Tribune,* Feb. 13, 1925, clipping.

90. *Ibid.*

91. *Ibid.*

92. *Daily Bulletin,* (Bloomington), Feb. 9, 1925; *Daily Pantagraph,* Feb. 10, 1925.

93. *Ibid.*

94. *Ibid.,* See *St. Louis Post Dispatch,* Feb. 12, 1925: *Drovers Journal,* Feb. 11, 1925, noticed that the House of Representatives passed the Strong-McLean bill embodying the recommendations of the President's Agricultural Conference without a dissenting vote. Under this measure the agricultural credits act was so amended as to make it impossible for agricultural credit corporations which are privately financed to discount paper through the intermediate banks of the farm loan board. This it was believed would stimulate the formation of agricultural credit corporations to aid in financing the live stock industry in the west.
There were also charges that Hoover claimed authorship of suggestions contained in the pending Capper-Williams farm relief measure (undated clipping).

95. E. D. Funk to Calvin Coolidge, Feb. 13, 1925; E. T. Clark to Funk, Feb. 13, 1925.

96. *Ibid.*

97. Herbert Hoover to Eugene D. Funk, Jr., Nov. 7, 1955, in answer to question prepared by the present author.

98. Funk to President, Feb. 14, 1925; To Jardine. Jardine was appointed March 4, 1925. Howard M. Gore of West Virginia filled the vacancy after the death of Wallace. Benedict, *op. cit.,* p. 221, declared that Jardine was appointed through the influence of Secretary Hoover. Jardine was unfavorable to McNary Haugen legislation.

99. H. H. Hall to E. D. Funk, Feb. 14, 1925.

100. E. D. Funk to H. Hoover, Feb. 18, 1925.

101. E. D. Funk to D. O. Thompson, Feb. 18, 1925.

102. E. D. Funk to Chas. Broyles, Feb. 18, 1925.

103. E. D. Funk to "Charlie," Feb. 18, 1925, also unfinished letter to "Fred" and E. D. Funk to N, H. Gentry, Mar. 13, 1925.

104. E. D. Funk to N. H. Gentry, Mar. 13, 1925.

105. E. D. Funk to Jas. O'Donnell, Mar. 22, 1925.

Chapter XXI

1. *Report American Seed Trade Association,* 1925, pp. 121-125.

2. *Ibid.,* 1921, pp. 79ff.

3. *Ibid.,* 1925, p. 131.

4. E. D. Funk, Annual Convention, *Ibid.,* 1926, p. 25ff.

5. *Ibid.,* p. 44; W. A. Wheeler & D. D. Hill, *Grass and Seeds,* (Princeton, N. J. VanNostrand 1957), p. 694; Interview with W. A. Wheeler, Apr. 21, 1955.

6. M. Benedict, *op. cit.,* pp. 219-255.

7. *Congressional Record*—House, 69th Congress, 1st Session, Jan. 29, 1926, pp. 2997ff.

8. *Ibid.*, p. 2999.
9. *Ibid.*
10. E. D. Funk to Henry Rainey, Jan. 27, 1926.
11. E. D. Funk to Gov. Lowden, Apr. 12, 1926.
12. Frank Lowden to E. D. Funk, April 14, 1926, Frank Lowden Papers.
13. E. D. Funk to Lowden, April 12, 1926.
14. Frank Lowden to Funk, April 16, 1926 (original in Funk Papers), Frank
    Lowden Papers; also Wm. T. Hutchinson, *op. cit.*, p. 561.
15. *Ibid.*
16. E. D. Funk to Frank Lowden, April 24, 1926, Frank Lowden Papers, copy in
    E. D. Funk Papers. The article was entitled "What we can do for the
    farmer." See W. T. Hutchinson, *op. cit.*, p. 552.
17. *Ibid.*, p. 553.
18. E. D. Funk to D. E. Davenport, May 12, 1926.
19. *Ibid.*
20. *Congressional Record,* House, 69th Cong., 1st Session, Vol. 67, Part 8, p.
    9003.
21. *Ibid.*
22. R. S. Woodrow to E. D. Funk, May 21, 1926.
23. E. D. Funk to Frank Lowden, May 24, 1926, Confidential Letter, Frank
    Lowden Papers.
24. Frank Lowden to E. D. Funk, May 26, 1926, *Ibid.*
25. E. D. Funk to Byron Burns, (Decatur), May 27, 1926, *Ibid.*
26. Wm T. Hutchinson, *op. cit.*, p. 559.
27. E. D. Funk to Frank Lowden, Nov. 24, 1926, Frank Lowden Papers.
28. Frank Lowden to E. D. Funk, Nov. 27, 1926, Ibid.
29. E. D. Funk to Frank Lowden, Dec. 14, 1926.
30. F. Lowden to E. D. Funk, Jan. 4, 1927, Frank Lowden Papers.
31. E. D. Funk to Frank Lowden, Jan. 6, 1927.
32. E. D. Funk, *Summary of Statement as Farmer,* before Hearing of Business-
    men's Commission on Agriculture, Chicago, Feb. 1, 1927.
33. E. D. Funk to H. Hoover, Feb. 19, 1927.
34. *Daily Pantagraph,* Feb. 21, 1927.
35. E. D. Funk to Frank Lowden, Mar. 14, 1927, Frank Lowden Papers.
36. E. D. Funk to G. D. Neavitt, May 3, 1927, *Ibid.*
37. E. D. Funk to Frank Lowden, May 3, 1927, *Ibid.*
38. Frank Lowden to E. D. Funk, May 4, 1927, *Ibid.*
39. Frank Lowden to E. D. Funk, May 4, 1927, Frank Lowden Papers.
40. Enclosure, Allen E. Walker to E. D. Funk, April 29, 1927, *Ibid.*
41. F. O. Lowden to E. D. Funk, June 10, 1927, *Ibid.*
42. C. F. B. to Funk, July 12, 1927, copy in Lowden Papers.
43. E. D. Funk to Clarence Buck, July 13, 1927, *Ibid.*
44. *Ibid.*
45. Frank Lowden to E. D. Funk, July 19, 1927, *Ibid.*
46. E. D. Funk to Frank Lowden, Aug. 17, 1927, *Ibid.*, for an estimate of the
    work of Clarence Buck, see W. T. Hutchinson, *op. cit.*, pp. 564-569.
47. Frank Lowden to E. D. Funk, Aug. 20, 1927, Frank Lowden Papers.
48. E. D. Funk to E. O. Brown, Chicago Stock Exchange, Sept. 24, 1927.
49. Wm. T. Hutchinson, *op. cit.*, pp. 565-573, also pp. 594-602.

Chapter XXII

1. William T. Hutchinson, *op. cit.*, Vol. II, pp. 563-573 and 594-602 for analysis of this situation.

2. Kansas City, *Star*, Oct. 28, 1927, Membership Committee: Henry A. Garfield, President Williams College, Chairman; Charles J. Barrett, President Farmers Union; William M. Doak, Vice President of Brotherhood of Railroad Trainmen; Eugene Funk, President of National Corn Association; Edmund E. Ladd, President North Dakota Agricultural College; R. Goodwin Rhett, President Chamber of Commerce, U. S.; J. W. Shorthill, Secretary, National Council Farmers Cooperative Associations; James W. Sullivan of American Federation of Labor; L. J. Taber, Master of Ohio State Grange; Professor F. W. Taussig of Harvard U., Chairman U. S. Tariff Commission; Theodore N. Vail, President American Telephone & Telegraph Co.; Henry J. Waters, President Kansas State Agricultural College.

3. *Ibid.*, see signed statement; see Frank M. Surface, *The Grain Trade During the World War.* (New York: Macmillan, 1928), Chapters 5 and 9.

4. E. D. Funk to Herbert Hoover, May 4, 1928. The Gross letter enclosed.

5. See above chapter on Price Fixing.

6. E. D. Funk to Herbert Hoover, June 1, 1928.

7. H. Hoover to E. D. Funk, Jr., Nov. 7, 1955, *Ibid.*, in answer to questions prepared by the author. Hutchinson, *op. cit.*, p. 599.

8. E. D. Funk to Herbert Hoover, July 3, 1928.

9. E. D. Funk to Herbert Hoover, July 11, 1928.

10. E. D. Funk to J. B. Johnson, Aug. 27, 1928.

11. E. D. Funk to Edgar C. Levis, Media, Ill., Aug. 28, 1928.

12. E. D. Funk to C. P. Bull, Sept. 13, 1928; *Daily Pantagraph*, Sept. 23, 1928.

13. E. D. Funk to J. G. Brown, Sept. 10, 1928.

14. E. D. Funk to John Brown, Aug. 30, 1928.

15. E. D. Funk to C. V. Gregory, Aug. 31, 1928.

16. E. D. Funk to Henry Wallace, See telegram, Sept. 11, 1928.

17. E. D. Funk to Sam. Guard, Nov. 8, 1928. He also referred again to his efforts to help young Henry's Grandfather with the *Farmer;* Russell Lord, *The Wallaces of Iowa*, (Boston: Houghton, Mifflin, 1947), pp. 277-279.

18. *Ibid.*, E. D. Funk to C. P. Bull, Sept. 10, 1928.

19. *Ibid.*

20. J. Oglesby to E. D. Funk, Sept. 24, 1928.

21. E. D. Funk to C. P. Bull, Sept. 25, 1928.

22. E. D. Funk to J. G. Brown, Sept. 25, 1928.

23. E. D. Funk to J. G. Oglesby, Sept. 25, 1928.

24. E. D. Funk to Renick W. Dunlap, Sept. 27, 1928, marked confidential.

25. Sample letter, E. D. Funk to Wm. Rebham, as a representative farmer from Raymond county, Oct. 5, 1928.

26. E. D. Funk to Renick W. Dunlap, Sept. 27, 1928.

27. E. D. Funk to John Oglesby, Oct. 9, 1928.

28. F. Fulkerson to E. D. Funk, Oct. 15, 1928. (Letter used with Fulkerson permission): Fulkerson recalled that he had refused $20.00 cwt. for his entire herd of hogs when that was a big price. He had thought to get more on the ratio of Pork to Corn promised by Mr. Hoover. He had listened to the request to make lard hogs around 300 lbs. At St. Louis 50 of his 118 hogs were taken at $17.50 and he was told the heaviest could not be used at any price. So then he returned home, bought all the $17.50 feeders he could and sold them for $21.00 cwt. and could have sold at $24.00 if he had kept them. He considered himself lucky for having been through the situation but "the other poor cuss" he believed, landed just where "those who would vote for Hoover would land". He also feared that lands would soon be in the hands of the peasants. Good old families were gone to the cities. He believed that Mr. Smith might be only a little better than Hoover

but he could not forget the 1918 situation. Probably, he concluded, it was not a case of the best "but of the least worst" .... Then he closed quite typically with the admonition to take the above "from a political view but do not let it affect our personal friendship." Upon returning from a trip to the southern part of the state Funk answered Fulkerson that he had been speaking on that very subject. He referred again to the fact that he and his cousin Lawrence had lost 8,000 hogs whereas Fulkerson spoke of 300. He explained again that they had taken their losses as the minimum under the circumstances. He had fought for what he could get rather than take additional losses. He honestly believed that the dip would have been great if they had not acted in this manner.

29. E. D. Funk to Frank Fulkerson, Oct. 19, 1928.
30. E. D. Funk to N. H. Gentry, Oct. 22, 1928.
31. L. J. Taber to E. D. Funk, Oct. 22, 1928.
32. E. D. Funk to L. J. Taber, Oct. 25, 1928.
33. E. D. Funk to Herbert Hoover, Oct. 23, 1928.
34. Will T. Carson to E. D. Funk, Oct. 23, 1928.
35. W. E. Dieckman to E. D. Funk, Oct. 23, 1928.
36. E. D. Funk to E. E. Stevenson, Oct. 25, 1928.
37. E. D. Funk to John Oglesby, Oct. 26, 1928.
38. E. D. Funk to Herbert Hoover, Western Union. Nov. 7, 1928.
39. Herbert Hoover to E. D. Funk, Jr., Nov. 7, 1955, in answer to question prepared by the author.
40. E. D. Funk to A. R. MacCusick, Adv. Illinois Blue Book, Nov. 24, 1928.
41. E. D. Funk to A. R. MacCusick, Dec. 12, 1928.
42. Gilbert C. Fite, *George N. Peek and the Fight for Farm Parity,* (Norman, Oklahoma: University of Oklahoma Press, 1954) p. 207.
43. *Ibid.* p. 217.
44. *Blue Book,* State of Illinois, 1929–30 (Springfield: Journal Print. Co. 1929) pp. 848, 855-856.
45. E. D. Funk to Frank Lowden, Dec. 13, 1928, Frank Lowden Papers.
46. E. D. Funk to Wilbur H. Coultas, Dec. 13, 1928, *Ibid.*
47. *Seed World,* Dec. 14, 1928.
48. H. E. Young, Sect'y Farmers Institute, Dec. 19, 1928.
49. Copy letter Chas. L. Meharry to Congressman Fred S. Purnell, Jan. 24, 1930, chapter 26 for additional discussion of this problem.
50. *Daily Pantagraph,* Nov. 8, 1930.
51. W. H. Young to E. D. Funk, Nov. 24, 1930. This list includes the following: C. P. Bull, L. B. Clore, W. L. English, E. D. Funk, P. G. Holden, A. N. Hume, C. B. Hutchinson, Wm. James, T. A. Kiesselbach, Lee G. Maxey, E. G. Montgomery, R. A. Moore, L. A. Moorehouse, M. L. Mosher, W. H. Mumford, W. H. Olin, Fred Rundern, H. J. Sconce, J. H. Shepard, A. L. Stone, S. N. Ten Eyck, Val Kuska, W. A. Wheeler, P. T. Winaco, H. P. Winter and W. W. Young.
52. E. D. Funk to George Stevenson, Dec. 23, 1930.
53. E. D. Funk to Fred McCulloch, Jan. 20, 1931.
54. E. D. Funk to Harvey Sconce, Jan. 20, 1931.
55. E. D. Funk to K. E. Beeson, Jan. 23, 1931.
56. E. D. Funk to Directors, Dec. 3, 1932.
57. Program, Letter Harvey Sconce to E. D. Funk, May 16, 1932.
58. Chas. D. Boyles to E. D. Funk, Oct. 30, 1931.
59. E. D. Funk Speech "Plant Breeding and What It Means to Illinois Agriculture," March 1, 1932.

60. E. D. Funk, Speech, W. L. S. April 9, 1932.
61. S. M. Hastings to E. D. Funk, Sept. 8, 1932.

CHAPTER XXIII

1. *The Peoria Star*, April 25, 1933, clipping.
2. Minutes of the Agricultural Committee of Illinois Manufactures Assocn. Jan.
   13; Feb. 10, 1933, March 16, 1933.
3. *Chicago Daily Tribune* clipping Nov. 2, 1932.
4. Paul Beshers Radio Talk, "Beshers Plan of Farm Relief," W. L. S. Chicago
   Jan. 9, 1933 (Gridley, Ill: Hawthorne Ptg. & Pub. Co.)
5. *Chicago Drovers Journal*, Jan. 26, 1933.
6. *New York Times*, Mar. 8, 1933.
7. *Daily Pantagraph*, Feb. 22, 1933, clipping.
8. E. D. Funk to Jewell Mayes, Mar. 2, 1933.
9. *Ibid.*
10. *Chicago Herald and Examiner*, clipping, Mar. 29, 1933.
11. *Ibid.*, April 12, 1933.
12. *Congressional Record*, 73rd Congress House of Representatives, Mar. 21,
    1933, also *Daily Pantagraph*, Mar. 25, 1933.
13. *Chicago Evening American*, Clipping, Mar. 4, 1933.
14. *Ibid.* Mar. 27, 1923.
15. *St. Louis Globe Democrat*, April 5, 1933, clipping.
16. *Chicago Daily News*, May 10, 1933.
17. *Daily Pantagraph*, May 4, 1933.
18. *Information For the Press*, U. S. Department of Agriculture Office of In-
    formation Press Service, May 8, 1933 and *The Use of Alcohol From Farm
    Products in Motor Fuel*, Summary of a Report by U. S. D. A. in response
    to Senate Resolution No. 65.
19. *Chicago Daily Tribune*, Mar. 18, 1933, clipping.
20. *Prairie Farmer*, April 29, 1933.
21. E. D. Funk to Wm. W. Buffam, Jan. 25, 1935. E. D. Funk to John J. Bogan,
    Feb. 2, 1935; E. D. Funk to John Oglesby, Feb. 6, 1935.
22. *Daily Pantagraph*, Feb. 12, 1935.
23. E. D. Funk to W. W. Buffam, Oct. 15, 1936.
24. E. D. Funk to C. P. Bull, Sept. 7, 1933.
25. E. D. Funk to L. M. King, Pres. A. S. T. A. Sept. 7, 1933.
26. E. D. Funk to L. E. Brandt (First National Bank, De Kalb), Oct. 30, 1933.
27. *Memorandum to the Board of Directors of Reconstruction Finance Corpo-
    ration*, June 17, 1935. *Ibid.*
28. H. E. Barnard to E. D. Funk, Aug. 30, 1935. Chapter 26 also *Terre Haute
    Tribune.*
29. E. D. Funk to Fred McCulloch, Mar. 8, 1934.
30. E. D. Funk to Henry A. Wallace, Dec. 22, 1934.
31. Report E. W. Rusk, "The Proof of the Pudding," *McLean County Farm and
    Home Bureau News*, Dec. 1934.
32. E. D. Funk to Louis Fitzhenry, Jan. 25, 1935.
33. E. D. Funk to Hamilton Lewis, Feb. 16, 1945.
34. *Daily Pantagraph*, May 14, 1935.
35. E. D. Funk to Everett C. Brown, May 28, 1936.
36. H. G. Atwood to E. D. Funk, Oct. 12, 1936: George W. Moffett to E. D.
    Funk (no date): E. D. Funk to George Moffett, June 15, 1939; Western
    Union telegram, George Moffett to E. D. Funk, Sept. 17, 1936.
37. E. D. Funk to J. A. McConnell, Sept. 17, 1937.

CHAPTER XXIV

1. Interview with Margaret Schertz, Nov. 25, 1954.
2. Interviews with the following people: Ross Vinson, Nov. 13, 1957; Boyd Frye, Oct. 27, 1954; Howard Holt, Dec. 14, 1957; Margaret Schertz, Nov. 2, 1954; Vaughn Dunbar, Nov. 2, 1954; Elias Rolley, Oct. 27, 1954; W. W. Alderman, Nov. 26, 1957; Howard Reeder, Nov. 26, 1957; E. D. Funk, Jr., Oct. 20, 1954; Dec. 7, 1957; Ira Beal, Dec. 14, 1957; LaFayette Funk, July, 1958; Paul Funk, Oct. 27, 1954; See Appendix for roster of employees.
3. *Seed World*, July 13, 1928.
4. Interviews with Eugene D. Funk, Jr., Dec. 7, 1957 and Earl Sieveking, March, 1956; also G. H. Dungan, J. R. Holbert and A. L. Lang, "Progress in Hybrid Corn Production," Illinois Farmers Institute, 1935–36.
5. Interview with J. M. Davison.
6. Interviews with Harold Goodwin, Nov. 2, 1954 and *Summary*, April, 1956: W. W. Alderman, Nov. 26, 1957; Ira Beal, Dec. 14, 1957; Ralph Savidge, Dec. 12, 1957; Howard Holt, Dec. 12, 1957.
7. Interviews with Lewis Falck, Nov. 13, 1957; Wesley Wilcox, Dec. 7, 1957; Eugene D. Funk, Jr., Sept. 1958; Boyd Frye, Oct. 27, 1954; Harold Abbott, Oct. 1954; E. D. Funk, Jr., June, 1958; R. J. Laible, Oct. 27, 1954; Ross Vinson, Dec. 7, 1957; Howard Reeder, Nov. 26, 1957; Bernard Dahlquist, Dec. 12, 1957; Lewis Falck, Nov. 13, 1957; E. D. Funk, Jr., Nov. 13, 1957.
8. Interviews with Robt. Spry, Dec. 1957; E. D. Funk, Jr., July, 1955; Ward Alderman, Nov. 26, 1957; E. D. Funk, Jr., Nov. 26, 1957; Mac Convis, Dec. 12, 1957; Joseph E. Barnes, Summary; Information from Personal Files, Funk Bros. Seed Co.
9. *Daily Pantagraph*, Dec. 23, 1940.
10. Tributes from friends and neighbors, 1940.
11. *Ibid.*
12. *Daily Pantagraph*, Dec. 2, 1941. The portrait was painted by Othman Hoffler.
13. P. G. Holden, Presentation of Portrait of E. D. Funk, Sr., Nov. 30, 1941.
14. Letters from friends, C. P. Bull to O. J. Sommers, June 5, 1941.
15. *Ibid.*, Edward J. Dies, June 25, 1941.

CHAPTER XXV

1. *Prairie Farmer,* Jan. 11, 1941; Timothy took the place of blue stem as a hay crop, because blue grass replaced blue stem as a pasture grass.
2. *Ibid.*
3. *Records,* Funk Bros. Seed Co., 1904–08.
4. See Chapter X.
5. *Prairie Farmer,* Jan. 1941, E. D. Funk "Crops Since 1924" pp. 108-109.
6. *Catalogue,* Funk Bros. Seed Co., 1909.
7. *Catalogues* Funk Bros. Seed Co., 1903–30.
8. W. A. Wheeler, *Beginnings of Hardy Alfalfa in North America,* Reprinted from *Seed World,* by Northrup King, 1951, p. 12 and Joseph E. Barnes, *Alfalfa, Its Origin, History and Development as a Forage Crop,* Typewritten copy, Dec. 1, 1956.
9. *Ibid.*
10. W. A. Wheeler, *op. cit.* p. 3.

11. *Ibid.*, pp. 809.
12. *Ibid.*
13. *Prairie Farmer,* Jan. 1941.
14. Barnes, *op. cit.*
15. *Catalogues,* Funk Bros. Seed Co., 1903–27.
16. Barnes, *op. cit.*
17. Interview with Harold Goodwin, July 2, 1958.
18. *Catalogue,* Funk Bros. Seed Co., 1924, p. 12.
19. Harold Goodwin, "Summary."
20. *Ibid.*
21. *Ibid.*
22. William Herr and G. L. Jordan, "The Pricing and Utilization of Legume and Grass Seeds", *Bulletin* 582, University of Illinois Agricultural Experiment Station, Dec. 1954, p. 3.
23. *Ibid.*
24. *Ibid.*, see chart p. 5: also Frank Beck, *The Field Seed Industry in the United States.* (Madison: University of Wisconsin Press). The last decade studied by Beck was 1929–38. Herr and Jordan analyzed 1939–48 and attempted to bring information to 1954.
25. Herr and Jordan, *op. cit.*, pp. 5-10.
26. *Ibid.*, Summary, p. 48.
27. *Ibid.*, pp. 21-25.
28. *Ibid.*, p. 25.
29. *Ibid.*
30. *Ibid.*, pp. 36-37.
31. *Ibid.*, p. 40.
32. *Ibid.*, Summary.
33. Interview with Eugene D. Funk, Jr., Jan. 1957.
34. Interview with Harold Goodwin, Jan. 1957.
35. S. R. Newell, "Farm Seed Statistics—Present and Future," A. S. T. A. Chicago, Illinois, Jan. 28, 1957.
36. *Ibid.*, p. 2.
37. *Ibid.*, p. 3.
38. *Ibid.*, p. 4.
39. Lloyd Brown, "Statistics Needed by the Seed Industry," A. S. T. A., Chicago, Jan. 28, 1957, p. 2. Mr. Brown is associated with Albert Dickinson Company.
40. *Ibid.*, p. 3.
41. Joseph E. Barnes, " A General History of Seed Technology," Aug. 9, 1956. Typed Copy, p. 1.
42. *Ibid.*
43. *Ibid.*, p. 5.
44. *Ibid.*, p. 8.
45. H. Dean Burch and G. Barnes Welch, "Modern Seed Processing," *Crops and Soils,* Oct. 1956, p. 18. The authors are associated with Mississippi Agricultural Experiment Station.
46. W. A. Wheeler, *Grassland Seeds,* (Princeton: D. VanNostrand & Co., 1957).
47. Harold Goodwin, "Summary," January, 1957.
48. Joseph E. Barnes, "A History of Alfalfa," pp. 12-14.

Chapter XXVI

1. Edward J. Dies, *Soybeans: Gold from the Soil* (New York; MacMillan, 1942) Gives 1919 as the date. Also E. F. Johnson, "History and Accomplish-

ments of American Soybean Association," *The Soybean Digest*, November, 1949 gives date as fall of 1920. George M. Strayer to E. D. Funk, Jr. Nov. 5, 1956 gives 1920 as the date.

2. Among the early pioneers well known to E. D. Funk, Sr., were John T. Smith of Tolono; W. E. Riegel; Charles Meharry; A. E. Staley; E. F. Johnson (Soybean Johnson); Wm. Shellabarger; E. K. Scheiter; Whitney Eastman; D. W. McMillen; John B. DeHaven; John H. Caldwell; J. W. Hayward; Otto Eisenschiml; J. L. Cartter; Prof. K. E. Beeson; I. F. Laucks; Charles B. Martin; Professor W. L. Burlison; Professor J. C. Hackleman and Ed. J. Dies; H. G. Atwood; J. A. McConnell; Wm. T. Morse; Frank Garwood.

3. Dies, *op. cit.*, pp. 15-16 also Interview with I. C. Bradley, July 22, 1955.

4. O. Eisenschiml to I. C. Bradley, I. C. Bradley Papers.

5. Dies, *op. cit.*, p. 16; also I. C. Bradley to W. H. Eastman, Dec. 5, 1930, and O. Eisenschiml to Bradley, Nov. 17, 1938, I. C. Bradley Papers.

6. Dies, *op. cit.*, p. 17 also I. C. Bradley to W. H. Eastman, Dec. 12, 1939, *I. C. Bradley Papers*, The DeHaven Oil Co. made some oil in 1910.

7. *Prairie Farmer*, Jan. 1941, and G. B. Breedlove, "Soy-Bean—The Magic Plant," Article XIX, *Chicago Journal of Commerce*, July 16, 1936. According to L. B. Breedlove in 1923 nearly 60% of seed beans was grown by the midwestern farmers using them, 30% from other producers and only 10% was received from local seed dealers. There was a recognized opportunity for processing mills in the area.

8. Records, Funk Brothers Seed Company, Directors Meetings, Vol. 1., p. 151. According to the agreement of July 21, 1924, the equipment was purchased for $20,000, one-half the sum was to be paid in 7% preferred stock in Funk Brothers Seed Company. The capacity to successfully manufacture soybean oil and "cake" was described in the amount of 15 tons per 24 hours. The capital stock of the Company was increased September 1, 1924 from $50,000 to $75,000 consisting of 650 shares of common and 1000 shares of 7% cumulative Preferred par value $100.00. Twenty shares of the 500 shares constituting the $50,000 of common stock had been returned to the treasury. The 480 shares were held as follows: E. D. Funk, Sr. 297; H. H. Miller 92; L. F. Funk, Jr. 11; E. D. Funk, Jr. 11, De Loss Funk 34; L. P. Funk 10; D. N. Funk 20; J. R. Holbert 5; increases had occurred when a stock dividend of 25,000 shares was declared December 23, 1920. This was accompanied by a revocation of the sale authorized in 1909.

9. E. D. Funk, Jr. Early Soybean History, typed copy, November 17, 1951 and Harold A. Abbott, *Interview*.

10. Interview with Eugene D. Funk, Jr., Oct. 5, 1956.

11. *Ibid.*

12. Interview with I. C. Bradley, July 1, 1955.

13. E. D. Funk, Jr., "Soybean History," Nov. 16, 17, 1951.

14. *Ibid.*, Nov. 17, 1951; *The Seed World*, Nov. 2, 1923; L. B. Breedlove, "Soybean, the Magic Plant," *Chicago Journal of Commerce*, June 6, 1936. Varieties gaining in favor during 1936, were Illini, Manchu, Dunfield, Mansoy and Larado. Varieties holding their own were Ebony, Virginia, Ilsoy, Peking, Black Eyebrow and Wilson. Varieties losing favor were Haberlandt, Mammoth Yellow, Hamilton, Ito San, A K and Midwest.

15. *Soybean Records*, Funk Bros. Seed Co.

16. *Soybean Records*, Funk Bros. Seed Co.

17. *Daily Pantagraph*, Feb. 11, 1927.

18. Interview with I. C. Bradley, July 23, 1954; see also Margaret Schertz, *Summary*, Nov. 30, 1955.
19. *G. L. F. Shareholder*, Jan. 1929, p. 27.
20. *Ibid.*
21. *Daily Pantagraph*, April 17, 1928; *G. L. F. Shareholder*, Jan. 1929, p. 27.
22. I. C. Bradley, "Summary," no date; see Eugene D. Funk, Jr. Papers, J. J. Quinlan (Vice President Executive Offices Wayne Feeds of Allied Mills, Inc.), to E. D. Funk, Jr., Jan. 30, 1927 for excerpts from *Minutes* American Milling Company, May 26, 1928 and Oct. 1, 1928 for statements that signed contracts for 32,000 acres were received by May 1, 1928 and 50,000 acres by October, 1928.
23. *Ibid.*
24. *Ibid.*
25. L. B. Breedlove, "Soy Bean, The Magic Plant," Article XIX, *Chicago Journal of Commerce*, July 16, 1936 states that competitors could have received beans at a lower price. Therefore contracting mills received contract and non contract beans on same basis. Contract buyers were compelled to take nearly 40 per cent more beans than intended.
26. Interview with J. A. Waring, Jan. 19, 1956.
27. J. C. Hackleman, *Annual Report of Crop Extension*, Dept. of Agronomy, University of Illinois, year ending 1928.
28. *Prairie Farmer*, Dec. 15, 1928; *G. L. F. Shareholder*, Jan. 1929, p. 27; and L. B. Breedlove, "Soy Bean, The Magic Plant," *Chicago Journal of Commerce*, Article XIX, July 16, 1936.
29. *G. L. F. Shareholder*, Jan. 1929, p. 27.
30. *The Prairie Farmer*, Feb. 23, 1929.
31. A. G. Heidrich of Allied Mills to E. D. Funk, Feb. 25, 1929.
32. L. B. Breedlove, "Soy Bean, The Magic Plant," Article XIX, *Chicago Daily Journal of Commerce*, July 16, 1936.
33. Original Contract for 1929, E. D. Funk Papers.
34. Funk Bros. paid $1.15 per bu., Nov. 7, 1927 and $1.25, Nov. 16, 1927.
35. Minutes of Meeting held at Funk Bros. Seed Co., Mar. 19, 1929, pp. 1-14. E. D. Funk Papers.
36. J. Armstrong to American Milling Co., April 2, 1929 and Armstrong to Funk, April 4, 1929, *Ibid.*
37. See original contract, *Ibid.*
38. L. B. Breedlove, "Soy Bean, The Magic Plant," Article XIX, *Chicago Journal of Commerce*, July 16, 1926.
39. Minutes of Board of Directors, Funk Bros. Seed Co. Vol. 1, p. 242, June 18, 1929. Cost of new elevator $37,727.00.
40. *Ibid.* p. 244. The purchase price was $55,000.00 with $30,000.00 assumed by the company of the first mortgage on the property; of the remaining $15,000.00, $10,000.00 was to be delivered to McKenzie Milling Company of 100 shares of 7.70 Preferred Cumulative Stock in Funk Bros. Seed Co. Fifty more shares constituted the balance to be paid to the McKenzie Company. The officers of the company took subscriptions for the 250 shares of stock to be sold to farmers around Taylorville. This stock could be paid for in soybeans.
41. *Daily Breese*, June 17, 1929, clipping.
42. J. W. Armstrong to E. D. Funk, Nov. 23, 1929.
43. L. B. Breedlove, "Soy Bean, The Magic Plant," Article XIX, *Chicago Journal of Commerce*, July 16, 1926.
44. R. W. Dunlap to Charles Adkins (copy) Mar. 21, 1920.
45. Adkins advised Armstrong to wait in this matter. He thought soybeans and oil

cake would be fairly well taken care of in the tariff. Charles Adkins to Armstrong, Mar. 20, 1930.

46. L. B. Breedlove, "Soy Bean, The Magic Plant," Article XVIII, *Chicago Journal of Commerce,* July 14, 1936.
47. E. D. Funk to J. W. Armstrong, Mar. 28, 1930.
48. Declaration of Soybean Oil Manufacturers Association, May 21, 1930.
49. I. C. Bradley Papers Original signed copy of Declaration and Minutes of Meetings, May 21, 1930. The signers of the original Declaration included:

1. Archer Daniels Midland Company	by W. H. Eastman
2. Allied Mills	by H. G. Atwood
3. Staley Sales Corpn.	by H. T. Norris
4. Funk Brothers Seed Company	by I. C. Bradley
5. Scientific Oil Company	by Otto Eisenschiml
6. Spencer Kellogg & Sons Sales Corp.	by Robt. G. Bennet
7. Shellabarger Grain Products Co.	by W. L. Shellabarger
8. Lafayette Milling Company	by B. C. Williams
9. Armstrong Paint and Varnish Works	by R. G. Dahlberg
10. Falk & Co.	by D. Lewis
11. Central States Chemical Co.	by Walter E. Flumerfelt

50. John Armstrong to E. D. Funk, April 19, 1930.
51. Soybean Marketing Association, Elevator Agreement, Sept. 18, 1930, Funk Bros. Seed Co. *Records.*
52. Agreement Funk Bros. Seed Co. with Soybean Marketing Association, Sept. 18, 1930, *Ibid.*
53. Agreement General Storage of Cleveland, with Soybean Marketing Assoc., Sept. 26, 1930, *Ibid.*
54. Agreement General Storage Co., with Funk Bros. Seed Co., Oct. 7, 1930, *Ibid.*
55. W. H. Eastman to *Champaign Gazette* (copy) Oct. 14, 1930, E. D. Funk Papers.
56. Receipts for Soybeans from Marketing Assoc. Oct. 31, and Nov. 12, 1930, Funk Bros. Seed Co. *Records.*
57. Funk said that his records showed from Oct. 1, 1930 when the first car of Soybean Marketing Association beans were received they purchased up to Dec. 31st., 40,000 bu. per Sept. 18th contract and additional off lots from farmer members of the Association to the amount of 1398 bu. These beans were local beans trucked in. This made a grand total of 41,398 bu. purchased of Association beans during Oct., Nov., Dec., for both Bloomington and Taylorville. During these 3 months 25,724 bu. of Association beans were processed and 617 tons, 790 lbs. of meal was sold at an average price of $40.18 per ton. There were 200,647 lbs. of oil made which stood on Funks books at that time Dec. 31 to be delivered at an average price of 0.538 per pound. Up to Jan. 1 we have been unable to get shipping instructions for any of our own oil and same was being held in storage tanks. The operating loss to Funks was quoted as $1,473.43. On Jan. 1, Funks had on hand 15,674 bu. of Association beans from original purchase of 40,000 bushels. Dec. 31 Funks agreed to take over additional lots of Association beans in 5,000 bu. lots. Included in statement from Jan. 1 to March 1 was 23,698 bu. processed during this period. Association beans on hand Jan. 1, were included in 368 tons, 1555 lbs. of meal as understood when agreement was made Dec. 31, 1930. Meal averaged $38.54 per ton and oil 0.536 per lb. Figures according to Funk showed an operating loss amounting to $1617.94 from Jan 1 to March 1 and on March 1, there remained 3930 bu. Association beans paid for at $1.17 per bu. but

unprocessed. Above figures did not take into account extra expense that the Association or Funks stood in the opening of new territory to create a demand for the soybean meal. See Funk to Smith, April 30, 1931.

58. E. D. Funk to E. Smith, April 30, 1930.
59. Agreement Funk Bros. Seed Co. with Soybean Marketing Assoc., May 8, 1931, Funk Bros. Seed Co. *Records.*
60. Agreement Allied Mills with Funk Bros. Seed Co., Oct. 6, 1931, *Ibid.*
61. Interview with J. J. Quinlan, Vice President, Wayne Feeds of Allied Mills, Feb. 1907.
62. Interview with Eugene D. Funk, Jr., May 24, 1956.
63. Board of Directors Meeting, Funk Bros. Seed Co., Vol. 1, p. 239.
64. Interview Eugene D. Funk, Jr., Oct. 5, 1956; Wheeler McMillen, *New Riches From Soil,* (N. Y.: D. Van Nostrand, 1946).
65. Board of Directors Meeting, Funk Bros. Seed Co., Vol. 1, p. 239. The sale was for $50,000. Allied Mills assumed the mortgage of $30,000 and interest after Sept. 1, 1932. The balance of $20,000 was to be paid to Funk Bros.
66. H. H. Miller to J. B. DeHaven, Aug. 31, 1935.
67. W. L. Burlison, *Recent Developments in Utilization of Soybean Oil Paint,* Circular 438 (University of Illinois College of Agriculture, Agricultural Experiment Station and Extension Service, 1935). This Bulletin is a reprint of Dr. Burlison's address delivered at the Annual meeting of American Soybean Assoc. Evansville and LaFayette, Indiana, August 21–23, 1935.
68. *Ibid.*
69. Interview with E. D. Funk, Jr., Sept. 26, 1956.
70. L. B. Breedlove, "Soy Bean, The Magic Plant," *Chicago Journal of Commerce,* Article XX, July 18, 1936.
71. *Ibid.*
72. *Bulletin of Information,* National Soybean Processors Association, Vol. 1 June 1, 1936, *E. D. Funk Papers,* E. D. Funk, Speech at Chemurgic Council, McMillen, *op. cit.* p. 33.
73. E. Dies, "Soy, the Miracle Bean" *Commerce,* June 1936.
74. L. B. Breedlove, "Soy Bean, The Magic Plant," Article XIX, *Chicago Journal of Commerce,* July 16, 1936.
75. *Summary* from Records of Soybean Processors Association.
76. Interview with Earl Sieveking, June 23, 1955.
77. *Report* 1942, E. D. Funk, Jr. Papers.
78. George M. Strayer to E. D. Funk, Jr. Aug. 30, 1943; also *Annual Report* of Committee by E. D. Funk, Jr., 1943.
79. W. L. Burlison to E. D. Funk, Jr. Sept. 10, 1943.
80. O. B. Combs to E. D. Funk, Jr. Aug. 28, 1944; also *Annual Report* of the Committee by E. D. Funk, Jr., 1944.
81. *Annual Report* of Committee by E. D. Funk, Jr., 1945.
82. W. L. Burlison to E. D. Funk, Jr., Sept. 9, 1946.
83. George Strayer to E. D. Funk, Jr., Aug. 1, 1926; see also Committee Report by E. D. Funk, Jr., Aug. 13, 1946., *Ibid.*
84. Annual Report, 1947, *Ibid.*
85. Interview with E. D. Funk, Jr., Oct. 5, 1952.
86. Soybean Oil Tank Survey, Jan. 29, 1943, E. D. Funk, Jr. Papers.
87. *Soybean Records,* Funk Bros. Seed Co.
88. Harold Abbott, "Soybean Processing," typed copy Dec. 5, 1956.
89. *Ibid.* p. 3.
90. *Ibid.;* also interview with Harold Abbott, Dec. 1956.

91. Harold Abbott, "Soybean Processing," p. 4 and "Plant Expansion for Solvent Extraction of Soybeans," April 19, 1948.
92. Delmar D. Walker, "Solvent Soybean Operations," Nov. 1956.

CHAPTER XXVII

1. Henry A. Wallace and Wm. L. Brown, *Corn and Its Early Fathers* (E. Lansing, Mich. The Michigan State University Press, 1956) p. 6.
2. R. Crabb, *Hybrid Corn Makers* stated that Shull came to consider his pure line idea as more theoretical than practical. He also stated that East and Shull agreed never to press the matter of priority.
3. Paul Mangelsdorf "Dr. Jones' Contribution to the Hybridization of Corn," *Growth and Development of the Corn Plant*, 1947, pp. 50-52.
4. G. H. Shull to E. D. Funk, Jan. 17, 1914, reprinted *Modern Agriculture*, January 1939.
5. Crabb, *op. cit.*, p. 98.
6. Mangelsdorf, *op. cit.*
7. *Twenty-Fifth Anniversary Booklet*, Funk Bros. Seed Co., Chapter 4.
8. United States Department of Agriculture, *Yearbook*, 1936, p. 468. As has been shown above the names of Beal, Gardner, Holden, East, Shull and D. F. Jones are especially well known in the development of Hybrid Corn.
9. *Twenty-Fifth Anniversary Booklet*, Funk Bros. Seed Co. Chapter 4.
10. Earl Sieveking, *Summary*.
11. *Catalogue*, Funk Bros. Seed Co., 1920.
12. *Ibid.*, 1921, p. 1.
13. James R. Holbert and George N. Hoffer, "Control of Root, Stalk and Ear Rot Diseases of Corn," Farmers *Bulletin 1176* U. S. D. A., November 1920.
14. Eugene D. Funk, "Corn Disease Investigations," *Illinois Farmers Institute*, 26th Annual Meeting, Danville, April 23, 1921.
15. Howard Leonard, Pres. Illinois A. A. to Henry C. Wallace, Jan. 30, 1922. *Records of Bureau of Plant Industry*, General Correspondence, National Archives.
16. C. R. Ball to W. A. Taylor, Feb. 25, 1922, *Ibid.*
17. Memorandum C. R. Ball to W. A. Taylor, Feb. 25, 1922, *Ibid.*
18. *Ibid.*
19. A. G. Johnson to E. D. Funk, Oct. 28, 1924, Ibid.
20. *Seed World*, Dec. 19, 1924.
21. H. A. Wallace to E. D. Funk, Feb. 17, 1925.
22. E. D. Funk to Henry Fields, Mar. 24, 1925.
23. *Ibid.*
24. *Seed Trade News*, Oct. 6, 1925.
25. *Seed World*, Oct. 25, 1923, also Sept. 25, 1924.
26. E. D. Funk to H. E. Young, Nov. 6, 1926, with enclosure.
27. *Catalogue*, Funk Bros. Seed Co., 1927. Professor Holden was with International Harvester at this time.
28. *Ibid.*
29. E. D. Funk to Samuel Guard, Nov. 10, 1927.
30. *Daily Drovers Journal*, July 15, 1926.
31. *Daily Bulletin* (Bloomington, Ill.) Oct. 17, 1926.
32. *Ibid.*
33. *Ibid.*, Oct. 20, 1926.
34. *Ibid.*
35. *Seed World*, Oct. 7, 1927.
36. James Holbert, *Weekly Management Letter*, Jan. 7, 1955.

37. *Ibid.*, Nov. 23, 1955. See James R. Holbert *et. al.*, "Resistance and Susceptibility of Corn Strains to Second Brood Chinch Bugs," *Iowa State College Journal of Science*, Vol. IX, p. 3, 1936.
38. James R. Holbert, United States Department of Agriculture, *Yearbook*, 1928, pp. 227-228 and *Yearbook*, 1938, pp. 160-164.
39. J. G. Dickson and J. R. Holbert, "The Relation of Temperature to the Development of Disease in Plants," *The American Naturalist*, July–August 1928.
40. J. G. Dickson and J. R. Holbert, "The Influence of Temperature Upon the Metabolism and Expression of Disease Resistance in Selfed Lines of Corn," *Journal of American Society of Agronomy*, April 1926.
41. James Holbert, *Weekly Management Letter*, Oct. 19, 1955, Funk Bros. Seed Co.
42. James Holbert, W. L. Burlison and A. G. Johnson, "Portable Refrigeration Chambers Studying Cold Resistance of Plants in Field," U. S. D. A. *Circular 285*.
43. *Phytopathology*. 1933, pp. 105-106; 1929, 21, 128, 1931.
44. Holbert, *et al.*, U. S. D. A. *Circular 285*.
45. E. D. Funk to Henry Ramsey, Sept. 13, 1928.
46. James Holbert, *Weekly Management Letter*, Dec. 5, 1955, Funk Bros. Seed Co.
47. James R. Holbert, *Weekly Management Letter*, April 4, 1956, Funk Bros. Seed Co.; see also C. S. Reddy and J. R. Holbert "Further Experiments with Seed Treatment for Sweet Corn Diseases," *Journal of Agricultural Research*, Feb. 1, 1928; C. S. Reddy and J. R. Holbert "Experiments to show the Effects of Certain Seed Treatments on Corn," *Phytopathology*, 14; 44-45, 1925; C. S. Reddy and J. R. Holbert and A. T. Erwin, "Seed Treatment for Sweet Corn Disease" *Journal of Agricultural Research*, Oct. 15, '26; *Phytopathology*, 16, 82, 83, 1926; James R. Holbert and Benjamin Koehler, "Results of Seed Treatment Experiments with Yellow Dent Corn," *Technical Bulletin 260*, U. S. D. A., Dec. 1931.
48. *Corn Booklet*, 1947, Funk Bros. Seed Co., p. 5.
49. *Ibid.*, p. 6.
50. *Ibid.*
51. James R. Holbert, *Weekly Management Letter*, Nov. 16, 1955, Funk Bros. Seed Co.
52. *Ibid.*
53. James R. Holbert, *Weekly Management Letter*, July 20, 1955, Funk Bros. Seed Co.
54. *Ibid.*
55. *Ibid.*, July 13, 1955.
56. *Ibid.*, Nov. 2, 1955.
57. *Ibid.*, Nov. 9, 1955.
58. *Daily Pantagraph*, Feb. 21, 1937.
59. *Fifteenth Annual Report*, June 30, 1957, Funk Bros. Seed Co.
60. James R. Holbert, *Weekly Management Letter*, Jan. 18, 1956.
61. *Ibid.*, Dec. 16, 1955.
62. Richard Crabb, *The Progressive Farmer*, Mar. 1954.
63. James R. Holbert, *Weekly Management Letter*, Dec. 21, 1955, Funk Bros. Seed Co.
64. *Ibid.*, Oct. 7, 1955.
65. James R. Holbert, Direct Testimony, Case *J. A. Batson* vs. *J. C. Robinson Seed Co.*, Sept. 24-25, 1956.
66. *Ibid.*, p. 77.

67. *Ibid.*, pp. 80-81.
68. *Ibid.*, p. 127.
69. *Ibid.*
70. *Ibid.*, p. 65.
71. *Ibid.*, p. 65.
72. *Ibid.*, p. 16-17.
73. Earl Sieveking, "Shifting Agricultural Production," *Weekly Management Letter,* Dec. 21, 1955, Funk Bros. Seed Co.

CHAPTER XXVIII

1. Circular 1934, "Corn With a Future, Funk's Hybrid," Funk Bros. Seed Co.
2. J. R. Holbert, G. A. Dungan, A. L. Lang, *Illinois Farmers Institute.*
3. R. J. Laible, *The Furrow,* Deere and Company, Moline, Ill. Nov., Dec., 1936.
4. Earl Sieveking, *Interview,* Dec. 18, 1955.
5. *Ibid.*
6. Eugene D. Funk, Jr., *Interview,* Feb. 1956.
7. Claire V. Golden, *Interview,* July 28, 1957.
8. E. D. Funk, Sr., to J. L. McKeighan, April 18, 1944. J. L. McKeighan Papers.
9. Earl Sieveking, to J. L. McKeighan, April 25, 1934, *Ibid.*
10. *Catalogue,* 1907, 1908, 1914, 1925, *Ibid.*
11. *Catalogue,* 1925, *Ibid.*
12. Interview with Richard and Olga Best, May, 1957; also *Carlinville Democrat,* March 29, 1922; Folder, Columbiana Seed Co., 1934 and 1937.
13. *Ibid.*
14. O. J. Sommer, *History of Sommer Bros. Seed Co.,* (North Newton, Kansas: Mennonite Press, 1955), p. 36.
15. *Ibid.*, p. 29.
16. *Ibid.* p. 54.
17. *Ibid.*
18. *Records,* Funk Bros. Seed Co.
19. *Meeting, Board of Directors,* Funk Bros. Seed Co., vol. 1, pp. 283-294. E. D. Funk, Sr. held 361 shares of 611 outstanding common; H. H. Miller, 125 shares; the four sons of E. D. held 25 shares each; Holbert, 15 and Bracken, 10. E. D. Funk, Sr. held 117 of 506 shares of preferred stock. E. D. Funk, Jr. held 85, Paul 67, Theodore and LaFayette 70 each, Miller 86, Holbert 5, M. Schertz 1, Rolley 5 in 1939.
20. *Ibid.*
21. *Ibid.*, Vol. 2, p. 32, Sept. 15, 1939.
22. Funks *Corn Circular,* 1947.
23. Interview with Eugene D. Funk, Jr., July 31, 1958.
24. Letters From Associates, August, 1958.
25. Booklet, 1947.
26. Letters from Associates, August, 1958.
27. *Minutes of Meeting,* Funk Bros. Seed Co. and Associate Growers, Aug. 5, 1939, E. D. Funk, Sr. was General Chairman.
28. *Minutes Third Annual Meeting,* Funk Bros. Seed Co. and Associated Producers, Illinois Hotel, Bloomington, April 9–10, 1940.
29. *Ibid.*, Sept. 30, 1940.
30. *Ibid.*, Dec. 11, 1940.
31. *Ibid.*, Dec. 19, 1941.
32. *Ibid.*, Dec. 19, 1941.
33. *Ibid.*

34. *Ibid.*
35. *Summary,* Letters from Associates and Others, Claire Golden to J. R. Holbert, Dec. 15, 1941.
36. *Ibid.* Clarence Akin to J. R. Holbert, Dec. 13, 1941.
37. *Ibid.* I. W. Hepperly to J. R. Holbert, Dec. 13, 1941.
38. *Ibid.* R. D. Herrington to J. R. Holbert, Dec. 13, 1941.
39. Memorandum of Understanding and Franchise Agreement, Funk Bros. Seed Co.
40. *Minutes of the Promotion and Advertising Fund,* Funk Bros. Seed Co.
41. Growers Contract, Funk Bros. Seed Co.
42. Interview with Eugene D. Funk, Jr.
43. *Ibid.*
44. *Ibid.*
45. *Report of the First Hybrid Corn Division Meeting.* (Chicago, American Seed Trade Association, 1946) Foreword.
46. *Year Book and Proceedings of the 64th Annual Convention,* American Seed Trade Association, Chicago, June 21–25, 1947. pp. 100-110.
47. *Report of Sixty-Fifth Annual Convention,* French Lick, Indiana, American Seed Trade Association, June 23–26, 1948.
48. *Journal of Commerce,* April 5, 1948.
49. *Ibid.*
50. Earl Sieveking, "Fertilizer and Tilth," *What's New in Production, Storage and Utilization of Hybrid Seed Corn,* (Chicago: Hybrid Seed Corn Division), A. S. T. A. 1948, pp. 40-44.
51. *Ibid.*
52. Donald F. Jones, "Changes in Hybrid Corn Production in the Future," *Progress in Corn Production,* (Chicago; Hybrid Seed Corn Division) A. S. T. A. 1949, pp. 1-17.
53. Wheeler McMillen, "Rainbows in the Cornfields," *Ibid.,* p. 86.
54. *Report of the Fifth Hybrid Corn Industry-Research Conference,* Chicago, Nov. 28–29, 1950.
55. *Report of the Sixth Hybrid Corn Industry-Research Conference,* Chicago, Nov. 28–29, 1951.
56. *Report of the Seventh Hybrid Corn Industry-Research Conference,* Chicago, Dec. 3–4, 1952.
57. *Ibid.,* p. 34.
58. *Report of the Eighth Hybrid Corn Industry-Research Conference,* Chicago, Dec. 2–3, 1953.
59. *Report of the Tenth Hybrid Corn Industry-Research Conference,* Chicago, Nov. 30, Dec. 1, 1955.
60. *Ibid.,* pp. 114-115.
61. Annual Meeting.
62. *Corn Booklet,* no date.
63. James Holbert, *Weekly Management Letter,* July 27, 1955, Funk Bros. Seed Co.
64. Eugene D. Funk, Jr., *Historical Background of Research Acres,* p. 1.
65. *Ibid.*
66. J. Davison, "A Trip Through Research Acres," typed copy, Oct. 30, 1956.
67. Paul Weatherwax, *Indian Corn in Old America,* (New York: MacMillan, 1954) pp. 206-207.
68. R. J. Laible, "Research Acres," typed copy, Oct. 30, 1956.
69. *Ibid.,* p. 2.
70. *Ibid.*
71. *Ibid.*

72. Davison, *op. cit.*
73. *Ibid.*
74. *Ibid.*, also interview E. D. Funk, Jr., Dec. 7, 1957.
75. *Ibid.*
76. Helen M. Cavanagh, "Funk Memorial at Research Acres," *Journal of the Illinois State Historical Society,* Dec. 1956.
77. W. L. Burlison, "Dedicate Plaques to Funk Pioneers of Hybrid Corn" *Seed Trade News,* July 16, 1958.

Chapter XXIX

1. Interview with Eugene D. Funk, Jr., July, 1927. *Fortune,* Feb. 1957, p. 136 explains that Corn Products was organized in 1906 in New York "of Standard Oil money and the old Glucose Trust. It dominated the wet milling industry; it had all of the glucose market and most of the starch market. Anti-Trust action loosened this hold and by 1930 the company had beat a genteel retreat to 45% of the industry's volume. To-day it has 40%" . . . Sales in 1956 exceeded $300,000,000 in the United States and $100,000,000 abroad. Since 1919 Corn Products has never missed a dividend.
2. *Interview* with Eugene D. Funk, Jr., July, 1957.
3. *Ibid.*
4. Earl Sieveking, "Report of European Trip," 1947 Funk Bros. Seed Co. *Records and Minutes Regular Board of Directors Meeting,* Funk Bros. Seed Co., Feb. 15, 1949.
5. *St. Louis Post Dispatch,* August 19, 1949.
6. *Ibid.*
7. Earl Sieveking, *op. cit.*
8. Wayne Runge to Dr. James Holbert, Sept. 25, 1949, (copy), Eugene D. Funk, Jr., Papers.
9. *Ibid.*
10. Wayne Runge to Dr. James Holbert, Oct. 14, 1949, *Ibid.*
11. Advertising Folder, Compagnia Ibridi Mais, E. D. Funk, Jr., Papers.
12. *Interview* with Wayne Runge, July 13, 1957.
13. *Ibid.*
14. *Ibid.*
15. Dr. James Holbert to Eugene D. Funk, Jr., August 27, 1954, E. D. Funk, Jr., Papers.
16. *Ibid.*
17. Claude Nardin to E. D. Funk, Jr., August 1956, *Ibid.*
18. Robert Holbert, MS copy, "Mexico Looks at Hybrid Corn."
19. Interview with Eugene D. Funk, Jr., July 12, 1957.
20. J. R. Holbert to Sam Sears, April 1, 1955, J. R. Holbert Papers.
21. E. D. Funk, Jr. to Wayne Runge, Eugene D. Funk, Jr., Papers.
22. Wayne Runge to James R. Holbert, Dec. 18, 1956, (copy), *Ibid.*
23. Interview with E. D. Funk, Jr., July 25, 1958.
24. J. R. Holbert to Robert Blattner, July 26, 1956, copy *Ibid.*, F. Grossman to J. R. Holbert Dec. 28, 1956, *Ibid.*, and information from Wesley Wilcox, July 25, 1958.

Bibliography

I. Original Materials, Manuscript.

I. C. Bradley, Papers, Taylorville, Illinois.

Eugene D. Funk, Sr., Papers and Diaries, Bloomington and Shirley, Illinois.

Eugene D. Funk, Jr., Papers, Bloomington, Illinois.

LaFayette Funk, Papers and Diaries, Bloomington and Shirley, Illinois.

Perry G. Holden, Papers, Michigan State University.

James R. Holbert, Papers, Bloomington, Illinois.

Leonidas Kerrick, Papers, Decatur, Illinois.

Frank Lowden, Papers, University of Chicago, Chicago, Illinois.

Files, Funk Bros. Seed Co., Bloomington, Illinois.
Agronomists Reports 1903–1905.
Corn Register 1902–1905.
Ledger
Minutes of Meetings, Board of Directors and Stockholders 1901–1958.

Files, Department of Agriculture, United States Archives, Washington, D. C.

II. Newspapers and Periodicals.

Breeders Gazette 1897–1908.
Corn (Chicago) 1907.
Country Gentleman July–Dec. 1902.
Drovers' Journal (Chicago) 1886–1908.
Farmers Voice (Bloomington, Illinois) 1912–14.
Farmers Voice and *National Rural* 1902.
Inter Ocean (Chicago) 1902–1904.
Iowa Homestead 1902.
Journal of Commerce (Chicago) 1936.
Morning News (Dallas) 1914.
Orange Judd Farmer 1899–1909 and 1917–20.
Pantagraph, Daily (Bloomington, Illinois) 1865–1875; 1900–06.

Pantagraph, Weekly (Bloomington, Illinois) 1870–1890; 1902–12.

Prairie Farmer (Chicago) 1870–1920; 1936; 1941.

Seed World (Chicago).

Seed Trade News (Chicago) 1925–1935; 1944; 1947–53.

Soybean Digest 1945–53.

State (Columbia, S. C.) 1913.

Times (Chicago) Jan.–April 1871.

Tribune (Chicago) May and July 1873.

World Herald (Omaha) 1908–1909.

III. Public Journals and Records.

Congressional Record, 69th Congress, First Session, House of Representatives. Vol. 67, Washington: Gov't Printing Office, 1925.

Congressional Record, 53rd Congress, First Session, House of Representatives. Vol. XXI, Washington: Gov't Printing Office, 1894.

Congressional Record, 53rd Congress, First Session, Vol. XXV, Part II, Washington: Gov't Printing Office, 1894.

Congressional Record, 53rd Congress, Second Session, Vol. XXLV, Part I, Washington: Gov't Printing Office, 1894.

Congressional Record, 53rd Congress, Second Session, Vol. XXVII, Part II, Washington: Gov't Printing Office, 1895.

Journal of the House of Representatives, 40th General Assembly, Illinois, Springfield: Phillips Bros., 1899.

Journal of the House of Representatives, 41st General Assembly, Illinois, Springfield: Phillips Bros., 1899.

Journal of the House of Representatives, 33rd General Assembly, Illinois, Springfield: H. W. Rokker, State Printer and Binder, 1883.

IV. Reports.

Catalogues, Funk Bros. Seed Co. 1903–1938.

25th Anniversary Booklet, Funk Bros. Seed Co., Bloomington, Illinois.

Illinois Blue Book, 1913–1914 (Danville, Illinois: Printing Co. 1914); also 1929–30, (Springfield: Journal Printing Co., 1929).

Official Program Premium List, Sixth National Corn Exposition, 1914.

Proceedings of the American Seed Trade Association, 1904–1940.

Report of the Second Annual National Corn Exposition, 1908.

Report of the Fourth Annual Meeting, Illinois Agricultural Association, January 21, 1919.

Report of the National Agricultural Conference, 67th Congress, Second Session, 1921–1922, House Documents, Vol. 115.

Reports of the Hybrid Corn Division, American Seed Trade Association, 1946–1955.

Transactions, Department of Agriculture, Illinois, 1911. Vol. 49. (No Publisher given).

Year Book, United States Department of Agriculture, 1895–1936 Washington, D.C.: U. S. Government Printing Office.

Weekly Management Letters, Funk Bros. Seed Co.

Reports of American Breeders Association, Vols. IV and V, 1908, 1909 (Washington: 1910, 1911).

V. Articles.

Cavanagh, Helen M. "Funk Memorial at Research Acres," *Journal of Illinois State Historical Society*, December 1956.

Burch, H. Dean and Welsh, J. Barnes, "Modern Seed Processing," *Crops* and *Soils*, October 1956.

Campbell, Wm. A., "National Corn Association," The *American Reviews of Reviews*, December, 1908.

Dickson, J. G. and Holbert, J. R., "The Relation of Temperature to the Development of Disease in Plants," *The American Naturalist*, July–Aug. 1928.

Dickson, J. G. and Holbert, J. R., "The Influence of Temperature Upon Metabolism and Expression of Disease Resistance in Self Lines of Corn," *Journal of American Society of Agronomy*, April, 1936.

Dies, Edward J., "Soy, the Miracle Bean," *Commerce*, June, 1936.

Funk, Eugene D., "Look Ahead Farmers," *Farm Magazine*, July, 1911.

Herr, Wm. and Jordan, G. L., "The Pricing and Utilization of Legume and Grass Seed," *Bulletin* 582, University of Illinois Agricultural Experiment Station, December 1954.

Holbert, James R. "Thirty Years Experience in Hybrid Corn Breeding," *Modern Agriculture*, Jan., 1939.

Destler, Chester, "Agricultural Readjustment and Agrarian Unrest in Illinois 1880–1896," *Agricultural History*, Vol. XXI, April, 1947.

Holbert, James R., *et al*, "Resistance and Susceptibility of Corn Strains to Second Brood Chinch Bugs," *Iowa State College Journal of Science*, Vol. 9, 1936.

Holbert, J. R. and Koehler, Benjamin, "Results of Seed Treatment

Experiments with Yellow Dent Corn," *Technical Bulletin* 260, United States Department of Agriculture, Dec., 1931.

Holbert, J. R. and Hoffer, George N., "Control of Root, Stalk and Ear Rot Diseases in Corn, "*Bulletin 1176,* United States Department of Agriculture, November, 1920.

Jones, Donald F., "Changes in Hybrid Corn Production in the Future," *Progress in Corn Production,* Chicago: Hybrid Seed Corn Diseases, A. S. T. A. 1949.

Mangelsdorf, Paul, "Dr. Jones' Contribution to the Hybridization of Corn," *Growth and Development of The Corn Plant,* 1947.

McMillen, Wheeler, "Rainbows in The Corn Fields," *What's New in Production, Storage and Utilization of Hybrid Seed Corn.* Chicago: Hybrid Seed Corn Division A. S. T. A., 1929.

Reddy, C. S. and Holbert, J. R., "Future Experiments with Seed Treatment for Sweet Corn Diseases," *Journal of Agricultural Research,* Oct. 15, 1926.

Reddy, C. S., Holbert, J. R., and Erwin, A. T., "Seed Treatment for Sweet Corn Diseases," *Journal of Agricultural Research,* Oct. 15, 1926.

Sieveking, Earl, "Fertilizers and Tilth," *What's New in Production, Storage and Utilization of Hybrid Seed Corn,* Chicago: Hybrid Seed Corn Division, A. S. T. A., 1948.

VI. Unpublished. (Typed copies)

Abbott, Harold, "Soybean Processing," 1956.

Brown, Lloyd, "Statistics Needed by Seed Industry," 1957.

Barnes, James, "Alfalfa, Origin, History and Development as a Forage Crop," 1956.

Bull, Coates P., "The Significance, Import and Purpose of the National Corn Associations," 1955.

Davidson, J., "A Trip Through Research Acres."

Holbert, Robert, "Mexico Looks at Hybrid Corn."

Funk, De Loss, "Historical Items."

Funk, Eugene, "Plant Breeding and What it Means to Illinois Agriculture," 1932.

  Address at Columbia, Missouri, 1922.

  Address: Some Results From Ten Years of Corn Breeding, 1938.

  Address to College Alumni of Bloomington, 1938.

  Speech to Shirley Lodge #582, Nov. 30, 1943.

  Speech Before Commercial Club, Omaha, Nebr., 1908.

  Account of Hunting Trip, 1884.

  Speech before Chicago Agricultural Club, 1936.

  Address at Colonel Fulkerson's Home, 1902.

  Organization and Progress of the National Corn Association.

Funk, Eugene, Jr., "Early Soybean History," 1951, and "Historical Background at Research Acres."

Goodwin, Harold, "Summary," 1957.

Holmes, Hazel Funk, "Memories of My Mother Sophronia J. Funk."

Holbert, James, "My Early Experiences with Plant, Ear and Germinator Selections With Open Pollinated Corn," 1956. "My First Specific Assignment with Funk Bros. Seed Co.," 1955.

Kerrick, Leonidas, "Address before the Board of Agriculture, Ohio." "Speech First Baptist Church, Bloomington, Ill.," 1904. "Reciprocity."

Laible, R. J., "Research Acres," 1956.

Newell, S. R., "Farm Seeds Statistics."

Rehtmeyer, Gladys Funk, "Remembering I, II, III," typed copies.

Wallace, Henry, "Speech at the Dedication of Monument to Isaac Funk Family," 1915.

Walker, Delmar, "Solvent Soybean Operation," 1956.

VII. Books.

Benedict, Murray R., *Farm Policies of the United States,* 1790–1950, New York: The Twentieth Century Fund, 1953.

Bogart, E. S. and Thompson, C. M., *The Industrial State,* Vol. IV, Springfield: Centennial Commission, 1920.

Bowman, M. L. and Crossley, B. H., *Corn,* Des Moines: The Kenyon Printing and Mfg. Company.

Cavanagh, Helen, *Funk of Funks Grove,* Farmer, Legislator and Cattle King of the Old Northwest, 1797–1865; Bloomington, Ill.: Pantagraph Printing Co., 1952.

Cavanagh, Helen, *Funks Grove Timber,* Pamphlet, Bloomington, Ill., Funk Bros. Seed Co., 1957.

Chapman and Brothers (eds.), *Portrait and Biographical Album of McLean County,* Chicago: Chapman, 1887.

Coit, Margaret L., *Mr. Baruch,* Boston: Houghton Mifflin, 1957.

Crabb, Richard, *Hybrid Corn Makers,* New Brunswick: Rutgers University Press, 1947.

Chittenden, Russell H., *History of the Sheffield Scientific School of Yale University,* 1846–1922, Vol. 1, New Haven: Yale University Press, 1928.

"Diary of Celinda Hines," *Transactions of Forty-Sixth Annual Reunion of Oregon Pioneer Association,* June 20, 1918.

Dies, Edward J., *Soybeans, Gold From The Soil,* New York: MacMillan, 1942.

De Vries, Hugo, *Plant Breeding,* Chicago: The Open Court Publishing Company, 1919, Copyright, 1907.

Dulles, Foster Rhea, *America's Rise to World Power,* 1898–1954, New York: Harper Bros., 1954.

Faulkner, Harold U., *From Versailles to the New Deal,* New York: Yale University Press, 1950.

Fite, Gilbert C., *George N. Peek and the Fight for Farm Parity,* Norman: University of Oklahoma Press, 1954.

Fuess, Claude M., *Calvin Coolidge,* Boston: Little Brown, 1940.

Funk, Eugene D., Sr., *Commercial Corn Breeding,* 1904.

Bogue, Margaret Beattie, *Patterns From The Sod, Illinois,* 1850–1900, PhD. dissertation, Cornell University, published Illinois State Historical Society, 1959.

Gee, Wilson, *The Social Economics of Agriculture,* New York, MacMillan, 1954.

Hill, James, J., *Addresses,* Series Presented by Hill Reference Library, U. of Chicago.

Holden, P. G., *Corn Breeding at the University of Illinois,* 1895–1900, Charlevoix, Mich.: 1948.

Hoover, Herbert, *Memoirs,* 3 vol., New York: Macmillan, 1951–52.

Hutchinson, Wm. T., *Lowden of Illinois,* Chicago: University of Chicago Press, 1957.

Kerrick, Leonidas, *The Farm and the Town.*

Lord, Russell, *The Wallaces of Iowa,* Boston: Houghton Mifflin, 1947.

McMillen, Wheeler, *New Riches from the Soil,* New York: D. VanNostrand Co., 1946.

Mowry, George, *Theodore Roosevelt and the Progressive Movement,* Madison: University of Wisconsin Press, 1946.

Mullendore, William Clinton, *History of the United States Food Administration,* 1917–18, Stanford University, Cal.: Stanford University Press, 1947.

Myers, Wm. S., *The Foreign Policies of Herbert Hoover,* 1929–33, New York: Scribners, 1940.

Myrick, Herbert (ed.), *The Book of Corn,* Chicago: Orange Judd Company, 1903.

Paine, A. E., *The Granger Movement in Illinois,* University Studies, Urbana: University of Illinois Press, 1944.

Pringle, Henry, *Theodore Roosevelt,* New York: Harcourt Brace, 1931.

Pringle, Henry, *The Life and Times of William Howard Taft,* New York: Farrar and Rinehart, 1939.

Osgood, Ernest Staples, *The Day of the Cattle Man,* Chicago: University of Chicago Press, Phoenix Books, 1929.

Parlin and Orendorff, *How to Grow Pedigreed Corn,* Buffalo: Gies & Co., Printers, 1894.

Shannon, F. A., *Farmers Last Frontier,* New York: Farrar and Rinehart, 1945.

Pyle, Joseph Gilpin, *The Life of James J. Hill,* 2 vols., N. Y.: Doubleday Page & Co., 1917.

Shideler, James H., *Farm Crisis, 1919–1923,* Los Angeles: University of California Press, 1957.

Saloutis, Theo. and Hicks, John, *Agricultural Discontent in the Middle West, 1900–1939,* Madison: University of Wisconsin Press, 1951.

Sommer, O. J., *History of Sommer Bros. Seed Co.,* North Newton, Kansas: Mennonite Press, 1955.

Taylor, Carl C., *The Farmers Movement, 1620–1920,* New York: American Book Co., 1953.

Surface, Frank M., *American Pork Production in the World War,* Chicago: S. W. Shaw Co., 1926.

Surface, Frank M., *The Grain Trade During the World War,* New York: MacMillan, 1928.

Wallace, Henry A. and Brown, Wm. L., *Corn and Its Early Fathers,* East Lansing: Michigan State University Press, 1956.

White, William Allen, *A Puritan in Babylon,* New York: Macmillan, 1938.

Weatherwax, Paul, *Indian Corn in Old America,* New York: Macmillan, 1955.

Wheeler, W. A., *Beginnings of Hardy Alfalfa in North America,* Northrup King, 1951.

Wheeler, W. A. and Hill, D. D., *Grassland Seeds,* Princeton: D. VanNostrand Co., 1957.

Wilbur, Ray L. and Hyde, Arthur M., *The Hoover Policies,* New York: C. Scribners Sons, 1937.

Wish, Harvey, *Contemporary America,* New York: Harper Bros., 1955.

Index